THE ASQ CERTIFIED MANAGER OF QUALITY/ ORGANIZATIONAL EXCELLENCE HANDBOOK

THE ASQ CERTIFIED MANAGER OF QUALITY/ ORGANIZATIONAL EXCELLENCE HANDBOOK

Fifth Edition

Sandra L. Furterer and Douglas C. Wood, Editors

Contributors
*Bill Craddock, Denis Devos, Grace Duffy,
Sandra L. Furterer, Susan Gorveatte, Jeff Israel,
Tim King, Jd Marhevko, Heather McCain, Eileen Serrano,
Joe Wojniak, Douglas C. Wood*

ASQExcellence
Milwaukee, Wisconsin

Published by ASQExcellence, Milwaukee, WI
Produced and distributed by Quality Press, ASQ, Milwaukee, WI

Library of Congress Cataloging-in-Publication Data
Names: Furterer, Sandra L., editor. | Wood, Douglas C., 1955– editor.
Title: The ASQ certified manager of quality/organizational excellence handbook / Sandra L. Furterer and Douglas C. Wood. editors.
Other titles: Certified manager of quality/organizational excellence handbook (American Society for Quality) | American Society for Quality certified manager of quality/organizational excellence handbook
Description: Fifth edition. | Milwaukee, Wisconsin : ASQExcellence, 2021. | Includes bibliographical references and index. | Summary: "This handbook is a comprehensive reference source designed to help professionals address organizational issues from the application of the basic principles of management to the development of strategies needed to deal with the technological and societal concerns of the new millennium. The content of this fourth edition has been revised to reflect a more current global perspective and to align with the 2014 Certified Manager of Quality/Organizational Excellence (CMQ/OE) Body of Knowledge (BoK). In order to provide a broad perspective of quality management, this book has specifically been written to address: Historical perspectives relating to the evolution of particular aspects of quality management, including recognized experts and their contributions Key principles, concepts, and terminology relevant in providing quality leadership, and communicating quality needs and results Benefits associated with the application of key concepts and quality management principles Best practices describing recognized approaches for good quality management Barriers to success, including common problems that the quality manager might experience when designing and implementing quality management, and insights as to why some quality initiatives fail Guidance for preparation to take the CMQ/OE examination. Organized to follow the BoK exactly, throughout each section of this handbook the categorical BoK requirements associated with good quality management practices for that section are shown in a box preceding the pertinent text. These BoK requirements represent the range of content and the cognitive level to which multiple-choice questions can be presented. Although this handbook thoroughly prepares individuals for the ASQ CMQ/OE exam, the real value resides in post-exam usage as a day-to-day reference source for assessing quality applications and methodologies in daily processes. The content is written from the perspective of practitioners, and its relevance extends beyond traditional product quality applications"—Provided by publisher.
Identifiers: LCCN 2020027688 | ISBN 9781951058067 (hardcover) | ISBN 9781952236068 (hardcover) | ISBN 9781951058081 (adobe pdf) | ISBN 9781952236082 (adobe pdf) | ISBN 9781951058074 (epub) | ISBN 9781952236075 (epub)
Subjects: LCSH: Total quality management—Handbooks, manuals, etc.
Classification: LCC HD62.15 .C42 2020 (print) | LCC HD62.15 (ebook) | DDC 658.4/013—dc23
LC recordavailableathttps:// lccn.loc.gov/2020027688

ASQ and ASQExcellence advance individual, organizational, and community excellence worldwide through learning, quality improvement, and knowledge exchange.

Bookstores, wholesalers, schools, libraries, businesses, and organizations: Quality Press and ASQExcellence books are available at quantity discounts for bulk purchases for business, trade, or educational uses. For more information, please contact Quality Press at 800-248-1946 or books@asq.org.

To place orders or browse the full selection of Quality Press titles, visit our website at: http://www.asq.org/quality-press.

Printed in the United States of America

26   25   24   23   22   GP   6   5   4   3

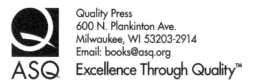

Quality Press
600 N. Plankinton Ave.
Milwaukee, WI 53203-2914
Email: books@asq.org
Excellence Through Quality™

Inspire Excellence

Table of Contents

List of Figures and Tables . . . . *ix*
Preface to the Fifth Edition . . . . *xiii*
Acknowledgments. . . . . *xv*
Introduction . . . . *xvii*

Part I   Leadership **1**

Chapter 1   A. Organizational Structures. **2**
  Organizational Design   2
  Vertical Organizational Design   3
  Horizontal Organizational Design   4
  Centralization/Decentralization.   5
  Types of Organizational Structures.   6
  Management Hierarchy and Influence on the Organization   12
  References.   13

Chapter 2   B. Leadership Challenges **14**
  1. Roles and Responsibilities of Leaders   15
  2. Roles and Responsibilities of Managers.   21
  3. Change Management   26
  4. Leadership Techniques.   36
  5. Empowerment   46
  References.   51

Chapter 3   C. Teams and Team Processes **54**
  1. Types of Teams.   56
  2. Stages of Team Development.   64
  3. Team-Building Techniques.   66
  4. Team Roles and Responsibilities   68
  5. Team Performance and Evaluation.   79
  References.   81

Chapter 4   D. ASQ Code of Ethics. **83**
  Reference.   85

Part II   Strategic Plan Development and Deployment **87**

Chapter 5   A. Strategic Planning Models. **88**
  References.   98

Chapter 6   B. Business Environment Analysis **99**
    1. Risk Analysis 99
    2. Market Forces... 104
    3. Stakeholder Analysis.. 110
    4. Technology 112
    5. Internal Capability Analysis 116
    6. Legal and Regulatory Factors 119
    References... 120

Chapter 7   C. Strategic Plan Deployment............................. **121**
    1. Tactical Plans 121
    2. Resource Allocation and Deployment 122
    3. Organizational Performance Measurement.......................... 128
    4. Quality in Strategic Deployment................................. 131
    References... 135

Part III   Management Elements and Methods. **137**

Chapter 8   A. Management Skills and Abilities......................... **138**
    1. Principles of Management 139
    2. Management Theories and Styles 142
    3. Interdependence of Functional Areas............................. 154
    4. Human Resources (HR) Management 161
    5. Financial Management 174
    6. Risk Management 185
    7. Knowledge Management 194
    References... 203

Chapter 9   B. Communication Skills and Abilities **205**
    1. Communication Techniques....................................... 205
    2. Interpersonal Skills 212
    3. Communications in a Global Economy 217
    4. Communications and Technology.................................. 220
    References... 228

Chapter 10   C. Project Management **229**
    1. Project Management Basics 231
    2. Project Planning and Estimation Tools........................... 239
    3. Measure and Monitor Project Activity 261
    4. Project Documentation 265
    References... 273

Chapter 11   D. Quality System..................................... **275**
    1. Quality Mission and Policy 278
    2. Quality Planning, Deployment, and Documentation 281
    3. Quality System Effectiveness.................................... 283
    References... 292

Chapter 12   E. Quality Models and Theories........................... **293**
    1. ISO Quality Management Standards 293
    2. Performance Excellence Models 300

3. Other Quality Methodologies 304
4. Quality Philosophies.. 317
References 325

Part IV Quality Management Tools 327

Chapter 13 A. Problem-Solving Tools 328
1. The Seven Classic Quality Tools 329
2. Basic Management and Planning Tools 336
3. Process Improvement Tools...................................... 343
4. Innovation and Creativity Tools 352
5. Cost of Quality (COQ) 361
References.. 365

Chapter 14 B. Process Management 366
1. Process Goals 367
2. Process Analysis... 371
3. Lean Tools.. 383
4. Theory of Constraints (TOC) 399
References.. 408

Chapter 15 C. Measurement: Assessment and Metrics.................. 409
1. Basic Statistical Use... 409
2. Sampling.. 416
3. Statistical Analysis... 419
4. Measurement Systems Analysis 427
5. Trend and Pattern Analysis 429
6. Process Variation 433
7. Process Capability 437
8. Reliability Terminology 439
References.. 443

Part V Customer-Focused Organizations 445

Chapter 16 A. Customer Identification and Segmentation 446
1. Internal Customers 449
2. External Customers.. 454
3. Customer Segmentation 456
4. Qualitative Assessment... 465
References.. 467

Chapter 17 B. Customer Relationship Management...................... 468
1. Customer Needs 469
2. Customer Satisfaction and Loyalty............................... 476
3. Customer Service Principles 497
4. Multiple and Diverse Customer Management 502
References.. 506

Part VI   Supply Chain Management **509**

Chapter 18   Supply Chain Management **510**
    A. Supplier Selection and Approval 511
    B. Supplier Risk Management 516
    C. Supplier Communications 518
    D. Supplier Performance 520
    E. Supplier Improvement 524
    F. Supplier Certification, Partnerships, and Alliances 526
    G. Supplier Logistics and Material Acceptance 531
    References 534

Part VII   Training and Development **537**

Chapter 19   Training and Development **538**
    A. Training Plans 540
    B. Training Needs Analysis 545
    C. Training Materials, Development, and Delivery 552
    D. Training Effectiveness and Evaluation 568
    References 576

Chapter 20   The Certified Manager of Quality/Organizational Excellence Body of Knowledge **577**

Appendix A   References *589*
Appendix B   Glossary and Acronyms *603*
Index *659*

List of Figures and Tables

Figure I.1   Evolution of quality, productivity, and information technology to business process management and business architecture methodologies xviii

Figure I.2   Conceptual business architecture elements xx

Figure 1.1   Functional departmentalization 7

Figure 1.2   Product departmentalization 7

Figure 1.3   Customer departmentalization. 8

Figure 1.4   Geographic departmentalization 8

Figure 1.5   Process departmentalization. 8

Figure 1.6   Matrix organization example 10

Figure 2.1   Causes for resistance to change 32

Figure 2.2   Analysis of an employee suggestion system 33

Figure 2.3   Logic tree analysis. 34

Figure 2.4   Maslow's hierarchy of needs. 37

Figure 2.5   A decision option hierarchy 41

Figure 2.6   Conflict-handling modes. 43

Figure 2.7   Traditional versus empowered organization 47

Table 2.1   Relationship changes in an empowered organization 49

Figure 3.1   Linking team structure. 60

Figure 3.2   Project staffing—KESAA requisites analysis 63

Figure 3.3   Team development phases 64

Table 3.1   Roles, responsibilities, and performance attributes. 70

Figure 3.4   Supporting factors for effective teamwork. 78

Figure 5.1   Overview of strategic planning process 90

Figure 5.2   A typical view of the hoshin planning process 92

Table 5.1   Setting objectives the S.M.A.R.T. W.A.Y. 94

Figure 5.3   Top-level means matrix format. 94

Figure 5.4   Linking goals, objectives, and means 95

Figure 6.1   Components of an environment analysis 100

Figure 6.2   SWOT analysis example 102

Figure 6.3   Failure mode and effects analysis example. 105

Figure 6.4   Stakeholder analysis example. 111

Figure 6.5   Generational features 117

Figure 7.1a   Action plan (front) 123

Figure 7.1b   Action plan (back). 124

Figure 7.2   The cascading concept (from QFD) used as a strategic plan
deployment tool 127

Figure 7.3   Examples of critical success factors for two organizations. 129

Table 7.1   Annual closed-loop assessment 130

Figure 8.1   Kolb's experiential learning model 144

Figure 8.2   Analysis of behavior template 146

Figure 8.3   The managerial grid 149

Figure 8.4   Major business processes. 158

Figure 8.5   New product design and launch process 160

Figure 8.6   Mutual investment in individual development......................... 170

Figure 8.7   Sample balance sheet 176

Figure 8.8   Sample income statement 178

Table 8.1   Types and forms of risks that could affect an organization 186

Figure 8.9   Bow tie analysis. 193

Figure 8.10   Transformation of data. 195

Figure 9.1   Communication path 206

Table 9.1   Some of the communication obstacles facing organizations
operating globally and possible remedies 218

Figure 9.2   Levels of information systems 222

Figure 10.1   Advantages and disadvantages of life cycle models. 233

Figure 10.2   Sample emergency department patient length of stay
improvement project risk analysis 240

Figure 10.3   ISO 9001 quality system implementation and registration 243

Table 10.1   A typical project-planning sequence 246

Figure 10.4   Customer response project—stakeholders 249

Figure 10.5   Deliverables (hypothetical) 250

Figure 10.6   Work breakdown structure (work package level) 251

Figure 10.7   Work breakdown structure (WBS)—building garage (outline format) 252

Figure 10.8   Gantt chart 253

Figure 10.9a   CPM data table 255

Figure 10.9b   CPM chart 255

Figure 10.10   Personnel resource requirements matrix............................. 257

Figure 10.11   Sample project budget 259

Figure 10.12   Calibration system project—sample variance report 262

Figure 10.13   Sample emergency department patient length of stay improvement
Lean-Six Sigma project charter 268

Figure 10.14   Sample stakeholder analysis for the emergency department
Lean-Six Sigma project. 270

Figure 10.15a   Action plan form (front) 271

Figure 10.15b   Action plan form (back). 272

Table 11.1   Example of a partial, hypothetical balanced scorecard. 284

Figure 11.1   Flowchart for quality audit   288

Figure 12.1   Baldrige criteria for performance excellence   301

Table 12.1   Examples for benchmarking a process   311

Figure 12.2   Sources of benchmarking information   312

Figure 12.3   APQC Benchmarking Code of Conduct   314

Figure 12.4   The Taguchi loss function   324

Figure 13.1   Flowchart example   330

Figure 13.2   Deployment flowchart example (also called a swim-lane chart).   331

Figure 13.3   Check sheet example   332

Figure 13.4   Cause-and-effect diagram example   332

Figure 13.5   Pareto chart example   333

Figure 13.6   Control chart example   334

Figure 13.7   Histogram example   335

Figure 13.8   Scatter diagram example   335

Figure 13.9   Network diagram example (activity on node)   337

Figure 13.10   Affinity diagram of "methods to improve team performance".   338

Figure 13.11   Interrelationship diagraph example   339

Figure 13.12   Matrix diagrams at various stages of completion   340

Figure 13.13a Priorities matrix—evaluating relative importance of criteria   341

Figure 13.13b Priorities matrix—comparing objects based on one criterion
               (acceleration)   341

Figure 13.13c Priorities matrix (partial)—evaluating all objects against criteria.   341

Figure 13.14   Process decision program chart example   342

Figure 13.15   Tree diagram example   342

Figure 13.16   PDCA/PDSA cycle.   346

Figure 13.17   DMAIC phase and activities.   347

Figure 13.18   Six Sigma tools by DMAIC phase   348

Figure 13.19   Process FMEA example   351

Figure 13.20   Mind map example.   354

Figure 13.21   Use of analogies for a gardening tool   355

Figure 13.22   Nominal group technique ranking table.   356

Figure 13.23   Multivoting example   356

Figure 13.24   Five whys example.   358

Table 13.1   TRIZ principles   359

Figure 14.1   SIPOC diagram example   367

Figure 14.2   Process management maturity assessment.   368

Figure 14.3   Deployment of strategic goals and objectives to process
               goals and objectives   369

Figure 14.4   Traditional process-mapping symbols.   374

Figure 14.5   Process map—non-grid format.   375

Figure 14.6   Process map—grid format.   376

Figure 14.7   A quality management system documentation hierarchy   377

Figure 14.8   Portion of a sample control plan 379

Figure 14.9   Typical U-shaped cell layout... 385

Figure 14.10   Value stream map—macro level (partial) 393

Figure 14.11   Value stream map—plant level (partial) 393

Table 14.1   Techniques, methodologies, and tools applicable to
               process management 402

Figure 15.1   Causal relationship in developing key process measurements............ 412

Figure 15.2   OC curves.. 418

Figure 15.3   Sampling decisions.. 419

Figure 15.4   Probability distributions 422

Table 15.1   Computer downtime log.. 424

Figure 15.5   Control chart for computer downtime 424

Figure 15.6   Run chart patterns 429

Figure 15.7   Bathtub curve 440

Figure 15.8   Reliability and validity.. 442

Figure 16.1   Product/service flow 449

Figure 16.2   Quality-level agreement 452

Figure 16.3   Preference segment patterns... 461

Figure 16.4   Segmentation concepts.. 461

Figure 17.1   Quality function deployment matrix "house of quality"................. 473

Figure 17.2   Sample QFD matrix for an automobile door 474

Figure 17.3   Quality function deployment using voice of customer (VOC) 475

Figure 17.4   Robust VOC system 477

Figure 17.5   System for utilizing customer feedback 479

Figure 17.6   The Kano model 480

Figure 17.7   A customer/client contact record, a sample LCALI form 483

Table 17.1   Perspectives of value to customers 491

Table 17.2   Levels of customer satisfaction....................................... 494

Figure 17.8   Successful customer-centric organizations excel in six critical areas 498

Figure 18.1   Supplier performance report... 522

Figure 18.2   Risks in sampling 532

Figure 19.1   Training versus education 539

Table 19.1   Deficiency analysis... 542

Figure 19.2   A training system model 544

Table 19.2   Distinguishing between performance and skill/knowledge issues 550

Figure 19.3   A curriculum development process.................................... 555

Figure 19.4   Levels of gamification 560

Figure 19.5   Levels of training evaluation 569

Table 19.3   Training form—example 574

Preface to the Fifth Edition

QUALITY MANAGEMENT—AN EVOLVING REQUISITE OF SOCIETY

We know the scope of quality management principles has evolved over the past four decades to much more than the control of manufacturing processes. Quality management tools and techniques are used for any process in any organization. We have seen the integration of organizational excellence models, various international systems standards, lean principles, and Six Sigma tools into the daily operations of an organization. For the most part, quality management professionals have led these efforts.

It is hard to grasp the amount of data available today and the speed at which they are delivered. Advances in technology within Industry 4.0, big data, and the internet of things have opened new opportunities to gain insights into what our customers/clients are thinking and how our processes are performing. Technology has profoundly changed the way we communicate with each other, allowing teams to effectively function globally. The rate of change only accelerates over time. Today's quality management professional must understand the impact of these changes and be able to apply the plethora of tools and techniques available to them in new ways. To remain relevant in society requires a broad understanding of the tools available and innovative thinking about how they are applied. The ASQ Certified Manager of Quality/Organizational Excellence (CMQ/OE) body of knowledge identifies the knowledge required to be successful. It knows not only what tools to use but also how to apply them to meet an organization's strategic needs in an ever-changing business environment.

The fifth edition of *The ASQ Certified Manager of Quality/Organizational Excellence Handbook* takes a fresh look across the broad range of current quality management practices while providing insight into new applications for these tools and techniques to meet the challenges of today's society.

CONTINUOUS LEARNING—PERSONAL EXCELLENCE AS A BASIS FOR ORGANIZATIONAL EXCELLENCE

ASQ's CMQ/OE certification recognizes an individual not only for a broad knowledge of quality management and organizational excellence principles but also for a deep understanding of the complex issues facing organizational performance. The CMQ/OE is a professional designation with rigorous prerequisite requirements in order to sit for an equally rigorous exam. It is the pinnacle of ASQ's professional accreditations.

The CMQ/OE exam body of knowledge is refreshed about every five years. This refresh starts with a job analysis survey of hundreds of quality management professionals around the world in order to capture current practices in the field. From there, teams of CMQ/OE thought leaders go through various workshops, from setting test specifications to item pool maintenance, item review, and, finally, an exam review. Thousands of CMQ/OE thought leaders have been involved with development since the exam's debut in 1995.

The way the CMQ/OE body of knowledge is developed helps ensure its relevance to current practices in quality management and organizational excellence. It is what organizations are looking for in a quality manager, director, or organizational excellence professional. The CMQ/OE body of knowledge changes as global economic conditions, societal concerns, and technology continue to change. This changing environment requires CMQ/OE professionals to recertify every three years in order to ensure their knowledge and skills remain relevant.

USE AND DEVELOPMENT OF THE FIFTH EDITION OF THIS HANDBOOK

This handbook was written to provide additional context to the CMQ/OE body of knowledge. It is an excellent reference for those preparing for the CMQ/OE exam. It can also be used by any professional wanting to understand the scope of quality management and organizational excellence practices. It is a practical guide for any professional to reference on a day-to-day basis when various quality management challenges occur.

While the most recent changes to the CMQ/OE body of knowledge are relatively minor, the fifth edition of this handbook has undergone some significant content changes in order to provide more clarity regarding the items in the body of knowledge. Examples have been updated to reflect more current perspectives, and of course, there is the addition of topics to the most recent body of knowledge.

Since the publication of the fourth edition of the CMQ/OE handbook, we have lost a great teacher and mentor. Russ Wescott has been the driving force behind this effort since the first edition was published in 1997. He touched many lives and is deeply missed. The editorial team of Dr. Sandra L. Furterer and Douglas Wood have taken the reigns, pulling this fifth edition together. Doug was a natural choice given his years of experience both developing and teaching the CMQ/OE prep course offered by ASQ's Learning Institute. Dr. Furterer has an extensive background in publications and editorial review as well as a great foundation in quality management principles. This editorial team recruited a team of recognized quality management thought leaders to contribute to this workbook. It was a true team effort.

Thanks to all of the team members who made the fifth edition of *The ASQ Certified Manager of Quality/Organizational Excellence Handbook* a reality.

—Jerry Rice, Chair, ASQ Quality Management Division

Acknowledgments

To our colleagues Bill Craddock, Denis Devos, Grace Duffy, Susan Gorveatte, Jeff Israel, Tim King, Jd Marhevko, Heather McCain, Eileen Serrano, and Joe Wojniak, who have contributed with us to this revised edition.

To the staff at Quality Press and the hardworking copy and production editors who have ably corrected grammatical errors and made valuable suggestions for improvement.

To the contributors to the first, second, third, and fourth editions, who laid the foundation for this edition.

—Sandra L. Furterer and Douglas C. Wood
Editors, Fifth Edition

I would like to dedicate this handbook to my husband, Dan, and three amazing children, Kelly, Erik, and Zach, from whom I derive the meaning of life.

—Sandra L. Furterer

Introduction

EVOLUTION OF QUALITY

The principles and tools of modern-day quality have evolved over the last one hundred years or so. They were first used mostly independent from productivity and information technology (IT) practices. However, as the tools and concepts evolved, so did the integration between the separate bodies of knowledge. They are now very seamlessly integrated principles and tools that enhance quality, productivity, and automated and streamlined processes that create value for our customers. We will step through the evolution of the quality, productivity, and IT bodies of knowledge, principles, and tools using Figure I.1 as a guide. All three disciplines evolved first as separate practices but integrated together through the years, as practitioners and academics better understood and applied the concepts and tools first in manufacturing industries before branching out into service industries, including healthcare, financial services, retail, and education, to name a few.

We will describe this evolution first with the quality practices. The quality body of knowledge (BoK) started with statistical process control in the 1920s.[1] Walter A. Shewhart introduced statistical process control (SPC) based on applications at Western Electric and Bell Telephone Laboratories. Shewhart published *Economic Control of Quality of Manufactured Product* in 1931 and *Statistical Method from the Viewpoint of Quality Control* in 1939.[2] Dr. W. Edwards Deming installed SPC in Japanese manufacturing as he assisted Japan in their rebuilding efforts after World War II. Total quality management (TQM) was a natural outgrowth of SPC, adding a process improvement methodology. The statistical concepts, along with the principles of the quality gurus Dr. W. Edwards Deming, Joseph M. Juran, Philip B. Crosby, Armand V. Feigenbaum, and others, became the foundation for total quality management (TQM), which became popular in the 1980s. Also in the 1980s, business process reengineering (BPR) encouraged completely throwing out the old process and starting over many times within the context of implementing major information systems changes.[3] These methodologies evolved to Six Sigma. The underlying principles of TQM, BPR, and Six Sigma progressed to business process management (BPM). BPM encompasses documenting, understanding, managing, and controlling key processes in the business enterprise.

On the productivity side, the Ford Production System was used to assemble cars, which was the basis for the Toyota Production System (TPS).[4] Just-in-time (JIT) production philosophies joined with TPS, which evolved into lean.[5] More recently, lean and Six Sigma merged to capitalize on the best of both improvement philosophies and methodologies, combining to form Lean-Six Sigma.

We add the IT stream to show the evolution of business process management systems (BPMS) and business architecture. At the same time that lean and Six Sigma were evolving, IT was advancing from nonintegrated material requirements planning (MRP) and material resource planning (MRP) II applications focusing on managing the shop floor and purchasing processes to integrated enterprise resource planning (ERP) and customer relationship management (CRM) information systems that are evolving into managing the entire supply chain.[6]

The key concept of BPM is the convergence of technologies with process management theories. BPM enables the process enterprise. The process enterprise is organized around core business processes that go across departmental and divisional lines. Processes should be standardized, measurable, repeatable, and reusable. BPM and BPMS both support Six Sigma process improvement through documentation of processes and automated collection of process metrics. Another evolution of the underlying principles has started merging BPM into BPMS and is evolving into business architecture. The goal of BPM is to improve products and services through a structured approach to performance improvement that centers on systematic design and management of a company's business processes.[7] An enterprise can use business architecture principles and methods as the foundation for identifying the processes that need to be improved to enable the business strategies. It provides the

Figure I.1 Evolution of quality, productivity, and information technology to business process management and business architecture methodologies.

Source: Sandra L. Furterer.

documentation of the business processes and the identification of the optimized business processes and components that can be used across multiple business units, markets, and processes. It enables standardization of processes and alignment of process improvement initiatives with the key processes that enable the business's strategic plan. The business architecture BoK is a natural progression from BPM principles. Business architecture is helping to provide a context and prioritization of business strategies that can help to focus Six Sigma and quality improvement efforts.

Now that we have seen the evolution of quality and a possible direction of the quality evolution, from which the CQM/OE BoK may eventually evolve, let us discuss how quality and an enterprise view can help us to better understand, model, and practice within the quality discipline.

ENTERPRISE VIEW

A BoK from systems engineering in business architecture focuses on modeling the key concepts and elements of the enterprise by aligning the business strategies and enabling processes to optimize the key groups of activities that enable optimized IT and process improvement initiatives. Our CMQ/OE BoK includes systems thinking, process improvement, and automation and technology that support quality. I have created a model, the strategic business process architecture (SBPA), to create an enterprise view of an organization's processes, people, and technology that can enable operational excellence. A simplified view of the key elements of the SBPA is shown in Figure I.2.[8] The elements of the SBPA describe the business system enterprise. The SBPA includes understanding customers and their expectations. Another important element of the business architecture is documenting the business's strategies and goals. The goals should relate to the capabilities that the organization requires to meet its goals. The value chain comprises activities that provide value to your customer.[9] The value chains are decomposed into the business functions. Each value chain and the subsequent business functions will be used to further decompose to the processes and their activities. This ensures traceability to value chains that provide customer value. The business capabilities enable the business functions. The business processes and their activities describe the sequence of activities that enable the business to meet the customer's expectations and provide value through the value chains. The conceptual information uses and enables the processes, activities, and optimized components. The optimized components help to leverage key services that automate and support the processes. Applying SBPA enables performance improvement across the entire enterprise, focused on the strategic direction of the organization.

FUTURE OF QUALITY

I briefly discussed the evolution of quality, Figure I.1, and then the conceptual business architecture elements, Figure I.2, that can help to model the enterprise, enhancing both quality and operational excellence by developing a process architecture repository that can aid the organization in its quality journey. These same elements can help to document and build a quality management system, whether

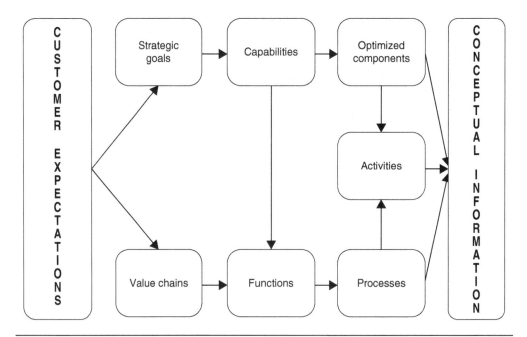

Figure I.2   Conceptual business architecture elements.

Source: Sandra L. Furterer.

using the Baldrige Criteria for Performance Excellence, the multitude of International Organization for Standardization (ISO) standards, or a homegrown system. So what does the future of quality hold? Change, most definitely. The world is becoming ever more complex; technology and product life cycles ever shorter. So how do we maintain and improve the quality of products, services, and the processes that develop and provide these products and services? It is by learning, applying, and evolving the quality management and operational excellence principles, tools, and methods that are so vital and so well presented in this handbook. We thank the wonderful contributors to this handbook who have helped you to continue evolving quality and operational excellence in your organizations.

STRUCTURE OF THIS HANDBOOK

The handbook follows the BoK scheme as set forth in Chapter 20. Throughout each section of this handbook, the categorical BoK requirements associated with good quality management practices for that section are shown in a box preceding the pertinent text. These BoK requirements represent the range of content and the cognitive level at which multiple-choice questions can be presented.[10]

There is some overlap of topics within the BoK. An attempt has been made to cover a given topic in depth in one section as it relates to that section of the BoK and cover it from a different perspective as it applies to a different section of the BoK. For example, failure mode and effects analysis (FMEA) is covered in Part II, "Strategic Plan Development and Deployment," as it would be used to augment the strategic planning process by identifying potential strategic risks to the organization and developing appropriate contingency plans to mitigate these risks. In Chapter 13, the FMEA is covered as a tool for risk management in processes and designs.

Additional references to material for each chapter are presented in Appendix A. When a topic is new to a test preparer, or knowledge has faded, the test preparer is urged to seek more information from one or more of the resources listed. There is no way this single handbook can provide the depth and breadth of knowledge you should have on any given topic in the BoK. There is a wealth of information that can be found on the ASQ website and from the ASQ Knowledge Center, www.asq.org, to prepare for the certification exam, including excellent training workshops.[11]

In order to provide a broad perspective of quality management, this book has specifically been written to address:

- Historical perspectives relating to the evolution of particular aspects of quality management, including recognized experts and their contributions

- Key principles, concepts, and terminology relevant in providing quality leadership and communicating quality needs and results

- Benefits associated with the application of key concepts and quality management principles

- Best practices describing recognized approaches for good quality management

- Barriers to success, including common problems that the quality manager might experience when designing and implementing quality management and insights as to why some quality initiatives fail[12]

Not every quality manager will possess equal expertise in each BoK section and topic. The handbook's primary purpose is to help readers properly focus their study efforts in preparation for the examination. However, this handbook should prove useful as a reference guide back on the job.[13]

TERMINOLOGY

The ISO definition of *product* as "the result of a process" includes categories of hardware, software, services, and processed materials. The word *product* is used throughout the handbook, with and without the accompanying clarification that it also applies to services. It is expected that the reader will have the flexibility to interpret the words in the context in which they are used and to substitute terms that are more apropos for their own industry or experiences to help them clarify the material.[14] The principles, concepts, and tools discussed in this handbook apply to any and all industries, including manufacturing, service (healthcare, financial services), retail, and technology, to name just a few.

DISCLAIMER[15]

The BoK for the CMQ/OE is largely based on conceptual ideas and models rather than on exact mathematical formulas or tangible items that can be held up as correct. For some of the areas of the BoK, there could be multiple correct views because of differences in industry, organizational maturity, geographic location, competitors' strategies, and so on. Even the gurus of quality differ in their philosophies, priorities, and approaches to quality. For example, multiple-choice questions often may appear to have at least two right answers. It will be your task to choose the one answer that best applies to the content and context of the question. (No one ever said that making decisions as a manager/director is simple.)

Furthermore, you should know that ASQExcellence policy maintains a strict separation between the people who prepare the examination, those who score the completed examination papers, and those who present material (in whatever medium available) for people preparing to take the examination. As a result of this separation, the content presented in this handbook may differ from the intent of the creators of the BoK and/or the writers of the examination questions. Therefore, any questions you may have regarding BoK intent or details about answer scoring cannot be answered by the editor of this handbook or by course instructors.

Success as a quality manager requires experience and a mature understanding of the various principles, concepts, and practices, as well as the specific knowledge obtained from this or any other reliable source. The best to you in your quest to become a Certified Manager of Quality/Organizational Excellence. *Good luck!*

Sandra L. Furterer, Editor

REFERENCES

1. D. Montgomery, *Introduction to Statistical Quality Control*, 7th ed. (Hoboken, NJ: John Wiley & Sons, 2013).

2. "About ASQ: Walter A. Shewhart," https://asq.org/about-asq/honorary-members/shewhart, n.d.

3. M. Hammer, "Reengineering Work: Don't Automate, Obliterate," *Harvard Business Review* (July 1990).

4. "Toyota Production System," http://www.toyota.com.au/toyota/company/operations/toyota-production-system, 2013.

5. J. P. Womack, and D. T. Jones, *Lean Thinking: Banish Waste and Create Wealth in Your Corporation* (New York: Simon & Shuster, 1996).

6. APICS (Association for Supply Chain Management), "Material Resource Planning," 2013, http://www.apics.org/industry-contentresearch/publications/ombok/apics-ombokframework-table-of-contents/apics-ombokframework-5.1; APICS, "Enterprise Resource Planning," 2013, http://www.apics.org/industry-contentresearch/publications/ombok/apics-ombokframework-table-of-contents/apics-ombokframework-5.1; APICS, "Customer Relationship Management," 2013, http://www.apics.org/industry-content research/publications/ombok/apics-ombokframework-table-of-contents/apics-ombok framework-5.1.

7. J. Chang, *Business Process Management Systems Strategy and Implementation* (Boca Raton, FL: Auerbach, 2006).

8. S. Furterer, *Lean Six Sigma in Service: Applications and Case Studies* (Boca Raton, FL: CRC Press, 2009); S. Furterer, "Lean Six Sigma Program Success Factors in a Retail Application," International Conference on Industry, Engineering, and Management Systems, Cocoa Beach, FL, 2008; S. Furterer, "Building a Conceptual Business Process Modeling Architecture Repository," *Journal of Management and Engineering Integration* 7, no. 2 (Winter 2015); S. Furterer, "Secure Operational Excellence, Business Architecture Methods That Blaze the Trail," *Industrial Engineer* (April 2009); S. Furterer, "Designing an Enterprise Lean Six Sigma Program," *Quality Management Division Forum* 37, no. 3 (Fall 2011); S. Furterer, "Enabling Enterprise Six Sigma through Business Process Architecture Modeling Techniques," *Quality Management Division Forum* 35, no. 3 (Fall 2009).

9. M. E. Porter, *Competitive Strategy: Techniques for Analyzing Industries and Competitors* (New York: Free Press, 1980).

10. R. Wescott, *CMQ/OE: The Certified Manager of Quality/Organizational Excellence Handbook* (Milwaukee: ASQ Quality Press, 2013).

11. Ibid.

12. Ibid.

13. Ibid.

14. Ibid.

15. Ibid.

Part I
Leadership

Chapter 1   A. Organizational Structures
Contributor: Bill Craddock
Chapter 2   B. Leadership Challenges
Contributors: Bill Craddock
and Sandra L. Furterer
Chapter 3   C. Teams and Team Processes
Contributor: Bill Craddock
Chapter 4   D. ASQ Code of Ethics

1. The only definition of a leader is someone who has followers.

2. An effective leader is not someone who is loved or admired. Popularity is not leadership.

3. Leaders are highly visible. They . . . set examples.

4. Leadership is not rank, privileges, titles, or money. It is responsibility.

—Peter F. Drucker

Leadership is not so much the exercise of power itself as the empowerment of others.

—Warren Bennis and Burt Nanus

If you want one year of prosperity, grow grain.

If you want ten years of prosperity, grow trees.

If you want one hundred years of prosperity, grow people.

—Chinese proverb

Chapter 1

A. Organizational Structures

It is appropriate that a book on the management of quality begins with the subject of leadership. Perhaps no other factor has a greater impact on an organization than how well it is led on both a strategic and an operational basis. Additionally, leadership is not solely the responsibility of those who reside at the higher levels of the hierarchy but is instead an activity in which anyone involved in the success of an organization can take part.

Strategic leadership includes defining the structures to achieve the overall vision and mission of an organization and its strategies and systems.

Define and describe organizational designs (e.g., matrix, flat, and parallel) and the effect that a hierarchical management structure can have on an organization. (Apply)

Body of Knowledge I.A

ORGANIZATIONAL DESIGN

A major role of leadership is to ensure that an organization is designed to carry out its mission, goals, and strategies. Understanding leadership requires a fundamental understanding of organizations and the design factors that must be considered.

The design of an organization is the formal framework for communication and authority and is determined by three major factors:

- *Complexity.* The number of different entities (for example, job titles, reporting levels, functional departments, and physical work locations) that will exist in the organization.

- *Formalization.* How much will the organization rely on standard guidelines and procedures to instruct and direct employee activities?

- *Centralization.* Whether decision-making authority is located primarily at upper management levels or is delegated to lower levels.[1]

These three aspects can be combined to create many different organizational designs. Purposes of organizational design are to:

- Divide the total work required into logical functional groupings (for example, departments and work units) and the jobs within the functions.

- Assign specific tasks and responsibilities to each individual job.

- Allow better coordination of diverse organizational tasks.

- Establish relationships among individuals, work units, and functions.

- Establish formal lines of authority and decision-making.

- Allocate and deploy organizational resources.

To create an appropriate design, a decision must be made as to how work activities will be organized both vertically and horizontally. The vertical structure typically categorizes positions as top managers, middle managers, first-line managers, and operations personnel. Creating the vertical structure includes determining these categories and defining the interaction between the levels by deciding who reports to whom and who has the authority to make what types of decisions. An appropriate organizational design will assist in aligning all of the employees, departments, and processes. Good work alignment is required to remove systemic conflict and achieve strategic goals.

VERTICAL ORGANIZATIONAL DESIGN

One concept used in creating the vertical structure is *unity of command*, or the idea that a subordinate should be directly responsible to only one superior.[2] Although structures such as a matrix organization do not follow this rule, the basic intent of vertical design is to avoid conflicts, misunderstandings, or misuse of resources. Organizational designers also must determine the level of authority and the amount of responsibility for the organizational members. Authority refers to the rights inherent in a managerial position to expect orders to be followed and is related to the position, not the person. Traditionally, authority is delegated downward to subordinate managers, giving them certain rights while specifying limits within which to operate.

There are also different forms of authority: line and staff. *Line authority* is the superior-subordinate relationship extending from the top of the organization to its lowest levels (along a chain of command). A manager with line authority has the right to direct the work of subordinates and to make certain decisions without consulting others. As organizations become larger and more complex, however, line managers may lack the time, expertise, or resources to do their jobs effectively. In response, staff functions are established, such as human resources, that have the authority to support and advise.

Organizations now recognize that one does not have to be a manager to have influence nor is influence always correlated to organizational level. Authority is an important concept in organizations, but focusing exclusively on authority produces a narrow and unrealistic view of sources of influence in organizations. Today, authority is recognized as only one aspect of the larger concept of power.[3]

For example, some individuals in an organization may have considerable informal authority due to their knowledge or personality.

Span of control is another design factor and refers to how many subordinates a manager can effectively and efficiently supervise. Although no consensus exists on an ideal number, many managers favor small spans—typically no more than six—in order to maintain close control.[4] The level at which this decision is targeted affects this number. As managers rise in the organizational hierarchy, they deal with a greater variety of complex and diverse problems. Typically, top executives have a smaller span of control than do middle managers, and middle managers require a smaller span than do supervisors. Therefore, to a large degree, the span of control determines the number of levels and managers in an organization. Other things being equal, the wider or larger the span of control, the more efficient the organizational design.

Today many organizations have reduced the number of managerial positions through restructuring while increasing the spans of control. The optimum span of control is increasingly determined by issues such as:

- Amount of employees' training and experience
- Similarity of subordinate tasks
- Complexity of the tasks
- Physical proximity of subordinates
- Degree to which standardized procedures are in place
- Sophistication of the organization's management information and internal communication systems
- Strength of the organization's culture
- Manager's preferred style[5]
- Employee turnover
- Available resources
- Financial and competitive pressures
- Organizational beliefs and values

HORIZONTAL ORGANIZATIONAL DESIGN

In addition to a vertical dimension, an organization's design also has a horizontal dimension that determines how work activities are organized at each level of the organization. This involves answering questions such as "How will work activities be allocated?" or "What form of departmentalization will work best?"

Division of labor means that rather than an entire job being performed by one individual, it is broken down into a number of steps, with separate individuals completing each step or group of steps. In essence, individuals specialize in doing part of an activity rather than the entire activity. Assembly-line production, in which each worker repeatedly does a standardized task, is an example of division of labor. Fast-food companies use the concept of division of labor to standardize the process of taking a customer's order and filling it quickly and properly. Because some tasks require highly developed skills, while unskilled workers can perform others, division of labor makes efficient use of the diverse skills and capabilities of employees. If all workers in an organization were engaged in each step of the production process, every worker would need the skills to perform both the most demanding and the least demanding jobs. The result would be that except when performing the most highly skilled or highly sophisticated tasks, employees would be working below their skill levels. Because skilled workers are paid more than unskilled workers and their wages tend to reflect their highest level of skills, paying highly skilled workers to do easy tasks would be an inefficient use of resources.

Historically, management has viewed the division of labor as an unending source of increased productivity. Eventually, certain drawbacks of division of labor exceed the economic advantages, including problems such as boredom, job stress, low productivity, poor quality, increased absenteeism, and high turnover. Organizations have discovered that giving employees a variety of activities to perform, allowing them to do a whole and complete piece of work, and putting them together into teams makes jobs more interesting, and higher quality often results.

CENTRALIZATION/DECENTRALIZATION

Centralization/decentralization refers to how much decision-making authority has been delegated to lower management levels. Few organizations could function effectively if all decisions were made by a select group of top managers nor could they do so if all decisions were delegated to the lowest levels of the organization. Fayol lists centralization as one of his fourteen principles of management and notes that the proper amount of centralization or decentralization depends on the situation.[6]

Organizations have traditionally been structured as pyramids, with authority and power concentrated at the top and with relatively centralized decision-making. As organizational environments have become more complex and dynamic, many organizations have begun to decentralize decision-making. Many executives now believe that decisions should be made by those people with the best information to make the decisions, regardless of their level in the organization.

More decentralization might be needed under one or more of the following conditions:

- The environment is complex or uncertain.
- Lower-level managers are capable and experienced at making decisions.
- Lower-level managers want a voice in decisions.
- Decisions are relatively minor.
- Corporate culture is more open to allowing managers to have a say in what happens.
- The organization is geographically dispersed.
- Effective implementation of the organization's strategies depends on managers having more involvement and flexibility to make decisions.

Organizational designers should select the amount of centralization/decentralization that best allows management to implement goals and strategies. What works in one situation might not be best for another.

TYPES OF ORGANIZATIONAL STRUCTURES

In resolving issues such as distribution of authority, reporting relationships, span of control, and amount of centralization/decentralization, the structure of the organization will result. It is worth noting that the current tendency is to move to flatter organizations having fewer hierarchical levels and more flexible reporting arrangements. Although a flatter organizational structure implies a wider span of control, information technologies have greatly simplified the processes of communication and decision-making, allowing authority to be more widely dispersed.

Organizations are becoming managed more as horizontal processes (for example, as a part of the supply chain or value chain), rather than vertical hierarchies. A *matrix structure* is one way of formalizing a structure that provides both effective horizontal and operational decision-making as well as allowing development of functional specialties. Another structure often used when an organization desires to implement a significant change is to create a temporary *parallel* or *collateral organization*, which consists of a group of employees (often a diagonal slice of the organization) who meet on a regular basis in order to guide the change process. Once the organization has made the transition, the parallel structure is dissolved.

Earlier, some of the aspects that affect organizational design—such as division of labor, distribution of authority, span of control, and employee knowledge and experience—were discussed. Many different structures can result from these decisions, and which one an organization selects is also affected by larger factors, both internal and external.

Each organization has its own way of grouping work activities (departmentalization). Groupings may be according to the:

- Work functions performed
- Product or service provided
- Customers served
- Geographic area or territory covered
- Product-customer process flow

The method(s) used should reflect the grouping that would best contribute to the attainment of the organization's strategic goals and objectives as well as the objectives of individual units. Following is a discussion of each of these structures, plus additional forms in which boundaries are more fluid.

- *Functional.* One of the most common ways to group activities is by the function performed. A manufacturing plant might be organized by separating engineering, accounting, manufacturing, human resources, and purchasing specialists into departments, as shown in Figure 1.1. Functional departmentalization can be used in all types of organizations, with the name of the functions changed based on the types of skills required to achieve organizational objectives. For example, a university hospital might have departments devoted to health research, patient care, facilities management, and finance.

• *Product.* Figure 1.2 illustrates the product departmentalization structure. Each major product group is placed under the authority of an executive who specializes in and is responsible for all aspects of that product line. A clothing retailer also uses product departmentalization, basing its structure on its varied product lines, such as women's and men's footwear and apparel and accessories. This type of structure allows portions of the organization to focus on particular categories of products, allowing greater expertise to be gained about the market and product technology.

• *Customer.* The particular type of customer an organization seeks to serve can also be used to define structure. The sales activities shown in Figure 1.3 for an office supply firm can be broken down into three departments: those serving retail, wholesale, and government customers. Textbook publishers often organize by customer, such as those serving primary schools, high schools, and college or university levels. The assumption underlying customer-stratified organizations is that customers in each grouping have a common set of problems and needs that will best be met by specialists who can focus on their needs.

• *Geographic.* Another way to organize is by geography or territory. An organization's sales function might have western, southern, midwestern, and eastern

Figure 1.1   Functional departmentalization.

Figure 1.2   Product departmentalization.

regions, as shown in Figure 1.4. A large school district might have six high schools to serve each of the geographic areas within its district. Geographic organization is valuable when an organization's customers are scattered over a large area, allowing the specific needs of the location to be addressed, as well as reducing business costs such as logistics.

 • *Process.* A flow form of departmentalization is shown in Figure 1.5, which illustrates the various production departments in an aluminum extrusion processing plant. Each department specializes in one specific phase (or subprocess) in the production of aluminum tubing. The metal is cast in huge furnaces and sent to the press department, where it is extruded into aluminum pipe. It is then transferred to the tube mill, where it is stretched into various sizes and shapes of tubing. It then moves to finishing, where it is cut and cleaned, and finally arrives in the inspect, pack, and ship department.

Figure 1.3   Customer departmentalization.

Figure 1.4   Geographic departmentalization.

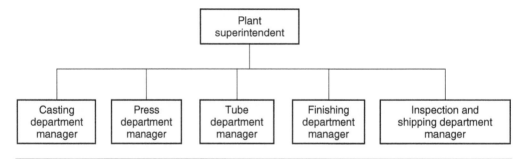

Figure 1.5   Process departmentalization.

- *Team.* The competitive drive for improvement has made organizing by teams more common. This structure often overlays or replaces the rigid boundaries of departmentalization, bringing together individuals with needed competencies for a particular mission. In a team-based structure, the entire organization consists of work groups or teams that perform the organization's work. Employee empowerment is crucial because no rigid line of managerial authority flows from top to bottom. Team members are free to design work processes in the way they think best and are held responsible for all work activity and performance results in their areas. For example, an insurance company reorganized its customer representatives into eight-person teams trained to expedite all customer requests. Rather than switching customers from one specialist to another, a team now takes care of every aspect of a customer request. A manufacturing example would be a plant expansion requiring skills from facilities, procurement, human resources, and process engineering to plan and execute the addition successfully. The team members each contribute knowledge from their own areas of expertise, and team discussions result in rapid and optimal compromises for completing the expansion on time, on budget, and without excessive risk to the organization. Such a project handled sequentially by each department would not have allowed an ideal outcome.

- *Matrix.* A matrix structure assigns specialists from different functional departments to work on one or more projects led by a project manager. This arrangement was developed in the 1960s by the U.S. aerospace industry to cope with the demands of managing a number of concurrent projects. Figure 1.6 shows a sample matrix organizational structure. In a typical matrix organization, specialists report to a line or project manager to integrate their expertise with those of other specialists. They also report to a functional manager responsible for departmental human resource issues such as hiring, skill enhancement, assignments to line or project units, and performance reviews.

- *Cells.* Parts of an organization may be structured in work cells. A *cell* is a self-contained unit dedicated to performing all the operations to complete a product or process or major portion of a product.

- *Boundaryless.* A different view of organizational structure is called the boundaryless organization (also referred to as a *network organization, modular corporation,* or *virtual corporation*). It is not defined by, or limited to, the boundaries imposed by a predefined structure. The *boundaryless* organization breaks down the artificial boundaries created by a design, such as departmentalization and hierarchies, and the external boundaries separating the organization from its suppliers, customers, and other stakeholders.

Many factors have contributed to the rise of the boundaryless organization. One is the need to respond to rapidly changing, highly competitive global markets. Another factor is new technology that permits organizations to work more effectively. For example, a world leader in credit card authorization systems has no corporate headquarters, secretaries, or paper mail. The chief executive officer calls his organizational structure the "blueberry pancake model, very flat, with all blueberries equal."[7] Employees have a vast amount of information at their fingertips through the company's e-mail network.

The authors of *The Boundaryless Organization: Breaking the Chains of Organizational Structure* discuss the means for structuring a boundaryless organization

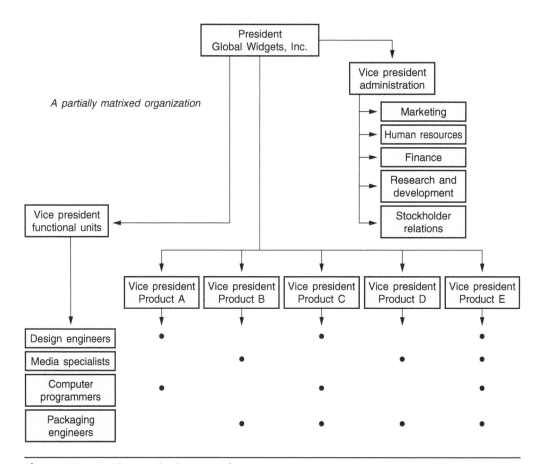

A partially matrixed organization

Figure 1.6 Matrix organization example.

attuned to the needs for integrating resources to serve the customer, strengthening the value chain, and crossing geographic boundaries.[8] Authors of *The Virtual Corporation* focus on the powers of information, new technologies, and a new kind of worker.[9] Beyond the ways an organization groups its work activities, there are other factors to consider. They are:

• *Strategy.* Since organizational structure will affect the ability to achieve strategic objectives, structure should be based on the organization's strategy. This means that if the strategy significantly changes, structure will likely need to be modified to support the change. A low-cost provider strategy may utilize a functional structure sharing the same support resources with many facilities (for example, centralized purchasing, human resources, and engineering), while a strategy to develop close, long-term customer relationships would call for a more decentralized structure (for example, sales offices for each major customer or geographic location).

• *Size.* The size of the organization affects structure due to the fact that a larger organization will tend to have more specialized and diverse activities to be managed. This increased differentiation can easily lead to narrowly focused or transactional management, although this may be mediated by where the company's product is in its life cycle. For example, a company that has grown large as a result of gaining a significant market share in a new product line may find a need for transformational management as the product enters the mature low-growth stage.

• *Technology.* Another factor affecting structure is the range of technologies used by the organization. Every organization uses various forms of technology to convert inputs into outputs, and the type of technology will have an impact on organizational structure. For example, a chemical firm using continuous-flow processes will be organized differently than a hospital or a law firm. The management styles are also likely to differ since professionals in a hospital or law firm are knowledge workers who would expect a freer rein than employees whose job is to load and unload railcars of raw material and finished goods.

• *Core competencies.* Organizations can be structured to focus on the core competencies that differentiate the organization from its competitors. Core competencies may consist of unique capabilities of its workforce, specialized technologies, the knowledge and experience of its management, its track record for innovation, world-class service policies and practices, a unique niche the organization's products and services fulfill, and so on.

• *Regulatory, legal, and other requirements.* Constraints and mandates due to regulations, laws, and standards may influence organizational structure. For example, ISO 9001 registrar organizations must clearly separate their registration-auditing organization and services from their consulting services organization. Certain customers may specify that the products they purchase be produced in facilities and by workers separate from products their supplier produces for other customers to protect proprietary designs and processes. Because of potential contamination, laws may prohibit the commingling of the production of certain products—for example, food products and chemicals. The types and levels of security mandated for certain industries—for example, products and services for the U.S. military— will influence organizational structure. Regulations governing occupational health and safety affect organizational structure, and laws governing allowable emissions are critical to certain industries.

• *Union.* Employees represented by a union are a kind of parallel organization within an organization. In an ideal situation, the union leader participates with the top management of the organization in strategy development as well as decisions affecting the ongoing business of the organization. In the more traditional situation, and sadly, still the more prevalent situation, the union and organization management may coexist in an adversarial relationship.

Union leadership may influence organization structure and reporting relationships, job design, work standards and practices, compensation and benefits, purchasing decisions, supplier selection, employee disciplinary actions, facility expansion or closure, process improvement initiatives, and so on. Disagreement over the terms of the labor-management contract can result in a production slowdown or strike.

• *Competition.* The competitive environment in which the organization operates will also affect organizational structure, as a higher pace of change requires a more flexible organizational design that can quickly adapt to new market opportunities. In this environment a team structure and participative style are more likely to succeed than a functional structure with autocratic management.

- *Workforce issues.* Availability of sufficient workers and/or of skilled workers is a factor affecting organizational design. All of the considerations necessary to attract and retain the workforce are factors—for example, availability of housing, transportation, schools, religious entities, shopping, entertainment, and adequate community infrastructure.

- *Facilities.* The present and future availability of land, buildings, utilities, rail service, roadways, an airport, and so on are important considerations. Some of these items may be termed infrastructure, but all are linked in a functional manner as facilities.

- *Other environmental factors.* The prevailing weather patterns, the political climate, and the presence or absence of crime are all factors as well.

- *Combinations.* Most large organizations will utilize a combination of methods of organization and management. At the local facility level, they might be organized in teams or in functional or process groups and at the division level organized by product. At higher levels there may be a geographic structure that allows focusing on a particular part of the world (for example, the United States, Europe, and Asia).

MANAGEMENT HIERARCHY AND INFLUENCE ON THE ORGANIZATION

To ensure that an organization achieves its desired outcomes, someone must plan, allocate resources, and monitor results. These are major activities for which management personnel have responsibility. *Top management* (also called *senior management* or *executive management*) is responsible for providing direction in defining the vision, mission, strategies, goals, structures, policies, systems, and objectives. These managers are also responsible for managing the boundaries between the organization and its major stakeholders, such as investors, business partners, and the communities in which the organization is located.

Middle managers are responsible for carrying out the policies and procedures necessary for achieving the mission, goals, and strategic objectives. Their emphasis is more operationally than strategically oriented, playing a key role in day-to-day communications and decision-making. Middle management's role also parallels that of top management in the sense of being responsible for leadership of a particular part of the organization.

First-level supervision (line management) is responsible for overseeing the workforce assigned to produce the products and/or services for which the organization is designed. Supervisors, while usually considered part of management, have the difficult role of thinking and behaving like a manager and, at the same time, dealing empathetically with the concerns and problems of the workers. In this role, supervisors must communicate downward the vision, mission, principles, and strategic objectives of the organization, take the actions necessary for their work unit to respond appropriately to those objectives, monitor and maintain the processes and people under their supervision, and be accountable for the quality and quantity of product and service required. How effectively supervision establishes a motivational environment has a direct effect on the stability of the workforce and the outcomes achieved by the organization.

Not an official member of management, the lead operator is often charged with the responsibility for some scheduling, instructing, and interwork unit liaison activities in addition to performing production work.

The role of supervisor, and to some extent the middle manager, may not be needed in some types of organizational structures—for example, where teams are the predominant structural element in a virtual organization or when information technology has adequately bridged the gap between the workers and management.

Organization culture has an overarching influence on organization structure. Culture may be determined by leadership views, by past practice, or by prevailing attitudes in the surrounding society. If the leadership places a high value on following orders, a narrow span of control may result. If an organization has been successful allowing relative independence of different divisions, adding linkages to control this independence will be difficult to include, even if there is good economic reason to do so. A society that values following the direction of authority will find difficulty encouraging individuals to innovate against the possibly poor direction of leaders.

REFERENCES

1. S. P. Robbins, D. A. DeCenzo, and M. K. Coulter, *Fundamentals of Management: Essential Concepts and Applications*, 9th ed. (Boston: Pearson, 2016).

2. H. Fayol, *Industrial and General Administration* (Paris: Dunned, 1916).

3. D. Kipnis, *The Power Holders* (Chicago: University of Chicago Press, 1976).

4. L. Urwick, *The Elements of Administration* (New York: Harper & Row, 1944), 52–53.

5. D. Van Fleet, "Span of Management Research and Issues," *Academy of Management Journal* 26, no. 9 (1983): 546–52.

6. H. Fayol, and J. A. Coubrough, *Industrial and General Administration*, trans. for the International Management Institute by J. A. Coubrough (London: Sir I. Pitman & Sons, 1930), 19–42.

7. T. Peters, "Successful Electronic Changeovers Depend on Daring," *Springfield Business Journal* (August 8, 1994): 15.

8. R. Ashkenas, D. Ulrich, T. Jick, and S. Kerr, *The Boundaryless Organization: Breaking the Chains of Organizational Structure* (San Francisco: Jossey-Bass, 1995).

9. W. H. Davidow, and M. S. Malone, *The Virtual Corporation* (New York: Edward Burlingame/Harper Business, 1992).

See Appendix A for additional references for this chapter.

Chapter 2
B. Leadership Challenges

I believe leadership lies more in character than in technical competence, but these two are interwoven. As people grow in competence, they gain awareness of a new dimension of their character. Then, as they begin to develop that aspect of their character, they find that their competence also increases.[1]

—Stephen R. Covey

When is a manager not a leader? When is a leader not a manager? The answer to these questions begs for a precise definition of *leader* and *manager*. Yet, try as we often do to differentiate between the two roles, ambiguity creeps in to blur the line of demarcation. The fuzziness is exacerbated by common usage (or "misuse," depending on your point of view). One observation is that the title *leader* is rarely found on organizations' lists of position titles, although occasionally *team leader* may appear. Does this mean that a leader is some ethereal entity who does not truly exist in the real world? Not so.

A *leader* is an individual recognized by others as the person to lead an effort. One cannot be a leader without one or more followers. A leader might or might not hold an officially designated management position or officially have people reporting to him or her. A leader leads people. An organization can also be referred to as a leader, in the sense that it is on the leading edge (in technology, innovation, products, services, market share) compared with its contemporaries.

A *manager* is an individual who manages and is responsible for resources (people, material, money, time). This is a person officially designated with a management position title. A manager is granted authority from above, whereas a leader's role is earned by having followers. Managers manage organizations, processes, systems, projects, and themselves.

According to Deming, "The job of management is not supervision, but leadership."[2] The roles of leader and manager can be fulfilled by the same individual. It is really what the individual does, how the individual does it, and from where the individual derives the power to act that relate to which term is most applicable in a given situation.

Leadership focuses on doing the right things; management focuses on doing things right.[3]

—Stephen R. Covey

This chapter discusses techniques and tools available to leaders that include those used to overcome organizational roadblocks (change management). Also discussed are techniques and tools used in applying, evaluating, and creatively using interpersonal skills (motivating, influencing, negotiating, resolving conflict, and empowering). These are leadership challenges.

Strategic leadership involves creating both technical and social systems that are effectively integrated and address the needs of both customers and employees. Operational leadership requires ensuring that organizational processes are effectively carried out on a day-to-day basis, monitoring performance and addressing constraints. It involves ensuring that employees understand what is to be done and are provided with the appropriate authority, responsibility, requisite skills, tools, and work environment with which to do it.

The levels of employee motivation and empowerment and how conflict is resolved shape as well as serve to measure the organizational culture. Leadership must effectively attend to these softer issues that also affect organizational performance.

In a Gallup study conducted from 2005 to 2008, a question was asked to elicit the words that describe what the most positive leader in your life contributes to you. The four most commonly expressed words were *trust, compassion, stability*, and *hope*.[4]

1. ROLES AND RESPONSIBILITIES OF LEADERS

Describe typical roles, responsibilities, and competencies of people in leadership positions and how those attributes influence an organization's direction and purpose. (Analyze)

Body of Knowledge I.B.1

Much effort and countless pages of print have been expended in attempting to develop a universal profile for a leader. It appears to be an endless and (perhaps) pointless task, each effort adding but another viewpoint on what constitutes a leader. It has already been stated that the line between the roles of a leader and those of a manager tend to be blurry and often overlap. Let us explore some of the attributes that tend to identify an individual as a leader, under several different situations:

- *Organization leader.* Most often holding a position with managerial or supervisory responsibilities, this individual exhibits leadership qualities that enable the person to accomplish more than the position calls for. This individual may be perceived as a leader by his or her subordinates, peers, and bosses for exhibiting one or more of these attributes:

  — Knowledge

  — Skills

— Experience

— Charisma

— Action

— Convincing speech

— Empathy

— Ethics

— Empowerment

— Collaboration

— Support

— Trust

— Multidimensional personality

- *Cause leader.* This individual may work either behind the scenes or be highly visible to followers. Through personal motivation and power of persuasion, this leader gathers followers to a common goal or cause, sometimes inciting the followers to take physical action against a targeted group. This type of leader has the ability to communicate in the language of the followers to stimulate their emotions, the stamina to build and sustain a high level of personal energy, and the ability to be seen as a fellow group member with issues the same as or similar to those of the group. This person is usually from the worker ranks of an organization or, sometimes, is a "hired gun" who looks and talks like the followers.

- *Transactional leadership.* A transactional style is one in which the manager views the relationship as one of getting the work done through a clear definition of tasks and responsibilities and providing whatever resources are needed. This view might be likened to a contractual relationship, with rewards (positive or negative) associated with achieving the desired goal.

- *Transformational leadership.* Transformational leadership is a style whereby a leader articulates the vision and values necessary for the organization to succeed. It is sometimes equated to charismatic leadership but is aimed more at elevating the goals of subordinates and enhancing their self-confidence to achieve those goals. Bob Galvin accomplished this transformational leadership at Motorola with the Six Sigma program, an approach that positioned Motorola to become a high-quality, reliable competitor in its market.

- *Other kinds of leaders.* Bass identifies several additional leadership types, namely:[5]

  — Educational leaders

  — Public leaders

  — Opinion leaders

  — Legislative leaders

To be a leader, one has to believe in oneself, but with reasonable doubt and humility. One has to have a zeal for the role and genuinely care for people (the latter does not apply to ruthless dictators who lead through fear). "Leaders of the future can no longer afford to maintain insularity. It is simply not an option in increasingly boundaryless organizations driven by customer power . . . now they must destroy those walls and replace them with bridges."[6] Key roles of a leader include being a:

- Facilitator

- Appraiser

- Forecaster

- Advisor[7]

- Enabler[8]

- Follower[9]

Requirements for good leadership are similar, regardless of the functional department a manager oversees. Some specific requirements for quality managers in leadership roles include the following:

- Personal commitment to process, product, and organizational quality

- Strong sense of value for others' work and leadership

- Skilled application of a broad base of knowledge of the quality field and an understanding of how to apply this knowledge in functional areas

- Wisdom about both people and things and an understanding of how to integrate them to get work accomplished

- Absence (or control) of temperamental or emotional characteristics that might interfere with the ability to work with others

Some critical personal attributes that leaders in the quality management area should exhibit include creativity, patience, flexibility, and self-discipline. Good listening skills, excellent coaching and training skills, sensitivity to customer and employee issues, and a personal commitment to excellence are all essential. Finally, a leader must be a mentor, capable of leading change and willing to empower followers.

In their book *The Leadership Challenge*,[10] Kouzes and Posner explain five practices that exemplary leaders use: (1) model the way, (2) inspire a shared vision, (3) challenge the process, (4) enable others to act, and (5) encourage the heart.

Just as organizational structures, processes, and priorities have changed in recent decades, so, too, have the defined roles and characteristics of an effective leader. Some writers have defined the difference between management and leadership as the amount of control exercised over people. Kouzes and Posner define leadership as a shared responsibility and state the difference as "Managers . . . get other people to do, but leaders get other people to want to do."[11] Warren Bennis defines the differences between the two as doing the right thing (leadership = effectiveness) versus doing things right (management = efficiency). Others have recognized that the type of leader needed often depends on the particular situation, such as the organization, its mission, its strategies, its competitive environment, and the makeup of the individuals being led.[12]

Some issues that make leadership difficult to define include:

- Leadership of an organization may be an appointed role (for example, president or department manager).

- Leadership may be taken on at various times by different people who are working together on a particular project. That is, the role of leadership is based on who has the competence necessary during a particular phase of a project.

- Increasingly, in a knowledge-based environment the person being led has more knowledge of the tasks to be accomplished than the individual who is regarded as the leader.

- The increase in virtual teams, in which a group of individuals is jointly responsible for a particular outcome but where team members do not have face-to-face contact (for example, where technologies are used to communicate).[13]

- Schein described paradoxes of leadership when stating that leaders of the future will be persons "who can lead and follow, be central and marginal, be hierarchically above and below, be individualistic and a team player, and, above all, be a perpetual learner."[14]

- Deming described the primary responsibility of leaders as "transformation of the organization."[15]

- Another leadership role is to ensure that the organization works effectively with respect to the interactions between individuals, groups, and business units both within and outside the organization and that behaviors meet accepted standards for business ethics.

The traits and actions of leaders will, or should, vary based on the contingencies they face. Hersey and Blanchard's situational leadership model focuses on three factors:[16]

1. Task behavior

   - The level of work-related detail and guidance a leader must provide to a performer

   - The extent to which direct action must be taken with the performer

2. Relationship behavior

   - The extent of the communication required with the performer

   - The amount of interpersonal support given a performer

3. Employee maturity or readiness

   - The ability of a performer to assume a task

   - The willingness of the performer to assume the task

Considering the maturity factor, the task and relationship behaviors comprise four situational leadership styles:

1. *High task, low relationship.* Specific instructions and close supervision of performance are indicated (a telling mode). For example, a new

or transferred employee is assigned a task for which he has no prior training and needs continual supervision until skill is developed.

2. *High task, high relationship.* Decisions are explained and there is opportunity to clarify and ask questions (a selling mode). For example, a newly trained operator is trying to apply the training to the task at hand but does not understand the need to follow the prescribed sequence of steps and requires supervisory support.

3. *High relationship, low task.* Ideas are shared, encouragement is provided, and the leader acts as a coach (a participating mode). For example, a trained operator is hesitant to assume full responsibility for the entire task assigned and needs help to build confidence.

4. *Low relationship, low task.* Responsibility for decisions and implementation are turned over to the employee (a delegating mode). For example, an experienced operator knows what to do and how to do it, as well as how to troubleshoot a problem should one occur, and assumes full responsibility for the task assigned without requiring direct supervision.

The keys to effective situational leadership are:

- Being able to determine, situation to situation, the leadership style most appropriate to apply in working with performers

- Realizing that one style does not fit all situations

- Realizing that the style used last with a performer may not be the best next time

- Realizing that other factors can influence performance, such as:

  — The performer's physical and/or mental health

  — Events in the performer's personal life

  — The influence of coworkers

  — Lack of material, tools, equipment, and so on

  — Inadequate working conditions

Another aspect to leadership is the emotional competence of the incumbent leader. Daniel Goleman identifies five dimensions, three personal and two social, and related competencies.[17]

The personal dimensions and related competencies are:

1. Self-awareness

   - Emotional awareness

   - Accurate self-assessment

   - Self-confidence

2. Self-regulation

   - Self-control

- Trustworthiness
- Conscientiousness
- Adaptability
- Innovation

3. Motivation

- Achievement drive
- Commitment
- Initiative
- Optimism

The social dimensions and related competencies are:

4. Empathy

- Understanding others
- Developing others
- Service orientation
- Leveraging diversity
- Political awareness

5. Social skills

- Influence
- Communication
- Conflict management
- Leadership
- Change catalyst
- Building bonds
- Collaboration and cooperation
- Team capabilities

Good leaders challenge the status quo. They inspire and enlist others. They encourage collaboration and enable others to take action. Effective leaders share their power and information to strengthen others. They look for and recognize people who are doing things right. Respected leaders set an example, recognize others' contributions, and celebrate successes. Exemplary leaders continually strive to improve both their intellectual intelligence (cognitive capacity) and their emotional intelligence. Leadership is a daily balancing act of juggling responsibilities and withstanding pressures.

2. ROLES AND RESPONSIBILITIES OF MANAGERS

The inherent preferences of organizations are clarity, certainty, and perfection. The inherent nature of human relationships involves ambiguity, uncertainty, and imperfection. How one honors, balances, and integrates the need of both is the real trick of management.[18]

—Richard Pascale and Anthony Athos

> Describe typical roles, responsibilities, and compe-
> tencies of people in management positions and
> how those attributes contribute to an organization's
> success. (Analyze)
>
> **Body of Knowledge I.B.2**

What Managers Do

Managers attend to the work and resources of the organization—a stewardship role. This may include obtaining, allocating, distributing, using, disposing, and accounting for the resources that fall within the purview of the position to which they are assigned. Primary categories of resources include:

- Money
- Time
- People
- Material
- Physical assets: equipment, facilities, land, and water
- Information
- Intellectual property

Managers may be assigned a variety of different position titles, some of which are:

- Chief executive officer, chief operating officer, chief finance officer, chief information officer
- Vice president of _____
- Director of _____
- General manager of _____
- Manager of _____
- Superintendent of _____
- Supervisor of _____
- Staff supervisor of _____

- Designer of _____

- _____ engineer

- Purchasing agent/buyer for _____

Labor laws differentiate between exempt employees (employees free from certain laws pertaining to hours and compensation) and nonexempt (employees covered by laws relating to hours worked and compensation). Generally, management employees are exempt (however, the nature of one's work and compensation received are key determinants of exempt versus nonexempt status; for example, some management employees receive overtime pay as nonexempt employees do).

As stated earlier, there is often overlap between the roles and responsibilities of a leader and a manager. A significant difference is that the manager's role is mandated by some higher authority and is in effect as long as the higher authority so states. The role of leader is less permanent and, in fact, may either be shared through rotation or acquired through acceptance by followers. Being recognized as a leader often has no relationship to an organizational position title. Thus, a manager may or may not be recognized as a leader. A worker may be recognized as a leader without having any managerial-type title or responsibility. Organizations often interchange the two terms—for example, by calling someone a project leader when the intention is really project manager. A chairperson may be a leader and/or a manager, depending much on the influence he or she may have on an organization and the decision authority granted.

Managers' roles may include:

- *Strategist.* Establishes direction for the enterprise through strategic planning and deployment of the plan's goals and objectives

- *Architect.* Builds an enterprise structure that supports the strategic goals and objectives

- *Organizer.* Organizes people, ideas, and things to achieve the enterprise's objectives

- *Business generator.* Grows and sustains a viable business by creating and retaining satisfied customers

- *Value creator.* Adds value to the enterprise's processes, products, and services

- *Innovator.* Continually seeks ways to introduce, improve, or replace processes, products, and services to further the strategic goals of the enterprise

- *Administrator.* Optimizes the use of results obtained from the resources available

- *Entrepreneur.* Redeploys resources from activities producing poor results to activities where improved results may be obtained

- *Supporter.* Provides visible support, personal involvement, and reinforcement in furthering the efforts of the workers in fulfilling the enterprise's objectives

- *Ethicist.* Embraces the principles, standards, morals, and norms of the society in which the enterprise operates

- *Environmentalist.* Operates the business with high regard for sustaining and improving the physical environment in which the enterprise exists, with responsible use of land, air, and water and safeguarding of wildlife

- *Mentor.* Provides a personal role model and guidance for the development of future managers

- *Motivator.* Creates and sustains a work environment that stimulates motivation in others

- *Coach.* Sets an example and guides others in achieving excellence

- *Trainer.* Imparts knowledge and teaches skills to others

- *Communicator.* Keeps others informed

- *Integrator.* Brings previously disassociated people and processes together

- *Harmonizer.* Balances and harmonizes major functions of the enterprise

- *Controller.* Oversees the financial affairs of an enterprise

- *Evaluator.* Tracks, measures, analyzes, and evaluates the performance, outputs, and outcomes produced by the enterprise and the contribution toward achieving the strategic goals of the enterprise and addressing the needs of society

Sometimes a person may be titled a manager even though she or he is an individual contributor (makes a personal professional contribution to benefit the enterprise) and is not responsible for managing people.

Management functions may be grouped as follows:

- *Planning*

  — Mapping the work unit's processes and interfaces with other work unit's processes

  — Defining the work unit's performance objectives and linkage with the organization's mission, strategic goals, and objectives

  — Identifying the actions and activities needed to achieve the unit's objectives

- *Organizing*

  — Acquiring or assembling the resources needed to meet the unit's objectives

  — Establishing the structural framework (systems and procedures) for managing the unit's processes and resources

- *Staffing*

  — Selecting, hiring, assimilating, and training personnel needed to achieve the unit's objectives

  - Developing the unit's individual and collective competence level to meet or exceed the planned objectives

  - Retaining the unit's competent personnel by creating a motivational environment

- *Directing*

  - Directing the actions and activities of the unit's personnel in achieving the planned objectives

  - Providing the support needed by the unit's performers in realizing the product or service produced by the unit

- *Controlling*

  - Monitoring unit performance and comparing actual results to plans

  - Taking appropriate corrective actions as needed

  - Identifying areas for continual improvement

Competencies needed by managers cover a wide range.[19] Typical managerial competencies may include:

- *Technical competence*, for example:

  - Value streams

  - Techniques and tools

  - Enterprise resource planning

  - Process and quality auditing

  - Process benchmarking

  - Information technology

  - Knowledge management

- *Business competence*, for example:

  - Strategic planning

  - Customer relationship management

  - Finance

  - Metrics

  - Risk analysis and management

  - Project management

  - Performance management

  - Organization structures

  - Marketing

  - Processes

  — Legal requirements

  — Ethics issues

  — Stockholders/ownership issues

  — Supply chain management

- *People competence,* for example:

  — Personality types

  — Managing styles

  — Diversity issues

  — Behavior management

  — Interacting

  — Communicating

- *Human resource competence,* for example:

  — Hiring

  — Training

  — Affirmative action

  — Benefits

  — Recognition and rewards

  — Compensation

  — Safety and well-being

  — Professional development

- *Environmental competence,* for example:

  — Factors affecting the world

  — Politics and power issues

  — Earth sciences

  — Competition

Drucker identifies four tasks of management:[20]

- *The task of economic performance.* Business enterprises exist for the purpose of economic performance—profitability. Other societal needs cannot be fulfilled without a surplus of economic resources.

- *The task to make work productive and the worker achieving.* Performance is accomplished through work. Achieving implies consideration of the human resource as human beings and not as things.

- *The task of managing the social impacts and the social responsibilities of the enterprise.* No institution can exist outside of community and society.

- *The task of managing within the dimension of time.* Management always has to consider both the present and the future, both the short run and the long run.

Persons holding management positions lower in the organizational structure are usually responsible for designated short-term outputs—for example, parts produced, engines serviced, reports generated, and so on. Managerial personnel at the high end of the organizational hierarchy are more likely to be responsible for longer-term strategic outcomes affecting the profitability, growth, and overall success of the enterprise.

3. CHANGE MANAGEMENT

> Use various change management strategies to overcome organizational roadblocks, assess impacts of global changes, achieve desired change levels, and review outcomes for effectiveness. Define and describe factors that contribute to an organization's culture. (Evaluate)
>
> **Body of Knowledge I.B.3**

3.1 Organizational Perspective of Change Management

Techniques for Facilitating or Managing Organizational Change

External change is inevitable; internal change is probable. Change can occur as a result of outside forces or inside forces. Organizations that continually improve their processes will have a greater probability of success than those who only react to problems. As an organization evolves, there are not only incremental changes but also increasingly major shifts in strategy, technology, and work organization.

Fear of change is also a real and valid concern. People are afraid of change because of its potential impact on them. Corporate downsizing and outsourcing cause major disruptions of people's work and personal lives, and continual improvement efforts are sometimes blamed for job losses.

Change management is a process for ensuring that the people affected by change understand the nature of the change and the reasons for it, with the expectation that the new methods of operating will be internalized without creating undue resistance, conflict, and fear. To reduce fear, it is important that the vision of the future be well communicated and that jobs be protected when feasible. Ongoing and open communication during any change process is paramount. Although these precautions will not totally remove fear, they can remove some of the uncertainty of not knowing the direction in which the organization is headed.

Change Agents

Change agents are individuals who play a specific role in the planning and implementation of the change management process.[21] They may be members of the organization or may be outsiders. Collaboration of an internal change agent with an external change agent who has extensive experience in the type of change to be implemented can be a useful strategy.

An internal change agent is a person within the organization designated, usually by management, to facilitate a particular change effort. Internal change agents possess an understanding of the organization's culture, infrastructure, and business and also have a vested interest in seeing change efforts succeed. However, they can be hindered by political pressures that can influence objective feedback when problems arise. They might also lack perspective of the big picture or have a vested interest in preserving certain traditions that keep them from seeing specific opportunities for improvement. The role of the internal change agent may be filled by a staff or line person, depending on the type and magnitude of the change being implemented.

An external change agent is a person from outside the organization who has been retained to advise and help facilitate the change process. An external change agent often has a greater degree of freedom and should be better able to objectively assess activities and provide honest feedback to senior management without fear of repercussion. Also, organizational members are less likely to have previous experiences with the change agent that might have an impact on effectiveness, and the agent does not have a vested interest in preserving long-held organizational traditions. The danger, of course, is that organizations can become so dependent on an external change agent that the change process is adversely affected when the agent leaves. Another disadvantage of external change agents can be their lack of familiarity with the specific corporate culture.

External change agents must work diligently to build a relationship with the client organization. This includes becoming familiar with company norms, shared beliefs, and behaviors, as well as understanding both formal and informal leadership structures. In most organizations, the change agent needs to become acquainted with persons who serve as informal leaders and to whom others turn for new ideas. Building a relationship between informal leaders can be beneficial because other members of the organization will check with them for affirmation that it is beneficial or safe to support the change process.

Deming emphasized the role of change agents in his view of organizational transformation by stating, "A system cannot understand itself. The transformation requires a view from outside."[22]

Guidelines for Implementing Change

The following steps are key to implementing change:[23]

1. Create an awareness of the need for change.

2. Organize a project with sufficient authority to guide the process.

3. Define the vision and strategies for achieving it.

4. Communicate the vision and demonstrate personal commitment to it.

5. Remove obstacles that prevent others from acting on the vision.

6. Go for early and visible successes.

7. Build on success by rewarding supporters and involving more people.

8. Institutionalize the new methods by aligning other systems with them.

The following are common errors made in managing change:[24]

- Not sufficiently emphasizing urgency and allowing people to be complacent

- Allowing personnel who do not have sufficient power to guide the process

- Lacking a clear and compelling vision or not communicating it strongly and/or frequently enough

- Failing to manage the forces that resist change

- Not ensuring some early successes that encourage others

- Celebrating victory prematurely

- Not changing the other organizational systems and cultural elements that are required for long-term continuation of the change

In Peter Senge's *The Fifth Discipline*, he refers to the parable of the boiling frog to emphasize how threats to corporate and personal survival are perceived when transformational change is taking place: A frog suddenly placed in boiling water—the turbulence of organizational change—will scramble out. Placing a frog in water that is room temperature will not upset the frog. In fact, the frog might even be calmed. Now the water can be gradually heated until it is boiling. As the heat increases, the frog will become groggier until it can no longer climb out. When the water is boiling, the transformation is complete. The frog's internal apparatus senses the change as a threat to survival and instinctively seeks to avoid the situation.[25] For effective organizational change, use a slow and gradual process change while paying attention to the subtle reactions from employees.

At the same time, a significant lesson that psychologists will emphasize is that the change process, from an individual perspective, is a progressive one that usually occurs over a considerable length of time. For major changes in culture, this is also true at the organizational level. Trying to shortcut the process may create an illusion of speed but will not produce the desired results.

Techniques and Roles of Change Agents

Change agents may assume several roles and use a variety of techniques, such as:

- Coaching top management to:
  - Create an environment in which change can take place with minimum resistance.
  - Develop and support an improvement plan.
  - Provide the resources to implement the plan.

- Supporting and advising management colleagues on how to:
  - Deal with technical issues.
  - Cope with intellectual and emotional resistance.
  - Measure, monitor, and report progress.
  - Handle behavioral issues.
  - Provide performance feedback, including reinforcement of top management for the decision it made and reinforcing the work of those implementing the change.
  - Use the change agent as a facilitator when needed.

- Managing a specific project or segment of a large project to:
  - Fill in where no other suitable resource person is available.
  - Serve as a role model for other project management efforts.

- Guiding the development of a network to:
  - Support the implementation of the change.
  - Deploy the principles and practices for managing change throughout the organization.

- Guiding the assessment of the results and closure of the change, including:
  - Reviewing lessons learned
  - Evaluating the economic case for the change
  - Documenting the change

Organizational Roadblocks

Organizational change is difficult, partially due to the inherent nature of how organizations are designed and operated. That is, by constructing an organization in one way (for example, defining the specific roles and processes to be used), other options are excluded by default. Although the boundaries of organizational structure, policies and procedures, and norms are actually quite permeable, the fact that they are defined, documented, and reinforced makes them appear permanent in the minds of many employees. This may be especially true in an organization with a history of success, where that success is linked mentally to the way things have been done in the past.

The division of labor in an organization, both horizontally and vertically, creates several roadblocks. Following are some examples, along with methods for reducing the effect on the organization's ability to change:

- *Lack of cross-functional collaboration.* Functional or other forms of work units are created in order to help clarify the mission and focus of each particular group in the organization. An organization, however, is a system with interdependencies in many different directions. When the interdependencies (for example, internal customer-supplier relationships) are not clearly defined and fostered, each work unit may view a request for change only as it relates to their own processes, rather than the entire organization.

A possible solution is to ensure that improvement initiatives, performance measures, and rewards are designed such that collaboration (teamwork across boundaries) will be necessary in order to achieve objectives. Develop internal customer-supplier agreements and performance measures, along with ongoing joint reviews of progress.

• *Lack of authority.* The reason for dividing up work processes and tasks is because time and/or skills constraints prevent any one person from carrying out all the necessary activities. This means that responsibility and authority are divided among many. When a change in work activity is required, however, new roles, responsibilities, and processes may not fit into the predefined boundaries.

A possible solution is to ensure that someone (for example, a champion/ sponsor) is identified who has authority over the entire area to be affected by the change and that they have a direct link to higher levels of the organization in the event they need additional support outside their area of authority.

• *Inward focus.* Similar to the lack of cross-functional collaboration is the problem of the boundaries between the organization and its environment. By definition, each organization consists of only certain processes and people, and outside these boundaries are suppliers, customers, regulators, and other stakeholders. The day-to-day attention of many members of the organization, however, is on internal processes, resources, and knowledge. Being willing to look externally for ideas, support, and feedback may not come naturally.

A possible solution is to have employees go outside of the organizational walls—for example, by visiting customer sites, locations where the final product/ service is in the hands of the final user, or where other sources of information on new ideas might exist (such as trade shows, conferences, workshops).

• *Internal competition for resources or rewards.* All organizations have limited resources and opportunities and must allocate them so as to best accomplish the mission with high efficiency. Limited funds, people, or promotions can cause employees to compete against each other—not wanting to suboptimize their area—instead of seeing their efforts as needing to be focused on maximization of the enterprise.

A possible solution is to ensure that strategic and operational plans clearly indicate the priorities and strategies of the organization and where and how resources are to be allocated. Involve employees in creating these plans through a catchball-type process.

• *Lack of understanding.* In a typical organization, there are so many different strategies, initiatives, projects, and day-to-day activities always going on that it is often difficult to keep everyone fully informed. People therefore put their focus where it seems best placed, but this may not agree with what is actually expected or desired.

A possible solution is to communicate, communicate, and communicate. The biggest problem noted in many employee surveys is lack of adequate communication. When people have gaps in their understanding, they often fill them in as best they can, even though what they hear or think may be incorrect. Management must ensure that information relative to organizational direction (for example, vision, mission, values, strategy, objectives, projects, and performance) is continuously communicated, with the amount and type of communication being adapted to the message and audience.

- *Slow decision-making.* Although an organization may have clearly communicated plans and good cross-functional relationships, levels of the hierarchy slow down and frustrate some people who are actively working on improvement initiatives. Vertical communication is meant to ensure ongoing alignment of goals and activities but is often slower than optimal due to the number of channels through which it may travel and differing time perspectives at each level.

A possible solution is to ensure that authority levels are clearly defined for typical situations and use an exception basis where a few key people have the authority to act if the decision involves crossing a particularly difficult organizational boundary. Specify decision-making channels that do not require everyone in the hierarchy to be involved in all decisions, especially those related to improvement opportunities.

Those who study human development discover a tension within many individuals who, on the one hand, want to improve their lives but, on the other, want a life that is stable and without chaos. Similar paradoxical issues have an impact on an organization's ability to change. Following are some examples:

- *Lack of willingness to invest for the long term.* Managers are often measured according to the end-of-quarter financial results. Yet a significant commitment of funds and other resources is usually required in the early part of organizational transformation, with the more strategic payoffs occurring perhaps three or more years later.

- *Wanting results fast.* Many of the cause-and-effect relationships dealt with on a day-to-day basis in organizations are quickly resolved. This gets translated into people's expectations for many other issues, although there is often a significant time lag between cause and effect. People become impatient and want to stop taking action if they are not seeing results.

- *Be selective in what to work on first.* Take the classic low-hanging-fruit approach. Make sure that initial efforts are focused on areas where success and payoff are highly probable.

- *Poor history of change.* Some organizations have a long record of unsuccessful change efforts, which causes people to become cynical and to want to avoid future attempts.

- *Learn from errors.* Study and admit past mistakes and ensure that future efforts do not repeat them.

- *Fear of the unknown.* By definition, change means that things will be different than in the past. People are often uncertain of what their new roles will be and whether they will be able to adapt to the changes, or want to.

- *Provide support for change.* Allow employees to talk with others who have been through similar changes. Provide reassurance that necessary support will be available throughout the change.

- Like the current condition
- Indicates time is wrong
- Poor history of change

- Don't like change
- Poorly communicated
- Wrong people, method, timing

- Future status unknown
- Fear of failure
- Additional workload

Figure 2.1   Causes for resistance to change.

Source: Reprinted with permission of APLOMET.

- Ensure that there is a common vision of change; communicate the purpose and importance. Figure 2.1 depicts the change process and causes for resistance to change. In the current state, people are comfortable with and like the current condition. There may be a prior history of poor attempts at change. The time may never have been considered right for change. When the change process is begun, people may not like the change. The required change may be poorly communicated. The organization may have the wrong people, method, and timing to make effective change occur. The future state and status may be unknown. People may have a fear of failure in the future state and fear additional workload.

- Understand the emotional impact of change.

- Understand the systems view—that is, be aware of how changing one process or part of the organization will affect other processes or parts.

- Communicate what will and what will not change.

- Model the behaviors that are desired.

- Provide effective feedback, rewards, and consequences.

- Be consistent in responding to resistance.

- Be flexible, patient, and supportive.[26]

Constraint Management

Managing change is particularly complex due to the fact that much of what must be changed often consists of intangibles such as beliefs, behaviors, and policies. These types of constraints are more difficult to identify and manage than issues such as the capacity limitation of a piece of equipment. Conceptual models or diagrams are useful for representing situations. It is important to provide models that are visual and aid in the understanding of intangible constraints that may need to be addressed. Following are some examples of how these diagrams can be used:

Identifying Constraints with an Interrelationship Diagraph. Creating the interrelationship diagraph is a method for representing several elements involved in a process and their cause-and-effect relationship. The diagraph involves first developing an affinity diagram, then analyzing and organizing the components into their respective relationships.

Figure 2.2 is an example of an interrelationship diagraph developed by an organization that was considering developing a suggestion system. Some people had reservations about whether it would be worthwhile, so the management team developed the diagram to represent its thinking about the issues involved. Team members included whether the relationships between components were positive or negative (for example, would or would not be beneficial), as some members of management had reservations about the costs, both resource and financial, of administering the program. They subsequently discovered that they could design the system to fit their particular needs rather than basing it solely on the systems they had seen and read about. The diagram helped them understand the true cause-and-effect relationships involved and that the design they selected would be the major driver for both costs and resources. An organization unhappy with an existing suggestion system might also learn from a similar analysis.

This type of analysis allows a group to develop a common view of how something is working or should work. The model can also be used as a diagnostic tool to guide collection of data to determine which components of the system are not working as desired. Managing constraints requires understanding the issues involved in the situation, how they are interrelated, which have the most leverage, and which will or may block the desired outcome.

Identifying Constraints Using a Tree Diagram. Another approach to finding constraints is to break the situation down into component parts using a logic tree diagram.

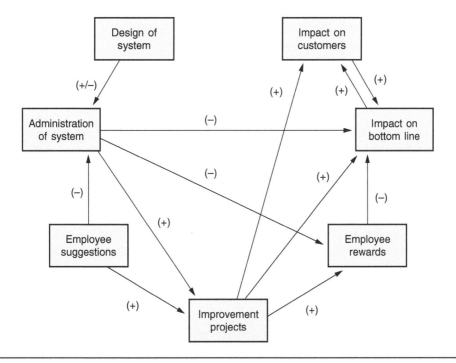

Figure 2.2   Analysis of an employee suggestion system.

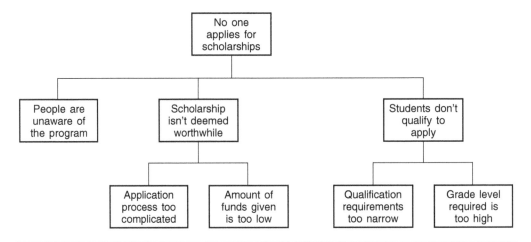

Figure 2.3   Logic tree analysis.

Figure 2.3 demonstrates the use of the process by an organization that offered a scholarship program for three years but had no applicants. The organization had widely publicized the program so elected not to look at that branch of the tree. By breaking down the other two branches, however, it found some likely sources of the problem. It may again ignore some of the branches (for example, keeping the required grade level at what is deemed necessary for true scholarship purposes) and either investigate or alter other aspects of the program in order to affect the next application period.

The logic tree diagram uses a top-down approach to analyzing the situation. As with many improvement tools, the process can also be enhanced by involving key stakeholders in developing the model and in gathering information to identify the constraint(s) for which action will be taken.

3.2 Factors That Contribute to an Organization's Culture

Schein defined culture as:

> The culture of a group can now be defined as a pattern of shared basic assumptions learned by a group as it solved its problems of external adaptation and internal integration, which has worked well enough to be considered valid and therefore, to be taught to new members as the correct way to perceive, think, and feel in relation to those problems.[27]

Culture includes the underlying assumptions and value that drive experiences in the organization. Culture is longer-term and typically enduring in an organization.[28]

Schein identified events and forces that help to understand culture: (1) group norms, or how people typically behave in groups; (2) espoused values; (3) formal philosophy; (4) rules of the game; (5) organizational climate, the meaning that organizational members attach to experiences within the organization; (6) habits of thinking, mental models, and/or linguistic paradigms; (7) shared meanings; (8) root metaphors or integration symbols; and (9) formal rituals and celebrations.[29]

Schein also analyzed culture at three levels: artifacts, espoused beliefs and values, and basic underlying assumptions. Artifacts include visible and feelable structures and processes and observed behavior. Espoused beliefs and values include: (1) ideals, goals, values, and aspirations; (2) ideologies; and (3) rationalizations. Basic underlying assumptions include unconscious, taken-for-granted beliefs and values.[30]

One must first understand the existing organizational culture before an attempt can be made to change it. Johnson suggested asking questions that can help to understand the culture aligned to several identifying artifacts:[31]

- Symbols, such as organizational logos, office layouts, and parking spaces

- Power structures, such as managerial groupings and the most powerful functional areas

- Organizational structures, such as organizational hierarchy (chart) and informal structures

- Control systems, such as performance measurement and reward systems

- Rituals and routines, such as the annual Christmas party and meetings around the water cooler

- Stories and myths, such as stories about mavericks and myths about promotion opportunities

- The paradigm, such as client satisfaction at all costs

Different areas of the globe apply different change management tools, including:[32]

North America (in priority order):

1) Strategic planning

2) Mission and value statements

3) Benchmarking

4) Customer satisfaction surveys

5) Growth strategies

Europe:

1) Benchmarking

2) Mission and vision statements

3) Strategic planning

4) Customer satisfaction measurement

5) Outsourcing

South America:

1) Strategic planning

2) Customer satisfaction measurement

3) Pay-for-performance

4) Mission and vision statements and total quality management

Country cultures can also impact organizational culture, which may require different change management strategies and tools, depending upon both the organization and the organization's country location where the change projects occur.

4. LEADERSHIP TECHNIQUES

> Develop and implement techniques that motivate employees and sustain their enthusiasm. Use negotiation techniques to enable parties with different or opposing outlooks to recognize common goals and work together to achieve them. Determine when and how to use influence, critical thinking skills, or Socratic questioning to resolve a problem or move a project forward. (Create)
>
> **Body of Knowledge I.B.4**

It is impossible for one person to motivate another person. Motivation is derived from within a person—a person needs to feel motivated. Therefore, motivating a person can only be done by creating an environment in which the person feels motivated. When one person (for example, a supervisor) says she is going to motivate a subordinate, she means (or should mean) she is going to do something that will cause the subordinate to become motivated. The idea that a "kick in the butt" will motivate a subordinate is incorrect; it may just move the subordinate and usually will make the subordinate angry and/or afraid. That kind of movement is erroneously perceived as motivation.

Theories of Motivation and Influence

Two types of motivation have been identified:[33]

- *Extrinsic motivation:* The satisfaction of either material or psychological needs that is applied by others or the organization through preaction incentive or postaction reward.

- *Intrinsic motivation:* The qualities of work itself or of relationships, events, or situations that satisfy basic psychological needs (such as achievement, power, affiliation, autonomy, responsibility, creativity, and self-actualization) in a self-rewarding process.

Abraham Maslow developed a model demonstrating a *hierarchy of needs* through which he believed people progressed.[34] Maslow's pyramid (see Figure 2.4) assumes that once humans satisfy the basic, physiologically driven needs, they will then

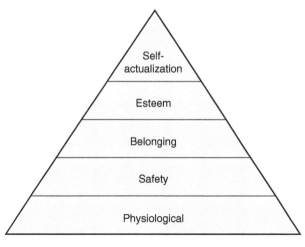

Stage	Process	Needs
1st	Physiological	To eat, sleep, have shelter
2nd	Safety	To have economic and physical security
3rd	Belonging	To be accepted by family and friends
4th	Esteem	To be held in high regard; status
5th	Self-actualization	To achieve one's best

Figure 2.4   Maslow's hierarchy of needs.

be motivated by higher-level needs, and this process will continue until achieving self-actualization. The workplace is obviously a key aspect in allowing an individual to satisfy physiological and safety needs, but someone who has satisfied these levels and is working to satisfy higher levels can quickly return to the bottom of the hierarchy in the event of a job loss. The workplace can also allow an individual to reach higher levels, assuming there are job opportunities that enable the person's personal desire for recognition and achievement to be satisfied. It is important to note that since Maslow's theory is based very much on values, it would not necessarily apply to people from all cultures or socioeconomic strata.

Frederick Herzberg identified two categories into which work motivation factors could be classified—*satisfiers* and *dissatisfiers*.[35] Dissatisfiers included factors such as work conditions, salary, company policies, and relationship with one's supervisor. He also called them *hygiene factors* since, although they create dissatisfaction if not adequately addressed, correcting the deficiencies would not create satisfaction. Satisfiers included items such as responsibility, achievement, advancement, and recognition.

There are also three motivational theories specifically related to recognition and rewards:

- *Equity theory.* Job motivation depends on how equitable the person believes the rewards (or punishment) to be.[36]

- *Expectancy theory.* What people do is based on what they expect to gain from the activity (Victor Vroom).[37]

- *Reinforcement theory.* What people do depends on what triggers a behavior initially (the antecedent) and the consequences that have in the past resulted from such behavior or the consequences the performer believes will happen as a result of a behavior (B. F. Skinner).[38]

What motivates one person may not motivate another. McClelland and others have posited that:[39]

- An individual who enjoys working closely with other people is motivated by affiliation.

- Someone who works in order to accomplish personal goals is motivated by achievement.

- A person who works in order to contribute to the well-being of others is motivated by altruism.

- Someone who wants to have control over her or his work is motivated by power.

These motivations are not mutually exclusive nor is any one person driven only by a single factor. In fact, in order to satisfy their many different needs, people are often involved in several different activities at work, in their local community, and in other organizations.

A paradoxical view of motivation is the division between intrinsic motivation and extrinsic motivation. Some people are driven more by their own internal needs or desires, while others are motivated primarily by external factors. This is partially a function of whether the person has an internal or external locus of control—whether you believe your future is influenced more by your own actions or by the actions/decisions of others.

Caution is advised in assuming that what stimulates motivation for an individual in one situation or time frame will continue to motivate the next time. Also, what provides motivation for one person may not do so for another. Consider this example: Work is backing up, and the manager tells her work unit personnel that the unit will have to work overtime each day for the next ten days. Rose, a young woman who is saving money to buy a dirt bike, is delighted about the prospect of extra compensation. Ray, a single father whose baby is cared for during the day by a babysitter, is distraught because he has to be home by 6:00 p.m. to relieve the babysitter and realizes that any other option will cost more than he will earn on overtime. Rose is motivated; Ray is not. Six months later, the same need for overtime occurs. Rose resents the mandate (she has purchased her dirt bike and wants to ride it in the early evenings before the sun sets). Ray's aunt has moved in with him and now cares for the baby. Ray needs the additional compensation to help with his expanded family. Ray is motivated; Rose is not.

Negotiation

In order for multiple parties, whether individuals or groups, to work together to achieve common goals, there must be agreement on the goals, the methods for achieving them, and what will occur when difficulties arise. Each party will typically have different values and priorities that need to be addressed, and that calls for negotiations resulting in an agreement acceptable to all parties. Management-union negotiations are perhaps the most widely discussed example, but negotiation also occurs as part of many other normal business processes, such as:

- Establishing specifications for purchased components for a new product
- Setting performance measures for a process or department
- Defining the desired outcomes for an improvement project
- Identifying personal development goals

Parties involved in such negotiations might include customers and suppliers, senior management and middle management, sponsor and team leader, or manager and employee.

A difficulty in the negotiation process is that the two parties often approach the task as though there were only two sides to the situation, when, in fact, multiple views could be taken. This is exacerbated when a win-lose attitude is taken, as the process will become divisive and usually result in outcomes that are not seen as beneficial by either party. There are four orientations to negotiation: win-win, win-lose, lose-win, and lose-lose. When both parties approach negotiation with an anticipation of achieving mutual benefit, both parties tend to win. The other three orientations leave the parties striving not to lose at any cost.

Principled negotiation based on a win-win orientation includes:

- Separating the people from the problem
- Focusing on interests, not position
- Understanding what both sides want to achieve
- Inventing options for mutual gain
- Insisting on objective criteria

Timing also affects negotiations, both long-term and short-term. For negotiations that recur on a long-term periodic basis (such as labor agreements), the years between sessions allow the parties to store up their frustrations and release them just as they come together to forge a new contract. At the same time, allowing a break between negotiation sessions allows the parties to back off from what may be an emotional discussion and reflect on their primary purposes.

Negotiations should take place in an environment that is conducive to open discussion and allows all involved to see each other face-to-face. Rather than making presentations to each other, both parties should focus on a conversation with each other, which means that listening in order to understand the other person's viewpoint is a key requirement. A set of ground rules or a third-party mediator may be useful if the negotiations involve a highly controversial or emotional subject.

Some techniques that have been found to improve the negotiation process include:

- Focusing on common objectives before discussing areas of difference
- Avoiding power strategies such as lying about one's priorities in order to get the other party to submit to lowered expectations
- Doing something for the other party, even if symbolic, to create positive energy

- Separating out discussion issues that are not interconnected so they can be discussed based on their own merit

- Bringing in other parties that may have additional or different information about the situation[40]

Additional techniques include:

- Identifying, up front, a range of acceptable outcomes—and why you want what you want

- Determining the real intentions of the other party: the goals, objectives, and priorities

- Being prepared with supporting information

- Not rushing the process

- Keeping the most difficult to resolve issues for last

- Being sensitive to face-saving needs of the other party

- Being firm, fair, and factual

- Always controlling your emotions

- Evaluating each move against your objectives and assessing how it relates to all other moves

- Being adept at formulating a win-win compromise

- Being aware of the effect of the outcomes of the present negotiation on future negotiations

- Actively listening and seeking clarity of expectations

- Being flexible with your position and being able to step back and look critically at your position—there may be multiple ways the same overall objective can be achieved. This view involves going up the vertical hierarchy of one's cognitive view of the situation, rather than only going horizontally across perceived options.[41]

Figure 2.5 is a portion of a decision option hierarchy for reducing deficit spending by a city government. Negotiations between city officials and the school board often focus only on option C, while negotiations with the citizenry focus only on options A and B. By limiting the focus to the *hows*, the larger picture of the higher *why* is often ignored, which means that option D is often not even understood as a possibility.

Negotiating is a skill very much needed in the project management arena. Often, the project manager/leader has less authority than ongoing operations managers, and that necessitates negotiating for needed resources. This is especially problematic when the project team is not dedicated solely to the project. Then, one of the largest problems is ensuring that the project team members get the time needed to work on the project.

Change management usually involves negotiation in eliminating organizational roadblocks and managing constraints. (Change management will also involve conflict resolution.)

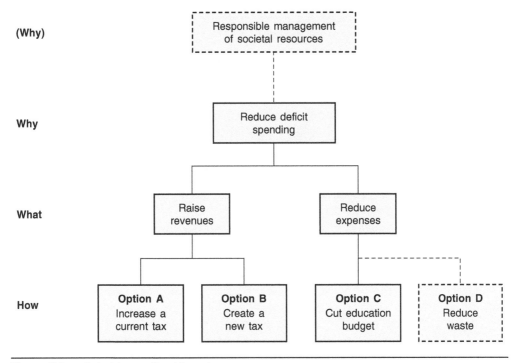

Figure 2.5   A decision option hierarchy.

Some common uses for negotiation are:

- Customer-supplier purchasing contracts
- Negotiation of compensation terms between a potential new hire and the organization
- Labor-management contracts
- Facilities/equipment rental contracts
- Negotiating for approval of the annual budget for a work unit

Having effectively completed negotiations usually means that the relationship between the parties will continue and that the agreement should be documented. The agreement should include the standards against which the compliance of each party will be compared, a frequency or process for reviewing performance, and what is to take place if a violation should occur.

Conflict

Sources and Views of Conflict. Because organizations consist of individuals and groups with different backgrounds and responsibilities, some conflict is inevitable. A conflict might occur between two individuals (for example, between a manager and an employee, or between peers), between groups (for example, departments or teams), or between organizations (for example, customer and supplier). Although conflict will often be created by disagreements over goals or resource allocation, beneath the surface are differences in values, priorities, roles, and personal styles that cause the conflict to become emotional and/or personal.

Conflict occurs when two or more options appear to be mutually exclusive, and a viable alternative is felt to be absent. Conflict cannot be resolved when the parties involved firmly believe that what each wants is incompatible with what the other wants.

Conflict may be due to personal issues or may be caused by underlying organizational issues (for example, incongruent policies or unclear boundaries). The effect is that energy that should be focused on the organization's mission instead gets transferred to activities that are unproductive. Regardless of whether the activities are unseen or visible, it is in the best interests of the organization to identify and address the conflict. Quality managers, because of their expanded role in facilitating cross-functional cooperation for strategic alignment and continual improvement, should be aware of and develop their conflict management abilities.

On the plus side, conflict can also be viewed as an energizing force. Management and resolution of differences between individuals and groups can unlock creativity. "Contrary to conventional wisdom, the most important single thing about conflict is that it is good for you. While this is not a scientific statement of fact, it reflects a basic and unprecedented shift in emphasis—a move away from the old human relations point of view where all conflict was basically seen as bad. In brief, in our new frontier environment, conflict is the order of the day."[42]

One model for understanding conflict resolution is based on the dimensions of assertiveness (extent to which a party attempts to satisfy his/her own concerns) versus cooperativeness (extent to which the party attempts to satisfy the other's concerns).[43] The resulting matrix (see Figure 2.6) has been incorporated in an assessment instrument that can be used to evaluate conflict-handling style. Interpretation of the instrument emphasizes that each conflict mode might be appropriate for a particular situation. The following list further expands on these options:[44]

- Approach it as a problem to be solved. Utilize facts and information that can be useful for looking at and evaluating different options.

- Smooth over the conflict by emphasizing the positives and trying to avoid the negatives. This is obviously only a temporary solution if the conflict is substantial.

- Transfer the problem to a higher level of authority.

- Resolve any scarcity of resources that is creating the conflict.

- Avoid the conflict if it is not in the organization's best interests to continue to pursue it.

- See if compromise will resolve it to the satisfaction of both parties.

- Change the minds of the people involved.

Since the latter option involves trying to change a person's mind, it is not a very viable one. Research indicates that people's basic personalities do not change substantially over their lifetimes, so changing a mind is obviously difficult. Additionally, organizations do not have the right to change a person's thought processes per se. The option is viable if interpreted differently—people may be transferred or otherwise removed from the conflict situation as a final option. In a quality organization, however, it is more likely that additional methods for resolving the situation would be attempted.

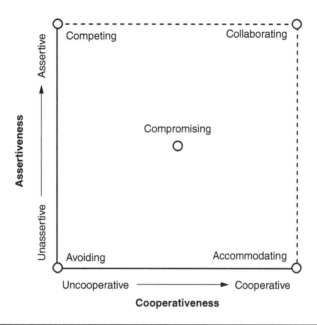

Figure 2.6   Conflict-handling modes.

Techniques for Conflict Resolution. The best method for resolving a particular conflict depends on the situation. If there is clearly a solution that simply needs to be identified and agreed to, and the parties involved are not adamantly opposed to each other, then simple discussions utilizing brainstorming, multivoting, and consensus may be sufficient. The brainstorming process can be used to identify several possible solutions, followed by a multivoting process that narrows the list to a smaller, more viable list. Looking at the positive and negative attributes of each option may then result in agreement of all parties on what action(s) will be taken. This discussion can be aided by looking at each activity required by each party in the conflict, the effort it would require, and the impact it would have both on resolving the issues and on the relationship between the parties.

A more difficult situation arises when, although there may be several viable solutions, the involved parties do not appear to be prepared to work cooperatively in order to reach a joint decision. A process such as *interest-based bargaining* (also called *principled negotiation*) might then be used to attempt to satisfy as many interests as possible using the following steps:

1. Define the problem in a way that distinguishes it from the people involved.

2. Clarify the interests of the parties (as opposed to their positions on the issue).

3. Identify new and creative options beneficial to all parties.

4. Determine objective criteria to be used to evaluate fairness of the outcomes for all parties.

Conflict resolution may also involve intervention by a third party. For example, a person trained in human process interventions might help parties involved in a conflict by engaging them in dialogue. Strategies that might be used include:[45]

- Helping the parties avoid the factors that trigger conflict
- Setting guidelines for interaction of the parties
- Helping the parties find ways to cope with the conflict
- Identifying and eliminating the underlying issues

Real dialogue involves not only listening to what the other party says but also taking care to truly comprehend his or her perspective and why it is important to him or her. It also requires that one understand the values and assumptions underlying one's own position and be willing to share them.

Core Issues in Conflict Management. Conflict management is difficult when people take a "What's in it for me?" viewpoint. A win-win approach provides the following benefits:

- A unified direction—a platform for achieving the organization's goals and objectives
- Higher employee satisfaction, especially when active listening is used, and the search for alternatives is expanded
- Improved health and safety of employees due to encountering less stress in their lives

Following are components of an approach to resolving conflict to the mutual benefit of all involved parties:

- Define the conflict as a mutual problem.
- Identify goals common to all parties.
- Find creative alternatives that satisfy all parties.
- Ensure that all parties understand their own needs and communicate them clearly.
- Emphasize mutual interdependence (as opposed to independence or dependence).
- Be certain that contacts are made on a basis of equal power.
- Communicate needs, goals, positions, and proposals openly, honestly, and accurately.
- State needs, goals, and positions in the opening offer.
- Empathize with and understand others' positions, feelings, and frames of reference.
- Reduce defensiveness by avoiding threats, harassment, or inconveniences to other parties.

A conflict is not likely to be resolved successfully when either party does the following:

- Defines the conflict as a win-lose strategy
- Pursues his or her own goals or hidden agenda
- Forces the other party into submission

- Increases power by emphasizing independence from the other party and the other party's dependence on them

- Tries to arrange contacts based on power relationships

- Uses inaccurate or misleading communications

- Overemphasizes needs, goals, and position in the opening offer

- Avoids empathy and understanding of others' positions, feelings, and frames of reference

- Would rather both parties lose (lose-lose) than have the other party get his or her way

Critical Thinking and the Socratic Method

Critical thinking is defined by Davis-Seaver[46] as "purposeful thinking that uses the skills of problem solving, decision making, evaluation, and metacognition to resolve conflicts, arrive at solutions and understand depth. It is that part of the creative thinking process that analyzes and evaluates the appropriateness and logicalness of the creative process or outcome." The constructivism perspective of critical thinking aligns best with the quality management aspects of critical thinking. This perspective incorporates critical thinking from an experiential one that requires curiosity and reflection.[47] There are many quality management and improvement tools that can enhance the ability to think critically. Taiwo used the term *critical systems thinking* to include the elements of total quality management incorporating customer focus, process improvement, and employee involvement.[48] From that perspective, systems thinking and the many quality principles can potentially unlock critical thinking and new solutions to enhance quality and improve efficiency. The Six Sigma and lean perspectives bring myriad tools into our tool kit that engage the tenants of critical thinking. Performing root cause analysis and applying such tools as cause-and-effect diagrams, why-why diagrams, and failure mode and effects analysis can help us to think critically and ensure that we identify and eliminate the root causes of quality and process problems. Seeing our processes as systems that create products and services while applying process mapping and value stream mapping tools ensures we consider the entire system and not just subsets or parts of the processes.

Socrates approached critical thinking by asking questions, called the *Socratic method*. These questions can help the thinker to examine assumptions and find evidence for facts. According to Merrill, there are four steps in critical thinking: (1) gather information, (2) test assumptions, (3) restructure thoughts, and (4) reach conclusions. Merrill also supports the need for systems thinking to enhance problem-solving and critical thinking.[49] The TRIZ methodology, or the theory of inventive problem-solving, developed by Genrich Altshuller, is focused on helping product designers design innovative products by thinking differently. "In the TRIZ methodology, the fundamental idea in the conceptual framework is the extraction of the essential conflicts from the problems and the eventual resolution of the conflicts. Altshuller asserted that an invention frequently appears when a contradiction between the engineering parameters is resolved. The contradictions can either be technical contradictions in the form of two mutually conflicting parameters within a system, or physical contradictions that are the direct opposite of two values for a parameter formulated by the same system."[50] TRIZ originated from Altshuller analyzing thousands of patents and identifying only forty fundamental inventive principles and was initially applied to product innovation and invention. It can be applied in service process design to incorporate critical-thinking approaches.

5. EMPOWERMENT

> Apply various techniques to empower individuals and teams. Identify typical obstacles to empowerment and appropriate strategies for overcoming them. Describe and distinguish between job enrichment and job enlargement, job design and job tasks. (Apply)
>
> **Body of Knowledge I.B.5**

One of the core components of quality leadership is having everyone in the organization involved in managing and improving quality of the processes for which they are responsible. This might be done as part of day-to-day operations as a member of a natural work team or a self-directed team, or in becoming part of a group that is going to take on a special process design or improvement project. Regardless of the way it occurs, it involves giving employees greater responsibility and authority and is commonly labeled *empowerment.*

Empowerment is based on the belief that employees have the ability to take on more responsibility and authority than have traditionally been given them and that heightened productivity and a better quality of work life will result. Different words and phrases are used to define empowerment, but most are variations on a theme: to provide employees with the means for making influential decisions. Juran defined empowerment as "conferring the right to make decisions and take action."[51]

Empowerment means different things in different organizations, depending on culture and work design; however, empowerment is based on the concepts of job enlargement and job enrichment. *Job enlargement* means changing the scope of the job to include a greater portion of the horizontal process. An example would be a bank teller who not only handles deposits and disbursements but now distributes traveler's checks and sells certificates of deposit. *Job enrichment* means increasing the depth of the job to include responsibilities that have traditionally been carried out at higher levels of the organization. An example would be if a bank teller also had the authority to help a client fill out a loan application and complete initial screening to determine whether or not to refer the customer to a loan officer.

As these examples show, empowerment of employees will require:

- A work environment and managing style that supports empowerment

- Training in the skills necessary to carry out the additional responsibilities

- Access to information on which decisions can be made

- Willingness and confidence on the part of the employee to take on greater responsibility

Empowerment also means management giving up some of the power traditionally held by it, which means management must take on new roles and responsibilities and gain new knowledge. It does not mean that management relinquishes all authority, totally delegates decision-making, and allows operating without accountability. It requires a significant investment of time and effort to develop mutual trust, assess, and add to individuals' competencies, as well as develop clear agreements about roles, responsibilities, risk-taking, and boundaries.

Empowerment is difficult to implement because it is often a major culture change from past ways of working. It involves behavioral changes in all members of the organization: management, operations personnel, and support staff. Therefore, it is critical that the organization lay the appropriate groundwork. To start, an organization should develop an operational definition of empowerment and communicate a strong commitment to it, starting with top management. It should develop a time-phased implementation plan and build or modify the necessary organizational systems to support empowerment.

Empowerment requires the transfer of authority with a clear agreement about expectations, responsibilities, and boundaries. This process takes place over a period of time as both managers and workers become comfortable with the concepts and implications of empowerment. Four principles that foster this transition are:

1. Give people important work to do on critical issues.

2. Give people discretion and autonomy over their tasks and resources.

3. Give visibility to others and provide recognition for their efforts.

4. Build relationships by finding them sponsors and mentors.[52]

Empowerment often also calls for restructuring the organization to reduce levels of hierarchy or to provide a more customer- and process-focused organization. Empowerment is often viewed as an inverted triangle of organizational power. In the traditional view, management is at the top while customers are on the bottom, whereas in an empowered environment, customers are at the top while management is in a support role at the bottom (see Figure 2.7).

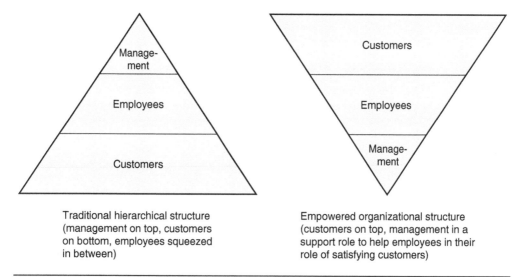

Traditional hierarchical structure (management on top, customers on bottom, employees squeezed in between)

Empowered organizational structure (customers on top, management in a support role to help employees in their role of satisfying customers)

Figure 2.7   Traditional versus empowered organization.

For empowerment to be successfully implemented, the leader's role must shift from that of a traditional manager to that of an enabler. Leaders must balance their need for personal control with the ability to provide freedom for others to act on their own authority. This is a mindset as well as a negotiated agreement between leaders and their subordinates. Leaders who empower others create an environment in which this balance can take place. They involve their subordinates in planning, delegating responsibility, clarifying the scope of authority, delineating boundaries, encouraging, providing a motivational environment, and rewarding accomplishments.

The process also needs to occur from top to bottom. Frontline managers need to understand how to implement the process and how to transition from a traditional role to that of an empowering leader. Middle management needs to work to remove barriers to empowerment and to help coach frontline managers in their new roles. Changes in performance review and compensation systems are usually required to align these systems with the new responsibilities.

People who are well matched with the jobs they hold do not require force, coercion, bribery, or trickery to work hard and produce quality work. They are internally motivated. An example of a mismatch is assigning a usually gregarious extrovert to spray-painting parts in an isolated room while wearing a protective mask all day. This would certainly be totally dissatisfying and lead to poor work for this individual. Another example would be reassigning an operator who formerly worked at a help desk solving customers' problems to a role as a telemarketer where he or she has to cold call prospective customers. Initiating customer contact may be a totally distasteful job for the individual. Type of personality, personal beliefs and interests, fear of danger, and so on are all factors to consider when matching people to jobs—assuming a motivated workforce is desired.

For a person to be internally motivated from the job itself, the person must:

- Receive sufficient skills training and knowledge to succeed in the job assigned

- Know what level of performance and results are expected

- Be provided with appropriate tools, equipment, and a workplace conducive to producing a quality product or service within a safe, secure, and healthful (physical and mental) environment

- Experience responsibility for the results of the work

- Experience a challenge but not be overwhelmed

- Have the authority to make decisions commensurate with the job responsibilities and personal competence and within preestablished boundaries

- Experience the work as contributing value

- Know how the results from personal work contribute to the organization

- Know how work is measured and evaluated

- Have the opportunity to improve the processes used in the work

- Know that management is aware of, supports, and appreciates the work

Table 2.1   Relationship changes in an empowered organization.

Issue for comparison	Traditional organization	Empowered organization
Employees' primary focus is on:	Management	Customers
Management's role is:	Monitoring and controlling	Facilitating and coaching
Management–employee relationship is:	Boss-to-subordinate	Peer-to-peer

Although work design is the most visible change in empowerment, the relationships of managers and employees is perhaps the most significant and difficult aspect of that change. Table 2.1 summarizes these changes, emphasizing the inherent difficulty in trying to change from a traditional to an empowered organization.

Common mistakes and barriers to empowerment include:

- A lack of a clear commitment. To succeed, top management must clearly communicate its support. Without this commitment, empowerment will be impossible to implement.

- Failure to define empowerment. Failing to develop an operational definition of empowerment results in confusion and inconsistent implementation. Many managers do not understand the term and can unwittingly block its effective implementation by sending conflicting messages.

- Failure to establish the boundaries within which employees can be empowered.

- Failure to provide appropriate training to management and the performers.

- Failure to implement appropriate incentives. People who have been rewarded for behavior that serves a traditional hierarchical system will resist transitioning to a new role unless incentives to encourage change are in place.

- Lack of an implementation plan. Empowerment consumes time, resources, and up-front costs for training and organizational support systems. An implementation plan is essential to prepare this groundwork. An organization that does not think through all of the implications sets up serious barriers to success.

- Inability to modify organizational culture. Many traditional organizations will hinder empowerment by virtue of their hierarchical structures, reward processes, and cultural values. Unless appropriate changes are made, empowerment will fail.

- Some people will resent a shift to empowerment. They often do not want to assume the responsibility involved. Others may feel management is trying to pass down their responsibility in order to save money or whatever.

- Not everyone will buy in at first. Some will wait and see if this is just another "here today, gone tomorrow" scheme of management. Some are terrified at the new freedom, fearful they might make a dreadful mistake and be punished for it.

- Middle and first-level management resent giving up their authority (and perhaps the curtain they have been hiding behind). Learning and practicing new behavior is tough on those who grew up in the traditional ways.

- If top management is not visibly and continually seen using empowerment techniques, the effort will likely not succeed.

- Changing the culture from a traditional hierarchical mode to one where empowerment is practiced takes a long time and costs money. A high level of sustained commitment is needed for years.

- The organization structure and reporting relationships will need to be changed.

- Major systems and processes will require modification or replacement—for example, the strategic planning process, compensation system, employee recognition and reward process, customer service processes, expense reimbursement procedure, and so on.

Benefits from Empowerment

Aubrey and Felkins reported a survey administered in several companies to evaluate the perceived benefits of employee involvement. It indicated significant improvements in attitudes and behavior. For example, results showed an increase in individual self-respect, increased respect for employees by supervisors, increased employee understanding of management, reduced conflict, and increased employees' awareness of why many problems are not solved quickly. A similar survey administered to management indicated that employee involvement seemed to increase productivity.[53]

Customer satisfaction also typically improves when personnel are given the authority to make decisions directly related to customer problems or needs. For example, a major credit card service organization reported that through its employee empowerment program, customer delight helped to propel the organization to the number two spot in the bank credit card industry and helped it win the Baldrige Award. Other Baldrige Award winners report similar results.

> *The very highest leader is barely known by men.*
> *Then comes the leader they know and love.*
> *Then the leader they fear.*
> *Then the leader they despise.*
> *The leader who does not trust enough will not be trusted.*
> *When actions are performed without unnecessary speech*
> *The people say, "We did it ourselves."*
>
> —Lao-tzu

This chapter has discussed a number of leadership challenges and issues. While the expression "_____ is a born leader" may be true in some cases, for the rest of us being a good, effective leader is a learned skill. In transforming ourselves to become a good leader, we may have to change our behavior—sometimes drastically. We may have to disregard traditional teachings and practices from our early years. We are in a rapidly evolving world that calls for innovative, adaptive, and ethical leaders. Relationships with people are critical, especially as technology tends to lead us toward dehumanizing internal and external organizational interactions.

REFERENCES

1. F. Hesselbein, "The Habits of Effective Organizations," in *Leader to Leader: Enduring Insights on Leadership from the Drucker Foundation's Award-Winning Journal*, ed. F. Hesselbein and P. M. Cohen (San Francisco: Jossey-Bass, 1999).

2. W. E. Deming, *Out of the Crisis* (Cambridge, MA: MIT Center for Advanced Engineering Study, 1986).

3. S. R. Covey, "Three Roles of the Leader in the New Paradigm," in *The Leader of the Future: New Visions, Strategies, and Practices for the Next Era*, ed. F. Hesselbein, M. Goldsmith, and R. Beckhard (San Francisco: Jossey-Bass, 1996).

4. T. Rath, and B. Conchie, *Strengths-Based Leadership: Great Leaders, Teams, and Why People Follow* (New York: Gallup Press, 2008).

5. B. M. Bass, *Stogdill's Handbook of Leadership* (New York: Free Press, 1990).

6. R. M. Kanter, "World-Class Leaders: The Power of Partnering," in Hesselbein, Goldsmith, and Beckhard, *Leader of the Future*.

7. D. H. Maister, C. H. Green, and R. M. Galford, *The Trusted Advisor* (New York: Free Press, 2000).

8. C. Farren, and B. L. Kaye, "New Skills for New Leadership Roles," in Hesselbein, Goldsmith, and Beckhard, *Leader of the Future*.

9. D. K. Smith, "The Following Part of Leading," in Hesselbein, Goldsmith, and Beckhard, *Leader of the Future*.

10. J. M. Kouzes, and B. Z. Posner, *The Leadership Challenge: How to Make Extraordinary Things Happen in Organizations* (Hoboken, NJ: John Wiley & Sons, 2017).

11. Ibid., 27, 135.

12. W. Bridges, "Leading the De-jobbed Organization," and E. H. Schein, "Leadership and Organizational Culture," in Hesselbein, Goldsmith, and Beckhard, *Leader of the Future*.

13. C. Handy, "The New Language of Organizing and Its Implications for Leaders," in Hesselbein, Goldsmith, and Beckhard, *Leader of the Future*.

14. Schein, "Leadership and Organizational Culture."

15. W. E. Deming, *The New Economics* (Cambridge, MA: MIT Press, 1994), 116.

16. P. Hersey, K. Blanchard, and D. E. Johnson, *Management of Organizational Behavior: Leading Human Resources* (Upper Saddle River, NJ: Prentice Hall, 2001).

17. D. Goleman, *Working with Emotional Intelligence* (New York: Bantam, 1998).

18. R. T. Pascale, and A. G. Athos, *The Art of Japanese Management* (London: Penguin Books, 1986).

19. R. T. Westcott defines "competency = knowledge, experience, skills, aptitude, and attitude—KESAA Factors" and discusses examples of competence requisites in "The Metamorphosis of the Quality Professional," *Quality Progress* (October 2004): 22–32.

20. P. F. Drucker, *Management: Tasks, Responsibilities, Practices* (New York: Harper & Row, 1974).

21. D. W. Hutton, *The Change Agents' Handbook: A Survival Guide for Quality Improvement Champions* (Milwaukee: ASQC Quality Press, 1994).

22. Deming, *New Economics.*

23. J. P. Kotter, *Leading Change* (Boston: Harvard Business School Press, 1996).

24. Ibid., 16.

25. P. Senge, *The Fifth Discipline* (New York: Random House, 2005).

26. D. W. Okes, "Developing Effective Change Agent Skills," 32nd Annual Quality Clinic, Knoxville, TN, March 1991.

27. E. H. Schein, *Organizational Culture and Leadership* (San Francisco: John Wiley & Sons, 2010).

28. B. Schneider, M. G. Ehrhart, and W. H. Macey, "Organizational Climate and Culture," *Annual Review of Psychology* 64:361–88.

29. Schein, *Organizational Culture and Leadership.*

30. Ibid.

31. G. Johnson, "Managing Strategic Change—Strategy, Culture and Action," *Long Range Planning* 25, no. 1: 28–36.

32. D. Rigby, "Management Tools and Techniques: A Survey," *California Management Review* 43, no. 2: 139–160.

33. J. M. Brion, *Organizational Leadership of Human Resources: The Knowledge and the Skills, Part I: The Individual* (Greenwich, CT: JAI Press, 1989).

34. A. H. Maslow, "Self-Actualization and Beyond," in *Challenges of Humanistic Psychology,* ed. J. F. T. Bugental (New York: McGraw-Hill, 1967).

35. F. Herzberg, "One More Time: How Do You Motivate Employees?," *Harvard Business Review*, January–February 1968.

36. J. S. Adams, and S. Freedman, "Equity Theory Revisited: Comments and Annotated Bibliography," *Advances in Experimental Social Psychology*, 1st Ser., 9 (1976): 43–90.

37. V. H. Vroom, *Expectancy Theory* (New York: Sage, 2013).

38. B. F. Skinner, "Herrnstein and the Evolution of Behaviorism," *American Psychologist* 32, no. 12 (1977): 1006–12, doi:10.1037/0003-066X.32.12.1006.

39. D. McClelland, *The Achieving Society* (Princeton, NJ: D. Van Nostrand, 1961).

40. K. W. Thomas, "Conflict and Conflict Management," in *Handbook of Industrial and Organizational Psychology*, Vol. 2, ed. M. D. Dunnette (Chicago: Rand McNally, 1976).

41. J. F. Brett, G. B. Northcraft, and R. L. Pinkley, "Stairways to Heaven: An Interlocking Self-Regulation Model of Negotiation," *Academy of Management Review* (July 1999): 435–51.

42. J. Kelly, "Make Conflict Work for You," *Harvard Business Review* 48, no. 4 (1970): 103–13.

43. K. W. Thomas, and R. H. Kilman, *Thomas-Kilman Conflict Mode Instrument* (Tuxedo, NY: XICOM, 1974).

44. M. A. Bittel, ed., *Handbook for Professional Managers* (New York: McGraw-Hill, 1985).

45. T. G. Cummings, and E. F. Huse, *Organizational Development and Change*, 4th ed. (St. Paul, MN: West, 1989), 171.

46. J. Davis-Seaver, *Critical Thinking in Young Children* (Lewiston, NY: Edwin Mellen Press, 2000).

47. C. Vejar, *Critical Thinking: An Academic Perspective* (Hackensack, NJ: Salem Press, 2019).

48. J. Taiwo, "Systems Approaches to Total Quality Management," *Total Quality Management* 12, no. 7 (2001): 967–73, doi:10.1080/09544120120096115.

49. P. Merrill, "Be Ready, Develop Your People and Process Skills, to Be a Part of Quality 4.0," *ASQ Quality Progress*, October 2019.

50. C-T. Su, C-S. Lin, and T-L. Chiang, "Systematic Improvement in Service Quality through TRIZ Methodology: An Exploratory Study," *Total Quality Management and Business Excellence* 19, no. 3 (2008): 223–43, doi:10.1080/14783360701600662.

51. J. M. Juran, *The Last Word: Lessons of a Lifetime in Managing for Quality* (Wilton, CT: Juran Institute, 1993), 332.

52. Kouzes and Posner, *Leadership Challenge*.

53. C. A. Aubrey, and P. K. Felkins, *Teamwork: Involving People in Quality and Productivity Improvement* (Milwaukee: ASQC Quality Press, 1988).

See Appendix A for additional references for this chapter.

Chapter 3
C. Teams and Team Processes

A team is a group of people who perform interdependent tasks to work toward a common mission. Some teams have a limited life—for example, a design team developing a new product or a process improvement team organized to solve a particular problem. Other teams are ongoing—for example, a departmental team that meets regularly to review goals, objectives, activities, and performance. Understanding the many interrelationships that exist between organizational units and processes, and the impact of these relationships on quality, productivity, and cost, makes the value of teams apparent.

Many of today's team concepts were initiated in the United States during the 1970s through the use of quality circles or employee involvement initiatives. The initiatives were often seen as separate from normal work activities rather than integrated with other organizational systems and processes. Team designs have since evolved into a broader concept that includes many types of teams formed for different purposes.

Difficulty with teams in the United States is often blamed on a cultural emphasis on individual accomplishments versus shared responsibility and success. The problems are also due to inadequate organizational support structures. For example, since reward systems often reinforce individual performance, it is logical that people would be less interested in sharing responsibilities. Formal gainsharing programs that reward individuals financially based on performance of the company, division, facility, product line, and/or project of which they are part are more likely to reinforce the need for working together toward common goals.

Just as individuals develop over their life span, groups tend to change over time. Being aware of this normal progression and ways to overcome difficulties that arise can help the team process be a very positive experience. As Senge pointed out in *The Fifth Discipline*, if a team really jells, the resulting experience can be a highlight of one's career.[1]

The team process also helps an organization change and begin working in different ways. If decisions are made in a multidisciplinary way, the team will consider a broader perspective and will be likely to better address problems. Other members of the organization will often more readily accept the decisions. Some work design changes mean that people from formerly separate functional areas now work together in a newly designed process. These types of changes require more significant attention to organizational change issues to help the group focus on its new mission.

Team processes offer the following benefits to the organization:

- Synergistic process design or problem-solving
- Objective analysis of problems or opportunities
- Promotion of cross-functional understanding
- Improved quality and productivity
- Greater innovation
- Reduced operating costs
- Increased commitment to organizational mission
- More flexible response to change
- Increased ownership and stewardship
- Reduced turnover and absenteeism

Individuals can gain the following benefits from teams:

- Enhanced problem-solving skills
- Increased knowledge of interpersonal dynamics
- Broader knowledge of business processes
- New skills for future leadership roles
- Increased quality of work life
- Feelings of satisfaction and commitment
- Sense of being part of something greater than one could accomplish alone

Numerous reasons have been noted for why teams often fail to reach their full potential. Common reasons are:

- Failing to integrate cooperative work methods into the organizational culture
- Lack of organizational systems necessary to support the team process
- Minimal up-front planning of how the organization plans to utilize teams
- Failure to prepare managers for their changing roles
- Failure to prepare team members for their new roles
- Inappropriate recognition and compensation systems
- Inadequate training
- Impatience of top management with the time needed for maturation
- Incomplete understanding of group dynamics

1. TYPES OF TEAMS

> Identify and describe different types of teams and their purpose, including process improvement, self-managed, temporary or ad hoc (special project), virtual, and work groups. (Understand)
>
> **Body of Knowledge I.C.1**

Team Configurations

Consider the differences between a baseball team, a jazz quartet, and a bomb squad. They differ according to the number of members, the range and complexity of skills required, the forms of leadership used, the frequency of working together, and the total time spent working together. As Louis Sullivan, a mentor of Frank Lloyd Wright, stated, "Form follows function," and this also applies to teams. Although they may take different names in different industries or organizations, this section presents eight types of teams:

- Process improvement teams
- Self-managed teams
- Temporary/ad hoc teams
- Work groups
- Cellular teams
- Special project teams
- Virtual teams
- Combinations of two or more of the above types

Process Improvement Teams. A process improvement team is a project team that focuses on improving or developing a specific business process and is more likely to be trying to accomplish breakthrough-level improvement. The team comes together to achieve a specific goal, is guided by a well-defined project plan, and has a negotiated beginning and end. Such teams are typically cross-disciplinary, bringing together people from different functions and with different skills related to the process to be improved. The team may have a management sponsor who charters the team and ensures that the team has the appropriate resources and organizational support.

The leader of a process improvement team is usually selected by the project sponsor, and the team meets on a regular basis (for example, weekly) to plan activities that will be carried out outside the meeting, review information gathered since the previous meeting, and make decisions regarding implementation of process changes. An independent facilitator who has no involvement in the process to be improved may also work with the team if team members do not have sufficient skills or experience with team facilitation.

In today's fast-paced environment, many organizations also perform process improvement through an accelerated team process sometimes called a *kaizen event* or *kaizen blitz*. These teams spend three to five consecutive full days focusing on a very narrow project scope and implement many of their recommended changes during that period. Gains on the order of 70% (for example, increase in productivity or reduction in changeover time) are not uncommon. In order to accelerate the pace of progress, the facilitator typically has more authority than with most teams.

Self-Managed Teams. Self-managed teams are groups of employees involved in directly managing the day-to-day operation of their particular process or department. They are authorized to make decisions on a wide range of issues (for example, safety, quality, maintenance, scheduling, and some personnel decisions). Their responsibilities also include processes traditionally performed by managers, such as setting objectives, allocation of assignments, and conflict resolution. These teams are also called *self-directed teams* or *high-performance work teams*. They give employees much broader responsibility and ownership of a work process.

The leader of a self-managed team is usually selected by the team members, and in many cases the role is rotated among the members over time. Also often rotated is the responsibility for providing within-team coordination of particular technical aspects of the team's processes, such as safety or scheduling.

All of the elements that apply to work groups also apply to self-managed teams. Self-managed work teams, however, require more up-front planning, support structures, and nurturing. The transition will usually take a significant time period and needs consistent support from management.

The following key lessons related to self-managed teams were identified during a study of a financial organization:[2]

- Implement a well-thought-out structure to design and guide the implementation process, such as a steering committee, a design team, and a pilot effort.

- Provide special training to managers and supervisors to help them make the transition from their current role to the new support role.

- Develop a careful plan to manage people throughout the transition. The new team structure will cause changes that will appear threatening to many involved, as they interpret the changes as a loss.

- Set realistic expectations that consider the long and energy-consuming time required for the process to become integrated into the business.

Comprehensive training is also critical in order to move from a traditional to a self-managed work environment. For example, one Fortune 500 company provides training in the following subjects:[3]

- Maintaining a focus on the customer

- Developing a vision and mission that are integrated with the larger organization's mission

- Understanding roles and operating guidelines

- Working together to make decisions, plan work, resolve differences, and conduct meetings

- Implementing concepts and strategy for empowerment

- Setting goals (objectives) and solving problems for continuous improvement

Self-managed teams are more likely to be successful when they are created as part of starting up a new facility (a greenfield site) since the cultural change required if an existing facility (a brownfield site) attempts to transition from a traditional work design is so dramatic. In order to smooth the transition to self-managed teams, an existing organization may begin by first implementing cross-functional process improvement teams and/or work teams as a means for learning.

Temporary/Ad Hoc Teams. In a flexible organization, a need for a temporary team may be identified due to a specific problem or situation. Although such ad hoc teams may not use the same formal structures (for example, agenda and regular meeting frequency), the same general principles and processes are still necessary. An empowered organization often sanctions the use of such teams when deemed useful to carry out a short-term mission. For example, many organizations regularly use temporary teams to conduct internal audits of compliance of their quality management system with the ISO 9001 standard.

A problem or situation may arise that requires immediate and dedicated attention. For example:

- A flood or fire has occurred, and decisions have to be made regarding temporary relocation of the process. What emergency plans need upgrading to deal with a similar future emergency?

- A major customer is sending in an auditing team to assess the adequacy of your quality management system. What needs to be done to prepare for the audit?

- Your information management computer system has been compromised by an outside virus. What processes have been affected, and what emergency steps must be taken to recover from the infected data and programs? What safeguards need upgrading or replacement to prevent a similar future disaster?

Usually, management designates the person to form the team to address the situation. Typically, and depending on the nature of the situation, the team will be small and cross-functional and will call on other technical expertise as needed.

Situations less critical than those listed may also be addressed by a temporary team—for example, the disposition of an unusually large return or recall of unacceptable product.

Work Groups. Work groups, sometimes called *natural teams*, are teams of employees who have responsibility for a particular process (for example, a department, a product line, or a stage of a business process) and who work together in a participative environment. The degree of authority and autonomy of the team can range from relatively limited to full self-management depending on the organizational culture. The participative approach is based on the belief that employees will be more productive if they have a higher level of responsibility for their work and are empowered. Since the team understands the work processes, the members should monitor and improve the processes on an ongoing basis. The team leader is usually the individual responsible for the work area, such as a department supervisor.

Work groups function similarly to quality circles, in which department personnel meet weekly or monthly to review performance of their process. They monitor feedback from their customers and track internal performance measures of processes and suppliers. These teams focus on continual, incremental improvements in their work processes. They are similar to process improvement teams, with the key differences being that they are neither cross-functional nor temporary. Again, a facilitator is usually available for teams if needed. Other outside personnel may be brought in as resources on a temporary basis.

More effective use of the work group team design involves applying it at all levels of an organization, with each level linked to the one above and below it (see Figure 3.1). The top management team monitors performance of processes for which it is responsible (for example, overall business performance), teams at the next level monitor and improve their processes (for example, logistics and delivery performance), and teams at the next level track and improve their performance. Since performance of a work area can be affected by issues outside the team's control, one work group might request that another (for example, the supplier work group) improve a particular process. Alternatively, a process improvement team may be organized that involves both departments working together.

Since work groups are an ongoing organizational structure, it is critical that the organizational systems and values support the effort. Certain basic elements should be considered when an organization is attempting to initiate work groups:

- Top management support

- Clear communication

- Improvement objectives and expectations

- Team training

- Appropriate competencies

- Supportive compensation and performance appraisal systems

Other issues to consider include:

- Team's scope of responsibility and authority

- Degree of autonomy

- Information needed by team and where obtained

- Decision-making process

- Performance measures and success factors

- Recognition and rewards for performance

- Competencies that must be developed

- Selection process for leaders and facilitators

- Risk management process

An implementation plan including the necessary support systems should be defined before initiating such groups. If work groups are being introduced into an existing

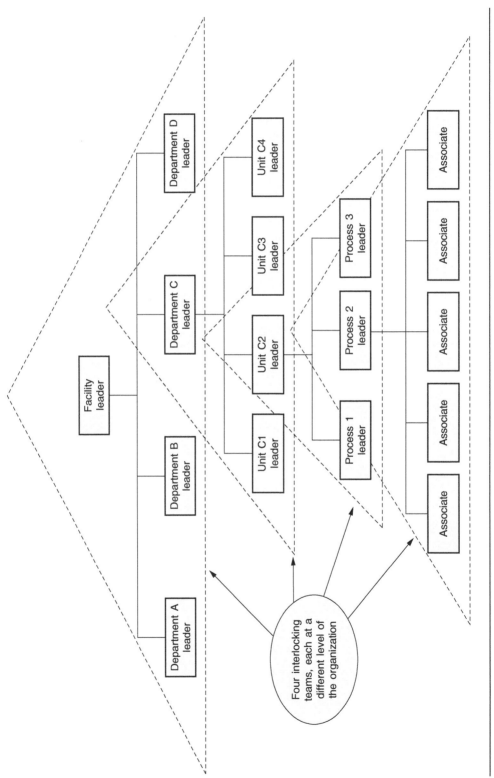

Figure 3.1   Linking team structure.

organization where a participative management style has not been used before, a pilot program in a department where it is likely to succeed is highly recommended.

Cellular Teams. When processes are organized into cells, the layout of workstations and/or machines used in a given part of the process typically is arranged in a U-shape configuration. This allows operators to proceed with a part from machine to machine, performing a series of sequential steps to produce a whole product or a major subassembly.

The team that operates the cell is usually totally cross-trained in every step in the series. Team effectiveness depends on coordination, timing, and cooperation. Team members' competencies must be as closely matched as possible to maintain a reasonable and consistent work pace and quality.

Cell team members usually assume ownership and responsibility for establishing and improving the work processes. Leadership of the cell team may be by a person designated as lead operator, or a similar title. In some cases the role of lead operator may be rotated among the members. The lead operator is usually responsible for training new team members, reporting team output, and balancing the flow of work through the process. A cellular team is a specialized form of a self-directed work group.

Special Project Teams. Often, a need develops to form a long-duration, totally dedicated project team to implement a major new product, system, or process. Some examples are:

- Reengineering an entire process

- Relocating a major segment of the operation

- Mergers, acquisitions, or divestitures

- Replacing a major information system

- Entering a new market with a new product

- Preparing to apply for the Baldrige Award

Such special project teams may operate as a parallel organization during their existence. They may be located away from the main organization and even be exempt from some of its policy and work-rules constraints. The core team members are usually drafted for the duration of the project. Persons with additional expertise may be called into the team on a temporary, as-needed basis. Usually, the project is headed by an experienced project manager. Depending on the nature of the team's objectives, external specialists or consultants may be retained to augment the core competencies of the team members.

Virtual Teams. In today's global and electronic business environment, it may be expedient to have team members who do not work in the same geographic location. These virtual teams also require many of the same roles and processes, but the substitution of electronic communications (for example, e-mail and video-conferencing) for face-to-face meetings provides an additional challenge to team leadership. A key competency of team members is the ability and motivation to self-manage their time and priorities.

Virtual teams have special needs, some of which are:

- Telephones, local area networks, satellites, videoconferencing
- Computers, high-speed and wireless connections, internet technology, e-mail, web-based chat rooms/forums, and so on
- Software for communications, meeting facilitation, time management, project management, groupware, accessing online databases
- Combinations of the above may facilitate communication and performance

The benefits of virtual teams are:

- Team members may work from any location and at any time of day.
- Team members are selected for their competence, not for their geographic location.
- Expenses may be reduced or eliminated, such as travel, lodging, parking, and renting/leasing or owning a building, office equipment, and furniture.

Team Selection

Management selects the team leader. Team members may be selected by either management or the team leader. When the choice of the team members is left to the team leader, however, some methods and tools may be used. To begin, the team leader should identify the competence needed. Competence comprises five factors (KESAA):

- *Knowledge.* Formal education, degrees, educational certifications, professional certifications, and self-study achievements
- *Experience.* Years spent applying knowledge and skills in pertinent types of organizations and industries and in jobs/positions held
- *Skills.* Skill certifications, training received, and demonstrated proficiency in the use of pertinent tools and equipment
- *Aptitude.* Natural talent, capability, capacity, innate qualities, deftness, knack, adaptability to change, natural ability to do things requiring hand-eye coordination, and fine motor skills
- *Attitude.* Manner of showing one's feelings or thoughts; one's disposition, opinion, mood, ideas, beliefs, demeanor, state of feeling, reaction, bias, inclination, emotion, temperament, mental state, frame of mind, and ease in accepting and adopting new or changed plans and practices

By analyzing the tasks facing the team, the team leader can complete a *KESAA requisites analysis* for each individual role, major task, or task cluster.[4] A sample from staffing a project team is shown in Figure 3.2.

In addition, the *Myers-Briggs Type Indicator* may be used to determine how each potential team member is best suited to the team tasks and team dynamics anticipated. Team leaders should also consider any problems obtaining cooperation from a selected person's boss relative to time constraints and conflicts, prior

---

Project Staffing—KESAA Requisites Analysis

[Define KESAA factors for each key project participant planned on the resource requirements matrix—personnel]

Task/work package name: Train project managers in using new Microsoft Project software
Task/WP number: 3.10.01.01
Job/position category/title: Application software specialist

Knowledge	• Knows proven techniques for designing and delivering software training to people with diverse knowledge, experience, and skills • Extensive knowledge of project planning and management techniques, tools, and practices • Received Microsoft certificate for completing the advanced MS Project five-day training program within last four years • Earned college degree (software major)
Experience	• Has instructed project teams in use of MS Project at a previous employer, two or more times • Used MS Project on two or more previous large-scale projects • Has demonstrated proficiency in providing software technical support for MS Project users working on large-scale projects • Has demonstrated proficiency in using thorough, rapid, and user-friendly techniques for training new software users
Skills	• Possesses excellent communication skills (reading comprehension, instructing, technical writing, and listening) • Proficient in using all Microsoft Office software • Trained in using proven instructional technology in training design, delivery, and evaluation
Aptitude	• Has capability to adapt the MS Project training to the special needs of each participant • Has worked well in a team environment that is subject to frequent changes. Fast learner.
Attitude	• Enjoys imparting his/her knowledge and skills to new software users • Measures his/her success on the improved performance of those trained by him/her • Believes that MS Project is the best selection of project management software, at this time and place • Exhibits "What can we do to make this happen?" demeanor

Additional comments:

_____

_____

_____

_____

Prepared by: Anna Lyst   Date: June 30, 2013

Figure 3.2   Project staffing–KESAA requisites analysis.

Source: Reprinted with permission of R. T. Westcott & Associates.

commitments (unfinished work on regular assignment), priorities (which work is most important?), and reporting relationships (to whom does the selected person report?).

A selected individual's reluctance to join a team may be because of the potential for losing interaction with colleagues from the same discipline and the potential for losing an opportunity for further education and training in the individual's chosen field, as well as potential impact on pay raises and promotion.

2. STAGES OF TEAM DEVELOPMENT

Describe how the stages of team development (forming, storming, norming, performing) affect leadership style. (Apply)

Body of Knowledge I.C.2

Teams will progress through stages of growth and maturity as the members work together over time. Understanding these development stages is valuable for the effective management of the team process. The stages can vary in intensity and duration depending on the type of team, the environment in which it works, and the individuals who constitute it. Since trust is essential for high-performance teams, successfully completing these stages is necessary for reaching a consistent high-performance level. A generic model for the phases of team development, described by Tuckman,[5] is shown in Figure 3.3:

- *Stage 1: Forming.* When team members first come together, they bring with them individual identities and the values and the priorities of their

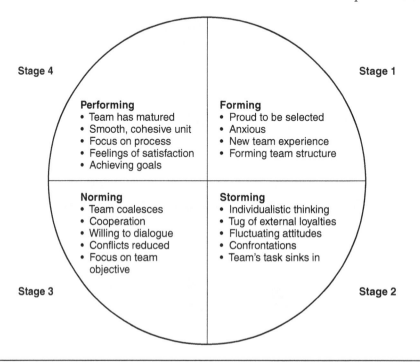

Figure 3.3 Team development phases.

usual environment. Each team is a new experience, even for those who have previously been members of teams. Individuals enter this situation cautiously, feeling uncertain of what their roles and performance will be in this new environment. During the forming stage, the team usually clarifies its purpose, identifies roles for each member, and defines rules of acceptable behavior (often called *norms*).

- *Stage 2: Storming.* During this phase the reality of the team's task sinks in. Team members still think primarily as individuals and might attempt to form decisions on the basis of their individual experiences rather than pooling information with other members. Collaboration has not yet become the norm as team members fluctuate in their attitude about the team's chances for success. The behaviors exhibited during this time may involve argument, testing the leader's authority, attempts to redefine goals, and competitive or defensive acts.

- *Stage 3: Norming.* In this phase the individuals coalesce into a team by shifting their focus from personal concerns to that of meeting the team-related challenges. Interpersonal conflicts and the tug of external loyalties are reduced. Team members are willing to discuss differences for the sake of the team, resulting in more cooperation and dialogue.

- *Stage 4: Performing.* At this stage, the team has matured to the point where it is working as a smooth, cohesive unit. Team members have a good understanding of each other's strengths and weaknesses and how they support the mission and are now able to work through group problems. There is a better appreciation of the team's processes and a general satisfaction with team membership. During this phase, the team is making significant progress toward achieving its goals.

Although the four stages of development indicate a logical sequence that occurs over time, the actual progress made by each team will vary. For example, a team that has progressed to stage 3 or 4 may fall back to stage 1 or 2. This may occur if team members learn that previous assumptions about one another are not true, information they have been using for decision-making is found to be inaccurate, or team membership changes. Some teams might never progress beyond an earlier stage because of limited project duration or poor resolution of group dynamics issues.

Some authors have added a stage to Tuckman's original model: *adjourning.* It is the process of closure that occurs when the team has accomplished its mission. The team should take time to review the lessons learned and what was accomplished, complete documentation, celebrate, and formally disband. Frequently, this stage is either skipped over or incompletely performed, or in some cases, project teams just continue to meet without "closing" the project and without a continuing business purpose.

Team development can be enhanced by making sure that team members have a basic understanding of how to (1) interact in positive ways, (2) deal with difficult people or situations, (3) contribute to accomplishing the team's goals, and (4) give or receive constructive feedback.

3. TEAM-BUILDING TECHNIQUES

> Apply basic team-building steps such as using ice-breaker activities to enhance team introductions and membership, developing a common vision and agreement on team objectives and identifying and assigning specific roles on the team. (Apply)
>
> **Body of Knowledge I.C.3**

Team Processes

There are two major groups of components in team processes—task type and maintenance type. Task-type processes keep a team focused and moving toward its goal, while maintenance processes help build and preserve the effectiveness of relationships between team members. Key task components include:

- Reviewing and documenting the team's objective(s).

- Preparing an agenda for every team meeting and staying focused on the agenda. If other issues come up that need to be addressed, the agenda can either be intentionally modified or new issues can be placed on a list for the next meeting agenda.

- Defining or selecting and following a technical process that fits the particular project mission (for example, a seven-step problem-solving model if the team is trying to solve a problem).

- Using decision-making techniques (for example, consensus, consultative) appropriate to the situation.

- Defining action items, responsibilities, and timing and holding team members accountable.

Maintenance tasks are somewhat less easily defined but can also dramatically affect team performance. An outsider might see only the tasks involved with meeting objectives as important, but for team members, the dynamics of interactions between team members can be just as critical. Theories and practices of team dynamics have come from fields as diverse as sociology, psychology, anthropology, organizational development, and political science, where group behavior has been studied in working, living, academic, and therapeutic environments.

Team maintenance tasks are meant to help alleviate the problems created by the fact that each individual on the team has her or his own perspectives and priorities. These are shaped by individual personality, current issues in the person's personal life, and the attitudes of both the formal and informal groups within the organization to which the individual belongs. This means that although the team may have a specific objective and agenda, each individual perceives things differently.

Preventing Problems with Team Process. Two common ways of preventing team dynamics problems are to use *norms* and *roles*. A list of behavioral expectations (norms) is defined by the team during the first meeting, or a predetermined set of norms used by all teams within the organization might be adopted. Following are a few examples of norms and the purpose of each:

- "Be on time for meetings." Emphasizes that meeting time needs to be used effectively and to wait for someone to arrive is a waste of others' time.

- "At least four (of five) team members must be able to attend." Recognizes that vacation, business travel, and other events may prevent some team members from attending a particular meeting while ensuring that meetings are not held and decisions made by only a small proportion of the members.

- "No side conversations." Ensures that members are fully present and listening to what is being said, making sure that each person's ideas are heard and considered.

- "Staying on the agenda." Although somewhat task oriented, this emphasizes that team meetings are not the place for personal gripes and that the team has an important mission.

- "Participation by everyone." Clarifies that all are expected to play an active role, even though the particular skills and activities may differ.

- "Use the *parking lot*." For issues not on the agenda that are set aside to be dealt with at a later time.

- "No phones or other electronic devices" are to be used in a team meeting unless specifically required to accomplish the task at hand.

- "The management of team members must be apprised that the need for absolute dedication to the team objectives by team members is not to be interrupted, except for extreme personal or business emergencies."

Having team members take on particular roles helps get them involved and reduces the likelihood of their feeling that their time is being wasted. Two common roles often rotated among team members are scribe and timekeeper. A *scribe* is responsible for capturing information from the team meeting in a record of meeting minutes and distributing them appropriately following the meeting. A *timekeeper* monitors how well the team is progressing against the time line spelled out in the agenda and will notify the team if it is straying off the scheduled times.

Another method for getting team members more involved and working together is to have them work in even smaller groups on narrow activities. For example, if the team needs to acquire some data that are readily available, having two team members work together to get and present the data will provide an opportunity for them to develop a closer working relationship that can carry over into the overall team process.

The first team meeting can set the tone for the entire team effort, and it is therefore important that it be well planned. Following are some actions that can enhance the first meeting:

- Have the sponsor or other stakeholders attend the meeting to emphasize the importance of the project and the support that will be provided

- Ensure that all team members have a full understanding of the team's mission and scope

- Allow team members to get acquainted

- Clarify team members' roles

- Work out decision-making issues

- Establish meeting ground rules (norms)

- Define or select the technical process improvement methodology/model to be used

- Define/review the project plan and schedule

- Draft the team's objectives (may be modified in second meeting)

- Define the structure for future meetings

Special exercises (often called *icebreakers*) can also be conducted during the first meeting to help team members feel more comfortable in the new environment. (Training material providers offer a plethora of such exercises.) Aside from structured exercises, team members can be asked to state what they hope to personally gain from the project experience. The team can come up with a name for the group. Team members can discuss previous experiences with working in teams and what they learned from them. Activities such as these allow the personalities and values of individual team members to become more visible and bring team members closer together.

Setting the Team's Objectives. Setting objectives not only gives the team some work to do but begins the team's development and helps to clarify the task ahead. It is likely that the first draft will require modification at a subsequent meeting. As a template, consider the *S.M.A.R.T. W.A.Y.* (Table 5.1).

Decision-Making Method. Consensus decision-making is the process recommended for major project issues. The approach is more time-consuming and demanding but provides the most thorough and cohesive results. It allows the team to work out different points of view on an issue and come to a conclusion that is acceptable. Consensus means that the decision is acceptable enough that all team members will support it. To achieve consensus, all team members must be allowed to express their views and must also objectively listen to the views of others. The decision and alternatives should be discussed until consensus is reached.

4. TEAM ROLES AND RESPONSIBILITIES

> Define and describe typical roles related to team support and effectiveness such as facilitator, leader, process owner, champion, project manager, and contributor. Describe member and leader responsibilities with regard to group dynamics, including keeping the team on task, recognizing hidden agendas, handling disruptive behavior, and resolving conflict. (Analyze)
>
> **Body of Knowledge I.C.4**

Of the seven roles described in Table 3.1, the roles of timekeeper and scribe are the only ones that are optional depending on the ability of a team member to effectively fulfill a dual role of participating member and either scribe or timekeeper. While the remaining five roles are essential, they may be combined in a variety of ways. Crucial roles for the success of the team, once it is formed, are the team leader and facilitator roles. The *team leader* is responsible for the content—the work done by the team. The *facilitator* is responsible for ensuring that the process used by the team and the team dynamics are the best for the stage and situation the team is in.[6]

There is a need for a trained facilitator when:

- No team member is trained for, capable of, or willing to assume this role in addition to functioning as a participating member.

- The team has been meeting for some time and is incapable of resolving conflicting issues.

- A new member has been added, thus upsetting established relationships.

- A key contributor has left the team.

- There are other factors, such as running short on resources, project cancellation, or major change in requirements that may disturb the smooth functioning of the team.

Supplementing the team with on-call experts can often compensate for a short-fall in either the number of members or members' competencies. Such temporary members must willingly share their expertise, listen attentively, abide by team norms, and support team decisions.

The selection of a team member to serve as a timekeeper may be helpful, at least until the team has become more adept at self-monitoring time usage. When a timekeeper is needed, the role is often rotated, giving consideration to whether the selected member has a vital role to play in the deliberations at a particular meeting.

For some team missions where very formal documentation is required, a scribe or notetaker may be needed. This role can be distracting for a member whose full attention may be needed on the topics under discussion. For this reason, an assistant, not a regular member of the team, is sometimes assigned to take the minutes and publish them. Care should be taken not to select a member to serve as a scribe solely based on the person's gender or position in the organization.

All team members must adhere to expected standards of quality, fiduciary responsibility, ethics, and confidentiality. It is imperative that the most competent individuals available are selected for each role. See Table 3.1 for attributes of good role performance.

Frequently, a team must function in parallel with day-to-day assigned work and with the members not being relieved of responsibility for their regularly assigned work. This, of course, places a burden and stress on the team members. The day-to-day work and the work of the team must both be conducted effectively. Being unable to be in two places at one time calls for innovative time management, conflict resolution, and negotiation skills.

Table 3.1 Roles, responsibilities, and performance attributes.

Role name	Responsibility	Definition	Attributes of good role performance
Sponsor	Backer, risk-taker	The person who supports a team's plans, activities, and outcomes	• Believes in the concept/idea • Has sound business acumen • Is willing to take risk and responsibility for outcomes • Has authority to approve needed resources • Will be listened to by upper management
Champion	Advocate	The person promoting the concept or idea for change/improvement	• Is dedicated to seeing it implemented • Holds absolute belief it is the right thing to do • Has perseverance and stamina
Facilitator	Helper, trainer, advisor, coach	A person who: • Observes the team's processes and team members' interactions and suggests process changes to facilitate positive movement toward the team's goals and objectives • Intervenes if discussion develops into multiple conversations • Intervenes to skillfully prevent an individual from dominating the discussion or to engage an overlooked individual in the discussion • Assists the team leader in bringing discussions to a close • May provide training in team building, conflict management, and so forth	• Is trained in facilitating skills • Is respected by team members • Is tactful • Knows when to and when not to intervene • Deals with the team's process, not content • Respects the team leader and does not override his or her responsibility • Respects confidential information shared by individuals or the team as a whole • Will not accept facilitator role if expected to report to management any information that is proprietary to the team • Will abide by the organization's Code of Ethics and principles

Table 3.1 Roles, responsibilities, and performance attributes. *(continued)*

Role name	Responsibility	Definition	Attributes of good role performance
Team leader	Change agent, chair, head	A person who: • Staffs the team or provides input for staffing requirements • Strives to bring about change/improvement through the team's outcomes • Is entrusted by followers to lead them • Has the authority for and directs the efforts of the team • Participates as a team member • Coaches team members in developing or enhancing necessary competencies • Communicates with management about the team's progress and needs • Handles the logistics of team meetings • Takes responsibility for team records	• Is committed to the team's mission and objectives • Has experience in planning, organizing, staffing, controlling, and directing teams • Is capable of creating and maintaining communication channels that enable members to do their work • Is capable of gaining the respect of team members; serves as a role model • Is firm, fair, and factual in dealing with a team of diverse individuals • Facilitates discussion without dominating • Actively listens • Empowers team members to the extent possible within the organization's culture • Supports all team members equally • Respects each team member's individuality
Timekeeper	Gatekeeper, monitor	A person designated by the team to watch the use of allocated time and remind the team members when their time objective may be in jeopardy	• Is capable of assisting the team leader in keeping the team meeting within the predetermined time limitations • Is sufficiently assertive to intervene in discussions when the time allocation is in jeopardy • Is capable of participating as a member while still serving as a timekeeper

(continued)

Table 3.1   Roles, responsibilities, and performance attributes. *(continued)*

Role Name	Responsibility	Definition	Attributes of good role performance
Scribe	Recorder, notetaker	A person designated by the team to record critical data from team meetings. Formal "minutes" of the meetings may be published and distributed to interested parties.	• Is capable of capturing on paper, or electronically, the main points and decisions made in a team meeting and providing a complete, accurate, and legible document (or formal minutes) for the team's records • Is sufficiently assertive to intervene in discussions to clarify a point or decision in order to record it accurately • Is capable of participating as a member while still serving as a scribe
Team members	Participants, subject matter experts	The persons selected to work together to bring about a change/improvement, achieving this in a created environment of mutual respect, sharing of expertise, cooperation, and support	• Are willing to commit to the purpose of the team • Are able to express ideas, opinions, and suggestions in a nonthreatening manner • Are capable of listening attentively to other team members • Are receptive to new ideas and suggestions • Are even-tempered and able to handle stress and cope with problems openly • Are competent in one or more fields of expertise needed by the team • Have favorable performance records • Are willing to function as team members and forfeit "star" status

Source: R. T. Westcott and G. L. Duffy, eds., *The Certified Quality Improvement Associate Handbook*, 3rd ed. (Milwaukee: ASQ Quality Press, 2015).

Steering Committee

Top management is ultimately responsible for organizational performance improvement. One of top management's key roles, then, is to identify and prioritize opportunities and initiate teams to address those of greatest value to the organization. Projects might be selected on the basis of new strategic initiatives (for example, developing a new service for a new market niche), customer satisfaction data, cost-of-quality reports, or other strategic or operational performance measures or initiatives (for example, capacity, throughput, and lean projects such as waste reduction).

In order to carry out this process and to simultaneously provide opportunities for learning, a special group called the *steering committee* is often set up for guiding and tracking team efforts. The group usually includes key leaders in the organization (for example, president, operations manager, quality manager), as well as others who represent particular interests. In an organization working under a union contract, the union representative is also likely to be a member of the steering committee. The steering committee is often a diagonal slice representing all levels of the organization.

One role of the steering committee is to initiate desired organizational improvement efforts. It is vital that each team have a clear understanding of its purpose and how that purpose is linked to and supports the organization's strategic plans. This is done through a written charter that defines the mission and objectives of each project, as well as key personnel (for example, team leader, members, and facilitator) and project timing. The charter is a formal document agreed to by both the team and by management. It legitimizes the team's effort and documents a tacit agreement from management to provide whatever support is necessary to sustain the team. The charter should also include boundaries of authority and responsibility and related limitations, relationship of the team to other teams or projects, the scope of work, the team's reporting relationships within the organization, and the expected deliverables.

If a process improvement team is chartered without a clear mission or objective, the team will either do nothing or will go in the direction it believes best. One way to test understanding is to ask, "What will you measure to determine whether the objective has been accomplished?"

The steering committee may also have the responsibility for approving the team's recommendations and certainly has the authority to enable implementation. This helps ensure that teams' recommendations are acted on. Inaction will result in the belief of team members that management is not serious about the process, and employees will be reluctant to get involved in future efforts.

Another role of the steering committee is to ensure that managers and team members are trained in all aspects of the team concept. This should include team dynamics, project management, process design and improvement methodologies, empowerment, managing organizational change, attributes of leadership and the transformation process, and how to motivate and reward efforts.

Team Structure

How a team is structured will depend on the scope of the process on which it will work. A cross-functional team is most widely used for process improvement, as it may be necessary to cover the full range of job functions that the process involves.

The dynamics of individual personalities will affect the team's development and performance and should be taken into account when selecting team members. Every team needs a leader, appropriate team members, and, in some cases, a facilitator.

Team Leader. The team leader is responsible for coordinating meetings, which includes scheduling meeting rooms, creating agendas, guiding the team through the agenda (including reviews of homework assignments), and reporting progress to the steering committee. The team leader may also coordinate implementation of the team's approved recommendations. The team leader should have a vested interest in the process and may be a process owner responsible for the results of the process. The team leader must have strong organizational and interpersonal skills and should be sensitive when dealing with diverse opinions.

Team Members. Other team members are those involved with the process to be improved and may also include internal or external customers and suppliers. Technical experts and outsiders with no vested interest in the process are sometimes added to help provide additional knowledge, objectivity, or creativity. The team members will generally have action items to accomplish outside the team meetings and will often take on special roles during a meeting (such as scribe or timekeeper).

Team Facilitator. The team facilitator has the responsibility of helping the team to work effectively. The facilitator can play a critical role by asking questions, thereby encouraging the group members to look at the technical process on which they are working from different points of view. It is important that the team facilitator understand quality management theory. In particular, he or she should recognize the impact of individual and social psychology in groups. The facilitator may also provide or arrange for training to assist the team with the technical tools of improvement, such as process mapping, selecting data collection strategies, using relevant analysis tools, and ultimately guiding the development of a project plan to carry out improvement recommendations.

Dealing with Team Process Problems

Team members are most productive in an environment in which others are responsive and friendly, encourage contributions, and promote a sense of worth. Peter Scholtes spelled out ten problems that frequently occur within teams and are typical of the types of situations for which team leaders and facilitators must be prepared. Following is the list along with recommended actions:[7]

Problem 1. Floundering or difficulty in starting or ending an activity. *Solution:* Redirect team to the project plan and written objectives.

Problem 2. Team members attempt to influence the team process based on their position of authority in the organization. *Solution:* Talk to the members off-line; clarify the impact of their organizational role and the need for consensus and ask for cooperation and patience.

Problem 3. Participants who talk too much. *Solution:* Structure meeting so that everyone is encouraged to participate (for example, have members write down their opinions, then discuss them in the meeting one person at a time).

Problem 4. Participants who rarely speak. *Solution:* Practice gatekeeping by using phrases such as, "John, what's your view on this?" or divide tasks into individual assignments and have all members report.

Problem 5. Unquestioned acceptance of opinions as facts or participants making opinions sound like facts. *Solution:* Do not be afraid to ask whether something is an opinion or a fact. Ask for supporting data.

Problem 6. Rushing to get to a solution before the problem-solving process is worked through. *Solution:* Remind the group of the cost of jumping to conclusions.

Problem 7. Attempting to explain other members' motives. *Solution:* Ask the other person to clarify.

Problem 8. Ignoring or ridiculing another's values or statements made. *Solution:* Emphasize the need for listening and understanding. Support the discounted person.

Problem 9. Digression/tangents creating unfocused conversations. *Solution:* Remind members of the written agenda and time estimates. Continually direct the conversation back on track. Remind team of its mission, objectives, and the norms established.

Problem 10. Conflict involving personal matters. *Solution:* Request that these types of conflict be taken off-line. Reinforce ground rules.

Solutions to conflicts should be in the best interest of the team. Team members should be nonjudgmental, listening to team discussions and new ideas. Group feelings should be verbalized by periodically surfacing any undercurrents or by giving feedback.

One important skill needed in working with teams is the ability to provide constructive feedback during and/or at the end of a meeting. Feedback is an important vehicle to help the team mature. This feedback can be provided by the facilitator or by team members.

There are two types of appropriate feedback: motivational and coaching. *Motivational feedback* must be constructive—that is, specific, sincere, clear, timely, and descriptive of what actually occurred in the meeting. *Coaching,* or *corrective feedback,* specifically states the improvements that need to be made. Scholtes provides the following guidelines for providing constructive feedback (obviously, destructive or degrading feedback is not acceptable behavior):[8]

- Be specific

- Make observations, not conclusions

- Share ideas or information, not advice

- Speak for yourself

- Restrict feedback to known things

- Avoid using labels

- Do not exaggerate

- Phrase the issue as a statement, not a question

Having a team do a self-evaluation at the end of each meeting can be useful in helping the team to further develop team skills and to take more responsibility for team progress. Team members can be asked to write down how well the team is doing on each of the norms (for example, on a scale of 1–5) and to list any additional norms they believe need to be added. A group discussion of the information can then result in revised norms and specific actions the team will take to improve in the future.

Team Facilitation Techniques

A *facilitator* is a person who helps a team manage the team dynamics and relationship processes. A facilitator does not normally get involved in the content—the technical aspects of what the team is working on. The role of the facilitator is instead to act as:

- A guide to circumvent the pitfalls of a stoppage or detour in difficult situations

- A catalyst to assist in developing a plan that provides follow-up to all management levels, thus maintaining continuity of support

- An objective evaluator and auditor of team progress, identifying any roadblocks to success and opportunities to improve performance[9]

Some specific responsibilities of the facilitator include:

- Cultivating an unbiased and impartial environment

- Ensuring that a full examination and discussion of issues take place

- Providing an objective framework

- Reinforcing focus on mission and objectives

- Helping organize multiple and diverse viewpoints

- Regulating interruptions

- Ensuring that everyone on the team has the opportunity to participate in discussions and decision-making

- Defusing destructive behaviors

- Encouraging visual or verbal tracking of ideas

In order to carry out these responsibilities, the facilitator typically does the following:

- Encourages reluctant participants to speak

- Helps to resolve conflict between team members

- Provides feedback to the leader and/or team

- Ensures that ground rules (agreed-to group norms) are followed

- Ensures that members are listening to and understanding others

- Legitimizes everyone's perceptions and feelings
- Verbalizes what is going on
- Checks for agreement
- Maintains or regains focus on the meeting agenda or topic of discussion
- Provides ideas on approaches for gathering or analyzing data
- Ensures consensus
- Periodically summarizes results

A well-trained facilitator is a valuable asset in any team situation. A combination of formal training and considerable experience will produce the best results. Facilitators should be trained in meeting process facilitation, conflict resolution, training and coaching skills, interpersonal skills in a group environment, basic behavior management skills, quality management principles and practices, and appropriate use of quality tools.

Facilitators are less necessary as the team becomes more experienced and capable. Initially, the facilitator is more of a coach and referee in the team process and therefore requires good communications skills as well as some technical knowledge of the subject, meeting facilitation skills, and the ability to resolve conflict when it occurs. If performance of the team remains dependent on the facilitator, however, then the facilitator has not done an effective job of helping the team to develop. A highly developed team should have the knowledge and ability to deal with problems that might arise, such as a deviation from the agenda, interpersonal conflict, or ineffective decision-making—in effect, it should become self-facilitating.

Sponsor. Each team usually has a sponsor responsible for ensuring success. The *sponsor* is an individual who has a significant stake in the outcome of a particular team project. She or he is often the process owner. Such a person must be at a level high enough in the organization to be able to address any difficulties encountered by the team. In the early part of a continuous improvement effort, the sponsor may also be a member of the steering committee. A sponsor's responsibilities include the following:

- Helping to initiate the team effort by authorizing the activity
- Defining the purpose and scope of the team
- Coordinating the front-end planning
- Helping to select the team leader, facilitator, and members
- Negotiating additional resources needed

During the team effort, the sponsor maintains an awareness of team progress, monitors team performance problems, acts as a liaison to the steering committee, top management, or other departments or teams, helps obtain any additional information and resources that are outside the team's authority boundaries, and acts as a coach to the team leader.

Team Leader. The *team leader* is responsible for the team's ongoing success. Responsibilities include:

- Organizing and managing team meetings
- Working with the sponsor to develop and monitor the project plan
- Keeping the team effort on track
- Providing status updates to the sponsor and steering committee
- Addressing group dynamics issues
- Serving as a liaison between the team and other parts of the organization
- Helping to resolve problems
- Handling administrative duties and keeping team records

A team leader is also responsible for contributing to the team's content, although he or she must be careful that those contributions do not receive greater status than those of other team members. When a facilitator is not involved, the leader also has the same responsibilities as a facilitator relative to team dynamics and relationships.

A team's growth is the responsibility both of individual team members and of the organization. As shown in Figure 3.4, both must create the cultural synergy that makes teams productive.

A new type of organizational leadership is necessary to provide teams with the authority they need to be successful. This requires a transformation from the old type of autocratic leadership to the new facilitating, coaching, and participative approach.

Figure 3.4   Supporting factors for effective teamwork.

5. TEAM PERFORMANCE AND EVALUATION

> Evaluate team performance in relation to established metrics to meet goals and objectives. Determine when and how to reward teams and celebrate their success. (Evaluate)
>
> **Body of Knowledge I.C.5**

Team members and top management will quickly become frustrated if teams are not making progress. The organization should be tracking progress to identify problems, such as poor meeting attendance, failure of other departments to provide the necessary support, or lack of specialized technical knowledge. Long-term projects also require more complex project management skills and processes. Measuring and communicating the effectiveness of a team can help promote necessary changes and stimulate improvement. The feedback is important to management to indicate the degree to which a team is meeting its objectives.

Objective measures directed toward the project goal could include data such as changes in process performance (for example, increase in first-time yield, reduction of customer waiting time), resource utilization (for example, number of person-hours invested in the project, funds spent), and timing against the project plan. The team may also use internally oriented measures such as overall percentage of team member attendance at meetings and the team's evaluation of meeting effectiveness. A team should take responsibility for self-evaluation, with appropriate measures reported to the sponsor and steering committee.

One way a team can evaluate itself is to select criteria based on team effectiveness guidelines included in team training materials or based on the team's list of behavioral norms. A list of questions and a rating scale can then be used at the end of each meeting to monitor how well the team performed. The evaluation criteria can also evolve over time as the team develops. Standard instruments available from providers of training and organization development materials can also be used.

Questionnaires or interviews can be administered to outside-the-team personnel—such as internal and external customers, other teams, or management—and used to capture metrics related to perceived progress on attributes such as relationship building, effectiveness of the team's progress, and efficiency of the team's process. Maintaining a list of lessons learned can also help the team to see what additional benefits are being gained, and these lists can be shared with others to accelerate organization-wide learning.

Teams, like individuals, deserve recognition for their efforts. This recognition can also provide encouragement for future progress and success. In an organization that is just beginning to use the team process, this might be the single most important factor for sustaining momentum. The following suggestions for recognition and rewards are described by Aubrey and Felkins:[10]

- Supportive comments and helpful suggestions provided by management during team presentations

- Public recognition through professional societies or through publication of results in such journals as *Quality Progress* or industry publications, as well as company newsletters and bulletins

- Performance appraisals that reflect employees' personal growth and contribution as team members

- Material rewards such as certificates, pins, coffee mugs, and lunches

- Gainsharing, or distributing some of the cost savings or revenue enhancements to team members

- Bonuses or other monetary rewards

What is measured (and recognized/rewarded) and how it is measured and administered requires careful thought and team members' input. Applying recognition and rewards fairly implies the creation of standard performance definitions and values. Ignoring some achievements, recognizing or rewarding under-standard achievements, and giving the wrong weighting to an achievement are reasons why care and good judgment are critical, and each are causes of disappointment, disillusionment, and discontent among team members.

Nonmonetary forms of recognition are used to acknowledge a team's efforts in a majority of cases. Examples are public recognition in articles published in the organization's newsletter and/or community newspapers, verbal mention at group meetings, plaques and certificates, T-shirts, pins, and other visible but low-cost items. Recognizing an entire team with one standard reward can be less effective than when team members choose their own rewards within a value range. Catalog programs have evolved to service this approach. Sustained performance excellence may be rewarded by promotions and preferred assignments for team members.

Rather than focusing on rewarding performance, some organizations create a pay-for-skills plan. As employees progress through a ladder-style development program, their pay is increased at predefined increments. This is especially relevant in a self-directed team environment.

In addition to external recognition, it is important that team members and leaders provide internal recognition for team progress when important milestones have been accomplished. Recognition might also be given to individuals whose contributions are exceptional or above expectations or to people outside the team who have provided valuable support.

The team goal must be focused on team success, and teams need to behave as if they are owners. This begins when the teams are given responsibility, encouragement, and knowledge. The focus must also be directed to external customers. This focus depends on limited organization layers, a general focus on business and customers, logical boundaries for the team, strong networks, and open communications. The focus also relies on helping teams know who the critical customers are, what their needs are, and how the business may meet those needs.[11]

Groupthink

In the team selection process, as well as when the team is functioning day to day, care must be taken to avoid groupthink.[12] *Groupthink* occurs when most or all of the team members coalesce in supporting an idea or a decision that has not been fully explored or when some members may secretly disagree. The members are more concerned with maintaining friendly relations and avoiding conflict than in becoming engrossed in a controversial discussion. Actions to forestall groupthink may include:

- Brainstorming alternatives before selecting an approach
- Encouraging members to express their concerns
- Ensuring that ample time is given to surface, examine, and comprehend all ideas and suggestions
- Developing rules for examining each alternative
- Appointing an "objector" to challenge proposed actions

Final Thought

An effective team leader can provide an environment in which team members feel motivated. This can be achieved by applying the *six Rs*:

1. *Reinforce.* Identify and positively reinforce work done well.

2. *Request information.* Discuss team members' views. Is anything preventing expected performance?

3. *Resources.* Identify needed resources, the lack of which could impede quality performance.

4. *Responsibility.* Customers make paydays possible; all employees have a responsibility to the customers, internal and external.

5. *Role.* Be a role model. Do not just tell; demonstrate how to do it. Observe learners' performance. Together, critique the approach and work out an improved method.

6. *Repeat.* Apply the above principles regularly and repetitively.[13]

REFERENCES

1. P. Senge, *The Fifth Discipline* (New York: Random House, 2005).
2. C. C. Manz, and H. P. Sims Jr., *Business without Bosses: How Self-Managed Teams Are Building High-Performance Companies* (New York: John Wiley & Sons, 1993).
3. Ibid.
4. R. T. Westcott, *Simplified Project Management for the Quality Professional* (Milwaukee: ASQ Quality Press, 2005), Chap. 5.
5. B. W. Tuckman, "Developmental Sequence in Small Groups," *Psychological Bulletin* 63, no. 6 (1965): 384–99.

6. R. T. Westcott, and G. L. Duffy, eds., *The Certified Quality Improvement Associate Handbook*, 3rd ed. (Milwaukee: ASQ Quality Press, 2015), Chap. 5.

7. P. R. Scholtes, *The Team Handbook* (Madison, WI: Joiner, 1988), 6–37.

8. Ibid., 6–24.

9. J. L. Hradesky, *Total Quality Management Handbook* (New York: McGraw-Hill, 1995), 57.

10. C. A. Aubrey, and P. K. Felkins, *Teamwork: Involving People in Quality and Productivity Improvement* (Milwaukee: ASQC Quality Press, 1988).

11. J. A. DeFeo, ed., *Juran's Quality Handbook*, 7th ed. (New York: McGraw-Hill, 2017).

12. J. E. Bauer, G.L. Duffy, and R. T. Westcott, eds., *The Quality Improvement Handbook* (Milwaukee: ASQ Quality Press, 2002), Chap. 3.

13. Ibid.

See Appendix A for additional references for this chapter.

Chapter 4
D. ASQ Code of Ethics

Identify and apply behaviors and actions that comply with this code. (Apply)

Body of Knowledge I.D

It is important that people in an organization know and understand the behaviors that are considered acceptable. Therefore, another critical role of leadership is to ensure that the organization has defined those behaviors and the principles behind them as clearly as possible. Documenting and communicating the values and principles that should be used as a guide for day-to-day decision-making is one way employees learn what is acceptable. Another way is through observation of the actions of persons in leadership roles and others in influential or powerful positions. Therefore, it is important that a leader's actions be congruent with the stated principles and values.

For some fields of professional practice, codes of conduct are defined by professional organizations. Following is the code of ethics for quality professionals established by the American Society for Quality (ASQ). It provides both general principles and specific actions designed to ensure that ASQ members demonstrate ethical behaviors in their relationships with the public, employers, customers and clients, and peers. The code is critical to quality decisions and behavior and valuable when designing systems as well as in day-to-day communications.

It is important for leaders in organizations to take action on the basis of how well employees meet ethical guidelines. Employees who demonstrate ethical practices, especially during difficult situations, must be commended for their actions, whereas those who do not must be dealt with appropriately.

Use the ASQ Code of Ethics as a model to assist your organization in developing its own code as well as using it to develop your personal code of ethics. Refer often to your organization's code and your own code. Ensure that you are behaving at or above the ethical level embodied in the code.

One thing to consider, though, is that unethical behavior in one country may be an acceptable behavior in another locale.

Although the term *supplier* is not specifically mentioned, the intent of an ethical relationship between a customer and a supplier may be implied from the intent

ASQ CODE OF ETHICS

Introduction

The purpose of the American Society for Quality (ASQ) Code of Ethics is to establish global standards of conduct and behavior for its members, certification holders, and anyone else who may represent or be perceived to represent ASQ. In addition to the code, all applicable ASQ policies and procedures should be followed. Violations to the Code of Ethics should be reported. Differences in work style or personalities should be first addressed directly with others before escalating to an ethics issue.

The ASQ Professional Ethics and Qualifications Committee, appointed annually by the ASQ Board of Directors, is responsible for interpreting this code and applying it to specific situations, which may or may not be specifically called out in the text. Disciplinary actions will be commensurate with the seriousness of the offense and may include permanent revocation of certifications and/or expulsion from the society.

Fundamental Principles

ASQ requires its representatives to be honest and transparent. Avoid conflicts of interest and plagiarism. Do not harm others. Treat them with respect, dignity, and fairness. Be professional and socially responsible. Advance the role and perception of the Quality professional.

Expectations of a Quality Professional

A. Act with Integrity and Honesty

1. Strive to uphold and advance the integrity, honor, and dignity of the Quality profession.

2. Be truthful and transparent in all professional interactions and activities.

3. Execute professional responsibilities and make decisions in an objective, factual, and fully informed manner.

4. Accurately represent and do not mislead others regarding professional qualifications, including education, titles, affiliations, and certifications.

5. Offer services, provide advice, and undertake assignments only in your areas of competence, expertise, and training.

B. Demonstrate Responsibility, Respect, and Fairness

1. Hold paramount the safety, health, and welfare of individuals, the public, and the environment.

2. Avoid conduct that unjustly harms or threatens the reputation of the Society, its members, or the Quality profession.

3. Do not intentionally cause harm to others through words or deeds. Treat others fairly, courteously, with dignity, and without prejudice or discrimination.

4. Act and conduct business in a professional and socially responsible manner.

5. Allow diversity in the opinions and personal lives of others.

C. Safeguard Proprietary Information and Avoid Conflicts of Interest

1. Ensure the protection and integrity of confidential information.

2. Do not use confidential information for personal gain.

3. Fully disclose and avoid any real or perceived conflicts of interest that could reasonably impair objectivity or independence in the service of clients, customers, employers, or the Society.

4. Give credit where it is due.

5. Do not plagiarize. Do not use the intellectual property of others without permission. Document the permission as it is obtained.

---

of the ASQ code. A code developed for use by a different type of organization would, no doubt, include specific principles applying to supplier ethics.

There is an increasing concern that the *social responsibilities* of an organization, its management, its employees, and its subcontractors be addressed in any code of ethics. Although this concern is not specifically mentioned in the ASQ Code of Ethics, it can be assumed the intent exists. The International Organization for Standardization (ISO) 26000 standard provides guidance.[1]

This is a short chapter, but the importance of embracing and sustaining ethical behavior permeates every aspect of organizations' operations. Laws and regulations have been enacted to control certain industries and types of organizations and punish wrongdoers. Behaving ethically, however, has to derive from personal values and integrity. Controls are useful reminders, but individuals must believe in and feel the need to conduct themselves ethically.

REFERENCE

1. American Society for Quality, ASQ/ANSI/ISO 26000:2010, *Guidance on Social Responsibility* (Milwaukee: *ASQ Quality Press*, 2010).

See Appendix A for additional references for this chapter.

Part II
Strategic Plan Development and Deployment

Chapter 5   A. Strategic Planning Models
             Contributor: Jd Marhevko
Chapter 6   B. Business Environment Analysis
             Contributor: Jd Marhevko
Chapter 7   C. Strategic Plan Deployment
             Contributor: Jd Marhevko

The transformation to world-class quality is not possible without committed, visionary, hands-on leadership.

—Steven George

Although strategic planning is billed as a way of becoming more future oriented, most managers, when pressed, will admit that their strategic plans reveal more about today's problems than tomorrow's opportunities.

—Gary Hamel and C. K. Prahalad

An environment which calls for perfection is not likely to be easy. But aiming for it is always a goad to progress.

—Thomas Watson Jr., IBM

The purpose of a business is to gain and keep customers.

—Fred Smith, Federal Express

Chapter 5
A. Strategic Planning Models

Define, describe, and use basic elements of strategic planning models, including how the guiding principles of mission, vision, and values relate to the plan. (Apply)

Body of Knowledge II.A

If you always do what you've always done, you'll always get what you've always gotten.

—Origin unknown

An organization's strategy defines what it strives to become and the means by which it will achieve it. Tregoe and Zimmerman define strategy as "the framework which guides those choices that determine the nature and direction of an organization."[1] Mintzberg further describes strategy as a plan or a course of action into the future, as a pattern providing consistency in behavior over time, as a position—namely, the determination of particular products in particular markets, and as a perspective—namely, an organization's way of doing things.[2]

Strategic planning is the continuous process of incorporating entrepreneurial decisions in a systematic way, with a view of the future. The efforts need to be carried out systematically and measured against the expectations, and feedback should be provided to identify stakeholders.[3] Planning is a continual process because the environment in which we work is dynamic. Changing factors include but are not limited to changes in demand and scope of customers, stakeholders, competitors, supply chain, and employee base. These groups are also referred to as *interested parties*. Effective, continual planning guides an organization toward achievement of goals and prepares it for changes in their internal and external factors that can affect its future.[4]

The origin of the term *strategic plan* has been traced to H. Igor Ansoff's *Corporate Strategy*, published in 1965.[5] For the following two decades, Ansoff continued to write about this concept of planning and managing with a strategic intent. By the mid-1990s, Henry Mintzberg had contributed a vast amount of writing on strategic planning. A critical factor in strategic planning is the subject of quality.[6]

Long-range planning, a term often confused with strategic planning, consists of extrapolating future plans based on what is known of current operations. In this sense, long-range planning and forecasting are synonymous. Strategic planning develops a view of the future, then delineates plans for the near term that will, when achieved, address the future needs as envisioned.

The Baldrige Performance Excellence Program criteria describe strategic planning as the process that addresses strategic and business planning and deployment of plans, with strong customer and operational performance requirements. The award's strategic-planning category emphasizes that customer-driven quality and operational performance excellence are key strategic business issues integral to an organization's planning.[7]

The span of a strategic plan may be as short as two or three months (for fast-moving organizations in a rapidly changing marketplace) to thirty years or more for a public utility (planning electric generation capacity for the future with an average of thirty years to find and acquire land, design, certify, and put a new plant into operation). For most organizations the long-term planning span is three to five years. While the time frame to be visualized will vary across industries, a twenty- to thirty-year span may be needed to allow some organizational challenges. In such a case, specialists in envisioning (futurists) may be used to help leaders see potential situations clearly. This vision is highly useful in strengths-weaknesses-opportunities-threats (SWOT) analyses or scenario analyses (see below).

STRATEGIC PLANNING CONCEPTS

Strategic plans communicate the organization's priorities throughout the enterprise. Note that some organizations can fall short of this and only communicate to a few levels in the business. This can cause confusion in the execution of the plan. A strategic plan provides a road map of how to get to specific targets and directs everyone in the organization to work to reach those same targets. Strategic planning should not be the work of a few select managers. It should involve people from all levels of the organization in the planning and execution of actions needed to help the organization focus on customer needs, remain flexible and responsive, retain employees, satisfy the needs of other stakeholders, and achieve excellence.

The development of an overall strategic plan is affected by various internal and external forces. Internal forces such as corporate culture, finances, worker skills, and other resources have an effect on the strategic plan. External forces such as changes in technology, customers' requirements, accrediting and regulatory agencies' rules, and competitors' actions relative to products/services have an effect on the strategic plan. In addition, various functions within the organization need to develop their own strategies that are closely aligned and integrated with the overall strategic plan. Examples of these are service strategies, marketing strategies, quality strategies, and operational strategies.

The strategic planning process is a continual process. As part of the planning process, there is opportunity to determine whether previous strategic plans have been met. If the plans have not been met, the organization needs to determine why. Answers might range from a flawed planning process that needs improvement, to unrealistic objectives, to organizational weaknesses.[8]

Controversy has arisen over the viability of strategic planning. Because strategic planning spans several years, it does seem somewhat less useful for organizations that face extremely rapid change, such as organizations in a volatile marketplace, organizations facing exploding technological advances, or organizations manufacturing products with fad or short-term appeal (for example, toy action figures and computer games). Nevertheless, organizations operating within such rapidly changing contexts also require an established strategic planning process to avoid falling prey to knee-jerk reactions. Yet, in order to be responsive, the strategic planning cycle in such cases must be sufficiently rapid to remain meaningful.

TRADITIONAL STRATEGIC PLANNING

Numerous strategic planning models have been developed to assist in the planning process. A generic overview of traditional strategic planning is shown in Figure 5.1. Planning is typically divided into three levels: strategic, tactical, and operational. Strategic plans articulate what an organization strives to become and the means to achieve it.

Tactical plans identify **how** the organization will implement the strategic plan. Tactical plans are those that occupy most of the attention of quality engineers, especially when a new product/service is being planned. The quality engineer works with suppliers, testers, designers, and market and financial analysts to specify what tasks need to be completed to ensure that a product meets its goals.

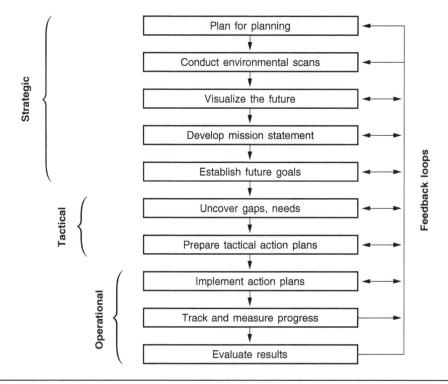

Figure 5.1   Overview of strategic planning process.

Operational plans, or action plans, are the day-to-day action-oriented plans concerned with the details of who performs what tasks and within what time frame. Operational planning includes scheduling inspections, tests, calibrations, process capability studies, training courses, and other essential day-to-day activities.

Another way to view these levels of planning is that strategic planning is composed of two phases. The first phase is formulation, in which strategies and objectives are formulated or defined. The second phase, implementation, encompasses the tactical and operational plans.

Involvement of people during the strategic planning process also changes as the process is deployed throughout the organization. Typically, the organization's leadership drives the strategic planning, with input from all functional areas. Next, functional areas formulate their own objectives and strategies (tactical plans) to support the strategic plan in achieving its vision. Further into the process, individual employees or teams become involved in developing action plans, budgets, and measures to monitor performance against the plans. A strategic planning process continues, with budget information being funneled back up through the organization to develop the functional budgets, division budgets, and overall corporate budget.

Measurements complete the process by providing feedback to the various levels. Individuals receive information on how well they are meeting their operational/action plans, functions and divisions receive information on how performance relates to their tactical plans, and the organization gets valuable feedback on how well it is achieving its vision. Measurements close the plan-do-check-act (PDCA) loop by providing the information needed to make course adjustments over time, thus ensuring that the strategic plan is met.

A potential shortfall of traditional strategic planning is that the resulting plan may, because of a lack of committed deployment (for example, ownership), end up on someone's shelf unfulfilled. For this reason, hoshin planning is presented as a model that completes the cycle from planning to deployment to planning again (plan-do-check-act). The Japanese term *hoshin kanri* loosely translates as *hoshin*, meaning policy or target, and *kanri*, meaning deployment or management.

HOSHIN PLANNING

The first stage of hoshin planning (Figure 5.2) is to develop, or revise as needed, the vision (for example, future state of the organization and its purpose) and mission of the organization using information from the environmental analysis. There is controversy over whether vision should precede mission or vice versa. The answer appears simple: do whatever makes the most sense for a given organization.

Let's say a healthcare organization has a long-standing mission to deliver exemplary healthcare (for example, efficient and effective care) to its community. That is a given—no need to change the mission. The environmental analysis, however, indicates that rapid and extraordinary changes must be made in the role healthcare will need to take in the future, or the continuance of the organization will be in jeopardy. A vision, or a revised vision, is in order. In this case, mission first, vision second.

Across town, an accounting firm is starting its first strategic planning process. It has neither a vision nor a mission on paper. It has, however, been functioning for years with the founding partners' unwritten concept of what to do, for whom they do it, and how well they do it. This concept needs to be captured in print and

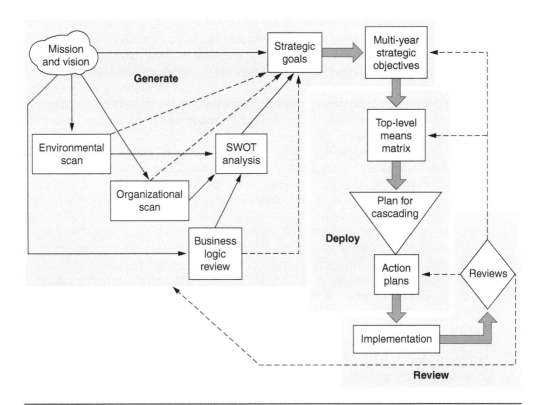

Figure 5.2   A typical view of the hoshin planning process.

examined for currency as well as future implications. A vision emerges from the planning team. The mission statement is then formulated to reflect the products and services it delivers now and will deliver in the foreseeable future. The firm views the mission statement as more likely to change to reflect changing client needs and as it expands into different service markets. In this case, vision first, mission second.

Creating a Vision Statement. The purpose of the vision statement is to express what the organization would like to accomplish and/or where it would like to be in the future. A vision statement should be brief, inspire and challenge, describe an ideal condition, appeal to all interested parties,[9] and provide direction for the future state of the organization. The following are examples of vision statements:

- To become a $125 billion company by the year 2000 (Walmart, 1990).

- To become the world's most loved, most flown, and most profitable airline (Southwest Airlines, 1989).

- To knock off R. J. Reynolds as the number one tobacco company in the world (Philip Morris, 1950s).

Why create a vision statement? To articulate a vision, an organization should visualize the future and define its role in it. Once the vision becomes clear, the organization can work toward achieving it by developing the strategic plan. Although the terms are often used interchangeably, mission statements and vision statements are distinctly different. "A mission is for today's goals and the vision is for tomorrow's goals."[10] Vince Lombardi, Super Bowl–winning coach of the Green Bay Packers, is credited with saying, "The best coaches know what the end result looks like, whether it's an offensive play, a defensive play, a defensive coverage, or just some area of the organization. If you don't know what the end result is supposed to look like, you can't get there. All teams basically do the same thing. We all have drafts, we all have training camps, and we all have practices. But the bad coaches don't know what they want. The good coaches do."[11]

Likewise, all organizations do basically the same thing. They all sell products and services to customers, and they all utilize the same resources (for example, people, equipment, and money). Successful organizations know where they are headed and have plans to get there.

Guiding Principles or Values. Some planners choose to develop guiding principles or values to specify how business is to be conducted (for example, the protocol for completing transactions). Guiding principles or values help establish and define the organization culture and form the basis for decision-making. Guiding principles or values may be customer focused, innovative, ethical, and risk-taking. These principles or values are the fundamental beliefs that guide actions.

Defining the Mission. To effectively develop a strategic plan with all its ancillary objectives, means, and action plans, the organization must state its mission. The mission defines the purpose of the organization. "Mission defines the core purpose of being, in terms of the accomplishments needed that will result in realization of the vision."[12] The mission statement is infrequently revised. The following are examples of mission statements:

- The mission of Levi Strauss & Co. is to sustain responsible commercial success as a global marketing company of branded apparel. We must balance goals of superior profitability and return on investment, leadership market positions, and superior products and service. We will conduct our business ethically and demonstrate leadership in satisfying our responsibilities to our communities and to society. Our work environment will be safe and productive and characterized by fair treatment, teamwork, open communications, personal accountability, and opportunities for growth and development.[13]

- TED: Spreading Ideas (two words).[14]

- Microsoft (at its founding): A computer on every desk and in every home.[15]

Establishing Strategic Goals. Keeping the vision and mission before them, planners integrate information derived from the environmental analysis to formulate strategic goals (strive for no more than three or four goals). This is often called an environmental scan.

Setting Multiyear Strategic Objectives. From the goals, planners then expand into multiyear strategic objectives (for example, what the objectives will be for the first year of the planning cycle, the second year, and so on). As with all objectives, they must be measurable. Each goal may have one or many objectives. Table 5.1 is a template for the S.M.A.R.T. W.A.Y. to establish objectives.

Table 5.1 Setting objectives the S.M.A.R.T. W.A.Y.

S	Focus on *specific* needs and opportunities.
M	Establish a *measurement* for each objective.
A	Be sure objectives are *achievable* as well as challenging.
R	Set stretch objectives that are also *realistic*.
T	Indicate a *time* frame for each objective.
W	Ensure that every objective is *worth* doing.
A	*Assign* responsibility for each objective.
Y	Ensure that all objectives stated will *yield* desired return.

Source: Reprinted with permission of R. T. Westcott & Associates.

● = The means was derived for this objective   ○ = The means has an impact on this objective

Figure 5.3   Top-level means matrix format.

Creating the Means Matrix. Using the goals and the objectives, a top-level means matrix is prepared. The means succinctly answer the how question. Additional data are added to the matrix—for example, estimate of resources required, persons responsible for each objective, and the basis for measurement. Each objective may have several means.

A typical means matrix format (Figure 5.3) displays the multiyear objectives (derived from the strategic goals) as columns and the means for accomplishing those objectives as rows. The relationship of a means to an objective may be coded—for example, a filled circle may mean there is a direct relationship, while an open circle may mean there is an impact on the objective. Primary and secondary responsibilities for each mean may be indicated as persons or functions. A macrolevel statement of resources required is entered for each of the means, as

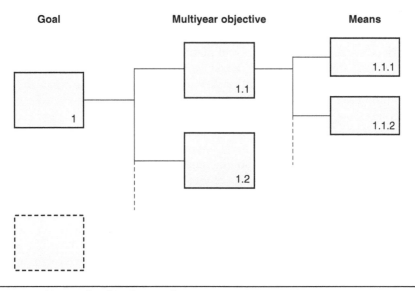

Goal   Multiyear objective   Means

Figure 5.4   Linking goals, objectives, and means.

well as the most appropriate measure. A Gantt charting of the time line for each of the means completes the matrix. If the time span of the strategic plan is five years, the time line would encompass the five years. As the planning team develops the matrix, it may well be a chart four to five feet long and ten or more feet wide. Figure 5.4 shows a tree chart of the relationships between the goals and the objectives and the objectives and the means.

Deploying the Plan. When the matrix has been reviewed and adjustments made (for example, for conflicting times and resources), the overall plans are deployed horizontally and downward throughout the organization. At this stage the strategic goals, objectives, and means are cascaded across the organization. The plans move in an iterative way—for example, up and down (vertically) and across organizational functions until consensus is reached, a process the Japanese call *catchball*.

Preparing Action Plans. Action plans are developed for each means by the individuals or teams responsible for executing the plans. There may be several action plans for each means. The action plans are implemented, continuously monitored, and reviewed.

Transitioning to the Next Year's Planning. By the end of the third quarter in the planning and implementation process, hoshin planning begins anew for the upcoming year. Results of the first year's implementation become additional information, part of the environmental assessment, for the following year. All goals, objectives, and means are carefully reviewed and adjustments proposed as needed. Typically, some action plans will not have worked out as planned, perhaps leaving work to be carried over to the next year. Some objectives and some of the means supporting those objectives may be no longer valid, require additional resources to complete, or be postponed to make room for a new or higher-priority activity.

Advantages and Disadvantages of Hoshin Planning. The hoshin planning process should not be confused with management by objectives, which it superficially resembles. Hoshin planning is a tightly knit planning and implementation system that can involve every member of the organization. Hoshin planning is a vehicle for communicating, through every organizational level, the direction of the organization and for controlling the outcomes. Every person in the organization knows where his or her efforts and ideas fit in the overall scheme. Documented evidence exists at every stage in the process to enable all planners to learn from the process, improve the process, and achieve the planned goals of the organization. Hoshin planning engenders and reinforces team-based problem-solving and decision-making. It literally forces management to "walk the talk" and to integrate the implementation of strategic plans with daily operations. It surfaces resource conflicts and forces trade-off analysis and resolution. Hoshin planning is a fact-based system for stimulating and managing the growth and development of the organization and its people.

Hoshin planning, through its catchball approach to resolving barriers and its insistence on constant tracking, measuring, and reviewing, succeeds where other less-stringent strategic planning efforts have faltered or failed. For the many years strategic planning has been around, it has always been implied that the plans must be cascaded down through the organization to be viable. The problem was that no effective and enforced process had previously been devised for making this happen.

Perhaps the single most troublesome area of hoshin planning for the typical American organization is the emphasis on involvement of the entire organization, with consensus at every level, before implementing the action plans. In hoshin planning, the ideal planning group often comprises the key top management of the organization, who coalesce into a smoothly functioning team, both to make the process work as well as to create a role model for lower levels. Also, the time required to fully implement hoshin planning can be daunting for smaller organizations. An answer, in many cases, is to take on fewer goals.

Hoshin planning is not an easy journey. It requires solid top-management support and personal involvement. For organizations that are not accustomed to soliciting feedback from below, or that have never before done formal planning, it involves a significant cultural change. An effectively functioning hoshin planning process might take three years, or even longer, to work out the smooth flow of information and to build realism into the planning.

SCENARIO PLANNING

Scenario planning is a disciplined method for imagining possible futures that companies have applied to a great range of issues.[16] By identifying basic trends and uncertainties leading to the future, a series of narratives or scenarios can be constructed. These stories challenge existing assumptions, providing a kind of looking glass for organizations to see themselves as never before. Scenario planning helps compensate for the usual errors in decision-making: overconfidence and tunnel vision. In its simplest form, scenario planning uses three macro (or all-embracing) scenarios: good future, bad future, and wild card. Once scenarios are visualized, alternate strategic (contingency) plans can be developed.

BARRIERS TO SUCCESSFUL STRATEGIC PLANNING

Undefined and ambiguous terms can be one of the biggest roadblocks to the strategic planning process. Terms can be easily misunderstood because they are often used interchangeably. The term *goal* is often substituted for *objective*. Likewise, *action plan* and *program* are sometimes used interchangeably. Organizations need to clearly define the terms they will be using in their strategic planning process and communicate them to ensure they are understood by all people involved. When priorities and strategies are unclear, people do not know what to aim for or what to do.

Strategic planning sometimes fails because reward and recognition systems do not support the results of the planning process or promote a sense of urgency. People are motivated to act quickly when they receive rewards and recognition, but in most organizations people are not rewarded for a sense of urgency.

At times, individual departments have their own set of plans, goals, and strategies that might or might not fit with those of other departments. When fragmented responsibilities and functional systems do not support the planning process, the organization cannot work together toward a common goal.

Additionally, when management does not "walk the talk" of strategic planning, people become confused by the mixed signals they receive. Excessive procedures, paperwork, and meetings choke out a sense of urgency by miring employees in mundane tasks (an example of lack of focus on the "vital few" of Juran). These problems are supported by the list of the ten most important pitfalls of planning as compiled by Steiner:[17]

1. Top management's assumption that it can delegate the planning function to a planner

2. Top management becomes so engrossed in current problems that it spends insufficient time on long-range planning, and the process becomes discredited among other managers and staff

3. Failure to develop company goals suitable as a basis for formulating long-range plans

4. Failure to assume the necessary involvement in the planning process of major line personnel

5. Failure to use plans as standards for measuring managerial performance

6. Failure to create a climate in the company that is congenial and not resistant to planning

7. Assuming that corporate comprehensive planning is something separate from the entire management process

8. Injecting so much formality into the system that it lacks flexibility, looseness, and simplicity and restrains creativity

9. Failure of top management to review with departmental and divisional heads the long-range plan they have developed

10. Top management consistently rejecting the formal planning mechanism by making intuitive decisions that conflict with the formal plans

When the appropriate model and structure for the strategic planning has been determined, the next step in the process is to conduct an environmental analysis.

REFERENCES

1. B. B. Tregoe and J. W. Zimmerman, *Top Management Strategy: What It Is and How to Make It Work* (New York: Simon & Schuster, Touchstone Books, 1980).

2. H. Mintzberg, *The Rise and Fall of Strategic Planning* (New York: Free Press, 1994).

3. P. Drucker, "The Information Executives Truly Need," *Harvard Business Review* 73 (January–February 1995): 125.

4. T. J. Cartin and D. J. Jacoby, *A Review for Managing for Quality and a Primer for the Certified Quality Manager Exam* (Milwaukee: ASQ Quality Press, 1997), 79.

5. H. I. Ansoff, *Corporate Strategy: An Analytic Approach to Business Policy for Growth and Expansion* (s.l.: McGraw-Hill, 1965).

6. Mintzberg, *The Rise and Fall of Strategic Planning*.

7. National Institute of Standards and Technology (NIST), Baldrige Excellence Framework, www.nist.gov/baldrige.

8. Ibid., 81.

9. Ibid.

10. J. R. Latham, "Visioning: The Concept, Trilogy, and Process," *Quality Progress* (July 1995): 89.

11. J. Madden and D. Anderson, *Hey, Wait a Minute, I Wrote a Book* (New York: Ballantine, 1985).

12. P. Mears and F. Voehl, *The Guide to Implementing Quality Systems* (Delray Beach, FL: St. Lucie Press, 1995), 32.

13. https://levisclothing.wordpress.com/mission-statement-2/ (2019).

14. https://www.ted.com/about/our-organization (2019).

15. Hubspot, 2019, https://blog.hubspot.com/marketing/inspiring-company-mission-statements.

16. P. Schoemaker, "Scenario Planning: A Tool for Strategic Thinking," *Sloan Management Review* 37 (Winter 1995): 82; T. Wheelen, J. Hunger, D. Hoffman, N. Alan, and C. Bamford, *Strategic Management and Business Policy: Globalization, Innovation and Sustainability*, 14th ed. (Upper Saddle River, NJ: Pearson Education, 2015).

17. G. A. Steiner, *Strategic Planning: What Every Manager Must Know* (New York: Free Press, 1979).

See Appendix A for additional references for this chapter.

Chapter 6
B. Business Environment Analysis

M any factors both inside and outside an organization can have a significant impact on short-term performance and long-term viability. For example, current strategy may be invalidated by a new entrant to the market or a change in product liability law, or new product or service opportunities may suddenly become possible due to new technological breakthroughs. A critical role of senior management, then, is to create and implement strategies to keep an organization viable over the long term, taking into consideration the interested parties, competitors, and society at large.

Development of strategy requires that an organization understand the external environment in which it operates, its own internal strengths and weaknesses, and how the internal and external factors can best be combined to create a competitive advantage. An organization might choose to be the leader in product or service design, or the low-cost provider in the general market, or may carve out a unique niche in the market that is not currently served by others.

Environment scanning and analysis, both external and internal, should not occur only once a year, just before strategy and budgets are set. In a fast-changing world, an organization must be continually monitoring factors known to be important to performance, as well as be on the lookout for changes that may bring new factors into consideration. Business environment analysis is a process that is done as a key input to the strategic planning process.

Figure 6.1 highlights some of the major components considered during an environment analysis. While much of the information gained during the analysis is on the same or similar issues, it is received from several different sources.

1. RISK ANALYSIS

> Analyze an organization's strengths, weaknesses, opportunities, threats, and risks using tools such as SWOT. Identify and analyze risk factors that can influence strategic plans. (Analyze)
>
> **Body of Knowledge II.B.1**

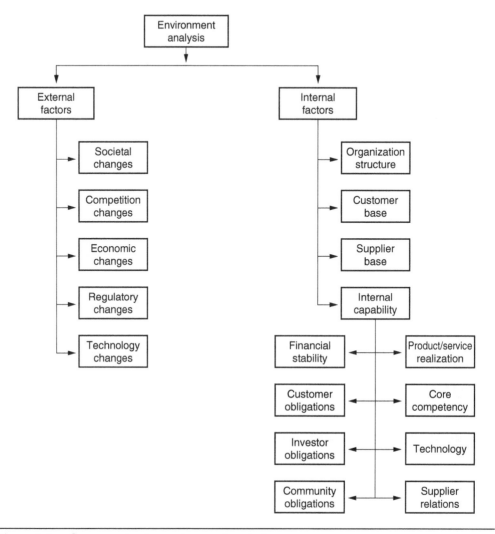

Figure 6.1   Components of an environment analysis.

SWOT Analysis

A common component of the strategic planning process involves looking at both current internal strengths and weaknesses of the organization's operations, as well as future opportunities and threats in the external marketplace. A strengths-weaknesses-opportunities-threats (SWOT) analysis is a systematic assessment of an organization's internal and external environment and identifies attributes that affect its ability to achieve its vision and to improve and protect its competitive position. A SWOT analysis looks at how the organization fits to the current reality. Following are some of the factors that are looked at in a SWOT analysis.

Strengths and *weaknesses* (focused on the internal environment) may include:

- How strong is the organization's image and/or name/brand in the marketplace?

- How strong (stable, effective, flexible) is the organization's leadership?

- How effective is the organization structure?

- How stable is the current and future financial strength of the organization?

- How do features and costs of products/services compare to competitors, and where are products/services in their probable life cycle?

- Is the organization well focused on a clearly defined vital few issues, or are efforts widely dispersed?

- How innovative is the organization? What is the track record of new products/services? Is there a strong research and development effort ongoing?

- How effective are the organization's efforts toward continual improvement?

- What is the condition (for example, age, flexibility, capacity) of major assets (for example, key employees, technology, facilities), and how does that affect the organization's capacity and capability to sustain the organization?

- What additional resources does the organization have available (for example, employees, stakeholders, capital) to enable change?

Depending on the answers to questions like these, the action might be to build on the strengths and address the weaknesses. In addressing the deficiencies, there are several options:

- Remove the deficiency by changing the goal or objective to make fulfillment achievable.

- Invest more in the people, technology, physical assets, improvement efforts, and so on to be able to turn the deficiency into a strength.

- Outsource parts or all of the process to another organization that can fulfill the process requirements more effectively.

- Sell the part of the business that causes the present deficiency.

Opportunities and *threats* (focused on the external environment) may include:

- What new competitors or products may enter the marketplace?

- What viable markets are not currently being served?

- How saturated is the marketplace?

- How are demographics or values changing in the marketplace?

- What new accreditation, legal, or regulatory issues might arise?

- Are customer/supplier partnerships or alliances effective for the organization?

- Does the likely future economic situation pose risks or potential rewards?

Figure 6.2 is an example of a SWOT analysis. Connie is the owner of the two stores that compose the Brides on a Budget Boutique. She met with her two store managers to commence their first strategic planning process. After an intense three-hour meeting, the items in Figure 6.2 were identified. Other issues were discussed, but the document represents the major items. Following the SWOT effort, Connie and her managers met again to begin to formulate a strategic vision. They prepared for this meeting by discussing answers to "What will this business be like five years from now?"

SWOT analysis should be based on objective data that review critical events from the past, the present, and the probable future in making comparisons with the marketplace, competitors, products and services, and company performance.

Strengths	**Opportunities**

• We are trend leaders in both cities in which the stores are located.
• Both locations are ideal for their market niche (high-traffic, multi-store malls).
• Customer retention indicates extreme loyalty and a high referral rate.
• Both stores show a 10% to 12% increase in business in last three years.
• Store A does a higher volume of cash business than store B.
• Layout, displays, and inventory carried is identical for both stores.
• Customer surveys and media coverage acknowledge the superb personalized customer service provided by personnel of both stores.
	• Find ways to improve profitability of store B.
	• Rethink inventory management practices and improve.
	• Assess the products (costs, quantity, style life, and pricing) carried to determine which products are most profitable and which should be dropped.
	• Assess the effectiveness of present advertising efforts and look for more lucrative media and approaches.
	• Examine the potential of new approaches to marketing:
	  – Offer home service (selection, fitting, delivery)?
	  – Explore alliance opportunities with other mall-store owners?
	  – Explore alliance opportunities with caterers, wedding planners, and so on?
	  – Consider presenting a fashion show?
	  – Consider opening an outlet store for previously owned bridal wear?

Weaknesses	**Threats**
• Connie is the only person who understands the billing system. • Because of taking advantage of a manufacturer's close-out, the business currently shows a negative cash flow. • Connie is stretched thin by her heavy work schedule and the growing pains of her business (hiring and retaining competent help, rising benefits costs, slowing economy, other stores closing in the malls, and so on) • Inventory obsolescence tends to be higher than for others in the industry. • An increasing number of crimes committed in the malls is affecting the attraction of potential buyers. • Store B is a cash drain (sales dollars low due to clientele tending to purchase lowest-price items, and number of bad debts increasing).	• Malls have both been bought from original owners, and a rent increase is rumored. • Connie could get sick. • Refurbishing of downtown areas is attracting customers away from the malls. • Malls are becoming hangouts for unruly teenagers, and could be a distraction for brides-to-be. • Mall owners' extension of the mall's business hours impacts personnel costs (often, we staff a store at hours when no potential customers appear, yet must comply with mall rules to be open).

Figure 6.2 SWOT analysis example.

Source: Reprinted with permission of R. T. Westcott & Associates.

Analysis of the information will typically be reviewed for items that provide significant advantages or risks that should be addressed by strategy, as well as the relative ratio of advantages to risks, which may have an impact on the aggressiveness of the strategy. Items affecting the firm's critical success factors must be reviewed in detail.

A SWOT analysis can be done at any time, but it is essential in developing the data needed for strategic planning. Also, there is no reason to prevent a critical discovery from the analysis from immediately being turned into an action plan—even before the strategic planning process is complete.

Failure Mode and Effects Analysis (FMEA)

Another form of analysis that has evolved for use in strategic analysis is a failure mode and effects analysis (FMEA). An FMEA is an analytical methodology used to ensure that potential problems have been considered and addressed throughout the process. Typically, an FMEA analysis is generally first applied to the design (DFMEA) of a product and then to the operational process (PFMEA) used to create the product. In the application and evaluation of business risks in strategic planning, a higher-level system FMEA approach would be used, similar to the PFMEA.

An FMEA is a tool that incorporates a systematic method to recognize, evaluate, and prioritize potential failures and their effects. Actions are then identified that could eliminate or reduce the chance of that potential failure occurring. From the strategic planning aspect, the FMEA can be used to develop contingency plans across the organization. FMEAs have been applied in market and competitive analysis, technology development, health, safety and environmental, and more.

From the perspective of strategic planning, an FMEA can help to identify the failure effects or symptoms if a strategy is not achieved. The impact would typically be from the perspective of the stakeholders. However, depending on the type of impact, the organization may consider the effect on any of its interested parties.

Across the typical PFMEA matrix, the following columns would fall under:[1]

- Identify output failures and impacts:
  - General strategy (the process step in the FMEA)
  - Potential failure modes
  - Potential failure effects (symptoms)
  - **Severity** (S) of the effect. This is usually a scale of 1–10, where 10 is the most severe.

- Assess inputs:
  - Potential causes
  - **Occurrence (O)**; frequency at which the potential failure mode could occur. This is usually a scale of 1–10, where 10 is the most severe, and the potential failure mode happens with a high frequency.
  - Current controls
  - **Detection (D)**; ability of the organization to identify if the failure mode has occurred. This is usually a scale of 1–10, where 10 is the most severe, and the organization is unable to detect the failure mode.

- Prioritize: A **Risk Priority Number (RPN)** is the multiplication of the $S \times O \times D$.

- Determine actions and impact:

  — Actions recommended; what countermeasures can be taken to protect the organization?

  — Responsibility; identify the individual(s) who have ownership of executing the countermeasures.

  — Actions taken; identify what has happened and how the occurrence and detection may now have been improved.

Refer to a portion of an FMEA example in Figure 6.3.

In evaluating any strategy, the golden circle reviews the failure effect (symptom), the failure mode (how), and the failure cause (why). By following the logic of the golden circle, the above example might be summarized as: the organization did not meet its budget (failure effect) because the margin was too low (failure mode) because the costs were too high due to a variety of reasons (failure cause[s]).

It is vitally important that future initiatives be aligned with findings of the SWOT or FMEA analysis. Success of previous strategic initiatives should be assessed to determine whether the desired outcomes were achieved. Success or failure may be a function of the method of deployment (for example, process reengineering) or may indicate an issue that will only be resolved through long-term and consistent action (for example, organization culture change).

2. MARKET FORCES

> Define and describe various forces that drive strategic plans, including existing competition, the entry of new competitors, rivalry among competitors, the threat of substitutes, bargaining power of buyers and suppliers, current economic conditions, global market changes, and how well the organization is positioned for growth and changing customer expectations. (Apply)
>
> **Body of Knowledge II.B.2**

For any product or service to be successful, it must be an effective fit to the economic environment. When shaping strategy, an organization should look for general trends in the marketplace, trends within the industry of which it is a part, and competitor strategies. The competitive landscape is affected by the strategies of customers and suppliers.[2]

Information on these issues may often be gathered from government sources, newspapers, television, the internet, direct marketing ads, industry groups or

		Identify output failures and impacts			Assess input				Prioritize	Determine actions and impact						
		Process step; Strategy	Potential failure mode	Potential failure effects (symptom)	Sev	Potential causes	OCC	Current controls	DET	RPN	Actions recommended	Responsible	Actions taken	New SEV	New OCC	New DET	New RPN
Column overview		What is the process step/strategy in review	How might the strategy fail	What is the impact on the key metrics or organizational needs	How severe is the effect to the interested party(ies)	What are the causes to this failure mode.	How frequently does this occur	What are the existing controls and procedures	How well does the organization detect the gap	Multiplication of $S \times O \times D$	What actions are being taken to mitigate the potential effect	Who has the responsibility for the actions	What actions have been taken	If changed, what is the new severity	If changed, what is the new occurrence	If changed, what is the new detection	Multiplication of the new values of $S \times O \times D$
Example		Improve margin	Margin is too low	Budget is not attained	8	> Pricing incorrect	6 (Example 60% of products)	> Limit on quantity sold	3 (Example) able to detect via margin analysis which SKUs do not meet the plan	$8 \times 6 \times 3 = 144$	> Rationalize nonprofitable SKUs	> Sam salesman	> Sales reduced nonprofitable SKUS	8	4	3	96
			Margin is negative	Organization loses money; potential bankruptcy	10	> Supplier pricing is too high > Excessive operational costs (scrap/rework) > Competitor is priced lower; must match		> Must have VP approval > DFSS methodologies to reduce cost		$10 \times 6 \times 3 = 180$	> Utilize LSS on nonprofitable SKUs	> Eric engineer	> Engineering improved processes to increase margin	10	2	3	60

Figure 6.3 Failure mode and effects analysis example.

Source: Used with permission of APLOMET.

publications, trade shows, customers and suppliers, and the annual financial reports of public companies. Some competitive intelligence gathering may be subcontracted to firms who specialize in this area, but management (and in the best organizations, all employees) should continually be on the lookout for changes that can provide opportunities or create threats to present and future strategies.

Some general marketplace issues for which information should be gathered include:

- Government subsidies that can help offset internal or raw material costs or make competitor products less expensive

- Trade restrictions or tariffs that limit (either by fiat or through economic incentives or disincentives) what can be sold to or purchased from particular markets

- Changes to international monetary exchange rates that have the effect of raising or lowering prices of raw materials used by the organization or the selling price for goods sold in global markets

- Social concerns, demographic or political changes, or other societal issues that may create opportunities or threats for the organization and/ or its products

- Inflation, deflation, or changes in lending rates that have an impact on the costs of borrowing money and of raw materials and labor

- Economic cycles that affect demand for various products (for example, luxury goods)

- Market expansion, stability, or contraction that influences demand for products (for example, in other countries, the opening up of new markets as a result of changes in political and economic philosophies)

- Social or economic differences (for example, values, relative purchasing power) between regions or countries

Some general issues to watch for relative to specific industries are:

- Amount of capacity currently in existence in the industry relative to total market demand and the rate at which demand and capacity are changing; for example, in industries where capacity is added in large blocks, if many organizations chase the same existing opportunity, an overcapacity situation may result, creating overstocking and pricing pressures

- Mergers and acquisitions that consolidate the number of players and may provide greater economic leverage for some

- Place in the life cycle of a particular product (for example, is it a brand-new or mature product?) and how that affects profitability and growth potential

- Potential for an entirely new product or service, or a less expensive version of the existing product or service, coming to market

- Speed of change in the industry and how it might call for breakthrough versus incremental change

- Trends toward or away from regulation of the industry

- Whether the product/service requires a local or globally focused design orientation

- Whether the cost of entry for new players in the industry is high or low and how this affects product, capacity, and pricing issues

- How much specialized knowledge and/or technology is required for the product/service and how much of a barrier that may create for new entrants

- How does/will the bargaining power of customers affect strategy? For example:

  — Just-in-time buyers offering long-term contracts but expecting price reductions

  — Large-volume customers demanding price and delivery advantages

  — Customers pulling back presently outsourced services

  — Customers changing to more standard products, making it easier for them to switch suppliers

  — Customers in a financial crisis expecting concessions from their suppliers

- Expiring patents

Competitive Analysis

Comparisons may be made of competitors' strategies and results in relation to one's own assumptions. For example, if a competitor formulates its strategies based on its assumption that birth rates in the marketplace served will increase over the next five years and the opposite is occurring, there is a strategic gap that can be exploited. If a competitor's strategies are significantly different than what the organization's management assumes, it could lead management to believe there may be an error in strategy that would seriously affect the organization's potential.

Porter provides a framework for comparing the organization with competitors that, among other factors, examines a competitor's "core capabilities, its ability to grow, its quick response capability, its ability to adapt to change, and its staying power."[3]

Comparisons at a product/service level can yield valuable information for strategy consideration: For example, Commercial Bank A compares itself with its competitors' products and services feature by feature. On the surface, all the banks studied appear to be offering similar services. Closer examination of time to process, contacts available, fees, and linkage to other services reveals that competitors have an edge in supplying direct loans to customers who export. Bank A, in servicing its exporter customers, provides faster service in furnishing letters of credit, at lower fees, and has a wider range of overseas contacts. This detailed type of comparison yields important insights for use in determining whether the strategy needs to be changed.

Both quantitative data and qualitative data can be examined in comparing against competitors. Scanning of pertinent news media (newspapers, magazines, radio, TV, and the internet) for qualitative data is productive in finding both factual and speculative indications of competitors' recent and potential next moves.

Types of questions to ask when analyzing an industry include:

- Who are the competitors? How many are there? Where are they located? How do they range in size (number of employees, number of locations, dollar sales, number of customers, and so on)? Which competitor dominates the industry?

- Are the competitors forming consortiums or other types of alliances?

- How aggressively are the major competitors pursuing new product or service opportunities?

- To what extent are the methodologies used by major competitors influencing attraction of new customers?

- What are the primary weaknesses and vulnerabilities of the major competitors?

- Is doing business globally a plus or a minus for the major competitors? What risks are they facing?

- What image and reputation do each of the major competitors have regarding ethical and fair practices, legal practices, leadership strength, type of employer, environmental conscientiousness, and so on?

Organizations in extremely competitive markets establish units of specially trained people to search out meaningful comparative data about their competitors as well as about the environment in which both operate—for example, the pharmaceutical industry and the computer industry.

The results of competitive comparisons not only shape top management's day-to-day decision-making but provide input to the business environment analysis, affecting the formulation of longer-range strategic plans.

Benchmarking

Competitive comparison differs from benchmarking. Competitive comparisons are done to assess the organization's strategic strengths and weaknesses as compared to the competition. Benchmarking targets performance of specific processes for input to the strategic planning process. It identifies other organizations known for their best practices in those processes and conducts a benchmarking study to help define how the practices observed can lead to improvement in one's own organization's performance. Remember, copying a better practice of a competitor makes an organization, at best, only as good as the competitor—not better!

From the process of conducting benchmarking studies, data critical to strategic decisions and plans may be available. These data should be integrated with business environment analysis. Examples of potential benchmarking study results include:

- Revelation that a whole new technological approach may be needed to maintain or improve the organization's position in the marketplace

- Identification of the potential for upgrading the organization's value chain, from supplier through delivery to customers, thus reducing cycle

time, improving quality and production, reducing costs, increasing
customer satisfaction, and improving profits

- An indication of how lean manufacturing techniques can reduce
  inventories, improve process flow and quality, and eliminate the need
  for additional facilities

- Insights as to how activity-based management can aid in pinpointing
  products that are unprofitable to continue to produce/provide

- New knowledge of how to identify and deal with constraints in a major
  process

When such data are collected and analyzed, the potential exists for initiating a
process reengineering effort or other breakthrough initiative that could have a significant impact on the organization—for example, making a heavy improvement
investment at the front end, resulting in a significant return on the investment later.

Knowledge of one's competitors is vital and will typically include looking at:

- Who is producing a new product that can be substituted for an existing
  product

- How competitors market their products or company (for example, how
  they try to differentiate their products or company from others) in ads or
  press releases

- Timing of announcements of new products

- Alliances or mergers between competitors that may have an impact on
  market coverage or financial leverage

- Other companies who are not already in the market but who may have
  the expertise, resources, and inclination to enter it

- Pricing strategies that might indicate inherent cost structures or new
  market initiatives

- Synergies within a competitor's value/supply chain, or within their
  own organization's product mix, that might give them leverage

- Strength of an organization/product as a brand and at which market
  niches the brand is targeted

- Core competencies of competitors

- Position of the company relative to competitor firms (size, image, capital
  access, niche served)

- Age of competitor organizations and their management and how this
  might have an impact on the probability of significant change

As the strategies of customers change, there will usually be a ripple effect calling
for adaptive change by those who supply them. Some issues a company might
watch for include:

- How good is the relationship between the company and various key
  customers (for example, regarding field failures, customer complaints)?

- How high or low a cost would customers incur if they decide to switch to a different source?

- How might the customer decide to vertically integrate, producing internally some of the products/services currently purchased externally?

- What large purchasing groups might exist or be formed that could pool their purchasing power, with increased economic power being one result?

- How much does the product/service need to be customized and for which market segments, applications, or other demographic factors?

- How easy is it for customers to compare prices/sources (for example, ability to shop around using the internet or other means)?

- How are final user priorities and values changing, and how will that have an impact on desired product/service features or methods of delivery?

Supplier strategies can also have an impact on a company. Examples include:

- Is the supplier the only one available for the product/service, and how might that affect its pricing strategy or willingness to adapt to different needs?

- What is the total dollar amount of what is being purchased relative to the total sales of the product for the supplier, and how might that have an impact on its flexibility?

- Might the supplier find other applications or buyers for the product that would cause the supplier to discontinue selling the product according to the existing agreement?

This information allows an organization to begin to more fully understand the environment in which it is working. It must first, however, be combined with additional factors before strategy can be finalized.

3. STAKEHOLDER ANALYSIS

> Identify and differentiate the perspectives, needs, and objectives of various internal and external stakeholders. Ensure that the organization's strategic objectives are aligned with those of the stakeholders. (Analyze)
>
> **Body of Knowledge II.B.3**

Stakeholders may be described as interested parties, as they are with the International Organization for Standardization (ISO) 9001, but in general they are individuals, groups, or organizations who will be directly or indirectly affected by an organization carrying out its mission. Although employees, suppliers, customers, communities, and shareholders are the stakeholders having the most directly at stake, others, such as competitors, accrediting organizations, unions, regulatory organizations, and special interest groups, can also affect outcomes and should therefore not be ignored.

All interested parties have particular issues, priorities, and concerns, and it is important that an organization understand each of these stakeholder groups and the issues most important to them. For example, one company may draw a large proportion of its workforce from college students who primarily desire part-time work to help cover tuition until graduation, while another company may consist primarily of middle-aged parents who are concerned about health benefits for their families.

The organization should take steps to identify not only each stakeholder group but also its interests relative to the organization. An assessment should be done to identify risks between the objectives and plans of the organization and the needs and interests of stakeholders and action taken to close the gaps where feasible (see Figure 6.4). The impact of these risks should be considered especially as it relates to legal risks, employee and community health, and viability of the product/service in the marketplace. Efforts should then be focused on the vital few issues.

Both the IATF (International Automotive Task Force) 16949-2016 and ISO 9001:2015 require an understanding of the needs and expectations of the organization's interested parties.[4] Below in Figure 6.4 is a template for evaluating organizational alignment to the needs and interests of those interested parties. There is not a required format, and this is only an example. An organization should only include those environmental scan features relevant to its own business needs.

Identify the relevant opportunities (risks or benefits) for each type of interest party: Cu = Customer, St = Stakeholder, Ee = Employee, Su = Supplier, Co = Community

	Categories	Relevant (Y/N)	Customer (Cu)	Stakeholder (St)	Employee (Ee)	Supplier (Su)	Community (Co)
External	Social	Y	1. Web/internet services 2. Conferences	1. News releases, brand association positive or negative	1. Company association positive or negative	1. Conferences	1. Social responsibility (EHS, compliance)
	Cultural	Y					
	Political	N					
	Legal	N					
	Regulatory	Y					
	Financial	N					
	Technological	Y					
	Economic	Y					
	Natural environment	Y					
	Competition - International	Y					
	Competition - National	Y					
	Trends	Y					
	Stakeholder relationships	Y					
Internal	Governance	Y					
	Organization structure	Y					
	Roles and authorities	Y					
	Policies	Y					
	Objectives	Y					
	Strategies	Y					
	Resource: Capital	Y					
	Resource: Employee	Y					
	Resource: Time	Y					
	Technological	Y					
	IT	Y					
	Information flows	Y					
	Decision-making process	N					
	Stakeholder: Internal	N					
	Culture	Y					
	Standards	N					
	Guidelines	N					
	Model is adopted by ACW	Y					
	Contractual relationships	N					

Figure 6.4   Stakeholder analysis example.

The needs and interests of interested parties can be obtained by directly involving them in the planning process or by gathering input that will be considered during planning. When interested parties will not be directly involved, it is often advisable to communicate advance information about organizational plans in order to reduce the likelihood of inaccurate conjecture being the only information available to these groups.

Social responsibility is an especially challenging facet of stakeholder analysis. Consider the impacts on stakeholders of each of the following organizational strategies and behaviors:

- Organizational restructuring/reengineering resulting in layoffs

- Diversity issues relative to race, ethnicity, gender, sexual orientation, age, and so on

- Privacy concerns relative to personal test results, chemical dependencies, and personal finances

- Sexual harassment

- Environmental concerns relative to quality of air and water, pollution, flora and fauna, and so on

- Business in locations where the local practices challenge the organization's ethics and beliefs, particularly in such areas as human rights, bribery, or gift giving

- Actions, initiated or defended, that offend or damage relations with the public—for example, insider trading, misrepresenting the organization's financial status, predatory pricing, and so on

To help ensure that the needs and interests of interested parties are met, they can be converted to a strategic goal supported by strategic objectives, with measures used to track performance. Interested party concerns can also be embedded in values or principles statements used to guide management action. A common mistake is to think of stakeholder interests as incongruent with the organization's interests; in most cases this is not the case if one takes a systems view of society. An organization truly interested in long-term value to society will find that a balanced interface with all stakeholders can be managed.

4. TECHNOLOGY

Describe how changes in technology can have long-term and short-term influences on strategic planning. Identify new and upcoming technologies that may have an impact on business strategy and quality, such as automation, autonomation, Quality 4.0, cloud computing, or machine learning. (Understand)

Body of Knowledge II.B.4

In today's rapidly changing world, a new technological development can have a dramatic impact on the life and sustainability of an organization. Organizations must have a means for detecting technology developments, assessing the potential for use in their industry and organization, and effectively implementing those technologies that will likely provide an advantage. Technologies may include:

- Electronic-based technologies used for communicating

- Product, production, or service technology, including:

  — Automation: The use of largely automatic equipment in a system of manufacturing or other production process.

  — Autonomation: When a machine is designed to effect the principle of *jidoka* used in the Toyota Production System (TPS) and lean manufacturing. It may be described as "intelligent automation" or "automation with a human touch." This type of automation implements types of supervisory functions rather than production functions.[5]

  — Quality 4.0:[6] Quality 4.0 blends new technologies with traditional quality methods to arrive at new optimums in operational excellence, performance, and innovation. The new technologies include machine learning (ML) and artificial intelligence (AI), connected devices and operations, new forms of collaboration like social media and blockchain, big data, cloud computing, and new apps like augmented reality/virtual reality (AR/VR) and mash-ups. The 4.0 is a reference to Industry 4.0:

    - The first (real) Industrial Revolution embodied three revolutionary changes: machine manufacturing, steam power, and the move to city living for people who had previously been agriculturalists.

    - The second industrial revolution occurred when the production line and mass manufacturing drastically reduced the cost of consumer and industrial products.

    - The third industrial revolution took place when electronics and control systems gradually penetrated manufacturing, allowing greater flexibility and more sophisticated products at a significantly lower cost.

    - The fourth industrial revolution is happening now. It is an extension of the digital impact of the third revolution and merges it with the physical and natural worlds. Advances in data, analytics, connectivity, scalability, and collaboration have enabled this movement. These advances connect people, machines, and data in new ways. In quality, these technologies are important because they enable the transformation of culture, leadership, collaboration, and compliance. The Quality 4.0 technologies include:

      - ML and AI. ML is the set of models and algorithms that do not rely on the analyst to determine the relationships between variables and different data elements.

      - Mobile technology, AR, and VR.

- Cloud technologies such as cloud computing. This is the storing and accessing of data and programs over the internet instead of your computer's hard drive. The cloud is just a metaphor for the internet.

- Connected devices and edge devices.

- Big data and data lakes:

  - *Big data* is a term for data sets that are so large or complex that traditional data-processing applications are inadequate. Challenges include analysis, capture, data curation, search, sharing, storage, transfer, visualization, querying, and information privacy.

  - A data lake is a system or repository of data stored in its natural format, usually in object blobs or files. A data lake is usually a single store of all enterprise data, including raw copies of source system data and transformed data used for tasks such as reporting, visualization, analytics, and ML.

- Social media and blockchain. Blockchain technology offers a way for untrusted parties to reach consensus on a common digital history. A common digital history is important because digital assets and transactions are in theory easily faked and/or duplicated. Blockchain technology solves this problem without using a trusted intermediary.

- Support systems technology (for example, designed to serve marketing, engineering, production, customer service, finance, human resources, suppliers, knowledge management, and so on)

Technological developments can enable the creation of entirely new products (for example, handheld devices, distance learning) or may be incorporated into a product or a service process to enhance functionality or reduce costs (for example, online flight reservations, e-tickets, self-printed boarding passes, and even biologically implanted monitoring devices). The fact that technological changes often occur outside an organization's industry means that organizations must be continually scanning the environment to identify potential threats and opportunities. A change in one technology can also quickly obsolete another technology (for example, the demise of camera film, typewriters, auto carburetors, and a myriad of other now obsolete technologies) or dramatically shorten an expected product life cycle.

Just because a technology is available, however, does not mean the organization should immediately adopt it. Some issues that should be considered include:

- Is the technology one in which design standards are necessary or will evolve? If so, can the organization help lead the way toward standardization, or might another source (for example, regulators, stronger competitors, the marketplace) take precedence? What are the risks of adopting the technology before standards have been developed? Will the standards be applicable in all markets, or might different countries have their own version (for example, electrical power standards throughout the world)?

- How quickly is the technology likely to diffuse within the industry or marketplace? Will it be widely accepted almost immediately, or will there be a process of conversion over time? How much of the company's R&D (research & development) resources should be allocated to exploring this technology versus maintaining and improving existing products?

- Does the organization have the technical and financial capabilities to effectively adopt the technology? Should it be a leader and innovator or a follower that shortens the learning curve by learning from others' successes?

As these questions show, technology is not a panacea and should be implemented with forethought and planning. Understanding the fit between the technology and the organization can be especially important when it involves changing business processes. In using technology to improve service, Berry suggests six basic guidelines:[7]

1. A technology strategy must also address behavioral changes that will be required.

2. Do not apply automation to bad processes.

3. Make sure the new technology solves a real problem.

4. Technology should allow users to gain more control over the process, rather than to become robots.

5. Choose the lowest technology that will do the job, rather than just going for the latest and greatest.

6. Technology should increase flexibility, customer service, and performance.

The internal capability of the organization becomes important. If there is insufficient knowledge to support the technology, then it can either be acquired or the depth to which the technology is adopted can be scaled appropriately to internal capabilities. The knowledge required may include how to effectively integrate it into the organization's products or business processes and how to maintain/support the technology itself.

The ability to patent technological developments may also be considered. If a firm cannot obtain a patent on a new product, competitors may quickly duplicate the offering and quickly erode profit margins. The ability to provide a unique design for which a patent might be obtained may depend on the creativity of design personnel as well as an understanding of the legal aspects of the patent process.

A match of a new technology to core competencies and other technologies currently used by the firm may also have an impact on whether a new development in technology can be converted to a viable competitive strength. The technology may be one for which not only are new skills necessary but perhaps an entirely new mindset.

The time needed to change organizational culture may mean that the organization simply will not be able to take advantage of what initially seems like an opportunity.

Technology is a never-ending challenge in that it affects both the internal capability of the organization and an organization's ability to stay ahead of or at least keep up with competitors' new developments. For example, in some industries, the introduction of web-based selling has totally restructured the marketing, advertising, sales, order processing, product and service delivery, customer billing, and other processes of organizations. The competitor's internal capability, however, is stressed in the attempt to meet the new needs. The strategy question is "Can your organization afford to join in the race, or can it afford not to?" Technology can be a competitive advantage today and a constraint tomorrow.

5. INTERNAL CAPABILITY ANALYSIS

> Identify and describe the effects that influence an organization's internal capabilities: human resources, facilities capacity, and operational capabilities. Analyze these factors in relation to strategy formation. (Analyze)
>
> **Body of Knowledge II.B.5**

Organizational Core Competencies

It is essential to have a clear understanding of the primary competencies that distinguish the organization and its products and services from the competition. Ask:

- What capabilities of the employees enable the organization to successfully compete in the marketplace?
    - What are the unique skills and experience levels of the workforce?
    - What creative and innovative talents are embodied in our workforce?
    - What organizational climate, work environment, and management style supports a highly motivated workforce?
- What process capabilities enable the organization to successfully compete in the marketplace?
    - What research and development is unique to this organization?
    - What state-of-the-art organizational structure, facilities, processes, equipment, and tools are unique to this organization?
    - To what degree is the organization integrated with its supply chain?
- What unique difference does our geographic location make?
    - Proximity to major customer segments?
    - Proximity to major transportation hubs, highways, terminals, and so on?
- What unique certifications and other recognition has the organization received?
- How does the organization's financial stability distinguish it from competitors?

Factors that should be considered in developing the organization's strategy are:

- Availability of human resources

  — Is the available labor pool stable, expanding, or contracting? How does the culture need to be supported?

  — Is the infrastructure supporting the labor force capable of accommodating the organization's expanded or changed strategies in the future? What about transportation issues and housing issues like utilities, taxes, and emergency services? What about schools and other institutions to support families?

  — Is the current labor force and available labor pool capable of acquiring the competencies required to support future organizational strategies? In 2020 there are five generations across the workforce:[8] the traditionalists, baby boomers, Generation X, Generation Y, millennials, and Generation Z (aka the iGen). Their differing styles in learning need to be taken into consideration (see Figure 6.5).

  — Are there currently, or planned, educational opportunities capable of assisting in the development of the organization's human competencies?

- Are there currently, or available in the future, the facilities, equipment, and operational capacity to expand and/or reconfigure to accommodate future strategies?

- Are there funds available or accessible to support growth plans?

- Are there adequate materials, supplies, and suppliers to meet the needs?

- Will the quality of leadership, the organization structure, and the predominant managing style support the planned growth?

Much of the information desired from the environment assessment can be gained directly from customers and/or employees. For example, customer feedback can help an organization understand opportunities for modifying product or service features to make them more value-added for the customers. Employee feedback can help to understand how management systems support or hinder implementation of strategy.

Generation	Traditionalists	Baby boomers	Generation X	Millennials	Generation Z
Demographic features	-Paper based -Networking -Team players -Relevant/ updated content -Loyal/reten-tion >3 years	-Web based/ electronic -Me based/ altruistic -Relevant/ updated content -Loyal but realistic	-Web based/ electronic -Entrepreneurial -Individualistic/ self-reliant -Want to make a difference -Into brands -Unimpressed by authority	-Electronic only/gadgets -Relevant/rapid content -Respect for authority -Work in teams -Relaxed work environment	-Electronic only/gadgets -Bores/tires easily -Needs fresh materials -Relevant/ updated content -Not brand based

Figure 6.5   Generational features.

A portion of the customer and employee information to be fed into the strategic planning process may come from common sources of information such as customer complaint data and employee exit interviews. Since this type of information is limited to problem areas, however, a special data-gathering process should be developed and implemented as part of the environmental assessment process in order to gain more strategically focused information. Following are some of the questions that such assessments should be designed to answer.

From customers:

- How well are current needs and wants being satisfied, and how could that satisfaction be enhanced?

- What new products/services/features would be value-added?

- How does the organization and its products/services compare to direct competitors or other suppliers with whom the customer does business?

- Does the customer intend to use the organization as a supplier in the future? Why or why not?

- What are some future plans of the customer for which the organization should be aligning internal capabilities and resources?

- Does operation of the organization show alignment with the publicly expressed vision, mission, and values?

From employees:

- How well does the organization's culture fit with its strategy?

- Are skills and rewards appropriate for the industry and strategic direction?

- Are management systems properly aligned to the espoused vision, mission, and values?

- Do employees have the authority needed to make decisions for which they are held responsible (are they empowered)?

- Do employees understand the organization's strategy, and would they be committed to the changes necessary (ownership)?

- Is there sufficient trust and communication to enable the organization to work effectively?

- Was past strategy implementation seen as appropriately deployed?

Significant opportunities or gaps in findings must be translated into action. This might involve:

- Modification of the vision, mission, or values to more clearly spell out what the organization stands for in its design or redesign of a product or service

- Partnering with customers to develop a more long-term, integrated working relationship

- Changes in organizational structure, management systems, technologies, and communications practices to better produce, support, and reward behaviors in line with customer and organizational needs

- Enhancement of strategy deployment and employee development processes

These changes would be accomplished through being identified as specific objectives of the strategy, with appropriate projects and resources provided to carry them out and progress monitored to evaluate their effectiveness.

6. LEGAL AND REGULATORY FACTORS

Define and describe how legal and regulatory factors can influence strategic plans. (Understand)

Body of Knowledge II.B.6

Legal Factors

Legal factors relate to laws, the lawmaking process, and rules for litigation. Laws are established by city, county, province, state, or federal governments—and are enforceable by threat of punishment. Understanding the legal requirements of the following is suggested:

- Employment-related laws and litigation

- Product/service liability

- Environment liability

- Protection of intellectual property (patents, copyrights, trademarks)

- Contract-related liability pertaining to customer orders

- Ramifications of the Sarbanes-Oxley Act

- Antitrust laws

- Trade protectionism

Regulatory Factors

Regulations are established by agencies within governments as well as outside organizations—for example, industry associations, self-regulating bodies, and professional societies. Regulations are enforced through self-regulation under the threat of disenfranchisement. Regulations are principles or rules designed to control or govern behavior. In theory, they are voluntary but often have the force of law. Regulations may span a whole industry, or segments within industries may each have their own specific regulations. Identifying and understanding the pertinent rules and regulations is critical.

REFERENCES

1. Automotive Industry Action Group (AIAG), *Potential Failure Modes and Effects Analysis (FMEA)*, 4th ed. (Southfield, MI: AIAG, 2008), 2.

2. P. Thompson, J. Gamble, and A. J. Strickland, *Crafting and Executing Strategy, The Quest for Competitive Advance*, 20th ed. (New York: McGraw-Hill, 2015).

3. L. L. Berry, *On Great Service* (New York: Free Press, 1995), 8–16.

4. ISO 9001:2015 (Milwaukee: ASQ Quality Press, 2015), 2.

5. Bing, https://www.bing.com/search?q=autonomation+definition&form=EDGEAR&qs =AS&cvid=9e09a5d3e9624beaa9f2aa118b55ee09&cc=US&setlang=en-US&elv=AQj93OA hDTi*HzTv1paQdnidQh%21f2c0rrVzxel2wmsSyg*Sp4W3JZpCQwqp03otRtnsdgrguH NTj3qvC76Xi6y6gZQKBxkTxWGBAA5935u7E&PC=DCTS.

6. D. Jacob, What Is Quality 4.0? [blog], https://blog.lnsresearch.com/quality40, July 26, 2017.

7. Berry, *On Great Service*.

8. Center for Generational Kinetics, https://genhq.com/five-generations-of-employees -in-todays-workforce/, January 2020.

See Appendix A for additional references for this chapter.

Chapter 7
C. Strategic Plan Deployment

Anyone can make pretty planning documents; transforming those plans into meaningful actions is the hard part.

—Executive who prefers to remain anonymous

This chapter completes the strategic planning cycle. Chapter 5 introduced several process models for strategic planning. Chapter 6 discussed various types of information gleaned from the business environment analyses. This chapter covers getting the plans deployed, acted on, and measured.

The individuals who own the action plans, having participated in the formulation of the plans, deploy the plans to where the action fits in achieving an organizational objective. The next step in the process is monitoring and measuring progress and achievement against each strategic objective. The last step, for the current plan, is to assess performance, the outcomes, and the effectiveness of the planning process itself and to pinpoint areas for improvement—then start over again from lessons learned.

A simple concept, but it does require discipline and solid top management support. Following are the key steps for successful deployment of the strategic plan.

1. TACTICAL PLANS

> Identify basic characteristics of tactics: specific, measurable, attainable, relevant, and time specific and how these are linked to strategic objectives. Evaluate proposed plans to determine whether they meet these criteria. (Evaluate)
>
> **Body of Knowledge II.C.1**

Action Planning

To transform the organization's strategic objectives into action, an action plan is needed. In actuality, the planning detail that an action plan comprises is a miniproject plan. There may be several action plans generated from one strategic objective. It is the systematic approach to initiating actions and the follow-up of those actions that closes the loop toward achieving the organization's strategy. An action plan should include:

- Project identification and description

- Date project completion is needed

- Link to the strategic objective and any pertinent mandates

- Project objectives

- Scope of the project—Where and for whom will the solution/ implementation be applied? What limitations or constraints will be encountered?

- Deliverables—including both outputs pertaining to the project objectives and outputs for managing the project and ultimate outcomes

- Criteria by which the project will be measured

- Assumptions affecting the project

- Description of the overall approach

- Start date to begin the project

- Estimate of the resources required—time, personnel, facilities, equipment, tools, materials, money

- Verification that there is sufficient organizational capacity and resources to accomplish the objectives

- Estimate of benefits versus costs

- Time line and person responsible for steps to complete the project (mini Gantt chart)[1]

Figures 7.1a and 7.1b show an action plan example for one of several projects linked to a strategic cycle time reduction objective. Note that the action plan form can also be used for other small projects—for example, corrective or preventive action, process changes resulting from regulatory changes, a kaizen blitz, or an internal audit.

2. RESOURCE ALLOCATION AND DEPLOYMENT

> Evaluate current resources to ensure they are available and deployed in support of strategic initiatives. Identify and eliminate administrative barriers to new initiatives. Ensure that all internal stakeholders understand the strategic plan and have the competencies and resources to carry out their responsibilities. (Evaluate)
>
> **Body of Knowledge II.C.2**

Action Plan		
Project title: Replace existing laser-cutting machine.	**Plan number:**	Q-5
Description: Determine, select, purchase, and install an appropriate laser-cutting machine that will meet our need for a five-year project life.	**Date initiated:**	03/29
	Date needed:	09/01
Linked to what (strategic objective, contract, policy, procedure, process, corrective or preventive action, customer mandate, or regulatory requirement)? PAR # 04-21—Resulting from process audit and council decision.	**Approval by:**	TBB
	Team leader:	SLF
Project objectives: To replace existing cutting machine with the most cost-effective laser-cutting machine that meets engineering specifications, capital equipment purchase policy, and production criteria by August 31, 2004. Must meet Single-Minute Exchange of Dies (SMED)–type setup requirements and accommodate manufacturing cell configuration changes as needed when lean thinking is applied in the plant.	**Team member:**	EDB
	Team member:	KLF
	Team member:	ZLB
	Quality team member:	WED

Scope (Where and for whom will the solution/implementation by applied? What limitations and constraints?): Up to ten equipment vendors will be contacted with our Request for Proposal. Up to five vendor proposals will be evaluated in detail. Up to three vendors' machines will be subjected to a live demonstration using our materials and specifications. Preference will be given to U.S. vendors if all other factors are equal.

Deliverables (include outputs re content, outputs re project management, and outcomes):
- Evaluation criteria
- Engineering specifications
- Request for Proposal
- Review of project status at weekly management meeting (time and cost expended)

By what criteria/measures will completion and success of project be measured?
- Deadline met
- Equipment meeting all specifications and production requirements selected, purchased, installed, tested, and turned over to production
- Purchase with capital project policy parameters

Assumptions made that might affect project (resources, circumstances outside this project):
Machine selected will not require predelivery design modifications.

Describe the overall approach to be taken, data needed, processes to apply:
- A three-person team will be formed (leader from quality, members from engineering and production)
- Within an extended work week (forty-eight hours) the team will:
- Research appropriate vendors and their equipment
- Prepare Requests for Proposals from selected vendors
- Evaluate proposals and select machines to subject to demonstration testing
- Select and place purchase order for equipment
- Arrange for appropriate operator and supervisor training
- Provide necessary changes to procedures and work instructions
- Install, test, accept, and turn over machine to production

When should project be started to meet the date needed/wanted? March 29

Estimate the resources required (time, personnel, facilities, equipment, tools, materials, money):
- Quality engineer for sixteen hours per week for twenty-two weeks
- Production engineering for sixteen hours per week for eighteen weeks
- Travel and Lodging (T&L) expenses for trips to machine demonstrations: $5,000
- T&L expenses for training first operator and supervisor: $3,000
- Machine replacement (transportation, rigging, etc.): $4,000
- Machine cost: $1,200,000
- Other expenses: $2,000

Is there sufficient organizational capacity, and are resources sufficient to meet the objectives?
Yes

Estimate the benefits versus costs value: Annualized decrease in setup costs = $75,000
- Annualized decrease in cycle time = $200,000
- Salvage value of obsolete machine = $5,000
- Project costs = $14,000
- Annual amortized machine cost = $240,000
- Total costs = $254,000
- First-year payoff = $26,000
- Second-year payoff = $35,000
- MARR: 16%
- Net present value (five-year project life): $92,105

Outline the major steps and dates on page 2.

Figure 7.1a Action plan (front).

Source: Reprinted with permission of R. T. Westcott & Associates.

Step number	Activity/event description	Predecessor	Start date	Finish date	Person responsible
1	Form project team and launch project		3/29	4/1	SLF
2	Prepare machine specifications and Request for Proposal	1	4/1	4/12	EDB
3	Research vendors	1	4/1	5/3	SLF
4	Select vendor and order machine	2, 3	5/3	5/10	KLF
5	Train initial operator	4	6/24	6/28	ZLB
6	Install machine	4	6/21	6/25	ZLB
7	Conduct trial runs	5, 6	6/28	7/12	ZLB
8	Revise documented procedures and operator training materials	7	7/26	8/2	SLF, WED
9	Train supervisor	8	8/2	8/31	ZLB
10	Place machine in production schedule	9	8/23	8/31	ZLB
11	Document project and disband teams	10	8/31	9/10	SLF

Figure 7.1b   Action plan (back).

Source: Reprinted with permission of R. T. Westcott & Associates.

Leadership and Management

Strong leadership, diligent management support, and personal involvement are necessary to develop and deploy strategic plans into action. Instituting strategic planning, whatever model is adapted to the organization, takes sustained commitment and a can-do attitude. The hard part of the process is deployment and management of the actions (projects) that will, collectively, accomplish the organization's strategic goals and objectives.

For most organizations, initiating strategic planning is a major cultural change. Communication to everyone and from everyone in the organization is critical at every stage in the process. Strategic communication to senior management assists with obtaining the encouragement and sustained support critical to the people who will be transforming the plans into action and achieving the results. The trade-off decisions about resources will require negotiating skills and conflict management. Leadership roles for each stage in the strategic planning process must be chosen wisely.

For leadership to provide the sustained support needed, measurement of performance in key areas and the organization as a whole is required. These measures are often deeper than the balanced scorecard and may include ad hoc measures covering new aspects of the organization and its culture. Often an excellence model helps to align principles with best management practices.

Resource Availability

One of the principal concerns is how to superimpose and/or integrate action plans resulting from the strategic planning process with everyday business activities.

Picture this: The strategic planning team, in its zeal to produce a great plan, goes beyond the capability of its organization to implement the strategic actions as well as continue to "make the donuts." Guess what falls out? Right—one or more of the strategic actions. Guess who gets blamed? Right—the people who compiled the action plans often catch the blame. So the strategic planning process must be suspect? Wrong—the process is fine—if it is followed properly.

This situation demonstrates another key to successful deployment and integration. Also, there needs to be an organizational culture that permits lower-level persons to challenge the actions they are being asked to implement. The front-line personnel must be heard and receive respectful answers to their challenges—without fear of retribution.

One of the several advantages of hoshin planning is that care is taken to ensure that the plans are deemed acceptable and doable by all involved. This includes a consensus on resources needed. A key question is: Can time be made in the day-to-day activity schedule to integrate the work involved in carrying out the action plans? Or is it just assumed that the time will somehow be found for these new actions and nothing will suffer? In this age, relatively few organizations have the slack time to assimilate a lot of new activities without sacrificing something. A strategic planning team needs to understand how far the organization can be stretched before something breaks.

Aside from daily activities, which are crucial, work on other potentially conflicting activities and programs may be underway or planned, such as:

- A process reengineering initiative

- A new quality management system (for example, International Organization for Standardization [ISO] 9001, International Automotive Task Force [IATF] 16949)

- A new information-processing system

- An outsourcing initiative that will result in downsizing

- A merger, acquisition, or divestiture of part of the business

- A new product/service line of business

- Major upgrades to machines and processes

- Turnover of personnel due to new, large employers entering the same labor pool area

- A Six Sigma initiative

- New products/services that threaten obsolescence

- Restrictive regulations mandating mass retraining, new procedures, and controls

If any of these conflicting activities or programs are underway, or soon will be, this must be considered in the business environment analysis. For example, assume that one of last year's multiyear objectives was to replace the present information system (IS) within the next three years. System design, programming, testing, and implementation tasks are still going on and severely draining existing resources. Strategic planning must assess this impact—before making commitments that will conflict. And if the people responsible for the means do not challenge the shortage of resources, those at the action level who will most feel the lack of resources must challenge the feasibility of completing the actions affected.

Allocation of Resources

Before action plans are fully developed (for example, including resource esti- mates), a spreadsheet (matrix) should be prepared showing the various types of resources required against each of the objectives. This matrix can be at any level of detail needed for decision-making regarding resources—for example, includ- ing the commitment of resources for day-to-day work. It is vital to know not only what type of resource is needed but also when it will be required and for how long. Many project-planning software programs are capable of providing such a document, as well as able to play out what-if scenarios to determine the best mix with the least conflict.

When adjustments have been made, the action plans are developed, and a revised master resource allocation plan is prepared. This becomes the resource allocation baseline against which actual use of resources is measured. Constant monitoring and in-course correction is necessary. Not only will the estimates by which the resource allocations have been made be tested in practice, but the resources available will be subject to changes as time goes on. People leave, train- ing replacements takes time, equipment breaks down, funds are jeopardized by external aberrations, and so on. As initial plans often cannot be static, neither can resource allocations be held constant. This does not mean planning is useless, but it does mean that without plans there is limited ability to see the potential con- straints and what must be done to achieve the objectives.

Deployment of Tactical-Level Means

Steps are taken to ensure horizontal and vertical alignment of plans, as well as inte- gration at midlevel and with functional management. One of the tools for surfacing potential priority and resource conflicts early in the process is a group review of the master means matrix prior to deploying to the action planning level. One organ- ization calls this meeting a walkabout. Each person responsible for a means posts a flip-chart paper on the wall showing, by name or job title, the anticipated people, machines, materials, and funds required and when needed. Each attendee, using colored sticky notes, walks about the room examining the postings. When a poten- tial conflict is noted, a sticky note is attached where the conflict is seen. Following this, negotiation and trade-offs take place to resolve the conflicts. Any unresolved conflicts are listed as issues to be resolved before plans are deployed downward. Inasmuch as many of the means are cross-functional in nature, the walkabout begins the integration and consensus process for the second layer (those below the initial planners). This iterative up, down, and sideways integration and conflict resolution process continues, both at the means level and the action levels, until agreement is reached, and the plans can be deployed.

Deployment of Action Plans

In some of the traditional strategic planning processes, the planners move directly from the objectives to action plans (often failing to convey a clear understanding of the linkage between objectives and action plans). Usually, a gap analysis is employed to surface the steps that may be needed to move from the current status toward the future goals.

In traditional strategic planning, it is implied that action planning is a natural extension of the deployment process. Unfortunately, this is where the traditional approach has sometimes faltered for lack of commitment to support and execute the plans. The hoshin planning process is designed to remedy this potential shortfall. The hoshin approach literally involves everyone in the organization with the action planning that pertains to their function. The action plans must be prepared and sent back up the planning hierarchy for acceptance and integration before the implementation of the plan can take place. This catchball technique not only ensures involvement of those persons responsible for implementing the action plans but also achieves better buy-in of the plans.

The summation of all the action planning details (that is, time and resources required, including dollars) is reviewed by successive organizational levels back up to the strategic planning team. At this point the plans are given final approval or adjusted and sent back down the organization for replanning and return. This iterative process aids in communicating the entire strategic plan to all employees and allows each employee to clearly understand his or her contribution to the overall plan. Figure 7.2 displays the concept of cascading from top-level (enterprise) objectives down throughout the organization to individual action plans.

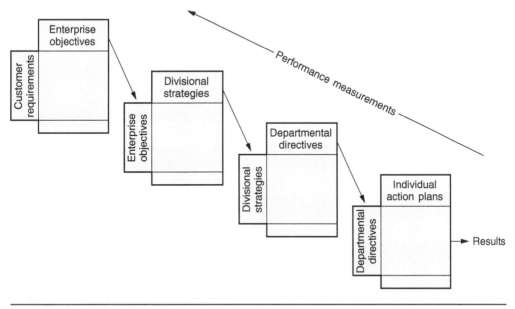

Figure 7.2   The cascading concept (from QFD) used as a strategic plan deployment tool.

3. ORGANIZATIONAL PERFORMANCE MEASUREMENT

> Develop measurements and ensure that they are aligned with strategic goals and use the measures to evaluate the organization against the strategic plan. (Evaluate)
>
> **Body of Knowledge II.C.3**

Designing Performance Measures

Measurements for processes are used to indicate the effectiveness of the processes in delivering products and services, such as product/service quality relative to customer satisfaction. Internal operational measures may include inventory turns, efficiency of the quality management system, cost savings from Six Sigma projects, and so on.

Feedback Loops. Consider the experience of folding and flying paper airplanes, hoping they would fly straight and true to their targets. Once launched, those planes went where they wanted to. Consider flying a model radio-controlled plane. When the wind blows the plane off course, the radio operator adjusts the rudder and ailerons, and the plane is back in control. This difference contrasts open-loop versus closed-loop performance measurement. In closed-loop measurement, monitoring is continual so that immediate adjustment to the action can be made.

The better the design and construction of the paper plane, and the more experienced the operator, the more likely the plane will fly close to its desired target. This is basic to open-loop operations. Good planning, anticipation of the potential causes of disruption, tightening the process so that it is not easily deflected from the target—all these are useful practices that are effective in the hands of skilled managers. However, closed-loop processes are more likely to succeed in reaching their objectives because they can better handle disruption from unforeseen causes.

Every process should have two outputs: (1) a valuable product or service to satisfy the customer and (2) the information to manage, control, and improve the process. A closed-loop process has many advantages over the open-loop operation. Unfortunately, many processes are open loop, and managers resort to intuition, emotions, and other ineffectual methods in an attempt to eliminate common causes of variation. Management by fact—that is, using closed-loop processes and trend data to monitor continuous improvement—is the preferred approach.

The contrast between open-loop and closed-loop operations shows up early in deployment planning stages. Typically, in open-loop operations, planning focuses on how to detect or measure problems in the inputs and how to plan for contingencies. "What if the Barlow shipment is late?," "How late is too late?," or "What if the weather is too cold?," and "How cold is too cold?" In contrast, closed-loop planning focuses on how to measure the outputs and how to determine the control points where adjustments can be made.

In the development of a closed-loop process, output measures should be considered from two aspects:

1. Effectiveness; the quality of the process. A process is in place for a reason, or it would not exist. Measures of effectiveness are typically relegated to the manufacturing aspect of the business. Systems such as Baldrige and IATF 16949 also require that an organization consider the evaluation of performance for all of its core processes.

2. Efficiency; the speed of the process. While this type of measure is also typically relegated to manufacturing, an efficiency evaluation of transactional business processes can also be quite effective in strategic review. Business processes such as Time for New Product Introduction from engineering or Time to Hire a replacement associate can be key to an organization's strategic success.

Balanced Measurements. A technique for measuring organizational performance is the balanced scorecard approach.[2] Consider the balancing of financial and non-financial measures supporting a strategic objective of increasing customer satisfaction, for example:

- Reduction of customer order-processing cycle time (order entry to order delivery)

- Number of certified suppliers for critical raw material

- Accuracy and completeness of customer billing

- Number of field service technicians qualified to service all of the company's products

- Overall product failure costs reduced

Critical Success Factors. Many organizations designate indicators called critical success factors (CSFs) by which to measure the outcomes of the strategic plans. These must be custom fitted to the specific organization. These CSFs, when considered together, provide the focus for steering the organization toward fulfillment of its vision, mission, and strategic goals and objectives. Typically, these CSFs may number eight to twelve indicators and target the life span of the strategic plans—for example, five years. Partial examples from two different industries are shown in Figure 7.3.

A not-for-profit organization		Company A	
CSF	**Target**	**CSF**	**Target**
Number of subscribers	28% of area population	Sales expansion	$2,800,000 in five years
Fund growth	32% increase in corporate contributors	Pretax income	8.5% of sales

Figure 7.3   Examples of critical success factors for two organizations.

Metrics and Organizational Alignment

It has been said that whatever gets measured gets done. This is true in many applications and organizations. Unfortunately, the organization that has too many measures dilutes its ability to achieve breakthrough results in any of them. When metrics are considered an integrated element of organizational strategy, they are a powerful means of plan deployment throughout the organization.

An annual closed-loop assessment process, such as the one shown in Table 7.1, can be based on the Baldrige Award criteria, state-sponsored award criteria, or independent criteria. In any case the overall organizational goal should be to assess progress toward excellence and initiate a new plan to close the gap. Relatively few (four to ten) strategic metrics can focus an organization's efforts and achieve breakthrough performance. A variety of different tactical measures would be important to individual departments or sites that support the strategic plan. Metrics should be limited to the actual process drivers because too many metrics can lead to ineffectiveness. A metric should directly relate to an action to attain an objective and be attainable.

Some measurements verify that the action item is underway, and other measurements verify that the objective is reached. Usually, both types of measurements are required.

Measurement costs money. There is the time involved in measuring, often equipment and space for collecting and/or displaying the measures, and training of employees in how to measure. Measuring can be seen as a diversion of resources from the main task of producing useful output.

Six factors influence how frequently measurements should be taken:

1. *Purpose.* Does the metric indicate a trend or control output?

2. *Cost.* How much time/money is spent measuring?

3. *Rate of change.* What is the maximum time between measurements?

4. *Degree of control.* Can an unfavorable change be corrected? How soon?

5. *Consequences.* What is the risk?

6. *Baseline.* Are there existing data on how the metric performs over time?

Process maps for closed-loop operations should indicate the points where measurements are taken in a process and the analysis of those measurements.

Table 7.1 Annual closed-loop assessment.

Annual closed-loop assessment	Use of metrics
1. Define "business excellence" for your business	Establish strategic measures of success
2. Assess your progress	Compare your progress to world-class competitors and to strategic objectives; identify gaps
3. Identify improvement opportunities	Set annual priorities and improvement goals
4. Deploy action plan	Align key metrics and deploy to all levels of the organization

Monitoring, Measuring, and Reporting Performance

Continual monitoring and review of each action plan/project takes place. This may necessitate various types of project adjustments as the plans unfold into action. Reviews of progress and problems take place at all levels, including assessing the effectiveness of the planning process itself. Formal review reports are presented on a scheduled basis at each level (usually quarterly). The results and lessons learned feed into the subsequent year's strategic planning process.

The hoshin approach—while it often takes several years to achieve a smooth transition from traditional or no strategic planning—does engender greater organizational awareness of the organization's vision, mission, goals, and objectives. Hoshin planning does involve absolute top management support as well as a high degree of participation and personal commitment in carrying out the plans. Usually, by the third year of implementation, the process becomes the way of doing business.

In addition to the metrics already implied or discussed—that is, measuring progress against action plan time lines and measuring resources used against resources planned—there are other measures and tools used for performance measures. Key questions to ask include:

- Why measure? To take action to ensure success in reaching goals

- What to measure? Key process elements to help monitor the process

- Where to measure? As close as possible to where variation could occur

- When to measure? As often as necessary, but no more often

- Who should measure? The person closest to the action

- How many metrics? Only as many as are truly useful in meeting the strategic objective

- How to measure? As consistently but unobtrusively as possible

4. QUALITY IN STRATEGIC DEPLOYMENT

> Support strategic plan deployment by applying continuous improvement and other quality initiatives to drive performance outcomes throughout the organization. (Create)
>
> **Body of Knowledge II.C.4**

Formulating Quality Policies

The quality function or department can take several types of support actions relative to the strategic plan's deployment, as well as ensure that the voice of the customer is addressed throughout the organization's processes.

Quality should be integrated with the organization's strategic plans. In a very small organization, most personnel are familiar with all of the organization's knowledge, goals, policies, and procedures, much of which may not be documented. As organizations grow in size and complexity, personnel are added, many of whom make significant decisions. To ensure consistency and understanding throughout the organization, quality policies need to be defined, documented, and communicated.

A *policy* is a high-level, overall plan embracing the general goals, objectives, and acceptable practices of an organization. Policies state how goals will be achieved and are intended to guide decisions. They are future oriented, sometimes for the indefinite future and sometimes conditioned on the presence or absence of some constraining factor. As visions, strategic goals, and objectives are unique to each organization, policies are also (in general) unique to an organization.

A quality policy is a formalized document created to communicate the overall intentions and directions of the organization relative to quality. The quality policy is a guide indicating the principles to be followed or what is to be done but does not stipulate how. The quality policy should summarize the organization's view on the definition of quality, the importance of quality, quality competitiveness, customer relations, internal customers, workforce involvement, quality improvement, planning and organization, and additional subject matter as required. Examples of quality policy statements are:

- Our products shall be free from all unacceptable substances that may cause property damage or have an impact on the personal health of employees, customers, or suppliers and shall meet all applicable standards and regulations.

- We will deliver products and services that meet or exceed customers' requirements, on time, and at competitive prices.

- Our policy is to build long-term relationships with customers and suppliers that commit to high quality and continual improvement, as we do.

- Our commitment to quality without compromise will be sustained through state-of-the-art technology, cost-effective solutions, customization, customer support and training, and investment in research and development of ever better products and services.

Establishing a quality policy is a focal point for development of an organization's formal quality system. A clear and brief statement can help people in the organization develop a common understanding about the aims of the organization in dealing with management processes and work activities that affect all aspects of quality performance. The policies should be viewed as adaptable.

In general, senior management formulates top-level policies. The process of formulating an effective quality policy and objectives should be based on inputs from many stakeholders: line organizations, such as manufacturing and distribution; staff functions, such as product design, budget/finance, human resources, and legal; customers; suppliers; regulators; shareholders; communities in which business is conducted; senior management; and enterprise planners. The quality function should contribute input to and support the organization's overall policies.

Quality policies developed by the quality function/department should be clear and provide guides for conduct. Make a quality policy actionable through example.

When the culture does not permit or fit, do not attempt to force one quality policy on multiple markets or divisions. Remember—a policy imposed is a policy opposed.

The ripple effect from policy changes, if perceived as negative by any stakeholder, can produce unfathomable damage. Organizations have suffered major losses, and some have been ruined, by the results of saying one thing and appearing to do another. On the positive side, upgrading the quality policy would have favorable effects.

Policies differ from guiding principles. Organizational policies (directives, procedures, guidelines, and rules) are more specific and directive. Usually, the most important are communicated to the workforce through employee handbooks, to suppliers through supplier guidelines, and to customers through product or service guides and warranty and disclosure information.

Defining Quality Management Principles

Business principles are the fundamental beliefs or values that are intended to guide organizational behavior. These principles may be integrated and documented as a part of the strategic planning process. Examples are:

- We believe it is better and easier for the organization to retain customers than to replace them.

- We value each customer and grow as they grow.

- We believe in honesty and mutual respect for our customers and employees. This forms the basis for our shared prosperity.

Quality management principles are the guiding beliefs that, when used for organizational decision-making, will ensure long-term success from the perspective of customers, employees, and other stakeholders. The quality management principles are the basis for objectives at all levels and demonstrate the depth of the organization's commitment to quality.

Well-formulated principles should be timeless, not dependent on temporary circumstances. The ISO 9000 series of standards includes eight such principles. Examples of specific quality principles are:

- Problems have special causes and common causes.

- Management must take responsibility for common causes.

- It is better to prevent defects from getting in than to sort them out.

The quality function should recommend wording for the quality principles and support the deployment of the principles throughout the organization. Policies and principles that are nicely framed and hung in the front lobby, but not deployed, are just window dressing.

Quality Objectives

To deploy organizational goals and objectives relative to quality, quality objectives are set to specify what specific actions will be taken, within a given time period, to achieve a measurable quality outcome. Examples are:

- Errors in processing insurance claims will be reduced from 150 per week to 15 or less per week by the end of the fourth quarter of this year.

- 80% of all platform personnel will be cross-trained and qualified to perform a minimum of five banking functions by the beginning of next year.

- Waste of floor-covering materials will be reduced from 15.6% to 0.5%, or less, by the beginning of the first quarter of next year.

- Cycle time for family product line 4 will be reduced from 20 seconds per item produced to no more than 1.7 seconds per item produced by August 1 of this year.

The quality function should position itself to review all quality objectives, provide recommendations, and support the deployment of the objectives. The quality function should promote the establishment of responsibility for quality objectives as an inclusion in creating job descriptions and individual objectives as an agenda item for discussion in all performance appraisals. Inasmuch as individual compensation typically depends on receiving a favorable performance appraisal, the inclusion of quality objectives as measurable performance appraisal factors helps close the loop—pay for performance and support for meeting objectives. Inclusion of quality measurements in the appraisal process supports the adage that what gets measured gets done.

The quality function should participate in identifying the voice of the customer (VOC) and deploying the VOC throughout the organization. Expertise in using quality function deployment (QFD) should enable the quality professional in facilitating the development and deployment of the QFD output.

The Institute of Management Accountants (IMA) has a significant body of knowledge on strategic planning development and deployment via their CSCA (Certified in Strategy and Competitive Analysis) certification. Both ASQ and the IMA have collaborated on the overall SPD body of knowledge and share many of the references.

Summary

A quality function should support the strategic plan deployment by:

- Participating in the strategic planning process

- Helping in promoting the communication (deployment) of the strategic goals, vision, mission, values, and objectives

- Formulating quality policy

- Defining quality management principles

- Setting quality objectives

- Ensuring that quality objectives are included in job descriptions and that performance relative to those objectives is a performance appraisal measure

- Ensuring that the voice of the customer is addressed throughout the strategy development and deployment

- Periodically auditing to ensure that the organization's quality practices meet the intent of published quality policies

- Continually providing performance and environment feedback to the organization's strategic planners—information that is pertinent to the attainment of the organization's strategic goals and objectives

- Identifying opportunities and/or initiating continual improvement efforts to improve the strategic planning process and the deployment of the plans

REFERENCES

1. R. T. Westcott, *Simplified Project Management for the Quality Professional* (Milwaukee: ASQ Quality Press, 2005).

2. T. Wheelen, J. Hunger, D. Hoffman, N. Alan, and C. Bamford, *Strategic Management and Business Policy: Globalization, Innovation and Sustainability*, 14th ed. (Upper Saddle River, NJ: Pearson Education, 2015), Chap. 11; A. Thompson, M. Peteraf, J. Gamble, and A. J. Strickland, *Crafting and Executing Strategy, The Quest for Competitive Advantage*, 20th ed. (New York: McGraw-Hill, 2015), Chap. 2; R. M. Grant, *Contemporary Strategy Analysis*, 9th ed. (Edison, NJ: John Wiley & Sons, 2016), Chap. 1, 2.

See Appendix A for additional references for this chapter.

Part III
Management Elements and Methods

Chapter 8   A. Management Skills and Abilities
             Contributors: Bill Craddock, Jd Marhevko, Denis Devos, and Tim King
Chapter 9   B. Communication Skills and Abilities
             Contributors: Bill Craddock and Denis Devos
Chapter 10   C. Project Management
             Contributor: Sandra L. Furterer
Chapter 11   D. Quality System
             Contributor: Denis Devos
Chapter 12   E. Quality Models and Theories
             Contributor: Denis Devos

He who runs his company on visible figures alone will soon have neither company nor visible figures to work with.

—W. Edwards Deming

Management's job is not to promote satisfaction with the way things are, but to create dissatisfaction with the way things are and could be.

—Edward M. Baker

Most Japanese companies don't even have a reasonable organization chart. Nobody knows how Honda is organized, except that it uses lots of project teams and is quite flexible.

—Kenichi Ohmae

Chapter 8
A. Management Skills and Abilities

Organizations, regardless of their size, are complex entities. They consist of and require the effective coordination and integration of goals, objectives, systems, processes, employees, information, technology, and equipment, including interfaces with customers, suppliers, and other stakeholders. This is the role of management—to plan, carry out, monitor, and initiate action to maintain the appropriate focus and results and to ensure viability of the organization in the future.

The complexity of organizations is reflected in the metaphors used to describe them. In the more stable environments of past decades, organizations were thought of in mechanistic terms. That is, they were considered as a predictable amalgamation of tightly linked components that could be relatively easily adjusted in order to achieve desired results. In today's chaotic environment, organizations are often thought of as living organisms that evolve in order to adapt to change. The components of today's organizations operate in more fluid relationships, inasmuch as unpredictability of the future and a need for more rapid change call for a more agile and adaptable way of working.

This also changes the role of management. While mechanistic organizations could operate effectively with a hierarchical structure, organic organizations typically have fewer levels. In many ways, however, the basic functions required for managing are still the same. What has changed is the style of management and how much more widely the responsibilities for management are deployed.

Total quality management (TQM) has contributed significantly to these changes. An emphasis on customer satisfaction means that people now look across the organization rather than up the hierarchy in order to find out how well they are doing. Involvement of everyone in process management and continual improvement means that employees must be more knowledgeable and committed to the organization's mission. Management personnel must now know more about how to acquire competent employees and organize them in ways that allow them to function effectively.

Also, the distinction between a manager and a leader is ever blurrier. While in the past managers were said to manage resources and leaders to lead people, today there is less of a demarcation—the two roles often blend.

There are three levels of management. *Top management* (also called *senior management* or *executive management*) is responsible for providing direction through defining the vision, mission, policies, goals and objectives, strategies, systems, and structures. Top management is also responsible for managing the boundaries between the organization and its major stakeholders, such as customers, suppliers, employees, investors, and business partners.

An organization that is committed to quality requires that top managers demonstrate their commitment through defining the values and principles by which the organization will operate and by leading the effort. Some of the core principles of a quality orientation include a passion for excellence, a focus on customer satisfaction, the involvement of all employees, and a systemic view of the internal and external relationships of all organizational processes.

Middle management is responsible for carrying out the policies and procedures necessary for achieving the organization's mission, goals, and objectives. The middle manager's role is more operationally than strategically oriented, playing a key role in day-to-day communication and decision-making. Middle management's role often includes being responsible for managing a particular part of the organization.

First-level supervision (often called *line supervision*) is responsible for managing the work of a functional unit, such as customer service, production scheduling, a sales territory, quality assurance, and so on. First-level supervisors have a daily balancing act to perform—for example:

- They have to follow upper management's strategies, goals, objectives, and directives—and enlist the support of their subordinates in meeting the organization's mission, goals, and objectives.

- They have to be empathetic to, and often defend, the needs and concerns of their subordinates, whose beliefs and attitudes may be opposed to or not completely in accord with upper management.

1. PRINCIPLES OF MANAGEMENT

> Evaluate and use basic management principles such as planning, leading, delegating, controlling, organizing, and allocating resources. (Evaluate)
>
> **Body of Knowledge III.A.1**

Planning, Organizing, Staffing, Directing, and Controlling (POSDC)

What business are we in? What resources do we need in order to succeed? How should those resources be organized? What skills and information do employees need in order to do their jobs? How do we know how well we are doing? What should we do if things are not going well or if we want to improve?

These are just some of the questions asked by management as part of attending to the processes for which it is responsible. The processes of management (POSDC) are often described in the following categories:

- *Planning* is the setting of goals and objectives and the methods for achieving them.

- *Organizing* involves structuring the organization and the work to be done and obtaining and allocating resources in order to carry out the plans.

- *Staffing* includes acquiring the right people and placing them in the right job as well as further developing their competencies.

- *Directing* is guiding members of the organization to achieve the mission, plans, and objectives of the organizational work unit.

- *Controlling* involves monitoring activities and results to ensure that desired outputs and outcomes are obtained.

On a macro or long-term level, *planning* involves defining the vision and mission of the organization as well as the values and principles by which the company will operate. It involves defining the business's goals, objectives, and strategies to be used for each product, service, and/or customer segment and ensuring that appropriate systems and structures are created to carry out strategy. Planning must occur for the overall organization as well as subunits within it (for example, divisions, departments, and work units).

Operational planning has a shorter-term perspective and involves activities such as:

- Setting short-term objectives (for example, which university courses will be offered during the upcoming semester)

- Analysis, planning, and allocation of capacity and material (for example, how many flu shots are expected to be needed by a local community health clinic and how many nurses will be needed where and on what days)

- Planning needed resources (for example, ensuring sufficient inventory of winter road salt for a highway department depot)

- Setting out time lines (for example, when user training and operational conversion to a new customer relationship management software package will occur)

Organizing at the strategic level includes determining the organizational structure and design and how work will be divided and authority allocated. It is at this level that basic policies and decisions are made relative to the systems to be used to manage aspects of the business such as finance, human resources, order fulfillment, and research and the types and locations of facilities to be used in carrying out the processes. At the operational level, organization involves making the appropriate resources available, both human and otherwise (for example, equipment, material, information, and funds), to implement and sustain the processes.

Staffing at the strategic level is identifying the human resources needed and the levels of competency necessary to achieve the organization's mission, goals, and objectives, the acquisition of these resources, the building of a competent workforce that meets or exceeds customers' expectations, and the care and development of the individuals that compose the organization.

Directing at the strategic level is the communication of vision, mission, values, and strategy in such a way that every business unit understands its role in the success of the organization. *Directing* at the operational level is the day-to-day delegation, empowerment, and coaching that enables all employees to effectively apply their knowledge and skills to satisfy the customer.

Controlling at a strategic level is the monitoring of strategy implementation and results, using macrolevel performance measures (for example, sales, profitability, market share growth, new product development, and customer and employee satisfaction). *Controlling* at the operational level is the monitoring of shorter-term measures such as performance against budget, on-time delivery, and customer complaint resolution. Controlling includes initiating corrective and preventive actions when necessary. It also involves recognition and rewards for work done well. Controlling also includes the organization's continual learning and continual improvement.

Core Values and Concepts

The Baldrige Performance Excellence Program (BPEP) embodies interrelated core values and concepts:

- Systems perspective

- Visionary leadership

- Customer-focused excellence

- Valuing people

- Organizational learning and agility

- Focus on success

- Managing for innovation

- Management by fact

- Societal contributions

- Ethics and transparency

- Delivering value and results

- Management of information, knowledge, and information technology

- Building a competent, effective, supportive, and valued workforce

- Organizational and personal learning

- Designing, managing, and improving work processes with a systems perspective and emphasis on creating value

- Achieving measurable and effective process, product, customer-focused, workforce-focused, leadership- and governance-focused, and financial- and market-focused performance outcomes

- Managing for innovation

- Social responsibility

These values and concepts are the foundation for integrating key business requirements within a results-oriented framework that creates a basis for action and feedback.

For those organizations using International Organization for Standardization (ISO) 9001 or other ISO standards, seven quality management principles are as follows:

- Customer focus

- Leadership

- Engagement of people

- Process approach

- Improvement

- Evidence-based decision-making

- Relationship management

2. MANAGEMENT THEORIES AND STYLES

Define and describe management theories such as scientific, organizational, behavioral, learning, systems thinking, and situational complexity. Define and describe management styles such as autocratic, participative, transactional, transformational, management by fact, coaching, and contingency approach. Describe how management styles are influenced by an organization's size, industry sector, culture, and competitors. (Apply)

Body of Knowledge III.A.2

Overview of Management Theories and Styles

The personal style one uses in working with others depends on many factors. One is the background and perspective of the individual manager, especially the assumptions made about what influences people's behavior. The characteristics exhibited by employees, individually and as a group, may also have an impact on how a manager will approach an issue. A final factor is the particular situation. For example, the manager may act quite differently when carrying out the following two tasks: (1) a one-on-one discussion with an employee about a performance problem and (2) communicating to the entire organization the opportunities for learning that will be embedded in a new company initiative.

Several theories of management have been proposed over time that can help to explain different management styles. Following are some of the more widely known theories.

Scientific Management. Frederick Taylor was one of the first contributors to the scientific theory of management, which focused on finding the one best way to perform a task to increase productivity. Taylor emphasized the efficiency, not the satisfaction, of workers. He did this by breaking a job down into small-task components that could be studied to find the most efficient way of doing the task. Essentially, he separated thinking tasks from physical tasks, repositioning thinking tasks as the province of engineers, not the shop floor. Happening at a time when the workforce comprised poorly educated people with few skills, Taylor's approach significantly increased production. Ultimately, though, as more workers became skilled and better educated, the boredom and dissatisfaction of doing repetitive, unchallenging work began to decrease production.

Frank and Lillian Gilbreth also focused on increasing productivity. They developed the motion and time study method in order to analyze work processes. Henry Gantt (developer of the Gantt chart) proposed the concept of providing incentives to employees based on output.

Classical Organizational Theory. As organizations became larger and more complex, the study of management began to look at the management not only of individual tasks but also of the larger enterprise. Henri Fayol developed fourteen principles of management that included issues such as how power and authority needed to be subdivided into reporting relationships and the subordination of individual interests to the common good. Max Weber believed bureaucracy to be the ideal organizational structure since everyone would clearly understand their responsibilities, and lines of authority would provide more predictable and efficient output. Mary Parker Follett added the factor of relationships, both within the organization and between the organization and its environment, as a consideration for management.

Human Relations Theory. In the 1930s researchers performed a series of studies at the Hawthorne Works plant of Western Electric Company to determine the best level of lighting, length of workday, and length of rest periods to maximize worker productivity. As the lighting in the plant was increased, production levels rose. Surprisingly, production levels also rose as light levels were decreased. Researchers eventually determined that the increase in productivity was correlated not to lighting levels but to the fact that the workers were involved in the study. This change in behavior due to being singled out for attention, now commonly called the *Hawthorne effect*, clearly shows the importance of human factors in motivating employees. Human relations theory then brought a focus on workers—both individually and as a social system.

Behavioral Theories. Behavioral theory is the background on which many motivational theories are based. Two landmark theories related to motivation are discussed in Chapter 2. They are Abraham Maslow's hierarchy of needs and Frederick Herzberg's two-factor theory (satisfiers and dissatisfiers).

Douglas McGregor formulated the *theory X versus theory Y* model. Theory X is a negative view of human nature, assuming that most employees do not want to work and will require continual prodding. Theory Y is a positive view, believing that employees want to work and will seek responsibilities that can offer solutions to organizational problems and their own personal growth. Consistently treating workers under either of the assumptions tends to be a self-fulfilling prophecy.

Learning Theories. There are several theories of how people learn. David Kolb formulated the experiential learning model whereby a person (1) has an experience, (2) reflects on the experience, (3) develops abstract theories based on the experience, and (4) applies what she or he has learned.[1] When the knowledge is applied, it then creates another experience, and the cycle continues (see Figure 8.1). The model is useful not only for designing training programs but also for understanding how people react to certain types of training since most people tend to prefer particular phases of the learning cycle. For example, some prefer hands-on learning (phases 1 and 4), while others prefer abstract thinking (phases 2 and 3).

Knowledge of one's style can be assessed by a learning-style instrument such as the *Learning Styles Questionnaire* by Honey and Mumford. The knowledge can be used to identify learning opportunities that one would find more comfortable or desirable or help people to know in what areas they might want to expand their learning repertoire.

Howard Gardner proposed that there are multiple types of intelligence and that people will learn better if the learning experience enables them to apply their own strengths. The intelligences include:

- *Linguistic.* Skilled in the use of words

- *Logical/mathematical.* Skilled in the analysis of concepts

- *Visual/spatial.* Skilled with manipulating symbolic relationships

- *Musical.* Skilled with sound

- *Kinesthetic.* Skilled in physical touch or movement

- *Interpersonal.* Skilled in relationships with others

- *Intrapersonal.* Skilled in self-analysis and development

Differences in skill levels in each of the seven intelligences affect how well one will learn about various subjects and in different environments. Most training has traditionally focused on the first two intelligences, while accelerated learning techniques often integrate others in order to take advantage of different learning styles and how each fits with a particular aspect of the topic.

Another view of cognitive learning style focuses on preferences of the learner from two different angles: (1) Do you prefer to receive information in a verbal format or in visual images?, and (2) Do you prefer a holistic view or to analyze the details? These two perspectives then create four different combinations of

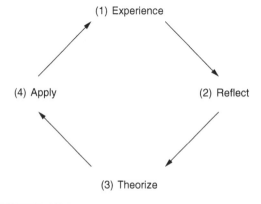

Figure 8.1   Kolb's experiential learning model.

learning styles. Instructors need to ensure that material is not presented in a way that puts one particular style at a significant disadvantage.

These concepts are also used in the final portion of the body of knowledge. In Chapter 19 on training and development, the experiential learning model and the multiple types of intelligences should be applied in making training plans, performing needs analyses, developing and delivering training materials, and assessing training effectiveness.

Behavior Management. Behavior management is an adaptation of B. F. Skinner's behavior modification/operant conditioning studies. Performance management is a technique involving an analysis of the antecedents of a behavior and the consequences of that behavior for the purpose of reinforcing desirable behavior to obtain or maintain positive consequences. The phrase "positive reinforcement for work done well" has become embedded in many of the processes for training and managing people in organizations.

A–B–C Analysis. The A–B–C analysis template is used in the systematic analysis of the behavior observed of an individual or a work group. The purpose of the analysis is to collect data that, when analyzed, may indicate what is causing or inhibiting specific behaviors.

Upon completion of an analysis, a manager can deduce whether the antecedent is appropriate and whether the consequences are positively reinforcing the behavior to the extent that the behavior is likely to be repeated. A–B–C means:

- A—*The antecedent, the trigger that initiates a behavior.* Examples include:
  — A work order received by a machine operator
  — A sign directing pedestrian traffic around an obstacle
  — A customer's inquiry about her stock market account
  — A nurse frowning when a patient flinches during an injection
- B—*The behavior initiated by the antecedent.* Examples include:
  — The operator starts the job.
  — Pedestrians follow the directions on the sign.
  — The customer service representative (CSR) looks up the account and answers the inquiry.
  — The patient complains about the pain inflicted by the nurse.
- C—*The consequences, to the observed person or group, from the behavior.* Examples include:
  — The worker is satisfied that the job started without a problem.
  — The pedestrians go about their business, without harm and mostly without noticing what they just did.

— The customer is satisfied with the response of the CSR but dissatisfied with the outcome of her investment.

— The nurse is defensive, stating that she could not help it, and it was only a slight "pinch." The patient grumbles and suggests the nurse learn how to do her job correctly.

An antecedent initiates a behavior, but the consequences of that behavior influence the performer's behavior in the next similar situation. In these situations:

- The machine operator may anticipate a trouble-free start-up of the next job.

- The pedestrians follow posted directions the next time they encounter a posting.

- The investor seeks out the same CSR when she has another question. The CSR thinks of ways to draw a positive inference from the negative performance of customers' accounts.

- The nurse gripes to other nurses about her experience. The patient tells everyone he encounters about the incompetent nurse. The nurse is nervous when making another injection, tending to make a poor and painful insertion of the needle.

Consider the following scenario: John, a new employee, has just undergone training as a bank teller. He is assigned a window and told to begin to serve customers as they step up. He is also told that his performance will be observed and that a discussion will be held, after John has been on duty for two hours, between John and the observer to mutually discuss ways John's performance can be improved.

One of the key points made in the training is to frequently use the customer's name during a transaction. It is this basic behavior that the observer will be targeting in the first improvement discussion. The observer prepares an A–B–C behavior collection form (see Figure 8.2) and stations herself as another teller (with a closed window) next to John. The observer collects data from the customer interactions. She analyzes the data and prepares to discuss the findings with John.

In the improvement discussion, John is made aware of his behavior and asked what he feels he can do to improve. The observer intervenes with suggestions to

Antecedent	Behavior	A/U	Consequences	P/N	I/D	Impact

A = Acceptable   U = Unacceptable   P = Positive   N = Negative   I = Immediate   D = Delayed

Figure 8.2   Analysis of behavior template.

Source: Reprinted with permission of R. T. Westcott & Associates.

consider, as appropriate. The two mutually agree on a plan of action. John returns to his window to try out the agreed-upon changes while the observer collects a new set of data. John is recognized for his use of the desired behavior, whether used once or used every time appropriately. The approach is repeated until John has mastered the desired behavior and has been recognized for work done well.

In this example the antecedent column may have something like "John is told about using the customer's name." The behavior column may have something like "John used the customer's name only once and used the wrong name a second time." In the *A/U* column, this may be coded as *U* or unacceptable. In the consequences column, the comment is based on observations such as "customer showed surprise and left the window showing some anger." The *P/N* column would show *N* for negative. The *I/D* column would likely be coded as *I* as the consequence was seen right away. If the consequence was that the customer later chose to take all her funds elsewhere, the I/D may be delayed. Impact is for comments regarding possible downstream effects.

Possible unintended outcomes from consequences are (1) feedback to the performer is unrelated to desired behavior (inadequate, incorrect for circumstances, not constructive, nonexistent), and (2) consequences tend to reinforce the wrong or inappropriate behavior (extinguishes good behavior rather than stimulating and sustaining desired behavior).

Performance/behavior management has been misused in some organizations and has received some bad press because it is perceived to manipulate people against their will. On the plus side, however, behavior management has achieved mutually beneficial positive outcomes for the individual and the organization when properly used with good intent.

Daniels states, "If you work with other human beings, you are subject to the laws of behavior. And if you don't understand them, more than likely you're impeding, possibly depressing, the performance of your employees, your peers, even yourself."[2]

Situational Leadership/Management. Paul Hersey and Ken Blanchard's *situational leadership* model and instrument is useful for the leader-manager in appropriately applying the right amount of direction and supporting behavior to followers as they progress through the four maturity levels.[3] It is also helpful in understanding why performance problems may arise when new procedures are introduced, reorganizations occur, and new members are added (or removed) from a work group or team. It is important for the leader-manager to realize that the process of progressing through the stages will need to differ from person to person, work group to work group, and situation to situation.

Systems Thinking. Peter M. Senge,[4] in *The Fifth Discipline*, discusses the five disciplines of the learning organization: systems thinking, personal mastery, mental models, building shared vision, and team learning. He points out that these disciplines should develop as an ensemble. Systems thinking is the fifth discipline; it blends the disciplines into a coherent body of theory and practice. Systems thinking shifts our mental focus from perceiving ourselves as separate from the rest of the world to being connected to the world.

Through a series of diagrams, Senge maps what he calls *systems archetypes*. Each archetype is described, and a principle is stated as well as one or more examples. These diagrams feature feedback loops. Upon mastering this systemic language, the subconscious becomes trained to think in terms of circles rather than straight lines.

Senge states, "While traditional organizations require management systems that control people's behavior, learning organizations invest in improving the quality of thinking, the capacity for reflection and team learning, and the ability to develop shared visions and shared understandings of complex business issues. It is these capabilities that will allow learning organizations to be both more locally controlled and more well-coordinated than their hierarchical predecessors."[5]

Complexity Theory. The growing body of knowledge on complexity theory and complex adaptive systems signals the emergence of a meaningful management concept. As a generalization, complexity theory is concerned with the interaction between the parts of a system, as well as the interaction between the system and its environment. A whole complex system cannot be fully understood by analyzing its elements. The interactions tend to change and shift. Consider that "the capacity for self-organization is a property of complex systems which enables them to develop or change internal structure spontaneously and adaptively in order to cope with, or manipulate, their environment."[6]

Okes discusses five ways complexity theory can be used to manage and improve organizational performance:

1. Ensure that the mission, values, goals, and priorities of the system are clear.

2. Provide only as much control as necessary for each system.

3. Ensure there is sufficient feedback from the environment for the system to detect and act on signals indicating a need for change.

4. Monitor a wide range of system performance metrics to understand more fully how well the organization is performing.

5. Make many small changes rather than major disruptions to improve system performance.[7]

As these examples indicate, many existing quality management practices support the view of organizations as complex adaptive systems. When and how each should be applied depends on the type of organization and its current situation. Complexity theory provides a lens through which such decisions can be made more easily.

Managerial Grid. Blake and Mouton proposed the managerial grid, shown in Figure 8.3. It is a two-axis perspective of managerial attention. The x-axis indicates the focus on accomplishing a task and the y-axis a measure of concern for people. A manager who has little of either, of course, is considered remiss in carrying out his or her duties. Someone high on task but low on people is focused on authority, while someone high on people but low on task is viewed as a "country club" manager. The ideal in this normative model is a high priority for both task and for people, asking for commitment by all to accomplishing common organizational goals. The "team management" manager shows both high concern and interest in her employees while also focusing on the tasks, skills, and processes of the work.

Seven Habits. Stephen R. Covey's model and instruments amplify his *Seven Habits of Highly Effective People*. Progressing from *dependence* through *independence* to *interdependence*, the basic model addresses:

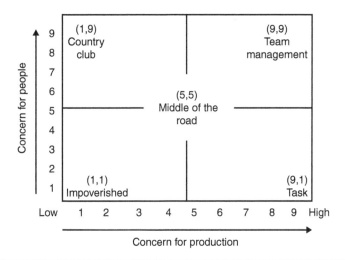

Figure 8.3   The managerial grid.
Source: R. R. Blake, and J. S. Mouton, *The Managerial Grid*, vol. 3 (Houston: Gulf, 1985).

- Being proactive
- Beginning with the end in mind
- Putting first things first
- Thinking win-win
- Seeking first to understand, then to be understood
- Synergizing
- Sharpening the saw (exercising the four dimensions of renewal)
  - Physical (exercise, nutrition, stress management)
  - Social/emotional (service, empathy, synergy, intrinsic security)
  - Spiritual (value clarification and commitment, study and meditation)
  - Mental (reading, visualizing, planning, writing)

Covey postulates that organizations function according to principles, whether or not leaders are aware of them. He emphasizes the importance of understanding these principles and how they interact with organizational functions to enable effective changes in quality. His term *principle-centered leadership* applies the seven habits to organizational change.[8] Covey and Gulledge assert that by applying the seven habits at four levels (personal, interpersonal, managing, and the organization's strategy, systems, and structures), an effective environment of trustworthiness can be attained to enable change to be perceived as positive.[9]

Interaction of Management Theories and Styles

The theories presented so far offer many different views of management. The personal style that an individual manager takes will be affected by the theories she or he believes to be more useful, as well as education, past experiences, and view of work and the world. Following are some of the resulting management styles:

• *Autocratic management.* Autocratic managers are concerned with developing an efficient workplace and have little concern for people. They typically make decisions without input from subordinates, relying on their positional power.

• *Participative management.* Participative managers are primarily concerned with people but might also attempt to balance this concern with the business concerns of the organization. Participative managers allow and encourage others to be active in the decision-making process.

Another approach to participative management is *management by walking around* (MBWA). It encourages managers to periodically roam throughout the organization and talk to employees, listen, and look for improvement opportunities. This technique motivates managers to stay in touch with the people who actually perform the work—those who experience problems firsthand.

• *Transactional leadership.* A transactional style is one in which the manager views the relationship as one of getting the work done through clear definitions of tasks and responsibilities and providing whatever resources are needed.

• *Transformational leadership.* Transformational leadership is a style whereby a leader articulates the vision and values necessary for the organization to succeed. It is sometimes equated to charismatic leadership but is aimed more at elevating the goals of subordinates and enhancing their self-confidence to achieve those goals. Bob Galvin accomplished this transformational leadership at Motorola with the Six Sigma program, an approach that, at the time, positioned Motorola to become a high-quality, reliable competitor in its market.

• *Management by fact.* A key emphasis of quality management is that decisions should be based on data such as performance measures and process improvement facts. This style is reinforced by the Baldrige Performance Excellence Program and the ISO 9000 series requirements.

• *Coaching.* A key differentiation in organizational performance is the ability to develop and effectively empower employees. Providing guidance and constructive feedback to employees to help them better apply their natural talents and to move beyond previous limitations has become a style of management. In this role, managers ask questions that will help others reach a conclusion rather than the manager making the decision for them.

• *Contingency approach.* Although many factors have the potential to positively affect performance, substantial obstacles often exist for managers who try to use a formula or single theory. For example, Locke and Schweiger, in their research into the subject of whether participation enhances productivity, did not find clear support for this premise.[10] One reason could be the difficulty of effectively implementing a participative management system.

Other management styles might be more productive in certain environments and conditions. For example, in some cases the costs of employee participation (ergo, training and support) might be greater than the potential cost benefits and intangible benefits that can be achieved. In some situations an autocratic management style might achieve superior performance over a participative style, such as when decisions must be made rapidly with information only available to the manager. For example, it is difficult to imagine that the captain of a sinking ship would have better results if he or she approached the crew using a participative style.

Different employees should be managed differently. This is an obvious statement, perhaps, but how can a manager understand and know when to apply different styles? There are several classifications of personality types. Two are listed below.

Tools

Dominance, Influence, Steadiness, Conscientiousness Instrument (DiSC). The DiSC profiling instrument is based on William Marston's theories. It measures characteristic ways of behaving in a particular environment. The DiSC dimensions are:

- *Dominance.* This dimension emphasizes shaping the environment, overcoming opposition, and accomplishing results.

- *Influence.* This dimension emphasizes influencing (or persuading) others in shaping the environment.

- *Steadiness.* The emphasis in this dimension is on cooperating with others within the existing circumstances in order to perform a task.

- *Conscientiousness.* The focus of this dimension is performing conscientiously to ensure quality and accuracy within existing conditions.

Within each dimension, the respondent's tendencies and desires are surfaced. An action plan is suggested, including the characteristics of other persons needed and the steps to be taken in order for the respondent to be more effective. DiSC increases self-awareness and points to ways the information can be used in relations with others.

Myers-Briggs Type Indicator. Isabel Myers and Katharine Cook Briggs devised a method of assessing personality type based on Carl Jung's theory of personality preferences. The Myers-Briggs Type Indicator™ (MBTI) looks at how one approaches life based on the following four bipolar dimensions:

(E)—Extraverted	or	(I)—Introverted
(S)—Sensing	or	(N)—Intuitive
(T)—Thinking	or	(F)—Feeling
(J)—Judging	or	(P)—Perceiving

Following is a brief summary of the pairs:

- An *E* gets energy by interacting with other people, while an *I* prefers to be alone to think things through.

- An *S* wants lots of detailed information in order to make a decision and is here-and-now oriented, while an *N* will go with a general hunch and is big-picture, future oriented.

- Someone who is a *T* makes decisions based on logic and facts, while an *F* places more consideration on the emotional and relationship impact of a decision.

- *J* people are concerned about getting things organized and completed, while *P* folks want to keep exploring alternatives and respond to here-and-now priorities.

Personal style is determined by the MBTI scores, defined in sixteen possible styles (for example, ENFP, INTJ, ISFP), with each having a relatively unique (but over-lapping) way of looking at the world. The model is useful for helping individuals understand their own behaviors as well as those of others.

The MBTI can therefore be used as a team-building tool whereby members of a team assess and discuss their respective styles and how it has (or will) affect their way of working together. It can also be used in forming groups—for example, making sure that membership is not too highly skewed in a particular direction (for example, making quick, intuitive decisions or wanting to collect more and more information to ensure that all possible viewpoints have been considered). The MBTI is in active use after many years of successful application.

The contingency approach is a good place to end this section. It emphasizes that there is no one right way to manage, to learn, or to look at the world, as high-lighted by Deming's system of profound knowledge. Managers need to have a good understanding of organizational theory, what drives people, and how learn-ing occurs if they are to effectively utilize the human resources that make up their organizations. Matching people to the job, matching training design to the learn-ers, and matching one's management style to the specific person and/or situation are fundamental to management.

Organizational Culture

The culture that results from the manner in which work is carried out, as well as outsiders' views (customers, suppliers, shareholders, the community, and com-petitors), shapes the way members of an organization relate to each other and to the world outside.

An organization is the integration of two major systems:

- The technical system, which defines how products and services are to be realized (and includes the equipment, work processes and procedures, and human resources to carry out the processes).

- The social system, consisting of how people communicate, interrelate, and make decisions. A manifestation of the social system is called *culture*, which is evidenced by employee behaviors.

Culture is a function of the artifacts, values, and underlying assumptions shared by members of the organization.[11] It can be shaped by communicating what stan-dards of behavior are expected and ensuring that policies, procedures, promotions, and day-to-day decisions are appropriately aligned. Culture is manifested in such ways as:

- How power is used or shared

- The organization's orientation toward risk or safety

- Whether mistakes are punished, hidden, or used to guide learning and improvement

- How outsiders are perceived and treated

- Vision, mission, principles, policies, protocols, procedures, and practices

- Artifacts, layout, and amenities (for example, furnishings, artwork, open versus closed workspaces, employee time-out spaces, signage, and so on)

Members new to an organization are soon acclimated to the culture through training and both formal reinforcement and peer influence.

The design of the organization has an impact on culture. If a hierarchical structure restricts cross-functional communications, then close relationships between interrelated functions will be more difficult. Similarly, in a unionized organization the relationship between organization management and union management will set the stage for how cooperatively people are able to work together toward common goals.

Culture will have a significant impact on quality when it is shaped by the words and actions of leadership, how work systems are designed, and what gets recognized and rewarded. If the culture is not proactive, is not focused on customers, and does not use data to guide decision-making, the organization is not likely to be highly successful in the continual improvement of quality.

Visible artifacts and the metaphors used to describe an organization are often superficial indicators of culture. For example, a company that talks of "killing the competition" and creates a graphic display showing competitors being "wiped out" would convey a focus on competitors rather than on customers.

Examining the beliefs and values espoused by members of the organization requires deeper probing than just observing obvious things. For example, in a family-owned business, the predominant values are often those of the founder(s). Those values may persist long after the death of the founding individual(s).

At an even deeper level are the shared tacit assumptions of which the organization's members may not be consciously aware. Failure to surface and consider these assumptions can result in serious blunders—for example, a failure to understand the mutual level of demonstrated trust needed for management to introduce major change in a unionized organization where an adversarial relationship persists.

The Juran transformation model and road map lists five breakthroughs for changing to a quality culture:

1. *Leadership and management* use strategy, engagement, empowerment, resources, rewards, audits, and nondelegable managerial practices to create positive and stable change. This is done in the first phase of the road map, *decide*.

2. *Organization and structure* is used to design and implement systemic operational systems that align functions into a smoothly functioning organization. This is the second phase of the road map, *prepare*.

3. *Current performance* is altered via the third phase of the road map, *launch*.

4. The fourth phase of the road map is *expand*. This *culture*-altering step may take three to five years.

5. *Adaptability and sustainability* arrive in the fifth phase of the road map, *sustain*. This continues as long as the organization meets its goals.[12]

Changing an organization's culture is difficult and requires time. Fear of change must be removed, poor labor-management relations must be resolved, and the company's focus must move away from the status quo. Employees should be convinced of the benefits that a quality management approach will provide and should buy in to the changes. This often means that employees at all levels will need to change behaviors or perform tasks in a different manner. If strong leadership, motivation, and enthusiasm are lacking, frustration and stress will result.

3. INTERDEPENDENCE OF FUNCTIONAL AREAS

Describe the interdependence of an organization's areas (human resources, engineering, sales, marketing, finance, research and development, purchasing, information technology, logistics, production, and service) and how those dependencies and relationships influence processes and outputs. (Understand)

Body of Knowledge III.A.3

The concept of an organization consisting of a system of interacting processes is widely accepted. The quality management system standard ISO (International Organization for Standardization) 9001 stresses this concept, up to a point. (ISO 9001 does not specifically include *all* of the functions of an organization.) The Baldrige Performance Excellence Program is more inclusive, covering all of the functional components of the business. Yet, in spite of the emphasis placed on systems thinking, many organizations still consist of functional silos or fiefdoms. Such internal silos tend to foster dysfunctional attitudes and behaviors, such as (partial list):

- Optimizing the operation of the subunit to the detriment of the overall organization (referred to as *suboptimization)*

- Having a "that's not my job" attitude—throw it over the wall for the next unit to worry about

- Inhibiting interunit communication and keeping knowledge in the unit

- Hiding mistakes; "Don't tell, it could make us look bad"

- Competing—attempting to get all of the resources we can get, regardless of other units' needs

- Protecting the boss's reputation at all costs, so he or she will protect us

- Being wary of the units who provide product or services to us and the units to which we provide product or services

- Ignoring the external customers—unless we are in sales or customer service, we have nothing to do with them

- Making sure we spend all of the budget money allocated to us; if we do not, next year's allotment may be reduced

- Resisting efforts to enlist our unit's people in cross-functional teams

And the list goes on.

The structuring of an organization into semiautonomous work units or departments developed with the hierarchical, autocratically run organization. The emphasis in this type of organization is centralization of decision-making (power and control), the specialization (education and experience) of the incumbents, and a focus on maintaining the status quo.

The modern perspective is a business organization as a system—a group of interrelated processes designed to accomplish a mission. Many of these processes call for specialized skills or functions. At the same time, the organization is not a stand-alone entity—it is part of a larger system that includes other organizations, society, and the world. An organization must ensure that its role in the larger system is carried out appropriately. This requires (1) an awareness of outside issues that affect the organization and (2) knowledge of how to manage the process of interfacing with those external functions.

Business functions can be classified as external or internal. *External* business functions are those that have dealings with the outside world, such as safety, legal, regulatory, product liability, and environmental and maintaining knowledge of laws, regulations, and standards mandated by authorities at the local, state, federal, and/or international levels. Other external business functions that must be managed include technological and process-oriented activities that might be driven by the competitive or industry environment within which an organization operates.

Internal business functions are those that operate within the boundaries of the organization, including sales, marketing, engineering, purchasing, production, human resources, finance, research and development (R&D), information technology, logistics, and other services. Collectively, these types of business functions affect the ability of the organization to meet and adapt to changes in customer and market requirements.

The distinction between external and internal functions exists in traditional, for-profit businesses as well as in not-for-profit educational or government organizations. Regardless of whether the organization is departmentalized according to function, product, customer, geography, process, or a matrix form, both internal and external business functions will exist.

The size and priority of a firm's various functions will also depend on the particular product or service being provided. For example, a firm that deals with dangerous chemicals or drugs will have larger legal, environmental, and safety functions. Companies in fast-changing fields, such as the telecommunications and computer industries, will have a larger research and product development function. In a labor-intensive business, human resources and training might be classified as separate functions; in a capital-intensive business, these functions might be combined, with training being a subset of the human resources function.

Internal Functions

Internal functions are those activities that create and operate the processes that enable the organization to accomplish its mission. Such functions would differ between a manufacturing organization, a healthcare organization, and an educational institution. The following list examines internal business functions found in a manufacturing setting. Although the names may change in a healthcare, banking, or government organization, the same basic processes typically occur.

• *Information technology* is a core enabler for an enterprise. The information technology function is responsible for providing technology that will allow the organization to effectively acquire, process, store, and access information that is of value for achieving results. Information technology strategy should be driven by business strategy rather than simply by adopting the latest technology. Because of the pace of change in information technology, all or parts of the function may be outsourced, and that requires an effective process for managing the subcontractor.

• *Finance* is responsible for planning, controlling, and reporting the flow of monetary funds into and out of the enterprise. It oversees the acquisition of both operating and capital funds. The finance function provides a structure used by the business for budgeting and accounting for operating receipts and expenditures and ensures that any excess funds are invested until needed. This group reports on the organization's financial status both internally (for example, for monthly operating reviews) and externally (for example, to the Securities and Exchange Commission [SEC] and to shareholders in the form of cash flow statements and balance sheets).

• *HR* is responsible for recruiting, training, and, as needed, terminating employment of the organization's personnel. It also oversees compensation systems, development of people for future needs (for example, career and succession planning), and resolution of people-problem issues in accordance with the organization's policies and any existing labor-management contract. The human resources function is also usually responsible for ensuring that company policies do not violate laws, such as the Americans with Disabilities Act (ADA) and discrimination laws regulated by the Equal Employment Opportunity Commission (EEOC). In unionized companies the function also coordinates, or is involved with, negotiating labor contracts and with ongoing labor relations.

• *Marketing* has the responsibility for ensuring that potential customers are aware of who the organization is and what it does, as well as helping translate potential customer needs into product or service opportunities for the organization. It develops communication channels—for example, advertising and timely news releases and using appropriate and available media—to keep the organization visible. Marketing is usually driven by and aligned with the strategic direction of the business to support growth, diversification, and broadening market penetration.

• *Product development* works closely with marketing and sales to develop the products that fulfill changing customer needs. This often drives technological breakthroughs.

• *Sales and customer service* functions work closely with present and potential customers to match their specific needs to current product offerings, resulting in a customer order. Customer service supports sales by ensuring that order requirements are clearly and accurately defined and are communicated to the scheduling function. It also monitors orders to ensure that they are fulfilled as contracted. Customer service also handles customer complaints and product returns.

• *Materials management* (or *logistics*) is often broken into three different functions: purchasing, inventory management, and production control. The *purchasing* process is responsible for identifying suppliers who can deliver needed materials for production—as well as maintenance, repair, and operations items—on time and at an appropriate quality level and price. The supplier management process also includes placing orders and monitoring supplier performance, often helping to improve suppliers or replacing them if necessary improvements are not made.

The *inventory management* function includes receiving purchased materials and issuing materials to production. This function also provides warehousing for raw materials as well as finished product. Disposition of scrapped material/product is also included.

Production control schedules production of customer orders and arranges for transportation of finished products to the customer. This process is often a key business measurable as customer order fulfillment is determined by both available quantity to meet requirements and on-time delivery.

- *Engineering* can take many forms depending on the particular industry, product line, or organization philosophy. The types of engineering functions include:

  — *Product engineering.* Converting the concepts from the marketing or R&D functions into viable products and specifications

  — *Process engineering.* Designing product realization work processes and procedures/instructions; developing, acquiring, and installing equipment (for example, machinery, tooling, gaging) that can consistently and effectively produce the organization's products

  — *Industrial engineering.* Optimizing workplace layout and material workflow, considering ergonomics in process design, and setting and monitoring production standards

  — *Facilities engineering.* Maintaining the building, land, central services (heating, ventilating, and air-conditioning [HVAC] and water), and machinery

- *R&D* is the process of exploring potential developments and new ideas in order to identify possible new products, services, or processes that can fulfill previously untapped opportunities and/or replace those that are in the later stages of the product life cycle.

- *Operations* (production) is the key element of any manufacturing organization. In fact, many plants have no responsibility but production, as all other functions are performed off-site. The production function manages the flow of material and its conversion from a raw state to a finished state. All resources—energy, materials, supplies, equipment, and human labor—are combined to make this conversion.

- *Quality* supports the other functions of the organization by defining and ensuring the use of operational systems that meet customer requirements. The quality function supports internal functions by providing special skills necessary for day-to-day operations—for example, supporting human resources in developing a quality-related training curriculum for new employees and assisting other functions in their continual improvement efforts. The quality function also provides quality control services—for example, product inspection, instrument and equipment calibration, and quality-related training.

Integrated Business Processes

A higher-level view of an organization is shown in Figure 8.4, demonstrating how the various functions must work together in order to become an integrated business system. Strategy development and deployment is the primary responsibility of senior management. Customer relationship management includes the processes primarily carried out by marketing, sales, and customer service. Product/process technology management includes R&D and various engineering functions that design new products and processes. Order fulfillment includes the functions that acquire and transform raw materials and deliver the final product to customers. Support processes are the staff functions that provide specialized expertise—for example, information, employees, performance reporting, and enabling the other business processes to work effectively.

This view of a business emphasizes the interrelationships of the many activities that take place. On a day-to-day basis, work occurs across organizational boundaries, requiring that employees have an understanding of the bigger picture. For example, to the patient who goes to an outpatient clinic at a hospital for an arm injury, it is a single organization. To those within the hospital, at least four different functions are involved—admissions, radiology, subacute care, and billing. Although a different individual oversees each function, and each may have its own mission statement, they must understand how their processes are interconnected in order to serve the overall organizational mission—and the patient.

One problem that often occurs is that each function or department within an organization tries to optimize its own performance without considering the impact on performance (suboptimization) of the overall enterprise. To continue with the arm injury example, consider what can occur if the admissions clerk tries to perform the activity as quickly as possible, attempting to reduce the queue of patients. Some of the effects on radiology, billing, the entire hospital, or the patient might be:

Figure 8.4 Major business processes.

- The patient gets lost due to poor directions to the radiology lab.

- The wrong type of X-ray is taken, and the patient is misdiagnosed and has complications and/or must have additional X-rays taken.

- The bill is sent to the wrong address.

- The treatment is incorrectly coded, and insurance refuses to pay.

It is therefore vitally important that people and functions within an organization understand the system in which they have a role and how their activities contribute to or detract from overall organizational performance. Optimization of one area often can conflict with efforts to optimize the overall system. Employees must collaborate across functional boundaries, a process for which team structures are vitally important.

A classic example of cross-functional collaboration is the process of *concurrent engineering* (also called *simultaneous engineering*), often used by manufacturing companies to expedite the development and launch of new products. The design and launch process has traditionally been done sequentially (see Figure 8.5) whereby sales talks to the customer and then tells product engineering what to develop. Product engineering creates specifications and drawings for the new product and hands them over to manufacturing engineering to figure out how it can be made. Manufacturing engineering designs and purchases equipment and tooling, then hands it over to production to operate. This process is frequently called "over the wall" product development, where each department believes that it has completed its task when the next department becomes involved.

In order to overcome the inherent problems with this process, concurrent engineering applies the team concept to get all key players involved simultaneously (see Figure 8.5). It is a multidisciplinary approach that typically involves product design and manufacturing engineers; sales, purchasing, quality, and financial personnel; and also key suppliers of raw materials and production equipment. By having all work together throughout the product and process development and launch cycle, many errors that would typically be found only after beginning production are prevented. Concurrent engineering invests the time in design changes before launch of the product, while the traditional method relies on continual engineering changes during production to address the problems. Cross-functional collaboration is a critical component of concurrent engineering and performance of any business process.

Systems Thinking

In thinking of an organization as an integrated business system, some caveats are:

- Be clear and objective as to what is to be changed or improved.

- Be specific as to what the desired outcomes from a change are.

- Be prepared to be flexible and adaptable as to the receptivity of feedback received.

- Accept that systems changes need effort and alignment from the outside in, not from the inside out.

A. Traditional method

B. Concurrent engineering method

Figure 8.5 New product design and launch process.

- The whole system is more important than its parts; relationships and processes are paramount.
- Every system is linked to other larger or smaller systems in a hierarchy of systems.
- The quest for achieving a steady-state balance, although desired, can be perilous in the rapidly changing world.
- Entropy must be reversed, or the system will perish.
- There are multiple ways to achieve the same preferred outcomes.
- Employees support what they participate in creating.
- Root causes and their effects typically do not occur within the same time frame and space.
- Systems consisting of many levels are too complex to fully comprehend and manage from a central control point.
- Solving problems at the level at which they were created is often not possible nor feasible.

Some of the advantages to systems thinking are:

- The organization is freer to commit to more than one approach or best practice relevant to achieving its strategy; for example, Six Sigma methodology is only one option of several available.

- Organizations can integrate multiple approaches, allowing:

  — Choice of the best management method or tool for the situation

  — Time to comprehend the principles and practices involved with each approach chosen, adapting each approach as needed

  — More effective integration of each individual technique or tool with other approaches

- With the advent of new, more easily adaptable approaches and methodology, the organization is better equipped to subsume the new approach into its system without the trauma traditionally encountered.

- Systems thinking makes understanding relationships, system to system, easier. This is especially important in understanding and managing supply chain relationships.

- Systems thinking, when it permeates the entire organization, causes all employees to think of the interrelationships within their organization, as well as beyond the physical boundaries to the external stakeholders (that is, customers, suppliers, investors, regulatory agencies, community, and so on).

4. HUMAN RESOURCES (HR) MANAGEMENT

> Apply HR elements in support of ongoing professional development and role in quality system: setting goals and objectives, conducting performance evaluations, developing recognition programs, and ensuring that succession plans are in place where appropriate. (Apply)
>
> **Body of Knowledge III.A.4**

Human Resources Functions

Depending on the size and purpose of the organization, the performance of the various functions relating to human resources may range from being wholly assumed by a person holding multifunctional responsibilities (as in a small organization) to a large HR department with several work units. Subfunctions of HR may include:

- Leadership development

- Human resource planning, including succession planning

- Staffing
  - Recruiting, interviewing, selecting, testing, hiring, assimilating
  - Relocation administration
  - Promotion, transfer administration
  - Job fairs
- Training
  - Employee orientation
  - Management/supervisory education and training
  - Nonmanagement skills training and education
- Capability and capacity planning
- Compensation
  - Wage/salary administration
  - Executive compensation administration
  - Job analysis
  - Job descriptions
  - Competency analysis
- Management performance appraisal
- Nonmanagement performance evaluation
- Payroll processing
- Benefits management
  - Insurance administration
  - Health and medical services
  - Vacation/leave processing
  - Pension/profit-sharing plan administration
  - Tuition aid/scholarship administration
  - Thrift/savings plan administration
  - Suggestion system administration
  - Employee assistance program administration
  - Recreation/social recognition program administration
  - Career planning and support
  - Stock plan administration
  - Retirement plan administration

- Labor relations
  - Complaint/disciplinary procedures
  - EEOC compliance, affirmative action administration
  - Union/management relations
  - Contract negotiation
- Safety, security, and employee welfare
  - Safety program administration
  - Occupational Health and Safety Administration (OSHA) compliance assessments
  - Security force management
  - Provide or arrange for counseling as needed (for example, substance abuse, family matters, health conditions, gambling, anger management, and so on)
- Employee termination, layoff, medical leave
  - Separation processing
  - Outplacement administration
  - Unemployment compensation administration
  - Workers' compensation administration
- Organization development
  - Employee satisfaction surveys
  - Organizational diagnoses
  - Organizational interventions
- Public relations
  - Community relations, fund drives
- Personnel records
  - Personnel records, reports, and database management
- Other
  - Employee communications, publications
  - Personnel research—for example, surveys
  - Food services
  - Library management
  - Travel arrangements administration
  - Administrative services (mail, phone, messengers, and so on)
  - Facility maintenance services

As you can see, HR is sometimes the home for diverse functions. However structured, there must be a strong collaborative relationship between the HR function, operations, and other staff functions.

Human Resources Responsibilities Shared by HR and Other Functional Managers. The responsibilities of managers of other functions, relative to HR, are to:

- Set functional human resources–related objectives aligned to the overall organization's strategic goals and objectives.

- Clearly communicate personnel resource requirements and specifications to the HR function.

- Learn and apply skills in interviewing job candidates.

- Follow the policies, procedures, and guidelines promulgated by the HR function.

- Learn and abide by the laws and regulations governing personnel behavior as they pertain to the function.

- Seek the counsel and guidance of the HR function on personnel legal issues, labor relations issues, safety, security, and employee welfare issues.

- Ensure that quality responsibilities are addressed in job descriptions and the evaluations/appraisals of employees' performance for all organizational levels within the function.

- Learn and apply a coaching style of managing, including effective performance feedback and recognition of employees for work done well.

- Support the continual development of the function's personnel (career planning support, promotions, lateral movement to gain additional competence, training and education, and other opportunities for personal development).

- Create and maintain a succession plan for key positions within the function.

- Ensure that all employees in the function are treated fairly and justly.

Identifying Job Positions. Finding employees who will be positive contributors to an organization's mission is an inherently difficult process. Ideally, each employee should be a good fit to the company's values, have an interest in the specific product or service being provided to customers, and have the skills required for a specific position. At the same time, when an organization wants to be flexible, there is also a need to ensure that not everyone thinks alike. Different ideas are the core of innovation; however, this section will focus on finding, hiring, and retaining employees who have the skills for a specific position.

To know what staff is necessary, an organization must first understand the tasks to be performed and the skills necessary. On the basis of the organization's product and process technology, management philosophy, and organizational structure, the work activities are organized into specific job functions/titles, each of which will typically have a description of the primary responsibilities.

The manager who oversees the position should develop the job description, with a review by HR. Having an employee currently in that position also review the description is useful. Job descriptions typically state any educational and/or experience requirements, as well as the level of accountability and authority allocated to the position. The document also includes the following:

- Position title

- Basic job functions

- To whom the individual reports

- Titles of positions reporting to the individual

- Knowledge and skill requirements (including educational and experience qualifications when applicable)

- Limits of authority (for example, maximum dollar limits with respect to decision-making)

- Specific job functions

- Performance standards

Any special physical requirements for the job (for example, ability to lift one hundred pounds) may also be included in order to reduce the likelihood of legal action regarding discrimination under the ADA.

Some key quality-related processes and activities likely to be spelled out in job descriptions for management personnel who are not in the quality department include responsibility for:

- Supplier quality management—purchasing or materials manager

- Product reliability, design for manufacture, design change control—engineering manager

- Quality of manufactured product—production or manufacturing manager

- Quality of training and organization development—function manager

- Clarity of product application and quality needs—sales manager

- Quality of information and the processes to support it—information technology director

These and other quality responsibilities can be further detailed and included in job descriptions of other personnel within these departments. Job descriptions must also be regularly reviewed and revised in support of organizational changes and continual improvement.

Personnel Selection. Personnel needed for job openings can be obtained by internal promotion or through external recruitment. Internally promoted employees provide the advantage of being a known entity, have a familiarity with the company's products and processes, and may become fully productive more quickly. A disadvantage of promoting from within the company is the possibility that past relationships or performance might affect others' views of the individual and influence the individual's ability to perform. Hiring from outside has the potential of introducing new concepts and ideas.

When a position is to be filled, a list of potential candidates is developed. This can be done by advertising the position both internally and externally, by contacting an external recruiter, or by working with placement personnel from educational, professional, or other institutions. Applicants are then screened through a review of résumés; those applicants whose résumés generate the most interest will be invited to interview for the position. Although special skills and experience could be necessary for some positions (for example, accounting or welding), organizations sometimes consider candidates whom they believe to have the aptitude, attitude, and flexibility for change and an ability to learn, since specific skills are often developed once the person is hired.

HR personnel specially trained in interviewing techniques and protocols, as well as the department manager, typically perform the interviews. Depending on the position to be filled and the work design of the organization, peers and customers of the position to be filled could also participate in the interview process.

Employers are increasingly turning to various forms of preplacement testing. Tests might check for cognitive ability, intelligence, physical ability, personality, and interests. Any test administered must be proven valid and reliable and appropriate for the position for which the testing was done to avoid possible liability or discrimination claims. Checking candidate references is also a valuable step in the hiring process, but legal constraints must be carefully observed.

Once the best candidate has been identified, an offer is made regarding pay and benefits. If it is declined, the next suitable candidate may be offered the position. When the offer has been accepted, the individual must be oriented as to company facilities, people, and practices. The quality manager should ensure that the company's quality policies and procedures are included in such orientations.

Organizational expectations must be made clear to new employees. This includes the specific goals, objectives, actions, and behaviors. Such information should be documented to support the communication process and to allow tracking of performance.

One mistake often made by managers is treating staffing considerations in a reactive mode, responding only as positions become vacant. A more proactive view is that of establishing a succession plan that looks at key positions and individuals in the organization over time. Developing people who will be able to move into other positions makes the organization more responsive to change. Quality managers should ensure that positions critical to quality, especially their own, are considered in the succession planning.

Personnel Selection, Hiring, and Assimilation

Key managers often may participate in recruiting at colleges and job fairs. To perform this role, the manager should develop competence in the following:

- Reviewing of candidates' résumés and choosing potential interviewees

- Interview scheduling at the college or event

- Managing time (interviews often may last only twenty-five minutes, with five minutes between each interview to record information gathered during the interview)

- Asking questions within the parameters of pertinent laws, organizational policies, procedures, and guidelines

- Acquiring the key information needed to determine if there is a match between the organization's needs and the candidate's competencies, interests, and attitude

- Deciding which, if any, of the candidates interviewed should be selected for further interviewing back at the organization's site

- Compiling interview notes and preparing a report of the recruiting effort

Except for very small organizations, recruiting at the organization's site is usually performed by the HR function. HR, working from personnel requisitions or other specifications, will seek candidates to fill open positions. HR may use a variety of sources—for example, job postings, ads (TV, radio, website, internet, newspaper), employee referrals, walk-ins, and so on. HR will screen and contact candidates for the hiring manager to interview.

Managers who conduct selection interviews will need competency in:

- Predetermining the questions they will ask a candidate and the criteria they will apply in recommending selection

- Managing time to ensure that the manager and the interviewee each obtain the information they require in making their decisions (for example, to consider working at the organization, to consider the candidate an acceptable fit for the organization)

- Asking questions within the parameters of pertinent laws, organizational policies, procedures, and guidelines

- Describing the organization's purpose, the requirements of the job/position under consideration, benefits, compensation range, and so on

- Deciding which candidate(s) are to be offered a job

Candidate interviews may be structured in several ways, such as:

- *One-to-one interview.* Hiring manager alone with candidate.

- *Panel interview.* Candidate faces more than one interviewer simultaneously.

- *Hierarchical interviews.* Candidate who passes interview with a lower-level manager is interviewed by the next higher-level manager with the possibility of being rejected at a succeeding level.

- *Peer interview.* Candidate is interviewed by his or her potential work peers. A variation is interviewing by persons who would be interacting with the candidate after hiring (for example, internal customers, suppliers, external officials, and so on).

- *Group interview.* Candidate is placed in a group with other candidates (often subjected to a series of scenarios) and required to respond to questions from several interviewers and interact with other candidates. In this competitive environment, candidates are evaluated against various criteria (for example, interpersonal skills, assertiveness, stress level, use of prior knowledge, adaptability, and so on).

The manager's responsibility is to collaborate with HR during the hiring process on the following matters:

- Determining the terms of the employment offer

- Obtaining necessary approvals for making the employment offer

- Negotiating terms with the candidate, if necessary

- Preparing for the new hire to enter the organization

  — Preparing coworkers

  — Preparing the workplace

  — Preparing an agenda for assimilation and training

  — Preparing informational materials the new employee will need

- Onboarding/New Employee Orientation (NEO)

New Employee Assimilation. A person is usually highly motivated upon reporting for a new job. It is what is done to the individual after hiring that increases or diminishes motivation. It is up to the manager to:

- Tell the new employee what performance is expected and how and when the employee's performance will be evaluated

- Provide any needed skills training and/or education the new employee will need to succeed

- Coach the employee as she or he develops the competency to perform the work assigned

- Provide effective performance feedback to enable the employee to correct and/or improve performance

- Support and recognize work done well

- Support the employee's self-development

Employee Development. The objective of employee development is to improve employees' performance in their current positions as well as to prepare them for future roles or positions. Successful companies recognize the importance of the continuous professional development of employees, as evidenced by the number of companies who operate corporate universities.

The need for professional development is closely linked to the organization's goals and objectives, the individual employee's goals and objectives, and the organization's current performance. Employee development should include the active involvement of both the employee and the manager, with a focus on individual and business performance. Opportunities for development are often identified during the performance evaluation process.

In order to keep professional development aligned with business needs, it is important that everyone know where the business is headed (for example, mission and strategy) and what skills will be needed in the future. The personal interests of each employee should be taken into account as well. Management must be cognizant of employees' skills and abilities and be able to ascertain whether these skills and abilities are sufficient for meeting the organization's current or future needs. Timely plans can then be created to define skills to be developed, explain how this will be done, and ensure the provision of adequate resources.

The quality manager has two primary responsibilities regarding professional development. The first is to ensure that the skills being developed throughout the organization include those that will allow other functions to perform their duties well. Another is to develop the personnel within the quality department. The ASQ's certification programs and professional development courses are valuable resources for developing quality-related skills.

In earlier times, development of individuals was considered to be a responsibility of employers. During those times, managers led employees in formulating career development plans. Organizations published career ladders and steps individuals should take to broaden their knowledge and skills for growth and development. This effort was not universally successful. It became more apparent that the real responsibility for development rested with individuals, not their bosses. Now, and especially with a more mobile, transient workforce, personal development is the individual's responsibility, sometimes with some resources and support from their employer.

Figure 8.6 is a model showing the mutual investment made by the organization and the individual leading to the individual's growth and personal development. The inner circle suggests what the newly hired individual brings to the workplace—for example, work and life experience, education, capabilities, and aspirations (each individual is different, as characterized by the unique symbol). Some combination of the options, shown in the center ring, affect growth and development of the individual over time—for example, assignments, feedback, exposure to experts, training and education, and so on. As time passes, and the individual continues to grow and develop, certain career enhancements occur—for example, advancement, more money, enriched self-esteem, and so on. The organization's investment is suggested by the factors outside the concentric circles, which fuel the development.

In summary, *development* is an all-encompassing term embracing much more than education and training. Inasmuch as managers cannot actually motivate an individual but can provide an environment in which an individual feels motivated, so, too, a manager cannot actually develop an individual but can provide opportunities and resources by which the individual, assuming a desire to do so, can grow and develop.

Performance Evaluation. Accurately evaluating staff performance is part of the continual improvement of an organization. Performance evaluation involves reviewing performance against expectations, identifying strengths and weaknesses, and creating an improvement plan. Performance evaluations are also considered for promotion and salary decisions and as input into disciplinary actions.

To be fair, performance evaluations must be continual, fact based, and founded on clear, established, and communicated expectations. They must result in the identification of areas where work is done well and areas for improvement and/ or corrective action. Performance evaluations should evaluate only areas deemed to be important since they will lose credibility if they focus on trivial matters.

Performance evaluations usually involve scoring the individual's performance against predefined criteria (for example, goals and objectives) and often include narrative comments. Common problems with performance evaluations are that ratings are either forced into a normal distribution or everyone is rated

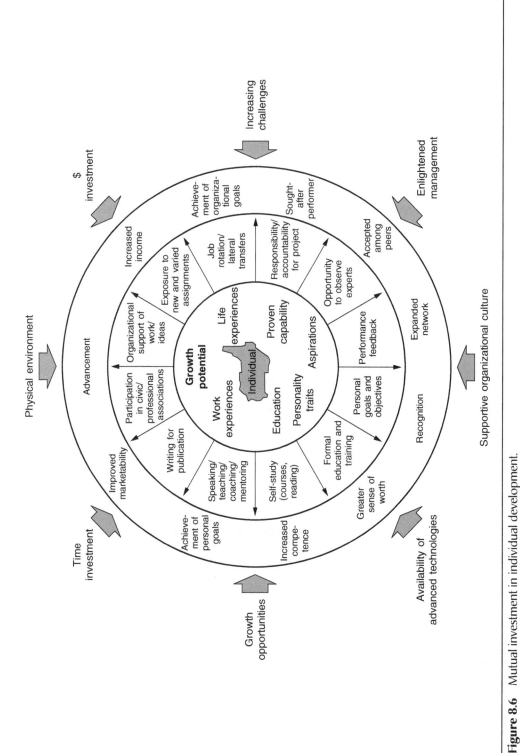

Figure 8.6 Mutual investment in individual development.

Source: Reprinted with permission of R. T. Westcott, *Stepping Up to ISO 9004:2000: A Practical Guide for Creating a World–Class Organization* (Chico, CA: Paton Press, 2003).

about the same. An additional source of information for evaluation is a record of critical incidents maintained by the manager, created at the time of applicable incidents. This involves reviewing a log of behaviors (good or bad) that the employee used when facing a significant or difficult situation. Critical incidents that will be logged should also be communicated on a more immediate basis in order to provide the employee with feedback for continual improvement or corrective action.

A more recent development in performance evaluation is the involvement of more than the manager and the employee. Known as *360° feedback*, this method solicits feedback from peers, subordinates, and internal and external customers.

A fair performance appraisal system exists when it allows for interaction between manager and employee and the following criteria are met:

- Expectations are clear and guidelines are established.

- The format (structure, time, place, and protocol) for the evaluation is consistent, with periodic meetings.

- Notes of performance, both good and bad, are discussed and recorded.

- Just-in-time training or coaching or both are used when work performance or behaviors are not appropriate.

- Disciplinary action rarely occurs as a result of the appraisal; however, if it does, an appeals process should be readily available.

- Assessments should consider consistency of output, presence of favorable or unfavorable environmental conditions, the ability to do a better job, the use of discretion (within limits), and the ability to work as part of a team.

- The evaluation should express whether the person grasps the quality aspects of the job and to what degree expectations were met.

Following are some problems that occur when a performance evaluation process is poorly managed:

- When appraisal is not done on a continuous or frequent basis, the performance review will result in some employees receiving unfair evaluation because of inaccuracies. Infrequent appraisals also fail to allow employees to rectify deficient performance in a timely manner.

- Annual reviews might be conducted late and done as a routine action to satisfy the higher-ups in the organization.

- Managers are not trained to give or receive feedback.

Experienced persons have expressed concerns about the use of performance appraisal systems. Deming stated that because the individual is part of a system, it is impossible to differentiate between the contributions of the individual versus the contributions of the system to the resulting performance.

An important role of the quality manager in the performance evaluation process is to ensure that the criteria used for evaluating personnel include measures related to product and organizational quality. Thoughtful and continual appraisal can help keep employees aligned with the mission of the organization.

Competency Analysis. Unlike job analysis, which is focused on the tasks contained within a job and the knowledge and skills required, a competency analysis focuses on the competencies of individuals performing the job. The five factors of competence—*knowledge, experience, skills, aptitude,* and *attitude* (KESAA) shows a KESAA requisites analysis form for collecting data.

Some of the reasons for conducting a competency analysis include gathering input to:

- Establish a job's level within a hierarchy of job levels and, as such, contribute to a determination of the compensation level of a job

- Determine the exemplary performer in a work unit performing similar tasks for the purpose of setting or modifying performance standards

- Help in selecting the members of a team

- Augment the job description with competency criteria

- Assess feasibility of job enlargement, job enrichment, and empowerment

- Help to establish the specifications for a new hire

- Conduct a competency gap analysis (desired versus present)

- Set objectives for improving competency

- Determine and articulate the organization's core competency

Staffing the Quality Function. Depending on the size of the organization, division- or corporate-level quality directors/managers could be involved in defining new strategic initiatives, integrating and standardizing quality methods across the organization, and transferring new technologies. They will often provide policy input to the operation-level quality function but might not actually have a staff reporting to them.

The range of quality activities within an organization is large and somewhat dependent on the industry; however, following is a list of typical job titles and activities within the quality function:

- *Vice president of quality.* Establishes the direction for the development and administration of the organization's quality initiatives. Consults with peers on the attitudes toward and practices of quality throughout the organization to develop an environment of continual improvement in every aspect of the organization's products and services. Acts as a champion for quality.

- *Director of quality.* Coordinates all aspects of the organization's quality program, such as developing and administering the program, training, coaching employees, and facilitating change throughout the organization. Responsible for participating in the establishment of strategic plans and policies, as well as procedures at all levels to ensure that the quality program will meet or exceed internal and external customers' needs and expectations.

- *Quality manager.* Ensures the administration of the organization's quality program within a defined segment of the organization.

- *Quality control engineer.* Designs, installs, and evaluates quality process sampling systems, procedures, and statistical techniques. Designs or specifies inspection and testing mechanisms and equipment, analyzes production and service limitations and standards, and recommends revision of specifications when indicated. Formulates or helps formulate quality procedures and plans, conducts training on quality concepts and tools, and interfaces with all other engineering components within the company and with customers and suppliers on quality-related issues.

- *Quality specialist.* As their primary assignment, performs a specific quality-related function within the company's quality program (for example, quality training, auditing, or reliability testing). Has either received direct training or has been performing the activity for a number of years. Shows a high degree of skill performing the activity.

- *Quality supervisor.* Administers the company's quality program within a defined function of the organization. Has direct reports that implement some aspect of the policies, procedures, and processes of the quality program.

- *Quality assurance engineer.* Works with the supply chain to maintain conformance and resolve issues; applies preventive methodology such as Advanced Product Quality Planning (APQP) or failure mode and effects analysis (FMEA).

- *Reliability engineer.* Assesses products and systems to identify and manage asset reliability risks that could adversely affect plant or business operations.

- *Quality analyst.* Initiates and/or coordinates quality-related data collection from production and service activities and interprets and reports these data using statistical techniques.

- *Quality coordinator.* Collects, organizes, monitors, and distributes any information related to the functions of the quality department. Might also communicate information on the latest standards, procedures, and requirements related to the company's products or services. Typically generates reports using computer skills and distributes these reports to various users in the organization, customers, or suppliers.

- *Quality technician.* Performs basic quality techniques to track, analyze, and report on materials, processes, and products to ensure they meet the organization's quality standards. Might calibrate tools and equipment.

- *Quality inspector.* Inspects and reports on materials, processes, and products using variable- or attribute-measuring instruments and techniques to ensure conformance with the organization's and customers' quality specifications.

- *Quality auditor.* Conducts system, process, product, and/or supplier audits of conformance to the organization's quality standards, customers' standards, and/or standards of a third party.

- *Quality trainer.* Designs and conducts quality training programs and/or instructs quality modules of wider-scope training programs. Consults with the organization's training function on the inclusion of quality content in other pertinent training programs. Designs and instructs a quality-related train-the-trainer program for personnel who will be instructing in quality programs.

5. FINANCIAL MANAGEMENT

> Read, interpret, and use various finance tools including income statements, balance sheets, and product/service cost structures. Manage budgets and use the language of cost and profitability to communicate with senior management. Use potential return on investment (ROI), estimated return on assets (ROA), net present value (NPV), internal rate of return (IRR), and portfolio analysis to analyze project risk, feasibility, and priority. (Analyze)
>
> **Body of Knowledge III.A.5**

Speak the Language of Management

Increasingly, today's quality professional realizes there is a need to speak the language of management—finance. Whether it is participating in the strategic planning process, seeking approval for a process improvement project, justifying a quality management system implementation and certification, or preparing for a Baldrige-type award—approval and support is mainly based on financial outcomes.

ASQ has mounted an effort to assist quality practitioners in developing an "economic case for quality." Many trade journals, representing a wide variety of industries, are urging their industry members to create an economic case for their activities.

Even past attempts to justify expenditures solely through a simple return on investment (ROI) have often failed because the proposal does not relate the request to the organization's bigger picture. For example, a quality manager seeking approval for a major process improvement effort may, considered alone, estimate a reasonable ROI. The proposed initiative, however, may be more than the organization can currently fund based on its financial health, or other strategic matters require the organization's more immediate attention and resources.

Learn some of the terms and tools of finance from guidance offered here and from suggested readings. Invest some time to get acquainted with the financial status of your own organization and the issues management considers important from a financial perspective. Importantly, determine where *quality* fits into the big picture and what it will take to link the measures of quality with the financial measures. Learn what "sells" to upper management and how to approach them.

Financial Reporting

Basic Statements. There are three basic financial statements. They are (1) the *balance sheet*, (2) the *profit and loss* or *income statement*, and (3) the *statement of cash flow*. These three are considered the required statements under the *generally accepted accounting principles* (GAAP) guidelines. The Securities and Exchange Commission (SEC) requires a statement of shareholder's equity in addition to the basic three.

Depending on the industry, size, and complexity of the organizational structure and special requirements dictated by governmental entities, industry norms, and accounting practices, there may be a number of related reports prepared. For example, one public utility company prepares:

- Consolidated reports and reports for each subsidiary
- Variance reports comparing figures from several past periods with the current period
- Cash flow comparisons
- Capital requirements, past and projected
- Sales and deliveries by business segment and by type of product/service
- Statement of shareholder's equity
- Statement of changes in net assets
- Statement of expenses by function
- Long-term debt comparisons
- Operating statistics—year-to-year comparison over five years

Bookkeeping Methods. There are two basic methods for bookkeeping: the *cash basis* and the *accrual basis*. The *cash basis* is simplistic: income is considered earned only when payment is actually received. Expenses are booked only when actually paid for. The cash basis is used by small organizations (small in physical size and small in the magnitude of transaction dollar amounts). The cash basis is simple, but from a control perspective, the revenues and expenses can mislead the decision-maker because of the time gap between an action taken and when money is disbursed or collected.

Using the *accrual basis*, income is considered earned when goods or services have been sold or performed and an invoice is created, although payment may not have been received. Expenses are booked as soon as a bill is received from a vendor, although they may not have been paid for.

The intent of the accrual basis is to be able to measure the results of operations by allocating to each period the income associated with operations of that period and all expenses and losses associated with the income of that period. This approach more accurately relates costs with income. The majority of organizations use the accrual method.

Many organizations prepare two types of financial statements: internal statements and external statements. *Internal statements* are produced at a macrolevel for management oversight and decision-making. These statements present information about the whole organization. Microlevel reports are used at department level or below and are oriented to operations, production, use of resources, and so on. *External statements* are prepared for disclosure to the SEC, lending institutions, investor-owners, the public, and other interested entities (depending on the organization's status as for-profit or not-for-profit). External documents are used by third-party auditors and accountants.

The Sarbanes-Oxley Act of 2002 (SOX),[13] enacted after a series of financial scandals, mandates strict requirements for financial accounting and for top management's responsibility and accountability in disclosing the financial status of their organization.

The Balance Sheet. A *balance sheet* shows the assets, liabilities, and owner's equity. See Figure 8.7. It is so named because it conforms to the formula:

$$\text{Assets} = \text{Liabilities} + \text{Owner's equity}$$

The balance sheet components typically are:

Company LMN
Consolidated Balance Sheet
December 31, XXXX
(In thousands of dollars)

Assets

Current assets

Cash	$ 20,178
Short-term investments	5,160
Accounts receivable (less allowance)	9,912
Inventories	33,428
Prepaid insurance expenses	966
Total current assets	69,644
Property and plant	55,113
Equipment, furniture, fixtures	99,875
Total property, plant, equipment	154,988
Less reserve for depreciation	53,288
Net property, plant, equipment	101,700
Goodwill	2,546
Total assets	173,890

Liabilities and owners' equity

Current liabilities

Accounts payable	$ 14,521
Dividends payable	1,085
Accrued wages and taxes	11,745
Federal, state taxes	5,639
Total current liabilities	32,990
Deferred income taxes	13,112
Long-term debt	31,524

Owners' equity

Preferred stock ($50 par value, 500,000 shares authorized)	
Common stock ($2 par value, 40,000,000 shares)	20,400
Retained earnings	75,864
Total owners' equity	96,264
Total liabilities and owners' equity	$173,890

Figure 8.7   Sample balance sheet.

- *Current assets.* Included are cash, short-term investments, accounts receivable (reduced by an amount for potential uncollectible accounts), inventory, and prepaid expenses. These assets are convertible to cash within a year. Adding the amounts for cash, short-term investments, and accounts receivable constitutes *quick assets.* Inventory may be valued by two common accounting methods: last in, first out (LIFO) or first in, first out (FIFO). LIFO would be used for materials that are usually stored loosely in piles (for example, sand and gravel). FIFO reflects the way inventory is typically used.

- *Property, plant, and equipment.* Such items are valued at *book value* (cost of acquisition) less applicable accumulated depreciation for the life of the asset.

- *Goodwill and other intangible assets.* This figure may represent the variance resulting from one company buying another for more money than the acquired company's net worth. Goodwill is usually amortized (decreased, written off) over some time period.

Total assets is one key determinant of an organization's size. Another is sales (reported in the income statement).

- *Current liabilities.* This figure represents liabilities that must be paid within a year. Included are accounts payable, dividends payable, accrued wages, and taxes. Current assets minus current liabilities = working capital (funds for current operating purposes).

- *Deferred income taxes and long-term debt.* These figures comprise amortization of investment tax credits over the life of the asset and debts that will be payable after twelve months, mortgages beyond the next year, long-term promissory notes, and bonds.

- *Owner's equity.* This amount consists of what the owners (stockholders) have invested plus any profits returned to the organization in lieu of paying dividends. Owners'/stockholders' equity may be called *net worth* or *book value.* Therefore, what the business owns (assets) equals the amounts owed creditors plus the claim (equity) owners have on the business.

The Profit and Loss (or Income Statement). The *income statement* shows sales, costs, expenses, and profits for a given period of time—for example, a quarter or a year. See Figure 8.8. The components of an income statement are:

- *Net sales.* This figure represents the organization's *gross* income from the sales of products and services (revenue in not-for-profit organizations). When all costs and expenses are deducted from net sales, a profit or loss results.

- *Cost of goods sold.* This figure shows the cost of all the products that were sold during the accounting period represented by the statement.

- *Selling and administrative expenses.* Often itemized, these figures show what the organization spent to sell the products and operate the organization.

- *Reserve for depreciation.* This figure represents an amount set aside to amortize the cost of assets over the lifetime of the assets. This reserve is depleted as depreciation is written off.

Company LMN
Consolidated Income Statement
December 31, XXXX
(In thousands of dollars, excepting per-share amount)

Net sales	$289,321
Costs and expenses	
Cost of goods sold	178,428
Selling and administrative expenses	55,743
Reserve for depreciation	7,725
Interest income	(1,335)
Total costs and expenses	240,561
Income before income taxes	48,760
Provision for income taxes	
Federal	12,856
State	2,865
Deferred	3,200
Total income taxes	18,921
Net income	$ 29,839
Net income per share	$ 1.46

Figure 8.8 Sample income statement.

- *Interest income.* This amount is the net interest earned on investments for the statement period. This other income is a deduction from expenses.

- *Total costs and expenses.* This amount is deducted from net sales to show *income* before income taxes. Income taxes are then deducted to arrive at either a *net profit* or a *net loss.*

- *Net income per share.* Net income divided by the dollar value of shares (taken from the balance sheet) results in net income per share.

Cash Flow Statement. The *cash flow statement* shows the incoming flow of cash and the outgoing flow of cash for the reporting period. The purpose of the statement is to make a determination as to whether the organization requires external financing or if the cash flow is sufficient to meet debt obligations and dividend payments. The statement often breaks down the organization's cash flow into three categories—for example:

- Cash related to operations

  — Net income

  — Depreciation and amortization

  — Deferred taxes and wages

  — Net change in accounts payable

- — Net change in accounts receivable
- — Net change in inventory
- Cash related to investing activity
  - — Capital expenditures
  - — Proceeds from sale of property
- Cash related to financing activity
  - — Increase in notes payable
  - — Repayment of debt
  - — Increase in common stock
  - — Payment of dividends
- Net increase in cash and cash equivalents
- Cash and cash equivalents at beginning of year
- Cash and cash equivalents at end of reporting period

The benefits of using a cash flow statement are:

- It records the actual cash generated at a given point in time.
- It offers more detail than the balance sheet.
- It indicates the quality of the organization's earnings, the cash backing up the earnings, and the organization's capability to pay interest and dividends.

Caution: The organization's cash flow statement should not be confused with cash flow reports for projects. Project cash flows typically spread the outlay of cash across the time period of the project—for example, expenditures made in each month by category of expenditure. Such statements for projects usually do not involve incoming cash.

Notes on Financial Statements. Most financial statements will show notes clarifying statement entries or describing important events or transactions. Notes should always be read. Examples of contents of notes are:

- Detailed costs of major capital expenditures, acquisitions, or initiatives
- Structural changes in the organization or operations
- Pending litigation
- Obligations for pensions
- Special contracts or transactions

Measures—Ratios

Ratios are used for several purposes. Investors and lenders use this tool to evaluate the viability of an organization before investing. Buyers and sellers use ratios as a means for establishing a fair price. Management uses ratios as a metric for assessing organizational performance and as a basis for determining incentive compensation amounts.

There can be four categories of ratios:

- Ratios that view an organization's liquidity and overall financial condition—derived from the balance sheet.

- Ratios that provide insight as to the organization's operations—derived from the income statement.

- Ratios that interrelate information from the balance sheet, the income statement, and other reports (for example, source and usage of funds to show how effectively the organization is using its resources).

- Other ratios compiled from reports other than those just mentioned. These ratios are derived from internal operating reports. They may help to analyze workforce utilization, cycle time, and industry-specific comparisons.

Ratios Derived from the Balance Sheet. These ratios are used to analyze the liquidity and financial health of the organization:

- *Current ratio*

$$\text{Current ratio} = \frac{\text{Current assets}}{\text{Current liabilities}}$$

Commonly, the current ratio should be 2.0 or greater to indicate that liquidity is not a problem.

- *Debt/equity ratio*

$$\text{Percentage debt} = \frac{\text{Total long-term debt}}{\text{Total long-term debt} + \text{Total owner's equity}}$$

$$\text{Percentage equity} = \frac{\text{Total owner's equity}}{\text{Total long-term debt} + \text{Total owner's equity}}$$

A capability to borrow additional long-term funds is critical to the organization's financial health. The larger the percentage of total capital that is reflected in existing borrowings, the more difficult it is to borrow more. The debt/equity ratio differs by industry; however, lenders universally feel that the greater the amount of owners' money that is invested in the organization, the lower the credit risk.

Ratios Derived from the Income Statement. These ratios are used to analyze the operations of the organization. *Gross profit* is the profit less the cost of goods sold (by a merchandising or manufacturing organization).

$$\text{Gross profit margin} = \frac{\text{Gross profit}}{\text{Net sales}}$$

A period-to-period trend analysis examines the movement of this ratio over time. Care must be taken when comparing this ratio with other organizations that what is included in the totals is comparable between the two organizations.

Cost of goods sold is another useful figure. The following example demonstrates how to determine it.

(thousands of dollars)		
	Inventory, January 1, XXXX	29,566
	Purchases	181,928
	Incoming freight	747
		212,241
	Less returns and allowance	385
		211,856
	Less inventory, December 31, XXXX	33,428
	Cost of goods sold	178,428

Interstatement Ratios. *Inventory turnover* represents the rate at which the organization sells its inventory.

$$\text{Inventory turnover} = \frac{\text{Cost of goods sold}}{\text{Average inventory}}$$

The higher the number of inventory turns, the lower the amount of cash required on hand. This means less borrowing for working capital and more available to invest to earn interest. Also, faster inventory turnover means less of a problem with nonsalable product. Many industries have recorded typical inventory turns for the industry.

The sooner an organization collects receivables due, the lower the amount invested in accounts receivable and the lesser the chance of bad debts.

$$\text{Days receivables outstanding} = \frac{\text{Average accounts receivable}}{\text{Net sales}} \times 365$$

$$\text{Average receivables} = \frac{\text{Opening plus closing balances}}{2}$$

The longer the period, the more a creditor's money is being used and less of the organization's funds.

$$\text{Days payables outstanding} = \frac{\text{Average accounts payable}}{\text{Cost of sales}} \times 365$$

To support increased sales, total accounts receivable outstanding and inventory tend to increase. Additional working capital is needed to increase sales.

$$\text{Working capital/dollar of sales} = \frac{\text{Average working capital}}{\text{Net sales}}$$

Average working capital = Average current assets – Average current liabilities

If the organization plans to increase sales volume (by an advertising campaign, hiring additional salespersons, and so on), the amount of additional working capital required by that sales growth must be determined.

ROI is the dollar benefit generated by an investment divided by the amount of the investment. This ratio is frequently used to justify a proposed project or quality initiative or in demonstrating the financial outcome of a project or initiative.

$$\text{ROI} = \frac{\text{Net dollar benefit}}{\text{Investment (Net costs)}} = \frac{\$675,000}{\$109,700} = \$6.15$$

$6.15 is returned for every $1.00 invested.

For example, net dollar benefit may consist of cycle time reductions, process improvements, productivity improvement, cost reductions, and so on.

There are some things to remember with ROI:

1. ROI and *benefits to cost analysis* may, depending on the figures used, produce the same ratio.

2. This computation does not consider the time value of money (money available now is worth more than the same amount in the future because of the potential earnings from using the money).

3. Net dollar benefit may be difficult to identify accurately for a specific project because of other influencing factors or ongoing initiatives.

Return on assets (ROA) is a measure of the return generated by the earning power of the organization's investment in assets. ROA is calculated by dividing net income by dollar value of tangible total assets. This ratio is used when there is a substantial capital investment to be made in physical assets. Things to remember with ROA include:

1. Net income may be difficult to isolate for a particular asset.

2. Payment for the asset usually spans several years and has an impact on cash flow.

3. During the time in which the asset is being paid for, the interest rates may fluctuate.

4. The computation does not consider the time value of money (money available now is worth more than the same amount in the future because of the potential earnings from using the money).

Other Ratios. A wide range of ratios have been developed for specific industry sectors and purposes. Examples of a few of these ratios are:

- Number of units accepted/number of units inspected
- Customer-accepted lots/lots shipped
- Warranty repair costs/sales
- Cost of quality/cost of sales
- Profit before income tax/number of employees
- Number of defectives/number of units inspected
- Cost to prepare drawings/number of drawings produced
- Number of engineering change orders/number of drawings

- Project overrun cost/total project cost
- Total operations personnel/customer service personnel
- Satisfied employees/total employees
- Information technology (IT) hardware uptime/total IT hardware operating time available
- Jobs completed/jobs scheduled
- Prevention costs/total cost of quality
- Nonproductive time/total time available

Product/Service Cost Structures

The traditional standard cost model is:

Product cost = direct material costs + direct labor costs + overhead costs

Different organizations use different methods for booking costs. For example:

- *Undifferentiated costs*—those costs known or assumed to be associated with producing the product or rendering the service. There is no categorization by cause or type of product or service.
- Costs allocated by a percentage of direct labor dollars or some other arbitrary factor such as amount of space occupied, number of personnel in work unit, and so on.
- *Categorized costs*—costs attributable to appraisal, prevention, or failure.
- Costs of materials and services allocated by the activity or process (cost drivers) by which they are consumed.

Traditional cost accounting practice involves computing the sum of all costs from the work unit accounts that have been identified as a part of the direct cost of goods, then adding to this sum the indirect expenses (utilities, space allocation dollars, cleaning and maintenance, and so on). In contrast, *activity-based costing* (ABC) uses a unique assembly of all the components of cost pertinent to each product or service. The ABC approach provides a much more accurate depiction of what it really costs to produce each type of product or service. Some organizations that use ABC curtailed or discontinued production of some of their products once the more realistic cost to manufacture became known.

Activity-based management (ABM) incorporates ABC as its data source. ABC is historical, whereas ABM is more proactive—what are the causes of the cost?

Budgets

Budgeting in larger organizations is an iterative process. As a result of the strategic planning process, a macrolevel estimated budget is prepared. Typically, this budget will identify a total of all projected income and expenses for operating the organization for the budgeted period. Operating units then prepare a tentative budget based on their estimated operating needs to meet the strategic plans. The operating budget numbers for all operating units are summed and compared with the top-level target budget. Depending on the organization's culture and practices, either negotiation or mandates occur to reconcile the operating budgets to the overall target budget. This usually involves several passes up and down the organization until agreement is reached. Sometimes, the top-level budget may be modified, but usually it is the operating units' budgets that will undergo change.

Once a budget is approved, the operating units manage their operations to attempt to stay in line with the approved budget. This balancing act requires continual monitoring and analysis of interim results, trade-off actions, and occasionally a request to approve an overrun due to a special occurrence. Measures to link budgets with strategic goals and objectives cascade throughout the organization.

The spreadsheet is the basic tool of the manager in managing his or her budget. The budget for most operating units will include an itemization of all planned expenses spread over the time periods in which the expenditures are anticipated. An income budget is not usually the concern of most operating units.

Managers' concerns include fears that:

- Not spending up to the allowed budget will result in a lower budget being approved for a subsequent period.

- Overspending the allowed budget will result in a poor performance rating and future curtailments to make up for the overrun.

- Concern for making budget may negatively affect customer satisfaction, employee satisfaction, and process and performance improvement initiatives.

- Concerns for financial performance will overshadow pertinent nonfinancial measures that are critical for decision-making.

Balanced Scorecard

The basic financial accounting model and reports are based on past events. The balanced scorecard was developed from a need for a measurement tool that includes both leading and lagging indicators.[14] The basic model contains four high-level groups of measures, from a financial perspective, customer perspective, internal business process perspective, and learning and growth perspective. The concept of the balanced scorecard can be adapted to any organization and to functions within an organization. By carefully selecting the key measures in each segment of the scorecard, management can more intelligently and confidently make critical decisions affecting the outcomes of the organization.

Communicating with Senior Management

While the quality professional may be driven by her or his needs to improve quality, customer satisfaction, and processes, senior managers react to an overarching need to show profitability during their time in office. Profitability not only pertains to satisfying the owners of the organization but also sustains the organization's growth and competitive position in the marketplace. Profitability is also the basis for senior managers' performance ratings and, often, their compensation.

Senior managers will tell those lower in the organization that "if we don't make money, we will all be out of a job."

An ASQ-sponsored survey revealed that a vast majority of American executives believe that quality has an impact on the bottom line. "Selling" quality initiatives and projects to management means:

- Calculating the risks and benefits involved

- Collecting and analyzing all the pertinent data derived from financial analysis, competitive analysis, benchmarking, and so on

- Crafting a salable picture of the benefits to the organization and to the executives who must approve the initiative

- Doing the homework before presenting the final proposal:

  — Soliciting critique and advice from key people in the organization who have or will have a stake in the outcome of the proposed quality initiative

  — Presenting a draft of the proposal to the people who furnished advice, with evidence that the proposal reflects their suggestions

  — Winning support from as many members of top management as feasible

- Presenting the proposal for approval, with the support of the people who participated in its preview

When seeking executive approval for a project or capital expenditure, think and talk the language of finance. It is imperative that quality professionals learn how to convert their requests and needs to financial performance language to achieve buy-in.

ASQ has embraced the concept of developing an "economic case for quality." ASQ provides tools and guidelines for quality professionals to use to sell the case for quality within their organizations. This trend is evidenced by the growing number of articles in a wide range of industry publications espousing the need to develop an "economic case for [insert industry name or function]."

6. RISK MANAGEMENT

> Identify the kinds of risk that can occur throughout the organization, from such diverse processes as scheduling, shipping/receiving, financials, production and operations, employee and user safety, regulatory compliance, and changes. (Apply)
>
> **Body of Knowledge III.A.6**

Types of Risks

Most everyone realizes that risk is present in our personal lives as well as in the organizations in which we work. Risks faced by organizations are:

- Events ranging from those causing minor disruption to those catastrophic events that affect the organization regardless of its location, financial stability, and so on

- Events that can affect each organization differently; a minor disruption to one organization can be a major disaster for another

A risk that becomes a negative event can seriously disrupt an organization's processes and make it unable to meet customers' requirements. Identifying and planning for potential risks is critical in the pursuit of customer satisfaction, organizational stability, and profitability, especially under adverse conditions such as market competition or economic recession.

Table 8.1 lists examples of risks that could affect an organization. This is not an exhaustive list. The proactive organization, regardless of size, makes an

Table 8.1 Types and forms of risks that could affect an organization.

Enterprise-level risks	• Poor quality, reliability
• Legal action	• Product/service obsolescence
• Noncompliance with regulatory requirements	• High rates of returns
• Environmental violations, such as oil spills	• High warrantee claims
• Financial investments	
• Significant marketplace shifts	**Operational process risks**
• Trade sanctions against foreign countries	• Order fulfillment errors
• New competitors	• Supplier errors
• Customer nonpayments	• Nondelivery of supplier products/services
• Civil unrest, terrorist attacks	• Poor planning
• Cyberattacks, computer hacking	• Lack of skilled employees
• Unexpected death or departure of key leaders	• Noncompliance with operational procedures
• Unauthorized release of corporate information	• Raw material defects
• Unsolicited takeover attempts	• Errors and omissions
	• Vandalism
Product/service risks	• Accidents, employee injuries
• Product/service is not suitable for intended market	• Inadequate operational controls
• Product/service does not meet regulatory requirements	• Inattention to warning signals from controls
• Product safety risks, injury to users	

assessment of the potential risks to which it is exposed and establishes feasible means to prevent or lessen their impacts.

Most often, quality professionals are called upon to identify and manage operational risks, rather than enterprise-level risks.

The Definition of Risk

Among quality professionals, there are two related definitions of risk. ISO 9000:2015, *Quality Management Systems—Fundamentals and Vocabulary*, defines risk as the "effect of uncertainty."[15] ISO 31000:2009, *Risk Management—Principles and Guidelines*, defines risk similarly as the "effect of uncertainty on objectives."[16] The element of uncertainty is central to the whole concept of risk and risk management. Risks are events or circumstances that may or may not occur. Uncertainty can result in both negative and positive outcomes. A positive risk outcome could be winning a lottery. The outcome is uncertain and would definitely have a positive effect on your life. For the purposes of this treatment, though, and the practical application by quality professionals, we will only consider the negative consequences of risk. That is, risks yield negative results on your objectives.

Since risks may or may not occur, analysis is required to determine which risks need mitigation and which can be accepted to manifest themselves naturally. The decision to accept a risk or to take mitigation actions involves two factors: the impact or severity of the event, were it to occur, and the probability of the occurrence of the event. Intuitively, this makes sense: An event that will have very little impact on you and is likely to never happen does not deserve a lot of thought. On the other hand, a highly impactful negative event that is almost certain to occur deserves a high level of consideration and the implementation of actions to avoid the event, minimize its impact, et cetera.

ISO 31000 and the Risk Management Process

It is important to consider those events that may occur and think of those in terms of how bad they would be if they happened (impact) and how likely they are to occur (likelihood). The impact of events may be very well understood, but determining likelihood is probabilistic and could involve statistical models.

According to ISO 31000, "All activities of an organization involve risk. Organizations manage risk by identifying it, analyzing it and then evaluating whether the risk should be modified by risk treatment in order to satisfy their risk criteria. Throughout this process, they communicate and consult with stakeholders and monitor and review the risk and the controls that are modifying the risk in order to ensure that no further risk treatment is required."[17] ISO 31000 is a standard to govern risk management, which it defines as "coordinated activities to direct and control an organization with regards to risk."[18]

When undertaking risk management, the first step is to understand and take into account the *context of the organization*. That context includes the following:

- The business(es) of the organization

- The nature of products/services provided

- The market climate, including domestic regulations and politics

- Social attitudes and norms of your society and foreign markets
- Demographic makeup of the workforce
- Ownership structure (a small family business or multinational corporation)
- Company culture
- Relationships with suppliers and partners
- The level of technology and speed of change in your marketplace

Managing risk within the proper context is the most important consideration for deciding an appropriate course of action. The risk of going to work tired is much different for someone working in a coffee shop than for an airline pilot or a heart surgeon.

Identification within Operational Processes

ISO 9001:2015 introduces the concept of risk-based thinking.[19] Risk-based thinking does not require the discipline or the rigor of risk management as described in ISO 31000 but rather provides an approach to considering risks as the basis for the implementation of appropriate levels of management control. Risk-based thinking is considered a preventive tool and as such requires that one think about risks during the design of business processes within a quality management system. Risk-based thinking is anticipatory: think about those things that can go wrong, how bad they would be, and how likely they are to happen. Thinking of these things ahead of time and then deciding upon the appropriate level of control that needs to be put in place to deal with these risk events if they occur is suggested. These controls are imposed proactively, before a problem occurs. Note that the appropriate level of control may be zero—many risks are of such low importance that no controls need to be imposed, and we will simply live with the risks and deal with their consequences if they occur.[20]

When a business process is designed, the design team must consider the risks characteristic in that process and whether or not controls are required to be built into the process. When considering risk, the team is always interpreting adverse events and outcomes through the lens of the context of their organization. Risks are weighed according to two factors: how bad would it be if this happened (impact/severity/criticality/consequences) and how likely it is to happen (likelihood/probability). Many risk assessment techniques, such as FMEA, use numerical rankings to quantify the level of severity and probability in order to create a prioritized listing for control and mitigation.

The first step is to generate a comprehensive list of risks for the process being assessed. The list can be derived from historical data such as incident reports, customer complaints, past corrective actions, et cetera, or can be brainstormed by a team of people who are highly familiar with the process. For example, there are certain characteristics in the process of hiring new employees:[21]

- The requirements for the job may be poorly defined.
- The method of outreach and recruitment may not find the best candidates.
- The job market may be highly competitive, and candidates cannot be found.

- Candidates may not be truthful on their résumés.

- Candidates may not be truthful during their interviews.

- HR may not be able to competently interview candidates for highly specialized positions.

- Candidates may not be a good "fit" for the organization.

- New hires may leave for a better job soon after hire.

The next step is to determine the impact and likelihood of each risk. For example, how bad would it be if a candidate misrepresented himself on his résumé, and how likely is that to happen? How bad would it be if a new hire left after a short time to take another job, and how likely is that to happen?

The final step is to assess the level of risk and the need for control or mitigation. If there is a risk that new hires leave for another job and that would be damaging to the organization, it might be necessary to pay above-average salaries and provide work schedule flexibility and a variety of attractive fringe benefits.

Again, context is important. If one is going to visit a friend at her home for a leisurely visit, being on time is not very important, and if the weather is good, being late is not very likely. One does not have to worry about leaving early in such a case. On the other hand, if one must travel to the airport for an international flight and the weather is bad, leaving very early to prevent being late would be appropriate. The risk of being late to the airport is much higher than the risk of being late arriving to a friend's house.[22]

ISO 9001 requires that risks be identified and managed for each business process within their quality management system. The above risk assessment should be done for each process.[23]

From the point of view of plan-do-check-act (PDCA), one would *PLAN* the risk assessment process, *DO* the assessment for each process and implement the selected risk management controls, *CHECK* on the effectiveness of risk mitigation strategies by reviewing operational data, and finally *ACT* on those lessons learned to continuously improve the appropriateness and effectiveness of risk management controls.

Internal audits of a quality management system should also be employed to assess the effectiveness of risk-based thinking. Since risks should be used as the basis for designing process controls, an auditor should also review the appropriateness of process controls through the lens of risk, in order to assess the effectiveness of the processes and management systems under audit.[24]

Examples of Selected Risk Assessment Techniques

ISO 31000 has a companion document, ISO 31010—*Risk Assessment Techniques*,[25] which includes thirty-one risk assessment techniques. Below is a brief description of seven selected techniques:

Brainstorming. Brainstorming is a very simple and effective technique for leveraging the knowledge and experience of a group of people who are familiar with a product or process. In a brainstorming session, a facilitator guides a group discussion around a particular topic. Participants are encouraged to think creatively in order to uncover ideas that likely would not have been considered before. The facilitator guides the discussion, keeps things on track, and uses techniques to solicit responses from everyone in the group. One way to do this is to proceed around the room in a clockwise fashion and get responses from every single individual. This prevents the problem of participants talking over each other and reduces the risk that good ideas from shy people will be overlooked.

Brainstorming can be used to identify risks and then combined with other risk analysis tools to complete the assessment. For example, a list of risks can then be brought into an FMEA for a more in-depth treatment of the severity of the consequence, the likelihood it will happen, the suitability of current management controls, and the need for further process controls.

Hazard Analysis and Critical Control Points (HACCP). Those who work in the food industry will already be familiar with HACCP. This technique can also be applied to risk-based thinking in the context of the wider quality management system. An HACCP analysis identifies those factors and issues that can affect product quality and determines what process parameters at what points in the process influence those factors in order to put monitoring and control in place to prevent adverse events. Similar to the risk assessment techniques described in this lesson, HACCP begins with a flowchart of the process and identifies hazards or risks to the process at each step along the way. In the automotive industry, a control plan is very similar to a HACCP plan.

The HACCP analysis determines risks, understands at what point(s) in the process they can be controlled, establishes process parameters and limits for those process variables, then monitors and controls those parameters. Furthermore, the HACCP analysis defines reaction plans to be taken when parameters fall outside of their prescribed limits and initiates product containment and corrective actions when required.

An HACCP plan follows each step of the process and defines which hazards or risks could be introduced or need to be controlled at that step. The plan quantifies the level of the hazard or risk and specifies process controls if applicable. The plan also includes the reaction plan for an out-of-control condition that describes what steps are taken and by whom, based on the nature of the abnormality. Since HACCP is used in the food industry, there are often very rigorous record-keeping requirements associated with ongoing measurement, monitoring, and reaction to out-of-control conditions.

Structured "What-If" Technique (SWIFT). This technique is similar to brainstorming, where a learned group of individuals work together under the guidance of a facilitator. SWIFT uses a set of "prompt" words to solicit responses to a variety of "what-if" scenarios. The purpose of this technique is to determine all of the ways that a system could fail, along with their associated outcomes.

The process must be mature, or at least well defined, in order for the SWIFT technique to be effective. The facilitator becomes familiar with the system under study in order to create an appropriate set of prompt words. Once the preparatory work has been done, the team convenes to perform the analysis. Like in brainstorming, it is essential that participants in the group have a high level of knowledge and experience with the process under review. Often, the group includes members of upstream (supplier) processes and downstream (customer) processes in order to fully investigate the impacts of a failure upstream and downstream of the process.

Once the list of prompt words is created (these could follow the Ishikawa diagram's 5Ms, etc.), the facilitator asks a series of questions, such as:

- "What if our machine breaks down for two hours?"
- "What if we run out of raw materials?"
- "What if the surgical nurse is absent for his shift?"
- "What if our restaurant customer is not happy with her meal?"
- "What if our bank customer slips and falls on a wet floor in the lobby?"

The answers to these questions are summarized, and then the team considers what controls are in place or need to be put in place to respond to these events or reduce the risk of occurrence. Often, these lists are then scored quantitatively according to severity and likelihood, in order to prioritize actions. The resultant plan can be a risk register with a listing of action items for risk reduction.

Scenario Analysis. Since ISO 9001 wants organizations to examine the context of their organization and risks and opportunities associated with achieving their strategic direction, scenario analysis can be a useful tool for assisting with this level of thinking. This technique considers a set of scenarios about the future and what risks and opportunities those future states could hold. Best-case and worst-case scenarios could be contrived, and then the impacts of those scenarios would be explored. Typical applications for scenario analysis include emerging customer preferences, emerging technologies such as *the internet of things*, demographics such as aging, political movements, et cetera. The organization could add "disruptive" scenarios to their list of future scenarios. This deliberate consideration of disruption is very compatible with risk-based thinking.

People within the organization (or consultants) with a knowledge of emerging trends can develop these scenarios and then work with senior leadership to assess what risks and opportunities might arise. After that identification step, the leadership team can determine what changes to strategic direction, processes, and controls might be appropriate to take advantage of those opportunities and mitigate those risks. Because the analysis is of a future state, the organization should have enough time to react to these anticipated issues and put proactive measures in place to deal with them.

The planning horizon will be different for each organization, but three to five years is common. Organizations should take into account potential changes in the regulatory environment, changing stakeholder needs, technological and social factors, et cetera. It is even appropriate to assess the variety of outcomes that could occur based on a very recent strategic decision. After this exercise, the organization should have a set of risks and opportunities (perhaps a strengths-weaknesses-opportunities-threats [SWOT] diagram) that can then be used as the basis for an action plan to capitalize on opportunities and mitigate risks. Naturally, there are pros and cons to this approach.

Cause-and-Effect (Fishbone) Analysis. No list of risk assessment tools would be complete without reference to one of the "seven tools of quality," the cause-and-effect (C&E) diagram. The C&E diagram is also called the fishbone diagram or the Ishikawa diagram, after the man who created it. Although the C&E diagram is a common root cause analysis tool, it can also be used proactively to anticipate risks and decide on appropriate actions to mitigate risk.

C&E analysis is a tool used in conjunction with brainstorming. When a group conducts a brainstorming session, the possible causal factors can be sorted into broad categories to assist analysis. Each group can create its own categories, but typical ones include man (people), machine, method, materials, and measurement. If one were examining the potential causes of losing a baseball game, for example, the categories might look something like *Hitting, Pitching, Injured/Absent Players, Opposing Team*, and so on.

The issues brought forth by the group are shown on a large display so that relationships and the relative number of potential risks in each category is apparent. After the brainstorming is complete and the picture of the risks has been established, the group can review which risks are most likely to cause an adverse event and determine what countermeasures might be put in place to mitigate those risks.

The C&E analysis is qualitative. Because the identified risks are usually contributory and not singular causes of a failure, it is not appropriate to try to assign a probability around each cause. It is up to the group to decide the importance of each and the magnitude of risk and put *a few* appropriate actions in place to mitigate the most important risks. Naturally, there are pros and cons to this approach.

Human Reliability Assessment (HRA). This technique, associated with the impact of people on processes and systems, can be especially useful in service industries where customer satisfaction is often very dependent on individuals and their behaviors.

It is well understood that many processes can fail because of human error, especially when people become distracted or have to complete tasks very quickly. Human error has been shown many times to be the cause of, or a significant contributor to, such disasters as industrial accidents or airplane crashes. Despite our best efforts to mitigate risks in mechanical and electrical systems, accidents still happen from time to time as a result of human error.

The Japanese have been working to identify and prevent human error for many years. *Poka-yoke* is the Japanese term for error-proofing systems to make them more robust to human error. In fact, ISO 9001:2015 (at clause 8.5.1 g) requires that (as applicable) actions be implemented to prevent human error. Needless to say, the identification of human factors that contribute to errors can be a very significant part of any risk-based thinking approach.

This approach begins with descriptions of the tasks within a process that people will perform, followed by an assessment by those with experience and expertise as to what can go wrong and how serious that error would be. After the review of how the person can make a mistake, two things happen. The process designers create a way of detecting the failure and recovering from it, and they look at ways of implementing controls to reduce the likelihood of the person's mistake. These human errors and their mitigation can then become part of other risk assessment tools such as an FMEA or an HACCP plan. Naturally, there are pros and cons to this approach.

Bow Tie Analysis. This technique is another graphic way for assisting in risk assessment. The bow tie diagram maps the pathways from the cause of a failure event through to its consequences. One of the benefits of this tool is that it considers the barriers (actual and proposed) that exist between the causes of a failure and the failure event and the barriers between the failure event and its consequences.

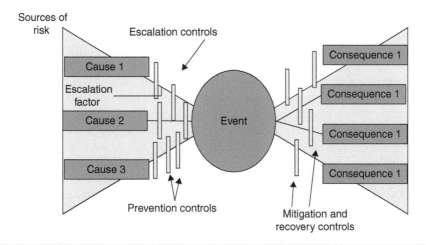

Figure 8.9 Bow tie analysis.
Source: IEC/ISO 31010:2009.

Causes	Barriers	Failure event	Barriers	Consequences
–Improper solvent storage –Electrical spark –Inadequate ventilation	–Practice drills on solvent use –Use only explosion-rated electrical devices –Increase air exchange rates	Paint shop explosion	–Ensure all protection equipment is in use –Construct one wall to allow explosive force to pass outside –Establish contingent capacity	–Injury of employees –Damage to adjacent production processes –Loss of capacity

Example bow tie diagram.

A bow tie can be created after fault trees or event trees have been created, or it can result from a brainstorming session with process experts. The bow tie diagram depicts a single failure event with its plurality of causes and consequences. The diagram then emphasizes identifying barriers (mitigating controls) along each pathway to block the cause(s) from causing the event or to block the failure event from resulting in serious consequences. See Figure 8.9.

Failure Modes and Effects Analysis. This technique is explained in Chapter 13.

Summary

This review of some of the elements of risk management is intended to build awareness of the need for assessing and managing the risks that can affect the organization. Recall that not every organization that has won the coveted Baldrige Award or other quality awards has survived. Failure has had little to do with their success in meeting the Baldrige criteria and more to do with how these organizations managed their businesses to withstand the risks encountered.

As quality management system standards such as ISO 9001 become less pre-scriptive, the responsibility for deciding what management controls need to be imposed on business processes rests more firmly on the shoulders of each process owner within the organization. Risk-based thinking requires that everyone con-sider risks and then decide on appropriate levels of control to mitigate those risks.

Furthermore, in this litigious society, organizations must carefully assess their potential liability from legal actions: actions arising from alleged product failures, end users' misuse of products, inappropriate actions of employees or alleged health, safety, and security violations, or negligence. Legal actions often result in huge payouts to the litigant if the company is found guilty or is forced to reach a huge out-of-court settlement regardless of alleged responsibility. Not being able to sus-tain a viable organization that fulfills customer requirements and supports your workforce is a quality failure—that is, a *quality of management* failure.[26]

7. KNOWLEDGE MANAGEMENT

> Use KM techniques in identifying core competencies that create a culture and system for collecting and sharing implicit and explicit knowledge among workers, stakeholders, competi-tors, and suppliers. Capture lessons learned and apply them across the organization to promote best practices. Idenfy typical knowledge-sharing barriers and how to overcome them. (Apply)
>
> **Body of Knowledge III.A.7**

What Is Knowledge?

One view is that knowledge is part of a hierarchy (see Figure 8.10). In this view, data are meaningless until something is done to them. Data can be stored in their raw form, or they can be manipulated (sorted, categorized, analyzed, calculated, summa-rized, and subjected to tests). When the manipulations are completed, the data may be synthesized into information. Information has meaning, but the meaning is based on the interpretation of the user of the information. The value of the information is determined by the uses for which the information is employed. Information can be stored for future use, disseminated to others for their use, or ignored (purposely or not). Typically, information is correlated/integrated with previously known informa-tion, as well as rules, policies, procedures, regulations, and so on, to build knowledge.

This new knowledge now has substance in the sense that it is framed by previ-ous knowledge. This enhanced knowledge may be used as developed, then stored (for example, in the human brain, the brains of a closely associated group of people, a computer, or documents in a file cabinet) or ignored and lost. Knowledge may be used in making decisions without the benefit of the next step in the continuum.

Wisdom is derived from the collective database of knowledge built from expe-rience, values, and expert insights. Wisdom provides the capability to exploit the

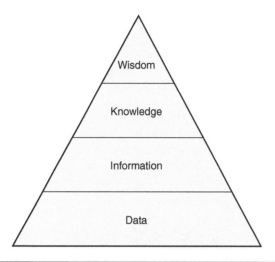

Figure 8.10   Transformation of data.

use of the knowledge for informed decision-making. Wisdom invokes unique capabilities, such as being able to:

- Visualize the connectivity among seemingly disparate knowledge sets (for example, the concept of a business organization as analogous to a biological system, the potential for adapting a space-age technological development for use in increasing agricultural output, the five-year strategic goals of an organization derived from an environmental analysis and synthesis of voluminous inputs)

- Know or sense the rightness or wrongness of an assumption, conclusion, or decision when objective data may not be available

- Solve problems of a nonlinear nature by attribution of nonquantitative characteristics and values to the pertinent knowledge sets to enable deduction of a solution

Tacit knowledge consists of all of the difficult-to-articulate know-how and techniques and processes that are part of an individual's and/or organization's expertise. It typically is not recorded and, while it is part of the corporate knowledge pool, there is no guarantee it will be passed on to the next generation. When an employee leaves an organization, usually the tacit knowledge retained by the employee also leaves.

Explicit knowledge is the captured and recorded knowledge that is codified and can be transmitted between individuals—that is, procedures, processes, standards, and other documents. Much of the current organizational *knowledge management* (KM) effort focuses on attempting to convert tacit knowledge into explicit knowledge without the loss of value.

In recent years, many organizations realized that their collective knowledge was disappearing. This may have happened because no effort was made to transform the mountains of data into knowledge for future generations to reuse. It also occurred when the human repositories of tacit knowledge left the organization.

For example, Chrysler created Books of Knowledge to stop the loss of internal automaking know-how and prevent future reinvention of the wheel. The armed forces videotaped and archived many of its war games and other activities as a source for learning. The purpose of these efforts was to enable sharing of knowledge, given the high turnover of personnel.

Not long ago, many people in organizations tended to protect and hoard their knowledge. Knowledge was perceived as power, and to share with another function was to give up this power. With the change from functional (silo) thinking to enterprise/systems thinking, organizations have realized the collective value of their knowledge bases, their intellectual capital. Knowledge, for those who use it wisely, is a key competitive advantage in the marketplace and must be leveraged with other core competencies.

How to Capture, Share, and Access Information

Knowledge management involves transforming data into information and the acquisition or creation of knowledge. The creation of knowledge from information requires human intervention, and applying wisdom is strictly a human function. Many of the mechanistic functions of manipulating data to generate information, and the storing and accessing of information for use in creating knowledge, can be done speedily and accurately by computers (for example, data mining, neural nets), whereby the software may find patterns of things not readily evident to the human eye. But interpretations from information to knowledge and wisdom typically involve a human capability.

Issues to consider for capturing, sharing, and accessing data include:

- Identifying the types of data to be captured and the media on/in which they are received

- Preparing the procedures for capturing the data and how they will be organized/categorized—for example, scanning documents into a computer database, filing the actual documents received, extracting key data for direct entry to computer storage, or point-of-sale transfer of data from a checkout register directly to computer storage

- Determining how the data may be used to create information (influences accessibility and design of storage medium) and whether certain data will be retained as *data* or in their upgraded form as *information* (for example, detailed machine or data recorder data or the summarized information version)

- For security purposes, identifying the customers who will use the data and protocols for access

- Designing methods for searching and accessing the data

- Establishing the policies and rules governing data use, maintenance of data (storage, handling, preservation, updating, and so on), retention duration, and disposal

- Determining the protocols for sharing, including whether the data will be made available on request (reactive mode) or will be disseminated to select individuals/departments based on an on-file profile of interests or needs (proactive)

- Establishing methods for continually evaluating the effectiveness of the knowledge management system and the means for improving it

Recognize that data sources may be proprietary, information is vulnerable if not properly cared for, and both data and information can disappear along with knowledge when people leave an organization. Information can be purchased, leased, rented, acquired as part of a merger or business acquisition, or generated within the organization.

No matter the source, there is a cost and a value associated with data, information, and knowledge. With some, the value may depreciate over time—for example, cash flow statements from five years ago or an economic analysis of the Pennsylvania Railroad from two years before its acquisition by Amtrak. Other data, information, and knowledge may appreciate in value over time—for example, lab notes from experiments in mapping DNA (data), the report summarizing the results of the experiments (information), and the board of directors' concerns and conclusions about the use of the information (knowledge). Other knowledge sets—for example, design documents for concept auto #CD0699 or the public communication program used during the construction of the Baldwin Bridge—may have instructional as well as historical value.

Initiating Knowledge Management

An organization-wide study may be conducted to determine what information and knowledge exists, where it exists, in what form it exists, and who does or will use it. The study team should include a variety of talents and backgrounds. It should probably not be directed and led by the information technology (IT) function in order to avoid emphasis on technology rather than content. Costs (acquisition, processing, storing, accessing, and maintenance) and values (worth to users) can be assigned and the knowledge sets displayed on a Pareto chart to aid prioritization. From the knowledge derived, decisions can be made about the knowledge management process (what to retain, how to retain it, who is responsible, who has access, how the activity will be funded, and so on).

The technology approaches used to support knowledge management are exploding in quantity and functionality. The advent of larger computer storage (in data warehouses or in a "cloud") and processing capability enables even smaller organizations to establish a knowledge management system. A very small organization can still reap the benefit of knowledge management concepts without the previous constraints of system complexity.

Consider the example of a small firm specializing in writing and publishing articles on business topics. The firm has established a four-hundred-item topic list. Supporting the list is an internal library of over one thousand books, approximately ten thousand documents (clipped articles, papers, conference proceedings, and so on), and over four hundred audio- and videotapes pertinent to the listed topics. The files are continually augmented by internet downloads, clipped articles from over fifty publications, and media purchases. This library of data is stored in easily accessible file drawers and on bookshelves. The topic list aids categorization of input and speeds access to data needed for a given topic.

The system is old-fashioned in that it is not computer based; however, it meets the needs of the small number of persons sharing the information, and it is cost- and time-effective. Its shortcoming is on those rare occasions when a cross-topical search is needed to locate data not specifically listed, when a computer "find" function would be useful. The cost and time involved to enter sufficient data into a computer database to support such a search, however, is not warranted for the few times it would be used. The system does meet present needs and far exceeds the functionality and focus of collections at nearby town libraries. Internet search capability supplements the physical collection.

Larger organizations are taking advantage of the innovative uses of intranets (dedicated internet-like internal systems) for sharing information and knowledge and data-mining techniques. Data mining is exploring, via computer, gigantic databases of millions of records to extract valuable data that can be transformed into useful information and knowledge. As an example, visualize the potential uses for information derived from exploring the correlation and permutations of data collected by a supermarket chain. It is the rare shopper who does not duti-fully present her or his shopping card to be swiped (bar code read) at the checkout counter. Bargains available only to the cardholder have successfully modified the behavior of the buying public to submit their card and hence allow the recording of their purchases for the company to analyze.

Other examples of applications of KM include:

- Organizations that carefully preserve the research and design work that went into creating a new product, whether or not the product was ever launched or was successful. All R&D persons assigned a new project must first access the database for pertinent information and knowledge. In these cases it is truly a policy to not reinvent the wheel.

- Legal firms that augment the existent case law (from publishers) with case details from their own experience with clients. It enables attorneys with the firm to access particulars of a case for applicability to a new case. This information also enables newer attorneys to learn how their peers have applied the law, as well as the firm's policies and practices in previous cases.

- Retail store chains that formulate patterns of buyers' habits from huge databases of captured customer data. These data facilitate how they provide the products people want when they want them—which products, from which distributors, in what quantity, when the product is needed, how retail space is allocated to each product, which products should be dropped, and how to schedule human resources for shelf restocking, checkout, and store maintenance. Also, the system is set to enable the issuance of pertinent coupons and notices to customers. Periodic searches of the customer database enable marketing to issue targeted advertisements to customers.

- The many companies that archive data, documents, and other physical objects that represent the company's history. These data and items not only are of historical interest to newcomers but are accessed in support of future planning, as background for publicity and advertising purposes and as objective evidence in legal matters.

- The corporate libraries that have expanded from their normal reactive services (acquiring, shelving, and loaning books and publications; data and information searches) to developing profiles of key users of the library and proactively feeding new information to users based on their profile and documented needs.

- A large organization that collects, catalogs, and makes available online to field salespeople a range of information. The information includes technical product information (their own and competitors'), sales presentations, sales and marketing practices and strategies, sales promotion materials, customer account information, analyses of buying patterns, and industry trend data.

- A company that annually measures the value of its intellectual capital and publishes it to its stockholders.

- Organizations who periodically mine their database for patterns and connections that remain virtually hidden to humans. The resulting information is used in determining the potential for new products and services, establishing new markets, segmenting the customer database, restructuring processes and the organization, and guiding the strategic direction of the organization.

The Learning Organization

As individuals must continue to learn, so must organizations. Essential principles for any learning organization include the following:

- Recognize that the database is not the KM solution; it is the people effectively using the database who are the real solution

- Build and reinforce an organizational culture that supports and promotes knowledge sharing, networking, and reusing knowledge rather than hoarding or reinventing knowledge

- Ensure that organizational management considers knowledge management a key strategy for growth and prosperity of the enterprise

- Institute a system of policies and procedures to identify what information and knowledge is essential and specify how the information and knowledge are to be captured, processed, stored, maintained, accessed, and used

- Nurture an open communication work climate that encourages the identification of new information and knowledge that can be exploited for individual and organizational learning and development

- Foster the valuing of knowledge management as one of the organization's core competencies in remaining competitive

As portrayed by Senge, organizational learning goes beyond the mere capture of knowledge to include gaining a deeper and complete understanding of how things work and involves five learning disciplines:

1. *Personal mastery.* A continual drive for personal and organizational development

2. *Mental models.* Understanding how our cognitive schema affect our view of the world and continually improving the accuracy of the models

3. *Shared vision.* Working jointly toward a common view to which all aspire

4. *Team learning.* The use of dialogue to move beyond mere conversation to true joint understanding

5. *Systems thinking.* Understanding the multiple cause-and-effect relationships and how they are interconnected in organizations, society, and other systems[27]

Core Competencies

A key to the long-term success of any organization is the ability to differentiate itself from competitors. One way of doing so is to possess a unique capability, a core competency that can be continually leveraged. For example, Honda has the ability to continually refine the technology of small gasoline engines, which has been applied to products such as lawn equipment, power generators, motorcycles, consumer automobiles, and racing engines.

Core competencies are a result of both specific knowledge and the ability to integrate various skills and other components of the organization to effectively apply that knowledge. In order for it to remain a core competency, the organization must continually increase the depth of knowledge and ability of employees to utilize it in new ways.

The Baldrige National Quality Award defines core competencies as "Your organization's areas of greatest expertise; those strategically important, possibly specialized capabilities that are central to fulfilling your mission or that provide an advantage in your marketplace or service environment."[28] This matters because an organization's core competency should then be a driver for company strategy and be maintained and improved through development of employees' skills and internal capabilities, as well as continual R&D in relevant knowledge areas. An effective knowledge management process supports the capturing, processing, and storage of information to make it available to those who need it while also maintaining the necessary security of that information.

Measuring the Outcomes of KM

Some best practices to measure the outcomes of knowledge management are:

- Focus the KM system on the organization's strategic objectives and measuring tangible outcomes.

- Define and clearly communicate the KM measures and how they will be used.

- Create interdependent KM measures tied to the organization's measures of its outcomes.

- Measure only what matters—with a primary focus on the customers of the KM system.

- Encourage the telling of success (and failure) stories of users of the KM system to reinforce the lessons learned aspect of measurements.

Organizational Hurdles to Overcome

To effectively implement KM techniques, a number of hurdles or barriers may have to be overcome, such as:

- Lack of top management's interest in, support for, and commitment to KM

  — A knowledge vision may be lacking.

  — The economic case for KM is not developed.

- Failure to consider KM a top-level strategy

  — KM as a competitive edge is not developed.

  — KM is not perceived as integral to doing business.

- Inter- and intra-organizational barriers

  — Organizational structures may either enable or hinder knowledge sharing.

  — Turf conflicts and tendencies to hoard knowledge are power issues.

  — Organizations not structured on a project basis may be less likely to understand and appreciate the value of KM in performing their assignments.

  — There can be conflict over funding for the KM system and services.

- Overcoming process barriers

  — Perceiving the IT function as the logical process owner of KM may be ill advised. With IT heading the KM effort, the emphasis may be more on processing data, not on the strategic use and value of the knowledge captured and retained.

  — In examining the process, questions include:

    - What data are to be captured?

    - Why are they needed?

    - Who will use the data and for what purpose?

    - What are the procedures and protocols for data capture?

    - What are the procedures and protocols for transforming data into information and knowledge?

    - How is information/knowledge access and retrieval to be accomplished?

    - Is there a competent person responsible for establishing quality criteria and maintaining the level of quality in selecting data for entry, correctly and completely capturing the data selected, maintaining database integrity and security, and providing accurate and timely access and retrieval of information/knowledge?

- In the case of a large database with a high volume of usage, have the users (internal customers) been segmented so as to optimize service (and costs) to the different segments?

- Infrastructure issues

— Who ensures that the electronic systems are adequate to serve the growing needs of the organization—that is, the expanding database, the ever-faster pace of business decisions, the increasingly innovative workforce, and the organization's commitment to continually improve?

— Who ensures that all persons interfacing with the KM system are properly trained?

- Cultural concerns

— Do the organization's strategy, the recognition and reward systems, the organizational structures, the predominant management style, and other cultural concerns help or hinder the realization of an effective KM system?

— Have cultural concerns, such as language usage and communication protocols, been updated to mesh with the KM system?

— Has the voice of the customer (external customer) been integrated with the design of the KM system?

- Individual barriers

— How resistant to change are the organization's employees?

— How reluctant will key employees be when required to submit their knowledge to a KM system—and perceive they have lost their power?

— How much individual fear has to be overcome—fear of failure, fear of exposing errors and mistakes in judgment, fear of giving up personal papers and notes?

Far from an exhaustive list of hurdles, barriers, and issues, this list provides an overview of concerns facing organizations implementing major new systems.

Product Development

Developing a product or service is often performed as a team consisting of representatives from marketing/sales, engineering, production/operations, quality, and finance. The physical location of the function varies from organization to organization, and it may even be outsourced. Numerous disciplines are usually involved, requiring the expertise of people with a wide range of knowledge and skills.

The development may include plans for:

- Funding

- Project planning and management

- Market research

- Customer needs/wants analysis
- Engineering design for manufacturability and for customer use (see below)
- Quality planning and management (design, processes, reliability, and so on)
- Consumer testing
- Marketing the product or service (promotion, selling, distribution, demand forecasting, assessing customer satisfaction, and so on)
- Product safety and liability

A process that has gained recognition is *human factors engineering* (HFE), an inter-disciplinary approach to evaluating and improving the safety, efficiency, and robustness of work systems, such as healthcare delivery. HFE is the practice of designing products so the user can perform the required use, operation, service, and supportive tasks with a minimum of stress and a maximum of efficiency. HFE is about designing for the user instead of forcing the user to accommodate the design. HFE scientists and engineers study the intersection of people, technology, policy, and work across multiple domains, using an interdisciplinary approach that draws from cognitive psychology, organizational psychology, human perfor-mance, industrial engineering, systems engineering, and economic theory. HFE addresses multiple aspects of work, including:

- Task analysis and design
- Device evaluation and usability
- Communication, collaboration, and teamwork
- Training
- Systems resilience, adaptation, and failure

HFE engages employees by getting them involved in the design process. It focuses on systems and environments designed by the employees, leading to the well-being and function of humans. Systems and environments designed through the HFE process are safer, more efficient, cost less, and reduce system downtime, maintenance, and injuries.

REFERENCES

1. J. Giles, "Learning How We Learn," in *Gower Handbook of Training and Development*, 2nd ed., ed. J. Prior (Brookfield, VT: Bower, 1994).
2. C. Daniels, *Bringing Out the Best in People: How to Apply the Astonishing Power of Positive Reinforcement* (New York: McGraw-Hill, 1994).
3. P. Hersey, and K. Blanchard, *Management of Organizational Behavior* (Englewood Cliffs, NJ: Prentice Hall, 1977).
4. P. Senge, *The Fifth Discipline: The Art and Practice of the Learning Organization* (New York: Currency Doubleday, 1990).
5. Ibid.
6. P. Cilliers, *Complexity and Postmodernism: Understanding Complex Systems* (London: Routledge, 1998).

7. D. Okes, "Complexity Theory Simplifies Choices," *Quality Progress* (July 2003): 35–37.

8. S. R. Covey, *The 7 Habits of Highly Effective People* (New York: Simon & Schuster, 1989).

9. S. R. Covey, and K. A. Gulledge, "Principle-Centered Leadership and Change," *Journal of Quality and Participation* (March 1994): 12–21.

10. E. A. Locke, and D. M. Schweiger, "Participation in Decision Making: One More Look," in *Research in Organizational Behavior*, ed. B. M. Staw and L. L. Cummings (Greenwich, CT: JAI Press, 1979).

11. E. H. Schein, *The Corporate Culture Survival Guide* (San Francisco: Jossey-Bass, 1999).

12. J. A. Defeo, ed., *Juran's Quality Handbook*, 7th ed. (New York: McGraw-Hill, 2017), chap. 2, 46–75.

13. See the Sarbanes-Oxley Act of 2002, a law that, among other stipulations, requires the principal executive officer or officers and the principal financial officer or officers of public companies to attest to the accuracy of financial reports and the effectiveness of internal controls.

14. R. S. Kaplan, and D. P. Norton, *The Balanced Scorecard: Translating Strategy into Action* (Boston: Harvard Business School Press, 1996).

15. ISO 9000:2015, *Quality Management Systems—Fundamentals and Vocabulary* (Geneva: International Organization for Standardization [hereafter cited as ISO], 2015).

16. ISO 31000:2009, *Risk Management—Principles and Guidelines* (Geneva: ISO, 2015).

17. Ibid.

18. Ibid.

19. ISO 9001:2015, *Quality Management Systems—Requirements* (Geneva: ISO, 2015).

20. D. J. Devos, "ISO 9001: Implementing Risk Based Thinking," *Proceedings of the ASQ World Conference on Quality and Improvement* (Milwaukee: ASQ, 2016).

21. Ibid.

22. Ibid.

23. D. J. Devos, "Risk Is the Compass—a New Approach to Auditing Using Risks and Controls," *Proceedings of the ASQ World Conference on Quality and Improvement* (Milwaukee: ASQ, 2006).

24. Ibid.

25. ISO 31010:2009, *Risk Assessment Techniques* (Geneva: ISO, 2015).

26. L. Scott, *Baldrige Key Terms*, December 18, 2018, accessed May 4, 2019, https://www.nist.gov/baldrige/self-assessing/baldrige-key-terms.

27. P. Senge, C. Roberts, R. B. Ross, B. J. Smith, and A. Kleiner, *The Fifth Discipline Fieldbook* (New York: Doubleday, 1994).

28. Baldrige Excellence Framework, Glossary of Terms, p. 47, accessed August 11, 2020, https://www.nist.gov/baldrige/baldrige.

See Appendix A for additional references for this chapter.

Chapter 9
B. Communication Skills and Abilities

In today's world, the quantity and diversity of available data, information, and knowledge is overwhelming for many people. Access to data from virtually any part of the world, even outer space, is nearly instantaneous. The quality of such data and information, as well as their usefulness, is often suspect, however. Not only is the capability to communicate quickly, succinctly, and accurately more important than ever but so is the ability to know what information to choose for a given purpose.

This chapter will review what communication is and how communication takes place and will present techniques and strategies for enhancing communication. In addition, the chapter will discuss how to effectively communicate in the global economy, as well as provide tips on how to use data produced by information systems technology to monitor and manage an organization.

1. COMMUNICATION TECHNIQUES

> Define and apply various modes of communication used within organizations, such as verbal, nonverbal, written, and visual. Identify factors that can inhibit clear communication and describe ways of overcoming them. (Apply)
>
> **Body of Knowledge III.B.1**

What Is Communication?

People working toward a common purpose cannot function without communication. Communication is a transmitting and receiving process that for effectiveness depends on both the transmitter's and the receiver's perceptions. This statement appears applicable to both human as well as technological communication. Important to each is the realization that there are filters affecting both what is transmitted and what is received. In the human communication process, these filters may represent cultural beliefs, the consequences of previous communications, conditions at the time of transmission, language disparities, education, experience, and

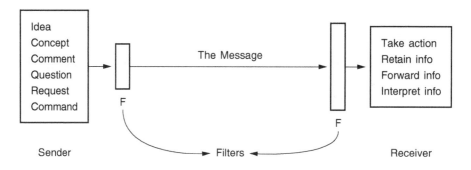

Figure 9.1   Communication path.

so on. In technological communication, filters are intended to reduce or eliminate noise (interference) along the communications path. Figure 9.1 depicts the communication path from sender to receiver.

Filters intended to help clarify the meaning of the message can, and too often do, muddle the message instead. (Note: some authors refer to *coder* and *decoder* rather than filters.) An aid to effective human communication is for the receiver to transmit back to the sender a paraphrased understanding of what the receiver heard or saw. Depending on the complexity of the message and its intent, this exchange may require repeating, in different words, until the intended understanding is reached. In technical transmission this clarification may be accomplished by various types of built-in checks for the technical accuracy of the transmission and then, for clarity of understanding, a return message confirming (repeating) the pertinent data. Keep in mind that unless there is direct machine-to-machine interface (no human intervention between the sending of data and the reaction to the data), even technological transmission may be subject to human filtering on both ends.

As far back as Socrates, it was pointed out that one must communicate with another on the other person's terms. This applies not only to language differences but also to cultural, educational, and experiential differences. Before communicating, the first consideration is, given the receiver's background, is this communication within the receiver's range of perception and understanding? In the technological realm, this potential for incompatibility is annoyingly prevalent in transmitting data from computer to computer. In this case the unknowing transmitter discovers that the recipient's computer and programs do not have the compatibility for receiving the data as sent—for example, the data appear garbled when received.

Hayakawa stresses that in communicating, the words or symbols are not the actual thing being discussed.[1] This concept emphasizes that for clarity of understanding on the part of the receiver, the sender must work at conveying what was meant by the message and strive to ensure that the receiver *got the message intended*.

Expectation is a critical factor in communication. Humans tend to see and hear mostly what they expect to see and hear. The unexpected message may not be received (ignored, blocked out). This suggests that some knowledge of the receiver's expectations should be known for communication to be effective. (Note: *recognize*, or *re-cognize*, means we see what we expect to see or have seen, ignoring what does not fit our mental model.)

Communication has occurred when action is taken. Action can range from immediately perceiving the message as an order and obeying it to deciding that the message contains information that may or will potentially be useful (or entertaining) at some later date and then storing the message for subsequent retrieval.

A significant problem in human communications is the difference between what the sender says and what the receiver often hears. Because the sender is translating thoughts into words and the receiver is then translating words into thoughts, many opportunities occur for differences in meaning. Misinterpretation can be caused by background, cultural biases, group norms, and emotional and health factors.

Direction of Communication

Organizational structure plays an important role in communication. Top-to-bottom vertical communication flows from managers to subordinates. The organization's vision and values, strategic goals, objectives and measures, and policies and procedures are typically communicated in this manner. Vertical communication also occurs when a manager assigns tasks to direct reports. Vertical communication also flows upward in the organization, in the context of feedback, problems encountered, and so on. In both downward and upward directions, the content of the communication is subject to filtering as the message passes from one person to another in the hierarchy.

For example, think of the telephone game. It goes like this: A group of people, say sixteen, are each separated by perhaps six feet. The first person softly reads a short story (up to a third of an 8 1/2 × 11-inch sheet of paper) to Person Number Two. Person Number Two repeats the story, from memory, to Person Number Three, and so on, until Person Number Sixteen has heard the story. Person Number Sixteen then repeats the story to the entire group. After a great laugh, the group discusses the changes that took place as the story passed from person to person. Often, the last person tells a version of the story that bears little or even no resemblance to the original.

Bottom-to-top vertical communication occurs when information flows from subordinates to management. Status updates on assigned tasks, employee suggestion systems, and various types of reports are examples of this form of communication. Upward communication may also include notification of deficiencies in materials, supplies, and work orders, as well as employee complaints.

Sometimes, management finds it more efficient to communicate some types of messages to all employees at monthly group meetings or via electronic communications such as e-mails. These communications are often announcements of presumed general interest to all (for example, new product/service, new large customer, facility upgrade) and may be used in situations in which the speaker desires an audience reaction.

In addition to vertical communication, information is also transferred horizontally. Information flow among peers or within a team or group is horizontal communication. Examples of situations in which horizontal communication occurs are (1) a cross-functional design team developing a new product, (2) a quality improvement team working on cycle time reduction, and (3) a field salesperson notifying the production scheduler of a pending large order.

In Chapter 7 the deployment of organizational goals and objectives was discussed. A critical feature of hoshin planning, used in strategic planning, is the *catch-ball* concept. This is using both vertical and horizontal means of communicating (down, up, and sideways). The aim is to ensure that everyone in the organization understands the organizational goals and objectives and identifies the part they are to play in achieving those goals and objectives. The communications, if carried out well, result in a tightly knit plan with clear linkages (and understanding) throughout every organizational level. Another type of vertical and horizontal communication is the 360° feedback process.

Methods of Communication

Communications can be written or oral (both are verbal communication) or nonverbal. Examples of written communications include policy and procedure manuals, performance reports, proposals, memoranda, meeting minutes, newsletters, e-mail, text messages, and online documents (for example, via company intranets). Examples of oral communications include giving orders, giving performance feedback, speeches, meetings (group or one-on-one), informal discussions, and voice mail. Computer transcription of recorded voice mails adds more complexity and chance for error to this process.

Body language—the expression of thoughts, emotions, and so on through movement or positioning of the body—is yet another form of communication. Detailed studies have been done to analyze the meaning of various facial expressions, positions of arms and legs, posture, and so on, for both females and males and within different cultures. Body language, especially if it is perceived to be negative (particularly if viewed as insulting, disrespectful, or threatening) from the receiver's perspective, can negate a positive oral message.

Picture one spouse giving an emotionally laden oral message to the other spouse, who is intently watching a televised sporting event. The "Yes, dear" replies do not reflect whether any of the spouse's messages were received. Also, body language may suggest that the messages, if received, failed to be interpreted as intended.

The negative nonverbal message that body language may communicate is a serious training topic for persons embarking on an assignment to a part of the world where the culture is different. Morrison et al. discuss some of the perils associated with inappropriate body language.[2]

Communication is also either formal or informal. *Formal* communication is planned and delivered as part of standard operating policies and procedures (SOPs) of the organization. A letter offering employment, a product test report, an environmental impact statement, the company's annual report, and performance appraisals are examples of formal communication. Signs, posters, and official posted notices are also formal communications.

Informal communication is not mandated or otherwise required but occurs as part of helping people function collaboratively. Examples include a discussion between a test engineer and a production supervisor to clarify a specification, or an e-mail message from one employee to another reminding him or her of the need for the two of them to prepare for an upcoming presentation. Classroom and online blended training are typically a mix of formal (for example, lecture) and informal (for example, discussion) communication.

The "grapevine" is informal communication. It is often of unknown origin and transmitted orally and/or by other fast, unauthorized media (unsigned posted notes on a bulletin board or e-mail, text messages, online postings, and so on). It may include rumor, opinions, gossip, false or true data, or valid information that has not yet been officially made known. Efforts to squelch or abolish the grapevine usually fail and often drive the communication further underground. Interestingly, management has been known to plant information for the grapevine to pick up for the purpose of testing the water to get employees' reactions or to communicate something that might be too embarrassing to document or say officially and publicly. To keep the grapevine from spreading misinformation, the frequency, accuracy, and honesty of management's communications to employees is crucial.

Other forms of informal communication include the pictures, cartoons, and quotations individuals post at their workplace and traditional greetings and rituals—for example, "Good morning, how are you today?"

Selecting Appropriate Media

Factors to consider in making the choice of media include:

- *Urgency of message.* If the building is burning, a loudspeaker evacuation notice from a top official would be appropriate, whereas the death notification and funeral arrangements for an employee over a loudspeaker could be perceived as poor taste.

- *Number and makeup (for example, culture, education, experience) of the receivers.* The bulletin board notification of critical safety rules may be inappropriate as the sole communication to workers with poor reading ability.

- *How dispersed are the receivers.* Will priority mail suffice for sending design changes to suppliers in different parts of the world? Or would another medium be more cost- and time-effective?

- *Culture and work climate into which the message will be received.* Would it be prudent for management to deliver its latest dictum on the "We must improve our quality and work harder to keep our customers" theme at an all-hands employee meeting when the workforce is embroiled in a labor contract dispute?

- *Best individual (for example, organizational level, functional responsibility, level of respect) to whom to send message.* Not only the content but also the authority level of the person sending the message will be a significant aspect of the message.

- *Physical and technical constraints (for example, facility size, transmission equipment capability/availability, time zones).* Will the conference room hold all the people needed to hear the message? Does the equipment have the needed capability? Will a phone call and ignorance of time zones awaken an irate customer?

- *Security/privacy/sensitivity issues (for example, of data and/or people).* Where will a manager and worker/associate discuss the performance review? Who might tap into a transmission and pick up proprietary organizational information (vulnerability to hackers)? What if the e-mail string gets in the wrong hands?

  — *Believability at the receiver based on the transmission method.* E-mails may look like "spoof" messages to the receiver. So many data breaches are due to "phishing," where plausible e-mails are used by receivers allowing access to sensitive data. Legitimate messages may flounder if receivers think they are fakes.

- *Safety, health, and environmental issues (for example, adequacy of facility, emotional state of receiver, impact of message on receivers' values).* Is e-mail too impersonal for communicating with certain receivers? In the interest of economy of time and space, will some of the niceties that typically are part of written communication—for example, use of titles, salutation, less direct language, and so on—be left out? Will the combination of message and medium convey a conflict of personal values to the receiver(s)?

- *Whether the communication (data or information) should be retained—that is, the methods for storing, maintaining (updating, preservation), accessing (including security requirements), and duration of retention.*

Questioning Techniques

Asking the right questions in the right way of the right people at the right time and for the right reasons is a skill that can be learned. Inasmuch as the quality professional relies heavily on data, information, and knowledge to fulfill responsibilities, this skill is important. The skill of questioning is critical to learning, and it needs to be developed somehow across the organization. Examples of a few of the situations in which good questioning skill is essential are:

- Identifying the process used by a bank loan processor in preparing a loan for approval or rejection

- Determining the root cause of a problem

- Getting facts about a customer complaint from a field service technician

- Confirming whether a direct-report employee understands what good performance is

- Confirming that trainees understand the skill and knowledge from their training

- Verifying the spikes on a control chart and obtaining the rationale for each

- Determining the facts behind a supplier's deteriorating quality

- Understanding new requirements, specifications, and other mandates

To obtain data or information from another person or group usually involves asking questions. What is asked and the manner in which it is asked influence the quality of the response received (that is, accuracy, completeness, timeliness, and relevance to other pertinent data). Skilled interviewers such as employment interviewers, consultants, complaint adjusters, systems designers, salespeople, talk show hosts, detectives, trial attorneys, and many others develop the skill of extracting the data they need to meet their purposes. Three basic methods are employed:

1. Plan beforehand what is to be learned.

2. Ask mostly open-ended questions.

3. Actively listen and capture the responses.

Additionally, and depending on the situation, these questioners create a setting conducive to the types of answers they are seeking. For example, they use a professional setting for questions about quality issues, individual performance, and so on, a threatening setting for questions about misbehavior, crimes, and so on, and a warm and comfortable setting for questions soliciting opinions and suggestions and the like.

Often, a questioner will start with a few short, close-ended questions to obtain demographic facts or identification—for example, "What is your employee number? What shift do you work? What accounts are you assigned to? To whom do you report?"

Then, to probe the subject of the interaction, the questioner shifts to open-ended questions, such as "Can you tell me exactly the chain of events that led up to Mrs. Smith filing a complaint about the service she received? From your perspective, what could have caused the missing pages in Tuesday's batch of policies mailed?"

The respondent's answers frequently open the opportunity for the inquirer to probe further by asking another open-ended question. Also, some responses may not be clearly understood by the questioner, so the questioner repeats what was heard in the form of a question. For example, "Did I understand you correctly when you said . . . ?" This closed-ended question will usually produce a *yes* or *no* answer, sometimes followed by further explanation or followed up by the questioner—for example, "Can you tell me about that?"

The technique of *active listening* in two-way communication involves paraphrasing the message received back to the sender. Here's an example:

> *(Sender)* "I need you to get the report you're working on out to Mr. Blank by noon today."
>
> *(Receiver)* "I understand you want me to get the analysis of perpendicular appendages for our Purple People Eater toy line to Mr. Blank no later than noon today, no exceptions."
>
> *(Sender)* "You've got it," or "No, that's not the one I mean, it's . . ."

In this scenario the sender knew what was needed, but the receiver could have been working on more than one report. Fortunately, the receiver listened actively by sending back the understanding of the order.

The speed of speech is said to be four to five times slower than the speed of assimilating the spoken word. Typing is often even slower. What is done about the gaps is the difference between an effective listener and a mind wanderer. The effective listener, instead of drifting off to other unrelated thoughts, focuses on the topic at hand, using the gap to begin to formulate questions to ask to learn more (cognitive multitasking or well-practiced serial tasking). Examples of questions to oneself using this technique are:

- "What is being said, and what does it really mean?"

- "How does that relate to what was said earlier?"

- "Where is this going, and what point is the speaker attempting to make?"

- "How is what I am hearing useful to me?"

- "Am I getting the whole story—what is being left out?"

- "What evidence is being given to back up the points made?"

- "Do I really understand what is being said, and should I ask for clarification?"

2. INTERPERSONAL SKILLS

> Use skills in empathy, tact, friendliness, and objectivity. Use open-minded and nonjudgmental communication methods. Develop and use a clear writing style, active listening, and questioning and dialogue techniques that support effective communication. (Apply)
>
> **Body of Knowledge III.B.2**

Using Interpersonal Skills and Techniques

Interpersonal skills and techniques the effective communicator may use include:

- *Showing empathy.* The communicator identifies with and understands the needs and interests of the receiver. The communicator fosters a harmonious relationship with the receiver.

- *Tactfulness.* The communicator is polite and respectful and avoids using insensitive, vulgar, or profane language.

- *Open-mindedness.* The communicator conveys her or his openness to consider other viewpoints and opinions. Without being hostile, the communicator provides constructive criticism when help is wanted.

- *Showing a friendly attitude.* The communicator evokes a feeling of warmth and helpfulness to the receiver.

- *Sensitivity.* The communicator is kind and caring, attuned to the receiver's feelings and concerns.

- *Trustworthiness.* The communicator is perceived to be and/or is known to be worthy of the receiver's trust.

- *Ethics.* The communicator embraces common codes of honor and integrity.

- *Fair-mindedness.* The communicator treats others as equals and is fair in communicating with all constituencies.

- *Authenticity.* The communicator is perceived as being congruent with reality. What you see and/or hear is what you get.

Benefits of Effective Communication Techniques

- Employees understand organizational strategies, goals, and objectives and their role in meeting them.

- Costs are reduced as the organization accomplishes tasks effectively, eliminating the costs and time delays associated with miscommunication.

- Open communication channels make it easier for management to perceive the real issues and problems.

- Employees are more receptive to change and prone to offer creative solutions for problems.

Organizational communication is most effective when the following are present:

- Open channels of communication are maintained. This enables employees to provide the correct information. Trust between the manager and the employee is enhanced.

- Employees are highly motivated.

- An appropriate recognition and reward system is in place.

- Communication is timely. When communication is timely, employees feel they can trust management and that management will act on the information provided. This applies to both top-to-bottom and bottom-to-top communications.

- The organization is flat. Reduction in the number of management layers helps reduce communication distortion.

- Employees are empowered. When teams or individuals are empowered, their participation and motivation increases, resulting in improved efficiency. Because they are closer to the problems, they are better positioned to make decisions rather than having to work through several management layers.

- Employee training in effective communication is provided.

Written Communications

The probability of distortion in formulating and conveying a message in writing versus orally depends on the competence of the sender in composing clear, concise, consistent, and comprehensive content. It also depends on the competence of the receiver in comprehending the intent, context, and content of the message. There is a tendency for the receiver to misunderstand written communication, especially when the message is shortened and the speed of transmission is increased. For example:

- A cryptic message delivered via a handheld device may be easily understood if communicated between two friends but could appear unintelligible to an outsider adult.

- A handwritten note attached to a document may rely heavily on the knowledge and experience of the receiver.

Consider this situation: A vice president (VP), noted for his stern demeanor and attention to perfection, habitually handwrote short notes on his personalized blue paper, attaching the notes to pertinent documents. The notes were written using blue or black or red ink. His assistant hand-delivered the noted documents to the addressees.

The receivers usually stopped their work to read the notes, making the following judgments: If the blue bullet, as the notes were called, was written in either blue or black ink, the action taken and the response to the message could be delayed (slightly). If the message was written in red ink, all work was stopped until the indicated action was taken or an answer to the question was determined, and a response was made to the VP.

All but one of the VP's direct reports reacted in this way. This person had made it a point to observe the VP writing the blue bullets and learned that the VP had a desk drawer full of blue, black, and red pens. When the VP wished to write a note to attach to a document indicating the action he wanted or the question he had, he reached in his drawer and grabbed a pen—any pen. The color had no significance! The employee also realized that some blue bullets were of much lower priority and could be "aged" to see if the message became self-evident, or meaningless, over time. If not, those remaining blue bullets were dealt with eventually.

• E-mail messages often lack attention to the feelings and beliefs of recipients. Messages sent via e-mail are usually short, blunt, and lack the typical politeness of letters. Such messages can lack the completeness a receiver may need to understand and react to the message. The use of *emojis* in e-mails to show emotional nuances has become more common, but often it just adds confusion. Does the receiver understand the small image the sender used? Also, because the message is not delivered face-to-face, the sender may deliver a more aggressive and/or offensive message. And e-mails are usually composed quickly and sent without much, if any, proofreading or fact checking. Haste sometimes does make waste. As a habit, all e-mails should be checked for spelling, grammar usage, and clarity of meaning—before sending. Text messages are similar, only to a greater degree. It has been said that nothing immortal has been written with just thumbs.

• The writer of the message does not have the advantage of observing the body language of the receiver, hence the writer is unable to judge how the message is being received. For example, does the receiver understand the message intent and content? Is the receiver disturbed (stressed, offended, confused) by the message and how it is worded? Is the relative importance or level of urgency the sender intended being correctly perceived by the receiver? Is the receiver perfectly clear about what action the sender intends the receiver to take, and when and how? Is the receiver clear about any confidentiality precautions the sender wants taken (whether the wishes are explicitly stated or implied)?

• Signage can be both the object of humorists and the curse of the confused. Two or more meanings attributed to a sign or a printed notice can produce unforeseen, even tragic results. On the humorous side, until recently, a sign on a major highway leading into San Diego read, "Cruise ships take next exit." A sign outside a university cafeteria said, "Shoes are required to eat in this cafeteria."

More seriously, a yellow notice attached to a new regulation for handling a dangerous chemical demanded, "Destroy this message after reading." A help wanted ad requested, "Person to handle dynamite. Must be prepared to travel unexpectedly."

Listening

I know that you believe that you understand what you think I said, but I am not sure you realize that what you heard is not what I meant.
—Robert McCloskey

Hearing and listening are distinctly different. People hear with their ears. They listen through their head, eyes, heart, and gut. Listening is often an afterthought in everyday communication. How often have you had a flashback to what you thought you heard and realized you had not listened carefully? Good listening should involve:

- Preparing yourself to listen

- Paraphrasing to clarify understanding

- Paying close attention to all that is being said and showing genuine interest

- Listening without judging—keeping an open mind

- Focusing on receiving data and information, not on the speaker's appearance, tone of voice, accent, beliefs, and so on

- Asking relevant and meaningful questions

- As the communication turns in a new direction, intervening with a summary statement of what you think you heard up to that point, which is better than waiting until the end to find you have been off track for much of the communication

- Clarifying objections—for example, what part of what was said prompted the objection?

- Responding with statements echoing similar situations to clarify your assimilation and application of what is being said

- As appropriate and comfortable, jotting down key words or ideas from the speaker

- Taking mental note of what you are learning, how it will benefit you, and what you can tell others

- Being aware of your talking-to-listening ratio, as it is a truism that we should talk less and listen more

What to avoid includes:

- Interrupting the person speaking

- Changing the subject in the middle of the communication

- Getting comfortable and drifting away to daydream

- Completing the sender's statements

- Solidifying your opinion or judgment of what is being said before you hear it all

- Attempting to document every word the speaker says

- Working on shaping your response while the other person is speaking

- Doing something entirely different during the communication, such as computer work, answering your cell phone, reading papers, and so on; avoid multitasking while communication is occurring

Feedback

Feedback may be informative, constructive, or a combination of both. *Informative communication* is passing information from one person or group to another person or group. Its intent is to inform, not to instruct, direct, or control.

Constructive communication (also called *corrective feedback*) is intended to provide information that will cause action by the receiver. For example, in providing performance feedback, the management person must:

- Refer to a standard, specifications, objective, or other basis by which the performer is being measured (the baseline)

- Give specific data related to performance in relation to the baseline

- Enlist the performer in jointly planning the action that will improve the person's performance

- Provide positive reinforcement for any performance improvement, including actions taken to attempt to improve performance

- Set a specific time for achieving the planned improvement and obtain mutual agreement

- Discuss the consequences for not achieving the desired performance level within the time frame planned

- Provide interim encouragement to the performer until the objective is reached

There is a world of difference between asking and telling. Making statements will engage a receiver but may make them defensive. Phrasing the same information as a question will more likely engage the receiver in common dialogue.

Roadblocks to Effective Communication

The disturbance or barrier distorting or blocking an intended message is often called *noise*, a term common to both human communication and technological communication. Examples of this noise include:

- The means for communicating is faulty or ineffective—for example, access to e-mail is blocked by a surge in usage due to a natural catastrophe occurring, there is congestion limiting delivery, security limitations prevent delivery, the location of the sender or the receiver is too loud for the person to be heard completely or accurately, or the cell phone connection keeps breaking up as the phone moves from location to location.

- The cultural differences between sender and receiver present obstacles due to language (including dialects), beliefs, habits, and practices.

- Communicators tend to selectively listen, not allowing themselves to hear the message as intended because of their own bias and beliefs.

- Sender and receiver place a different value on the message and from whom it is received, preventing reception of the entire message and/or understanding the intent and content of the message.

- The level of trust may cause either party to pay undue attention to the search for an underlying agenda and perceived manipulation or falsification rather than the face value of the message itself. This may be affected if the sender has made statements that cause the receiver to discount the message.

- Detection of, or perception that, the information conveyed in the message has been manipulated or altered to portray a more positive spin than the data warrant. For example, the subordinate tells the boss what the subordinate thinks the boss wants to hear—rather than the true and complete facts.

3. COMMUNICATIONS IN A GLOBAL ECONOMY

> Identify key challenges of communicating across different time zones, cultures, languages, terminology, and business practices and present ways of overcoming them. (Apply)
>
> **Body of Knowledge III.B.3**

The obstacles shown in Table 9.1, and more, complicate and hinder effective communication within a global enterprise. Overcoming each obstacle requires:

- A commitment to find a way to overcome the obstacle

- The willingness to adopt and adapt to new ways of communicating and to integrate those ways with the practices of the organization

- The ability to accept that there may always be differences, but the best approach that can be expected has been subjected to discussion with and consensus of the parties involved and agreement as to the practice or protocol

- Top management's commitment to continual improvement for the mutual best interest of all stakeholders

Table 9.1 Some of the communication obstacles facing organizations operating globally and possible remedies.

Obstacle encountered	Possible remedies
• Differences in cultures (politics, religion, social practices, business practices, and so on) Example: The business practices are alien to employees of the organization's new plant opened in China.	• Set the learning about the differences as a strategic objective for foreign facility management and headquarters management (immersion training) • Establish and distribute a newsletter to all employees, with side-by-side articles published in each of the languages used in the organization's locations • Create a position at each organization's location that will be responsible for answering employees' questions regarding the organization's policies and practices • Periodically convene a diagonal slice of the organization's employees, at each location, to assess the effectiveness of internal communications and uncover areas for improvement • Carefully monitor complaints or any hints of displeasure with the handling of cultural issues and take corrective and preventive action as needed
• Language differences (multiple languages and dialects, even in the same country) Example: The workforce hired by the new plant will be drawn from a multiethnic population comprising persons from three different tribes (each with their language variations), as well as two large groups originally from India and China (each with different language variations).	• Cross-train key personnel from both offshore locations and headquarters in everyday common business languages of the offshore locations and headquarters • Provide glossaries/dictionaries to personnel in the offshore locations as well as headquarters containing the common business terms and idioms in use • Provide orientation training for new hires in offshore locations stressing critical oral and written expressions and warnings that could affect their safety and security
• Time differentials (time zones as well as differing perceptions of time) Example: Most of the local population place a low emphasis on adhering to schedules.	• Establish and publish the business hours and protocols for communications to and from offshore locations • Through orientation and daily communication, address the importance of the day and time issue with offshore employees
• Additional risks (disaster- and political unrest-prone geographic areas, financial instability of regions and/or industries, predominant ethical and moral attitudes and customers of a geographic area) Example: Operating in a country where extreme poverty exists, crime and corruption are rampant, and the local leaders expect the incoming organization to "contribute" to the community in exchange for protection and ease in transacting business.	• Assess and continually update the assessments of additional risks that are likely when operating in specific offshore locations • Establish the responsible person, in both the offshore locations and headquarters, who will continually administer the programs and actions necessary to minimize or eliminate the risks (this may be outsourced)

Table 9.1 Some of the communication obstacles facing organizations operating globally and possible remedies. *(continued)*

Obstacle encountered	Possible remedies
	• Establish a system of listening posts (key people who will watch for local events and actions that could affect the risk exposure of the organization) and the means for reporting and acting on the information gathered • Understand and adhere to applicable anticorruption regulations
• Incompatibility of organizational structures and managing styles Example: Working with local tribal leadership.	• Recognize and address local perceptions of how the location/facility should be organized and managed • Accommodate local preferences as long as such preferences can be integrated into the business practices without negative impact to the organization
• Incompatibility of managerial and workforce competencies • Incompatibility of organizational structures and managing styles Example: Newly hired managers have no experience in coaching and participative management techniques. The newly hired workforce expects to be told what to do and does not expect to offer improvement suggestions.	• Assess and address the differential in managerial and workforce competencies between what the organization normally expects and what exists at the offshore location • Establish training and education to address the gaps in knowledge, experience, skills, aptitude, and attitude • Establish temporary coaches and advisors to facilitate operations until trained local personnel are fully capable • Establish appropriate incentives for individuals' improving their competencies
• Incompatibility of financial matters (currency, rates of exchange, accounting methods, pricing issues, inventory valuation, invoicing practices, payment collection practices, and so on) Example: Local payment collection practices vary based on from whom the payment is due. Some payments from certain constituencies may be waived in exchange for favors.	• Assess and address differences in handling financial matters • Establish training and education programs to clarify the organization's objectives and to ensure that pertinent policies, procedures, and regulations are understood and followed • Establish auditing programs to surface deviations from accepted practices and identify areas for improvement
• Incompatibility of electronic interfaces Example: Customer order data are garbled in transmission from the United States to a plant in Malaysia.	• Assess and address incompatibilities due to equipment design and operation and/or incompatible programs • Set up a corrective action team, including users and supplier, to work out solutions to the problems (may be a virtual team) • Create temporary communication processes to mitigate the condition and enable communication to continue • Establish help desks and remedial programs to quickly correct problems • Form preventive action teams to continually improve electronic interface systems

Succeed in the Global Workplace

The following is not intended to be a complete list of competencies in the global workplace, but merely suggestive:

- Study and understand the philosophies, beliefs, regulations/laws, and strategies of the global markets in which the organization does or will operate.

- Understand pertinent global business protocols, procedures, and practices.

- Develop global networks, both personal and organizational.

- Learn the business language of the pertinent global location.

- Gather information about, study, and understand the pertinent global cultures, especially as they relate to doing business.

- Modify the communication media, protocols, and styles to address the needs to be faced in the targeted global location, with care taken to sustain the organization's ethics and social responsibilities.

- Build or modify negotiation and decision-making skills to effectively deal with persons from the pertinent global location.

4. COMMUNICATIONS AND TECHNOLOGY

> Identify how technology affects communications, including improved information availability, its influence on interpersonal communications, and etiquette for e-communications. Deploy appropriate communication methods within virtual teams. (Apply)
>
> **Body of Knowledge III.B.4**

Uses of Information Systems

Information technology (IT) plays a fundamental role in organizational communications. Following are examples of just a few changes that have occurred in organizations since computer technology became a core part of business systems:

- A bank teller checks his or her employee benefits information by looking on the corporate intranet instead of reading a printed brochure formerly mailed home.

- A professor sends students a text message asking why they have missed class, rather than sending an e-mail.

- A technician monitors performance of a machine by looking at a graphic display in a control room miles away instead of reading an analog dial located at the machine site.

- A sales agent checks availability of a product by using a cell phone (accessing the inventory database through a wireless link) instead of waiting to look it up from a wired computer.

- A construction firm checks the status of a shipment using the shipping company's web-based tracking system.

- A VP or sales director shares sales trends by using a webinar application and sharing computer screens.

Information systems are used by organizations for three primary types of tasks: operations support, day-to-day decision-making, and strategic analysis. Operations support includes processing transactions—for example, a bank ATM, a point-of-sale connection in a retail store, or an online registration for a conference or course. Operations support also includes process monitoring and control. Monitoring and control applications might be a robotic assembly operation or the automatic pilot on an aircraft. Day-to-day decision-making is the analysis of process and business performance measures. Examples would include tracking of sales, on-time delivery, cycle time, and quality indicators, as well as financial and customer satisfaction metrics. Strategic analysis of longer-term indicators provides data for supporting decisions made from examining market sector and product line trends in order to project future business performance requirements.

Following are a few examples of how an effective information system enables analysis, control, and/or projection of performance:

- A regional salesperson can compare sales with objectives, verify that the product mix is appropriate, see if the plant or warehouse is experiencing difficulty meeting requested delivery dates, and check on commissions earned in the period to date.

- The regional sales manager is able to reference an artificial intelligence-driven status board to help manage development of specific customer types, manage the sales force, and provide performance feedback and direction to local salespersons.

- The VP of sales can access data for deciding how to allocate sales territories, manage the regional sales managers (support, coaching, performance feedback), and look at actual-versus-budget comparisons.

- The marketing VP can use cumulative information for forecasting buying trends, look at geographic differences in product preference, and do forward-trending analysis to evaluate the impact of possible new regional advertising.

- The operations plant manager can have early indications of actual changes or even projected product mix changes that will affect production schedules, inventories, purchases of raw materials, and the need for additional resources.

- The finance VP can use a simulation model on potential upward or downward trends in sales revenue to anticipate issues and plan for improvements in the financial position of the organization.

- The human resources VP and staff can utilize early indications of potential needs for staffing and training.

- The product development group can see how recently introduced products are selling, where traditional product sales are slumping, and where new needs may be developing.

Information systems are used to manage data about customers, suppliers, employees, finances, products, and processes. A well-designed system will allow the information generated at one level to be used at other levels. Figure 9.2 shows an example of some of the processes a bookstore might integrate into an information system.

Some of the more important information needed by an organization for long-term success is not generated internally. Information system design should consider the need for input of external information about competitors, markets, noncustomers, and societal trends. Sources for acquiring such information should be identified, as well as how it will be analyzed and integrated with, or compared to, company-specific information. Additionally, information systems increasingly need to be able to communicate information externally, such as for supply chain optimization.

The importance of information systems can be clearly seen by looking at their impact on various aspects of quality management. For example, both process management and problem-solving require accurate and timely information. A well-designed and maintained information system can simplify decision-making through the use of graphic displays of statistical and trend analysis. Information systems are also key to successful employee empowerment (see Chapter 2) and cross-functional collaboration since distributed information access is required in order for groups and employees to make quick and accurate decisions.

Figure 9.2 Levels of information systems.

The Technology in Information Systems

Depending on the types and volume of information, as well as differences in distribution needs, many information systems, like organizational structures, combine aspects of both centralization and decentralization. Mainframes or server farms may be used to manage organization-wide information pertaining to products and customers, while personal computers (decentralized) handle functional or process-specific information (for example, a computer-aided design [CAD] system for engineering, a workstation computer showing machine operations status). Local networks and the internet allow the information on these separate systems to be shared with or accessed by others. Wireless technology also expands the availability of information to and from any location and allows tablets or cell phones to perform some of the up-front data processing. Information may be stored in cloud-based storage anywhere in the world.

Technology decisions are also important to having a reliable information management system. Redundancy of portions of the hardware or software and databases is necessary to enable some processes to operate if a system fault occurs. These redundant data files will need to be updated or synchronized. Staying abreast of changes in technology while also maintaining a common core (for example, customer databases) is vital to competitiveness. Control of both applications software and databases is increasingly seen as proprietary to the business and, therefore, requires confidentiality and security. With the increasing trend toward external (cloud) data storage systems, this security issue becomes a business risk, as does the rise of government-supported actors seeking to obtain confidential data.

As data theft becomes more complex, the area of data security becomes simultaneously everyone's job and the job of specialists. The specialists keep abreast of new modes of hacking, and everyone needs to be made aware of their role in countering data theft.

Design of the information system, although enabled by new technologies, should be based on the organization's strategy, structure, and business systems. That is, information system strategy should be driven by business strategy, rather than vice versa. Organizations frequently have a chief information officer whose role it is to facilitate this integration. In an organization where the information system is well integrated with strategy, the system becomes a business model of the organization, showing what is measured, what is considered important, and how widely information is dispersed. This means that as strategy, structure, and/or business processes change, the information system will also need to be modified. The particular measures tracked and reported, at least at the decision-making and strategy levels, will also shift. The effect of rapid technological change and the increasingly competitive environment means that IT investment has become a growing proportion of the capital investment of most organizations.

Employee competency must be adequate for effective use of the IT applications provided, meaning that proper training and ongoing technical support of hardware and software are critical to the successful use of technology. The design of any information system should consider these fundamental questions:

- What specific information is needed, and by whom?

- What precision is needed, and how often should data be collected and analyzed?

- What standard reports should be available, and how should they be delivered?

- How long should the information be maintained (for example, archived)?

Not only is information itself vital to quality performance; the quality of the data themselves is critical. This requires that the process for collecting the data, whether manual or automatic, be validated. It is also important to ensure that the process for subsequent (and often automatically generated) computer analysis of the data be confirmed. For example, ensuring that auto accidents are correctly recorded (location, time, people and property involved, and cause) is important for each insurance claim. Accident information may then be automatically compiled for a state highway department, which relies on correct accident categorization and geographic grouping by the computer's software. The more automated the data collection becomes, the harder it is to maintain high-quality data.

Distribution of Information

In formatting data and reports, consider that some situations for which the information will be used are structured and predictable, while others are unstructured and unpredictable. In many cases users need the ability to look at the information in different ways. For example, sales data are useful when organized by segment. Allowing data to be viewed as text, numeric summaries, or graphics allows users to look for different types of patterns. Multidimensional graphics—for example, three-dimensional and color, as in geographic information systems (GISs)—and computer data mining can surface complex relationships that would otherwise not be discernable.

Big data, or data mining, is crucially dependent on accurate data. Most big data projects will spend 80% of their budget on data cleansing. Some firms have abandoned their big data efforts due to these costs and related delays.

Of course, not all information will be viewed or analyzed on a computer screen. Processes must be defined for distribution of appropriate information, usually in summary form, to other sources for communication such as bulletin boards, management reports, meetings, newsletters, e-mails, or the company website. Reports should take into consideration different personal decision-making styles and how information may need to be presented in a variety of formats.

Information must be available at the point of use. It should enable each user access to something on which to act or that provides a broader picture to allow the user to make more system-based decisions. As much as possible, the information should be integrated into the process being carried out rather than having it captured at a different location and then reported to the user. The purpose of process information is to:

- Allow action to be taken to have an impact on current performance

- Verify that past actions were appropriate

- Predict actions that need to be taken (or not taken) in the future

Not all information captured by an organization is of the same level of importance. In some cases analysis and reporting can be done on an exception basis, although the rules for what is to be considered an exception must be carefully defined and those definitions maintained. Computer models, expert systems, neural networks, artificial intelligence, and other techniques can be useful when the decisions to be made involve many variables or a complex and dynamic process, or when it is vital that many people take similar actions based on the same information.

Using Information for Managing Organizational Performance

Alignment and integration of business processes and performance measures is necessary in order for the information captured to support the organization's strategic goals and objectives. Alignment includes both vertical and horizontal aspects.[3] *Vertical* alignment makes sure that performance measures used at lower-level processes in the organization support the measures used in higher-level processes, while *horizontal* alignment means measures at one process will support effective performance of upstream and downstream processes, including those of suppliers, customers, and other stakeholders. *Integration* calls for making sure that the various systems, and their performance measures, work together rather than against each other and that the measures effectively implement the organization's stated values and strategies.

Analysis of performance measures should be defined according to who is responsible for the analysis (and subsequent action) and the frequency of the review. Reviews might be done by individuals or groups, and the frequency varies from continual to perhaps monthly or quarterly. In general, lower-level measures (for example, operational) are monitored much more frequently than higher-level (for example, strategic), although modern IT is allowing this to change (for example, an organization that is able to perform a traditional type of financial closing at any time, within an hour). The information needed to support the deployment of strategic goals, objectives, and action plans, and the monitoring, measuring, and reporting of actual versus planned performance, is critical to sustaining a viable strategic planning process.

Some related issues and concerns are:

- Care must be exercised to alleviate personal information overload to the extent possible.

- Security of data and information, and potential for misuse, requires increasing vigilance.

- The high risks of upgrading to the newest technology must be carefully assessed.

- Care must be taken to not emphasize technology to the detriment of stakeholder relations and needs.

- Service excellence is measured from a different perspective when looking from the inside out, rather than as perceived by the service receiver.

- Information systems can be either a competitive advantage or a disadvantage, depending on how used—for example, in the impact of these systems on an organization's customers, in their ability to be responsive to the marketplace, and in their capability to support a high level of performance (quality and quantity).

- An information system is only as effective as the quality of the planning that created it, the quality of the people who manage it, and the quality of the uses to which it is put. A highly sophisticated system poorly designed, poorly operated, inappropriately used, or inadequate to meet the needs for which it was intended is a drain on the resources of an organization.

Living with Ongoing Obsolescence

Few areas of a quality manager's role are as fraught with continual change as communications technology. As soon as a new device or communication mode is established, it becomes obsolete. Examples of technology changes and changes in users' habits are:

- *Cell phone.* Cell phones have rapidly evolved into smartphones, which provide instantaneous business and personal communication worldwide. This ability to review, prepare, send, and receive documents as well as follow world news and events has transformed any location where we might be into an effective business office. With these technological advances, problems have developed. Many professionals find it difficult to distinguish when business concludes and how to separate personal activities from professional activities.

- *Internet.* The World Wide Web (www) offers a myriad of means and methods for communicating, reactively as well as proactively. Even the most obscure business can now portray itself as a major player through the magic of animated and interactive websites. Bona fide sharers of information can post their articles, newsletters, and viewpoints and join chat groups to discuss issues. Sellers can directly accept customers' orders and payments through their websites. Buyers can track the progress and shipping status of their orders. Researchers can access a seemingly infinite number of resources through powerful search engines. Social media can instantly make or break a reputation. Weblogs (blogs or vlogs) created by individuals or organizations provide another outlet for recording and disseminating news and views. Short seminars (webinars) are offered, often in fifteen- to twenty-minute chunks, for learners with a myriad of interests and needs. Many educational institutions provide degree programs that can be completed without ever attending the brick-and-mortar site.

It is mostly true that if you want information and know how to search for it, you will find more than you ever expected, needed, or wanted. Also, larger organizations have implemented *intranets* that operate within the organization and its physical locations.

On the negative side is the outrageous quantity of data and information considered objectionable by many internet users (for example, pornography, solicitations for participation in unprintable acts, criminal advice, hate messages, and so on). Such material is so easily accessed that organizations have had to issue policies and disciplinary guidelines to attempt to quell the curiosity of their employees.

- *E-mail.* The expansion of electronic mail has replaced most regular mail. An e-mail message takes seconds to transmit and be received. Even with lengthy attached electronic documents, the elapsed time is negligible. Documents with electronic signatures are now widely accepted. Basic e-mail etiquette is continually being updated. Lists and suggestions range from discussions of brevity to grammar and punctuation usage, layout, font type and size, and things not to do.

Access one of the many websites by searching "e-mail etiquette." The speed with which e-mail is usually composed and the informality of its use has caused concern. Oft forgotten by e-mail users is the fact that the received e-mail is a direct reflection of the organization issuing it. Sloppy grammar, misspellings, incomplete information, incorrect information, and lack of good manners can, without careful checking by the sender, convey the sending organization's image, bad or good.

There are ways to manage these newer forms of communication. There is no doubt that these new devices have made communications management more complex. According to Smarsh (a Portland, Oregon, advisory firm),[4] there needs to be "clear policies and a technology foundation that allows for capture and supervision. Supervising your company's electronic communications data can help you realize more effective risk detection, mitigation, and management in the long run."

The recommendation from Smarsh includes five principles:

1. A sound data governance framework: leaders who meet to discuss challenges and make action plans

2. A culture of risk avoidance and compliance: this is part and parcel of a quality manager's role, visible in many other portions of the body of knowledge

3. A constant drive for efficiency: collaboration and sharing of risk-detection resources with other departments will help when budgets are tight

4. Innovative technology that supports risk detection: while risk starts with people, having tools to retain and evaluate content from employees allows for spotting problems before they become large

5. A commitment to constant improvement: once again, this fits in with the rest of a quality manager's role

The International Risk Management Institute suggests seven steps to manage e-mail:[5]

1. Automate tasks

2. Preview messages

3. Discipline yourself

4. Do not duplicate

5. Stay safe

6. Establish an electronic communication policy

7. Block junk and offensive mail and teach employees how to use filtering tools

Multifunction electronic devices. The wireless laptop computer has evolved to notepad technology and in some cases, cell phone or smartphone technology. These miniature electronic devices are replacing desktop and laptop computers. Their ease of use and small size makes them very convenient for professionals required to travel or who work from different locations. And, with voice-over internet capability, the laptop competes with the smartphone for visual, as well as verbal, contact with the other parties involved in the call or meeting. As new applications (apps) are developed to add functionality to smartphones, they become stronger contenders for primary communication devices.

These technological advances have transformed your automobile into a mobile communications center. Voice interaction, including access to cell phone messages, the internet, and emergency services, is provided by most vehicle manufacturers. Voice-activated internet access devices have become very popular, but who is listening and how do they avoid "eavesdropping"?

Social media. The widespread use of various and changing social media outlets has created many kinds of communication risks and opportunities. These currently (2020) include YouTube, Facebook, Instagram, Pinterest, Snapchat, LinkedIn, and Twitter. These are often relied on by individuals for news, new products, references or referrals, and background information. Not tracking these outlets may allow reputational risk to accumulate, and often very quickly.[6]

Assess the Risks

Highly integrated systems are, like any multipurpose machine, subject to breakdown if any one component fails to function properly (the weakest link). Before considering and buying the latest and greatest information-age system, care must be taken to think through the multitude of possible scenarios that a malfunction could cause and assess the impact and risks of each. Can a disabled information system be survived? For how long and at what cost? If the organization chooses to buy it, what data safety and backup provisions will be needed? What security issues may be created with use of the latest technology?

REFERENCES

1. S. I. Hayakawa, *Language in Thought and Action* (New York: Harcourt Brace Jovanovich, 1972).

2. T. Morrison, W. A. Conaway, and G. A. Borden, *Kiss, Bow, or Shake Hands: How to Do Business in Sixty Countries* (Holbrook, MA: Adams Media, 1994).

3. L. L. Silverman, and A. L. Probst, *Critical Shift: The Future of Quality in Organizational Performance* (Milwaukee: ASQ Quality Press, 1999), 96–97.

4. *Five Keys to Managing Risk within Electronic Communications* (blog), May 30, 2019, accessed June 1, 2019, https://www.smarsh.com/blog/five-keys-managing-risk-within-electronic-communications/.

5. S. Anderson, "Managing Electronic Communications," International Risk Management Institute, July 2000, accessed June 1, 2019, https://www.irmi.com/articles/expert-commentary/managing-electronic-communications.

6. K. Spisak, *Business 2 Community*, January 2019, accessed January 13, 2020, https://www.business2community.com/social-media/2019-social-media-trends-statistics-02156179.

See Appendix A for additional references for this chapter.

Chapter 10
C. Project Management

P*roject management* is a collection of proven techniques for proposing, planning, implementing, managing, and evaluating projects, combined with the art of managing people.[1] Projects are actions performed by people, usually with limited resources. Projects have a beginning and an end, whereas most everyday operations are ongoing. Projects may be needed at any organizational level. They can range from a massive effort (for example, a satellite global warming monitoring system) to a small, short-term project involving a few people from a single organizational entity (for example, a weekend relocation of a ten-person function to an office on another floor).

Projects are initiated for a variety of reasons, such as to:

- Develop or modify a product or service

- Start up a new business

- Implement a new process or system or introduce new equipment, tools, or techniques

- Reengineer a process to reduce customer complaints, decrease cycle time, and eliminate errors

- Relocate or close a facility

- Reduce environmental impact

- Comply with regulatory mandates

- Address a community issue

Activities and/or events that can trigger the initiation of a project may include the need to:

- Implement strategic goals and objectives by deploying strategic plans downward in the organization to where action plans (projects) are initiated

- Respond to an audit finding

- Take action resulting from a deficiency uncovered in a management review of existing processes

- Resolve an existing or potential process, product, or service deficiency identified through trend analysis

- Prepare to address identified threats to market share, customer retention, and profitability

- Address identified opportunities to expand and/or change focus in how products/services are marketed, produced, and delivered

- Take advantage of unrealized core competencies, strengths, or resources by initiating an innovative service development

Short-term projects are generally those that can be completed within one year. The short-term objectives that trigger these projects are called *tactical objectives.* Typical characteristics of short-term projects are:

- They require less rigorous or no risk analysis.

- They require fewer resources.

- They are typically not cross-functional.

- They may produce immediate cost savings.

- They require only a limited set of project management tools and at a lower level of sophistication.

- They are easier to obtain approval, funding, and organizational support for.

Examples of short-term projects include:

- Improving the quality of residential electric service installations by 25%

- Reducing defects on production line 2 from 5% to 1%

- Reducing the cost of claim-processing data entry errors by 10% within the calendar year

- Assisting the hospital's pharmacy in reducing cycle time in fulfilling drug orders

Long-term objectives are strategic and lead to projects typically taking longer than one year to implement. Typical characteristics of long-term projects are:

- They require risk and feasibility analyses.

- They are most often cross-functional.

- They have a major impact, over a long period, on internal and external organizations.

- They typically require a large commitment of resources.

- They are often a breakthrough initiative.

Examples of long-term projects include:

- Establishing or buying a new business

- Designing and implementing a customer-supplier strategic alliance between a custom packager and a distributor

- Implementing a quality management system in a contract metal products fabricating company and certifying it to the International Organization for Standardization (ISO) 9001 standard

- An educational institution preparing for and applying for the Baldrige Award

- Designing and implementing a municipal waste treatment program and facility

All but very small projects tend to be cross-functional, meaning they require direction, cooperation, and resources from multiple contributors, functions, or departments. For example, in a manufacturing environment, changing a component's outer case from aluminum to plastic would affect engineering, purchasing, production, shipping, sales, and possibly other functions (including suppliers). Because there may be a number of initiatives competing for the same resources, project leaders should take into account the needs of all the affected organizational entities.

1. PROJECT MANAGEMENT BASICS

> Use project management methodology and ensure that each project is aligned with strategic objectives. Plan the different phases of a project: initiation, planning, execution, monitoring and controlling, and closure. Ensure the project is on time and within budget. Consider alternate project management methodologies (linear, evolutionary, or iterative) as they apply to the project. (Evaluate)
>
> **Body of Knowledge III.C.1**

Project Life Cycle

The life cycle of a project may be defined in five stages:

1. Initiating the project

2. Planning the project

3. Executing the project

4. Monitoring and controlling the project

5. Evaluating and closing out the project

Understanding a project's life cycle leads to better estimation of what resources need to be applied and when. Identifying the stages also provides for intermediate decision points (go/no-go) as a stage nears completion. The advantage of planning by stages is that fewer contingencies need be built into the estimates of the total project, as funding and resource allocations are made stage by stage, with greater knowledge of actual requirements just prior to each new stage.

Initiating the Project

According to the Project Management Organization, *a project is a temporary endeavor undertaken to create a unique product, service, or result*.[2] Projects can occur at all levels of the organization and be of all sizes and lengths. Typically, projects become more complex and prone to risks the larger they grow, which requires more extensive project management methods and tools. To initiate a project, some type of project charter should be developed to identify the purpose, objectives, goal, scope, stakeholders, and potential benefits of the project. Projects should align to and support the strategic goals of the organization. Projects drive change and organize the people, activities, and deliverables that help to ensure a successful project. The Project Management Institute's (PMI) *Project Management Body of Knowledge (PMBOK)* guide identifies several reasons for projects and project management methods and tools: technological changes, competitive forces or actions, market or customer demand, political or regulatory changes, economic issues, process improvements, strategic goals, and environmental or social changes.[3]

Planning the Project

Planning determines the activities to be performed, who needs to do them, and by when to achieve the project's objectives. There are nine major components to be determined in the planning phase:[4]

- Objectives: the measurable goals or targets of the project
- Program: the strategy and major actions to achieve the objectives
- Schedule: the detailed plan including the activities, time lines, and resources to achieve the objectives
- Budget: the estimated expenditures of resources required for the project
- Forecast: the expected estimate of what will happen within a certain time frame
- Organization: the organizational structure of how the people will be organized within the project
- Policy: the overarching guide for decision-making
- Procedure: the detailed steps for how work will be performed
- Standard: the expected levels of performance

Additional planning activities and tools will be discussed in the next section.

Life Cycle Project Management Methodologies

There are three main life cycle project management categories of methodologies: (1) waterfall, linear, or predictive; (2) evolutionary or incremental, and (3) iterative or agile. Traditionally, most projects were performed using a waterfall, also called

Model	Advantages	Disadvantages
Waterfall, linear, predictive	• Can be easier to manage • Enables a more detailed plan early in the project • More predictable estimates of costs and schedule if requirements are stable • No partial solutions are given to the customer	• Can be rigid and inflexible • Requirements changes can cause increases in schedule and delivery times • Testing and feedback can be late in the project plan
Incremental and iterative	• Responsive to changes in the technology and requirements • Good method if requirements are not clearly defined early in the project • Interim functionality can be delivered earlier in the project	• More expensive because each new increment or iteration is a new project • Typically can take much longer to deliver a finished product • Difficult to predict final costs and time lines • Active customer involvement is critical throughout the project

Figure 10.1   Advantages and disadvantages of life cycle models.
Source: Sandra L. Furterer.

a linear or predictive project management approach. The project followed a linear method starting with project initiation, planning, execution, monitoring and controlling, and project closure. All of the customers' and stakeholders' requirements would be developed for the entire project, product, or process once in the requirements analysis phase, then designed, developed, tested, and implemented. The scope, project plan, and resources are developed early in the project. The scope is closely managed throughout the project.

In the evolutionary or incremental method, the product is produced through a series of iterations that add functionality within a specified time frame. The functionality is considered complete only after the final iteration.

In the iterative method, the scope is determined early in the project, but the time and cost estimates are routinely modified based on the team's increasing knowledge of the project parameters and requirements. Iterations develop the product, process, or service in a series of iterative cycles. There are advantages and disadvantages to the different life cycle models, as shown in Figure 10.1.[5]

Waterfall, Linear, or Predictive Project Management

The waterfall life cycle is the traditional way that projects were performed until agile or iterative methods were created in the early 1990s. The waterfall cycle includes multiple phases that are followed sequentially, where the deliverables and knowledge from each phase flow into the next phase. The knowledge builds and becomes more detailed and also moves from conceptual to design-oriented or physical. For software projects, the waterfall phases are:

1) Requirements analysis and definition: The requirements are elicited and defined from the customer for the product, service, or process

2) Design: Definition of the design specifications that achieve the requirements

3) Implementation: Building the product

4) Testing: Verifying and validating the product

5) Installation: Installing the finished product

6) Maintenance: Maintaining the finished product

7) Disposal or retirement: Retiring or replacing the product and disposing of products, services, or processes

Evolutionary or Incremental Project Management

The evolutionary or incremental life cycle model provides initial capability of the product, service, or process, which is then followed by successive deliveries until the final product is delivered. An evolutionary or incremental life cycle model is used when rapid exploration and implementation of part of the product is desired, the requirements are unclear at the beginning, funding is constrained, the customer wishes to remain flexible and allow new technology to be applied later, and experimentation is required to develop successive prototypes or versions.[6]

Iterative Project Management, Including Agile and Scrum

Agile and Scrum methods typically are considered to be provided using an iterative project management methodology.[7] However, the PMI *PMBOK* describes leveraging both incremental and iterative approaches, as this allows for iterating on increments of the functionality.[8] Iterative development processes provide several distinct advantages:[9]

• Continuous integration and testing of the evolving product

• Demonstration of progress more frequently than in a waterfall model

• Early warnings of problems

• Early delivery of subsets of capabilities or functionality

Agile Methodology

The agile project management method is an iterative, adaptive, and interpersonal approach that focuses on delivering what the customer truly needs.[10] The agile method began in software development but has migrated to use in other industries, including financial services, consulting, traditional metal manufacturing, and defense industries.[11]

Nerur, Mahapatra, and Mangalaraj contrasted the traditional software development approach to the agile development approach across several elements. In traditional development, the systems are considered fully specifiable and predictable and can be built through extensive planning. In agile development, the systems have high-quality, adaptive software that can be continuously developed and improved in small teams, with rapid testing and feedback. The control mechanisms for the traditional methods are process centered, while agile is people centered. The management style for traditional is command and control, while leadership and collaboration is key for agile methods. The knowledge management is explicit and well documented for traditional approaches but tacit and embedded within people in the agile method. The communication for a traditional approach is formal, versus informal for the agile method. The customer is important in identifying and validating requirements for the traditional approach but considered critical in the agile method. In the traditional method, the project cycle is managed by tasks and activities, while in the agile method it is guided by the product features. The development model for the traditional method is some variation of the life cycle model, such as waterfall, spiral, or a variation of these, while an evolutionary model is applied for the agile method. The desired organizational structure is bureaucratic and formalized for the traditional method yet very flexible and organic in the agile method. The agile method favors object-oriented technology, while there is no technological restriction in the traditional approach.[12]

The Agile Manifesto states four principles that the authors value:[13]

- Individuals and interactions over processes and tools

- Working software over comprehensive documentation

- Customer collaboration over contract negotiation

- Responding to change over following a plan

The authors of the Agile Manifesto defined twelve agile principles:[14]

- Our highest priority is to satisfy the customer through early and continuous delivery of valuable software.

- Welcome changing requirements, even late in development. Agile processes harness change for the customer's competitive advantage.

- Deliver working software frequently, from a couple of weeks to a couple of months, with a preference to the shorter timescale.

- Business people and developers must work together daily throughout the project.

- Build projects around motivated individuals. Give them the environment and support they need and trust them to get the job done.

- The most efficient and effective method of conveying information to and within a development team is face-to-face conversation.

- Working software is the primary measure of progress.

- Agile processes promote sustainable development. The sponsors, developers, and users should be able to maintain a constant pace indefinitely.

- Continuous attention to technical excellence and good design enhances agility.

- Simplicity—the art of maximizing the amount of work not done—is essential.

- The best architectures, requirements, and designs emerge from self-organizing teams.

- At regular intervals, the team reflects on how to become more effective, then tunes and adjusts its behavior accordingly.

A study by Lappi et al. identified important project governance elements in agile projects, categorized by goal setting, incentives, monitoring, coordination, roles and decision-making power, and capability-building practices.

The following lists the key agile practices within the governance categories:[15]

Goal setting:

- Customer and team cooperation for setting initial and flexible requirements and team-level goals

- Product backlog and vision guide the prioritization and iteration process

- Deliverable definition based on user stories

Incentives:

- The agile philosophy is the best incentive for gaining team members' commitment

- Peer recognition, project-based organizational structure, decision-making authority, and customer contact supports team dedication

- Limited monetary incentives and risk and opportunity-sharing addressed for motivation with agile

Monitoring:

- Monitoring by teams using sprint and iteration reviews with customer feedback

- Standard and quantitative measures, with agile-specific qualitative measures

- Visual tracking for deliverables

- Testing is important to validate user stories, with emphasis on automated testing

Coordination:

- Real-time communicating of information between empowered teams

- Iterative project planning with product vision and backlogs

- Providing infrastructure and practices for customer involvement and team autonomy

- Managing change through continuous prioritizations

- Facilitating frequent customer deliveries

Roles and decision-making power:

- Agile project teams with cross-functional roles and customer involvement

- Agile project team has total autonomy in decision-making

- Adaptive leadership by the project manager

- Agile coach oversees agile capabilities; Scrum master manages sprints and project team performance

Capability building:

- Clients' capabilities are key to success

- Optimal capability of agile team needs to address tensions between high- and low-skilled workers and specialization versus cross-functionality

- Key knowledge exchange within the team, with key stakeholders and permanent organization

- Agile practices and tools support routine and continuous learning

There are several methodologies that align with the statements and principles in the Agile Manifesto and include:

- Scrum: A framework to deliver high-quality products, quickly. Scrum will be discussed further below.

- Lean (including kanban): A methodology focused on reducing waste and improving the productivity and speed of processes and projects. Some of the lean tools applied to agile projects are kanban (signals for production based on customer demand), visual control, pull, value stream mapping, value analysis, and waste analysis, to name a few.

- Extreme Programming (XP): An agile software development framework applying engineering practices for software development.

- Crystal: An agile software development approach focusing mainly on people and their interactions, rather than processes and tools.

- Dynamic systems development method (DSDM): An agile project delivery framework that is both iterative and incremental, incorporating agile methods and principles including continuous customer involvement.

- Feature-driven development (FDM): An agile software development methodology focusing on product features.

- Rapid application development (RAD): An agile software development methodology that focuses on rapid prototype releases and iterations.

Scrum

Scrum is defined by its creators as *a framework within which people can address complex adaptive problems while productively and creatively delivering products of the highest possible value.*[16] Scrum has been used for many different applications, such as software; hardware; embedded software; networks; autonomous vehicles; schools; and government, marketing, and managing organizations.[17]

Scrum is a simple yet incredibly powerful set of principles and practices that helps teams deliver products in short cycles, enabling fast feedback, continual improvement, and rapid adaptation to change:[18]

- A product owner creates a prioritized wish list called a *product backlog*.

- During *sprint planning*, the team pulls a small part of functionality from the top of that wish list, a *sprint backlog*, and decides how to implement those pieces.

- The team has a certain amount of time—a *sprint* (usually two to four weeks)—to complete its work, but it meets each day to assess its progress (daily Scrum).

- Along the way, the *Scrum master* keeps the team focused on its goal.

- At the end of the sprint, the work should be potentially shippable: ready to hand to a customer, put on a store shelf, or show to a stakeholder.

- The sprint ends with a sprint review and retrospective.

- As the next sprint begins, the team chooses another part of the product backlog and begins working again.

Scrum Tools and Activities

User Stories. User stories are typically narrative descriptions of the functionality to be delivered. The user stories represent the customers' needs and requirements for the product, system, or service.

Scrum Burndown Chart. The Scrum burndown chart is used to track the productivity of the team and to identify how much work remains and when it will be complete. The chart graphs the work remaining in hours (y-axis) versus the number of days worked. The slope of the curve represents the burndown velocity or rate of productivity (hours per day). The days to complete is equal to work remaining (hours) divided by the rate of productivity (hours per day).

Product Backlog and Sprints. The product backlog is a prioritized list of ideas for the product. This helps to break the functionality into small increments, or sprints. Sprints are typically one to four weeks. At the end of the sprint, the functionality should be shippable to the customer, or complete, and meet the customer's requirements based on the items identified to be worked on for the sprint.

Sprint Planning. During the sprint planning, the team pulls a small group of the items from the highest-priority items on the product backlog. The team then determines how best to accomplish those items during the next sprint. A review and retrospective ends the sprint.

Daily Scrum. A daily meeting where the team meets to assess progress and make needed adjustments.

Scrum Master and Scrum Team. The Scrum master leads the Scrum team to the project's goal. The Scrum master removes barriers to successful project completion. The Scrum teams work due to the interpersonal nature of the team. The teams meet daily to assess progress and self-correct their direction. The teams are cross-functional and have all the competencies needed to accomplish the work. In large projects, multiple Scrum teams could work together to coordinate the work of the project. The product owner is responsible for the product vision and achieving the project's goals.

Scrum of Scrums. The Scrum of Scrum is a daily meeting for the Scrum teams to coordinate across multiple Scrum teams, typically for larger Scrum projects.

2. PROJECT PLANNING AND ESTIMATION TOOLS

> Use tools such as risk assessment matrix, benefit-cost analysis, critical path method (CPM), Gantt chart, PERT, and work breakdown structure (WBS) to plan projects and estimate related costs. (Apply)
>
> **Body of Knowledge III.C.2**

Risk Assessment

Risk Assessment—Determining if the Project Is Feasible. All projects that consume organizational resources involve risk. Risk assessment is important inasmuch as the project might not achieve a level of results acceptable to stakeholders, might not be accomplished on time, or might require more financial capital than initially anticipated.

Potential risks can be identified through brainstorming by a team, input from stakeholders, or reviews of other projects. Quantifying risks involves looking at the probability of a particular event's occurrence and its resulting impact by using a tool such as failure mode and effects analysis. Project managers should carefully consider the risk orientation of the particular organization and stakeholders for which the project is being undertaken and not allow their own perspective to overly influence subsequent decisions. Benchmarking may be an initially useful tool to help determine what levels of performance other organizations have achieved, how the results have been accomplished, and what benefits were derived from the project.

As businesses respond to changes in markets, technology, and strategic emphasis, they allocate or reallocate financial resources for many purposes. The careful selection and successful implementation of business projects play a large role in organizational change. An organization's future economic success and long-term survival are dependent on the financial benefits of projects outweighing the associated costs. A basic rule of thumb is that all projects should be frequently assessed from the earliest stage through completion and implementation.

A simple project risk analysis for an emergency department Lean-Six Sigma project is shown in Figure 10.2.

The project risk assessment is typically performed as part of the initial project charter development. It describes the key risks that may potentially derail the project. It includes the following fields:

Project risk analysis			*Required*
Brainstorm the potential risks to a successful project, identify the likelihood that each will occur, the potential impact, and develop a mitigation strategy.			
Potential risk to successful project	Occurrence of risk	Impact of risk	Risk mitigation strategy
Resource availability	High	High	Coordinate with leadership team
Conflict with other projects	Low	Moderate	Coordinate with other project leaders
Financial status of hospital	High	Very High	Monitor status, implement quickly
Weather potential of hurricanes	Low	Very High	Monitor weather, develop contingency plans to continue project after hurricane hits

Figure 10.2   Sample emergency department patient length of stay improvement project risk analysis.
Source: Sandra L. Furterer.

- Project risks: potential risks that could impact a successful project

- Occurrence of risk: the probability that the risk will occur during the project. Typically rated as low, medium, or high but could have additional levels, such as very high, high, moderate, low, or very low.

- Impact of risk: the potential impact of the risk should it occur during the project. Typically rated as low, medium, or high but could have additional levels, such as very high, high, moderate, low, or very low.

- Risk mitigation strategy: the strategy that could help to mitigate or reduce the occurrence or impact of the risk.

Cost-Benefit Analysis (or Benefit-Cost Analysis)

Benefit-Cost Analysis. Top management must approve funding for projects that require significant financial resources. Therefore, before a proposed project is initiated, a benefit-cost analysis using projected revenues, costs, and net cash flows is performed to determine the project's financial feasibility. This analysis is based on estimates of the project's benefits and costs and the timing thereof. The results of the analysis are a key factor in deciding which projects will be funded. Upon project completion, accounting data are analyzed to verify the project's financial impact on the organization. In other words, management must confirm whether the project added to or detracted from the company's financial well-being.

In today's competitive global environment, resource allocation is complicated by the fact that business needs and opportunities are greater and more diverse and that improvements are often more difficult to achieve. Many of the easier projects have already been done. Therefore, top management requires that project benefits and costs be evaluated so that projects can be correlated to overall revenues, costs, customer satisfaction, market share, and other criteria. These factors are analyzed to maximize business returns and to limit risks and costs. Therefore, quality improvement projects are considered to be business investments—as are all cash or capital investments—in which benefits must exceed costs. Quality managers are additionally challenged in that many of these benefits and costs are not easily quantifiable, as is normally expected by executives, accountants, and financial officers.

Benefit-cost analysis strives to evaluate the benefits and costs associated with a project or initiative. Two types of benefits can be evaluated: direct or indirect. *Direct benefits* are easily measured and include issues such as increased production, higher quality, increased sales, reduced delivery costs, higher reliability, decreased deficiencies, and lower warranty costs. *Indirect benefits* are more difficult to measure and include such items as improved quality of work life, increased internal customer satisfaction, and better-trained employees. Similarly, two types of costs can be evaluated. *Direct costs* include equipment, labor, training, machinery, and salaries. *Indirect costs* include downtime, opportunity costs, pollution, and displaced workers.

$$\frac{\text{Sum (\$) of all benefits anticipated (say, \$855,000)}}{\text{Sum (\$) of all costs anticipated (say, \$90,000)}} = 9.5$$

This means $9.50 in benefits for every dollar expended.

Typically, a benefit-cost analysis is conducted on the basis of direct costs and direct benefits to:

- Assist in the performance of a what-if analysis

- Compare the benefits, costs, and risks of competing projects

- Allocate resources among multiple projects

- Justify expenditures for equipment, products, or people

Because many indirect benefits and costs are difficult to quantify, and time is needed to identify such costs, some worthy quality projects or initiatives could fail to obtain the necessary funding.

Quality professionals are expected to help their organizations profit from quality investments, so no project should receive automatic approval and resource allocation. To be competitive, companies must find ways to increase profitability while providing customers with high levels of satisfaction. The challenge, then, is to find the link between critical business performance measurements, such as profitability, and quality investments for improvement projects, programs, and initiatives. Although some quality benefits and costs are difficult to measure or are unknowable, the quality manager still must help determine and measure quality's effect on the organization's finances. One way is by measuring the cost of quality.

Project Selection Decision Analysis. Understanding the relationship between quality and profitability requires knowledge of:

- How meeting customer quality requirements affects customer satisfaction

- How quality initiatives are linked to satisfying customer requirements and expectations

- The relationship between quality investments and gross profits
- How to ensure that quality improvement focuses on the greatest returns
- How to track elements of the cost of quality
- How customer returns and customer satisfaction affect revenues
- How to quantify customer satisfaction

Projects approved and funded by top management affect an organization's growth and development as well as its ability to remain competitive and to survive. Success depends on a constant flow of new investment ideas that are activated through these projects. Accordingly, well-managed organizations go to great lengths to develop an effective process for submitting project proposals.

Project screening procedures must be established so that projects with the most merit are approved. Screening quality capital expenditure proposals can be a complex activity. Benefits can be gained from a careful analysis, but such an investigation has its own costs. Projects should be selected not only on the basis of their potential financial payback but also on the basis of their fit to overall business needs (for example, new product development, improvements in support systems, or improvement of the order fulfillment process).

Ranking and Prioritizing Projects. Several methods are commonly used to rank and select projects for inclusion in the organization's cash/capital budget. Projects may be accepted or rejected based on the limitations of capital or other resources. Five analysis methods are discussed:

1. Payback period
2. Net present value (NPV)
3. Internal rate of return (IRR)
4. Potential return on investment (ROI)
5. Estimated return on assets (ROA)

- *Payback period.* The payback period is the number of years it will take the results of the project to recover the investment from net cash flows. The first formal method developed to evaluate capital budgeting projects, the payback period is easily determined by accumulating the project's net cash flows to locate the point where they reach zero.

The payback period method provides a measure of project liquidity, or the speed with which cash invested in the project will be returned. Organizations short of cash may place greater value on projects with a high degree of liquidity. The payback period is often considered to be an indicator of the relative risk of projects inasmuch as managers generally can forecast near-term events better than those more distant. Overall, projects with relatively rapid returns are generally less risky than longer-term projects.

- *NPV.* To improve the accuracy of cash/capital project evaluations, discounted cash flow techniques were developed to take into account the time value of money. One such method, NPV, consists of finding the present value of each cash flow, discounted at an appropriate percentage rate, which is determined by the cost of capital to the organization and the projected risk of the flow. The higher the risk, the higher the discount rate required. Compute the project's NPV by adding the discounted net cash flows. When the NPV is positive, determine if the project is a prospect for acceptance. If two projects are positive, the one with a higher NPV is a more likely choice.

- *IRR.* This is a discount rate that causes NPV to equal zero. If the IRR is greater than the minimum required by the organization (for example, cost of capital or alternative investment options), the project is likely to be accepted.

- *ROI.* This analysis method is used both as an estimating tool to determine the potential return on an investment contemplated, as well as a measure of actual pay-off upon project completion. ROI tends to be more useful for evaluating the payoff potential of shorter-term projects inasmuch as it ignores the time value of money.

The four methods just discussed may be applied either to projects involving a one-time investment—for example, purchase of a major facility or equipment—or to a project involving cash outlays over several time periods. Figure 10.3 is an example of the latter.

Here's a scenario: Assume an organization is considering implementing a quality management system and seeking certification to the ISO 9001 standard. The time frame from start through registration is estimated to be eighteen months. Following certification, the registrar will conduct semiannual surveillance audits. The contract with the registrar will be for three years. One driving force for considering the project is the potential for acquiring a major new customer's business upon certification. Management's policy is to approve only major projects that can begin to produce a payback within three years from implementation and an ROI ratio of at least three to one.

Using a spreadsheet and the *insert function* capability, the quality manager constructs a table. The manager employs the *finance* functions of the spreadsheet to compute the NPV, using a 9% discount rate, and the IRR. Estimates of benefits are gleaned from internal sources—for example, marketing, for the value of additional business. The computations and analysis indicate a payback in the third year (one and one-half years following registration), an NPV of $53,457, an IRR of 99% (obviously positive), and a 3.19 to 1 ROI ratio. The manager presents his proposal to management, and the project is approved for inclusion in the annual

Rate	9%						
			D	E	F	G	H
A Year	B Cost	C Benefit	Net cash flow	Cumulative investment	Cumulative benefits	ROI ratio	Cum. net cash flow
1	$(15,000.00)	$800.00	$(14,200.00)	$15,000.00	$800.00	0.05	$(14,200.00)
2	$(12,200.00)	$5,600.00	$(6,600.00)	$27,200.00	$6,400.00	0.24	$(20,800.00)
3	$(4,000.00)	$45,000.00	$41,000.00	$31,200.00	$51,400.00	1.65	$20,200.00
4	$(4,000.00)	$61,000.00	$57,000.00	$35,200.00	$112,400.00	3.19	$77,200.00
Totals	$(35,200.00)	$112,400.00	$77,200.00				
NPV	$(29,952.40)	$83,409.55	$53,457.15	(Excel NPV calculation)			
IRR			99%	(Excel IRR calculation)			
Payback			In year 3	(See column H)			
ROI ratio			3.19	(Column G = Columns F/E)			

Figure 10.3 ISO 9001 quality system implementation and registration.

budget. (Note: The IRR computation was not really useful for this particular decision, but was included to show how the spreadsheet function is used.)

In practice, all of the capital decision rules described previously are used; however, these methods can lead to different conclusions. Obviously, the best method is the one that selects the set of cash/capital projects that will maximize value to an organization.

Three properties must be exhibited by a project selection method if it is to lead consistently to making favorable capital budgeting decisions. The method must consider all cash flows throughout the entire life of the project and the time value of money such that dollars acquired sooner are valued more than later dollars. In addition, when a method is being used to select from a set of mutually exclusive projects, it must choose the project that will maximize the organization's value.

In the example, the payback method fails the first two considerations by not addressing all cash flows and ignoring the time value of money. Both the NPV and the IRR provide appropriate financial accept/reject decisions for independent projects, but only the NPV method indicates maximization under all conditions. The ROI ignores cash flow and the time value of money, thereby rendering the method useful for only rudimentary analysis, or smaller, short-term projects.

Return on Assets or Return on Net Assets. Projects that involve primarily the acquisition of assets are often proposed on the basis that the asset will earn more than the asset cost. Capital invested in an asset is recovered through the money derived from the use of the asset over the useful life of the asset.

Here's an abbreviated example: Assume an asset has an initial cost of $5000 and an estimated useful life of five years, with an estimated salvage value of $1000. The interest rate is estimated at 6%. The total estimated benefit derived from use of the asset over its useful life is $475,700.

The simplified ROA ratio calculation is:

$5000/5$ years $= $1000 + ($1000 \times 6\%) = 1060 [asset cost per year]

$1060(5$ years$) = 5300 [gross estimate of asset's cost for useful life]

$5300 - $1000 = 4300 [asset cost less estimated salvage sale value]

$475,700 \div $4300 = 110.63 [estimated net ROA—$111 return for every $1 spent]

Factors complicating the computation of ROA could be adjusting for the time value of money (not included in the previous calculation), the varying rates at which benefits are realized during the life of the asset, and an asset being paid for incrementally over several years having an impact on the cash flow, possibly meaning a time-delayed investment and different interest costs. As a tool for selection and prioritization, ROA may be computed using only direct costs and primary benefits to develop a ballpark estimate.

Portfolio Analysis. Usually, the comparative value of the proposed projects to the organization is a major consideration in the acceptance of projects. This comparative value pertains to the financial impacts of ongoing projects relative to the potential impact on resources of the proposed projects. A common fallacy is to accept new projects solely on the basis of their projected positive ratios, ignoring the fact that the organization may not be able to absorb further depletion of its resources within the time frames projected. For these reasons, it is prudent to create a comparative table or chart (for example, a decision tree) showing the relative financial impacts of ongoing projects versus proposed projects. The results of each of the five computations may be displayed in a table or spreadsheet for analysis of the projects (present and proposed). Thus, analyzed as a portfolio, decision-making tools may be applied to aid in the selection, postponement, or elimination of proposed projects.

The Boston Consulting Group developed a framework for analyzing portfolios (BCG matrix) that focuses on three aspects of each alternative considered: sales, growth of market, and cash absorption or production. The goal of the analysis is to develop a balance between the alternatives that use up cash and those that supply cash. Porter discusses the use of this analysis technique.[19]

Prioritization Matrix. A two-dimensional, L-shaped matrix that compares project alternatives against weighted criteria.

Strategic Fit Analysis. The basic question is "Does the project fit within the organization's near-term and long-term strategy and available resources?" A potential project may suggest unsurpassed benefits to the organization but not be feasible given the organization's debts and volatility of the market. Essentially, this is a form of risk analysis.

With the strategic decision that a project should be planned, the planning and estimating stage begins.

Methodologies for Planning the Project

Table 10.1 shows a typical project-planning sequence. The sequence of steps will vary depending on the organization's needs. Following are a few examples of the variations:

- Project would not need to be justified if it has already been mandated by management or a regulatory requirement. Jump to sequence number 3.

- Project is small, involves only one work unit, should be completed in six weeks, and will cost less than $20,000, including a capital expenditure to replace one machine. Follow sequences 1, 2 (benefits-to-cost ratio only), 3 (project scope and objectives), 5 (pick two members of unit familiar with the situation), 6 (probably can skip unless revision is needed), 7 (list all deliverables), 9 (do, and add persons responsible as notes to the time lines), 10 (probably can skip if Gantt chart clearly shows dependencies at a glance), 11 (combine with budget), 13 (combine budget and resource requirements), 14 (define metrics and reports), 15 (detail depends on policy of organization—a simple memo approval may be all that is needed).

- Project involves a major reengineering of a whole product line, including product redesign, new facilities, and new processes. Use the full range of the project-planning sequence, including PERT charting and interim stages/gates.[20]

- Project plan is not approved on the first pass, necessitating a return to any pertinent place in the sequence to recast the plans and work back up to the approval stage.

Table 10.1   A typical project-planning sequence.

Seq.	Tool/technique	Comment
1	Statement	The kernel of an idea, basic concept, problem, deficiency, or opportunity to be realized is carefully defined to help later in clarifying project scope.
2	Project justification • Payback period • Net present value (NPV) • Internal rate of return (IRR) • Return on investment (ROI) • Return on assets (ROA) • Benefits-to-cost ratio	Risk analysis and feasibility assessment leading to a go/no-go decision.
3	Drafts: • Mission statement • Project scope • Project objectives	Documents to clarify the overall direction of the project, what it is to accomplish, breadth and depth of project, and the measurable objectives by which progress and completion are to be measured.
4	Stakeholder requirements • Matrix • Process map (to identify areas from which potential team members should be selected)	Listing of stakeholders and their requirements: (1) those with a direct commitment to the project team, and (2) those without involvement but who can influence project results.
5	Project team formation • Matrix (from sequence 4) • Myers-Briggs Type Indicator* • DiSC profile* • KESAA assessment*	Team members selected from stakeholder groups to be represented and/or based on specific skill sets needed. *Discussed in Chapter 8, Section 2 (See Chapter 3 about teams and team processes.)
6	• Mission statement (updated) • Project scope (updated) • Project objectives (updated) • Project charter • Request for project planning funds	Team members refine the original drafts, prepare charter and request for funds to plan the project. (A benchmarking study could be appropriate to better define target outcomes. See Chapter 12, Section 3.)
7	Deliverables • Project outputs (objectives of project) • Outputs used to plan and manage the project	Team members compile a list of all contractually required or agreed-on outputs (identify, define, and document). Internal outputs used in managing the project are also listed.
8	Work breakdown structure (WBS)	Project work is further defined by breaking the work into a hierarchy of work categories (clusters/families of like work, down to individual task level). Boxes in the WBS diagram may be annotated with "person/work unit responsible," "resources required," "cost estimate," and various other cross-references.

Table 10.1 A typical project-planning sequence. *(continued)*

Seq.	Tool/technique	Comment
9	Gantt chart (matrix)	Major project steps or task clusters are listed vertically on a timeline chart, with each such item's estimated start to finish time shown as a horizontal bar across the chosen time intervals (days, weeks, months, quarters). As the project progresses, the same chart may be used to show actual time expended adjacent to the estimated timeline. Major milestones (check points, action dates) may be shown as points along the time bar for each listed item.
10	Time-dependent task diagram: • Activity network diagram (AND) • Critical path method (CPM) diagram • Program/project evaluation and review technique (PERT) diagram	Depending on the size, complexity, and duration of the project, the Gantt chart may not be sufficient for plotting the time dependencies of each task in relation to other tasks. AND shows the interrelationships of each task, or task cluster, in the project. CPM adds the dimension of normal time estimated to complete tasks and allows for computing the critical path (longest time line through the project steps). PERT adds two additional time estimates for each task (optimistic and pessimistic) allowing computation of what-if estimates of timing. Typically AND is used for short-term, simple projects. CPM is used where there are data or knowledge available to make reasonably accurate estimates of times. PERT is most often used for projects when there are no prior estimates known.
11	Resource requirements matrix (RRM)	An RRM is used to identify and describe the various types of resources needed, when they are needed, quantity, and cost (for example, personnel, facilities, equipment, materials, consultants, funding).
12	Linear responsibility matrix (LRM)	Used in larger projects, the LRM defines who has responsibility for what tasks, and to what degree (e.g., primary, secondary, resource only, need to know).
13	Project budget • Summary project budget • Cash flow budget	An itemized budget, prepared by the team, based on the project time and cost estimated.
14	Measurements and reports • Milestones/stage gates • Project monitoring • Data analysis methodology • Reporting protocols	The quantifiable measurements, defined by the team, whereby the project progress and project completion will be determined.
15	Completed project plan • Executive summary • Backup documents supporting plan • Funds request • Plan approval sign-off	Final approval to proceed with project is obtained.

Source: Reprinted with permission of R. T. Westcott & Associates.

Project Concept/Scope Statement. To initiate the planning sequence, a clear, concise statement is needed. This statement describes the situation and gives an overall concept of what the project is to accomplish, including long-term outcomes as applicable.

Stakeholder Requirements Matrix. Identify stakeholders and their needs. Stakeholders are those persons or groups who will be directly or indirectly affected by the project and its outcomes. A process map can be used as an aid to ensure that all stakeholders are identified. In addition to helping to identify areas from which team members should be selected, a process map provides the project team with an understanding of the current process. The stakeholder analysis for a customer response project is shown in Figure 10.4.

All stakeholders have their own interests, priorities, and concerns regarding a project's outputs and outcomes, as well as the processes used. Any stakeholder groups that will not be represented on the project team should have an opportunity to provide input. Their information is important for identifying processes to be used, boundaries (for example, of authority) to be observed, and performance measures to be tracked.

Project Team Formation. The team should consist of representatives of as many stakeholder groups as is feasible. It is especially important that those responsible for implementing any project recommendations are represented on the project team. Team membership must also take into account any particular technical skills that may be required. When the need for a member with specialized skills will vary over the life of the project, such a person may be called in on an as-needed basis.

When an opportunity exists to be selective in project team membership, the level of sincere interest shown by potential project team members is a primary consideration. Some organizations take into account the personal styles of potential members (as identified through a personality profile, such as the Myers-Briggs Type Indicator) to ensure team diversity.

The process for selection of team members can vary. Team members may be selected by the project sponsors (for example, a management group) or may be representatives appointed by the various stakeholder groups affected. The project team leader may be appointed and given the authority to select or solicit other team members. The approach used to select members may depend on the scope and importance of the project, likelihood of success or the potential impact of failure, the culture and values of the organization, or the dominant style of management within the organization.

Deliverables. The project team collects, categorizes, and documents all contractual requirements and all planned deliverables expected from the project. Also, where applicable, use of required documents and/or actions required by regulatory agencies may also be documented. In addition, the outputs needed to manage the project are also listed. An example of project deliverables is shown in Figure 10.5.

Work Breakdown Structure. Except, perhaps, for extremely small, short-duration projects, a *work breakdown structure* (WBS) is created by the project team. If any pertinent organizational groups are not represented on the project team, such groups should be consulted before committing them to work responsibilities on the WBS.

Typical terms for the descending levels of a WBS are *project level*, *subproject level*, *work unit/component level* (optional), *work package level*, and *task level* (may be

Stakeholder	Requirements	Impacts
Project team	• Project plans • Project management	Approval Successful implementation
Customer	• Timely initial response • Courteous response • Timely call-back response, if needed • Satisfaction with action taken or reasonable explanation as to why no action will be taken	Satisfaction with complaint response and resolution process
Customer service rep (CSR)	• Effective procedures, tools, and techniques for handling customer complaints • Positive reinforcement for work done well • Organizational objective to achieve a balance between serving volumes of customers quickly and serving customers satisfactorily • Well-trained and available support/supervision	Productivity loss due to overload of inadequately handled customer complaints. Customers' mood and satisfaction with responses. CSRs' demeanor and satisfaction in serving customers. CSRs' morale and motivation.
Complaint investigators (experienced CSRs removed from customer contact duties)	• Reduction in number of complaints to investigate • Reassignment of CSRs to customer contact duties	Elimination of complaints escalated to CEO's office. (Average = 2000/month with investigation cost of 20 CSRs/month)
Customer service management	• Senior management commitment to customer satisfaction as top priority • Revised measurements that reflect more appropriate balance between achieving customer satisfaction and productivity	More satisfied customers Lower operating costs Less employee turnover, fewer grievances and disciplinary actions Time better spent on preventive actions
Operations management	• Senior management commitment to preventive action to reduce occasions causing customer complaints	Reduction in customer complaints
CEO	• No poorly handled customer complaints to deal with	Time better spent on future planning, attracting and retaining investors
Stockholders	ROI	Investor confidence in company

Figure 10.4 Customer response project–stakeholders.

Source: Reprinted with permission of R. T. Westcott & Associates.

Name of deliverable	Description/purpose of deliverable
Project management outputs	
Time and cost tracking system	Procedure, software to collect project data
Progress reports	Weekly "exception" reports of variables
Evaluation report	End-of-project evaluation of results
Project documentation	Critical documents for knowledge base
Team effectiveness evaluation	Members' performance evaluated
Team celebration	Members recognized for contribution
Project work outputs	
Engineering specifications for machine	For use in selecting and purchasing machine
Vendor selection criteria	For use in selecting vendor
Purchase order	For purchase–lease of machine
Floor plan	Layout for new machine workspace
Installation plan	For replacement of old machine with new
Operator training plans	For off-site and on-site operator training
Trial run plans	To test new machine, acclimate operators
Revised work instructions	For changed process
Revised plant scheduling system	For changes in production scheduling
Turnover plans	Turning over responsibility to production
Post-installation process audit	To determine if planned outcomes were achieved

Figure 10.5 Deliverables (hypothetical).

Source: Reprinted with permission of R. T. Westcott & Associates.

optional). Usually, cost accumulation reaches down to the work package level. Figure 10.6 shows a three-level WBS under development (project level, subproject level, and work package level only). The task level has not yet been added, nor have the identification numbers for each box (usually a decimal hierarchy to aid accounting in building costs from the lowest to the highest level), the name of the person or function responsible, or time and cost estimates.

The WBS is the focal point for planning. It provides the structure of the project and the basis for estimating time and costs. The WBS also enables the project team to visually see the relationships of all parts to the whole: the deployment of tasks and responsibilities and the accounting structure by which costs will be accumulated and measured against budget.

Note: A WBS may be created in outline format, the line indentations indicating the levels of the structure. Advantages of the outline format are that the outline is easy to compile (word processing) and easy to modify. A disadvantage is the difficulty in clearly seeing the overall view of the project and its interfaces. The input to some project management computer programs that compile the WBS and other documents is similar to the outline format. A sample WBS in outline format is shown in Figure 10.7.

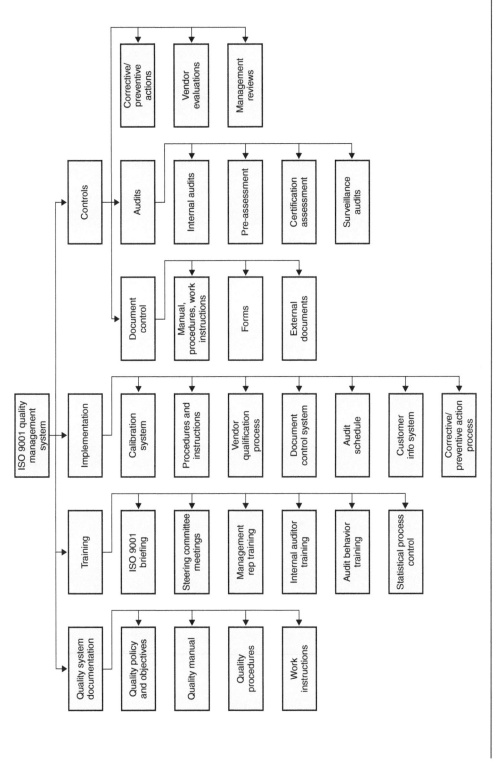

Figure 10.6   Work breakdown structure (work package level).

ID #	Activities	Resp. person	Start date	Finish date	Time est.	Cost est.	Depends on
02	New garage project	Russ	040113	092213	102	42,125	0
02.01	Purchase drawings	Russ	040113	040113	1	25	02
02.02	Select builder	Russ	040113	041213	2	0	02.01
02.03	Obtain permits	Russ	041413	043013	1	150	02.02
02.04	Order building materials	Bud	050513	052713	2	3,000	02.03
02.05	Construct garage	Bud	050513	091313	88	36,150	02.04
02.05.01	Lay foundation	Bud	051713	052713	5	3,500	02.05
02.05.01.01	Prepare lot	Ron	051713	052013	3	1,500	02.05.01
02.05.01.02	Set forms and pour concrete	Bud	052413	052713	2	2,000	02.05.01.01
02.05.02	Erect structure	Bud	060713	081113	45	19,350	02.05.01.02
02.05.02.01	Framing	Pete	060713	063013	15	6,750	02.05.02
02.05.02.02	Roof	Bill	062113	071913	12	5,400	02.05.02.01
02.05.02.03	Windows and doors	George	072113	073013	3	450	02.05.02.02
02.05.02.04	Siding	Al	072213	081113	15	6,750	02.05.02.03
02.05.03	Finishing structure	Bud	072613	091313	38	13,300	02.05.02.03
02.05.03.01	Electrical work	Oscar	072613	081813	15	5,250	02.05.03
02.05.03.02	Plumbing work	Tony	072813	082013	10	3,500	02.05.03
02.05.03.03	Interior finish, painting	Stan	082313	083113	7	2,450	02.02.03.02
02.05.03.04	Exterior finish, painting	Stan	083113	091313	6	2,100	02.05.03.03
02.06	Property reconstruction	Bud	081613	092213	8	2,800	02.05.03.02
02.06.00.01	Driveway	Rashid	081613	083113	4	1,400	02.06
02.06.00.02	Landscaping	Rashid	083113	092213	4	1,400	02.06.01

Figure 10.7 Work breakdown structure (WBS)—building garage (outline format).

Source: Reprinted with permission of R. T. Westcott & Associates.

Gantt Chart. After the WBS has been created, the tasks or steps are time phased on a *Gantt chart*. Gantt charts may be created at any level of detail needed for managing the project, although not generally at the work unit level. Figure 10.8 shows a partial Gantt chart at a work package level. As project planning progresses, the chart can be amended to display milestones (critical points for measurement) and as work progresses bars added representing actual times elapsed and other symbols to indicate project status.

Advantages of a Gantt chart include:

- It is easy to understand and modify.

- It is a simple way to depict progress status.

- It is easy to expand to identify tasks that are critical to monitor.

18-Month ISO 9001 Quality Management System Implementation Project

Task	Weeks 1–13	Weeks 14–26	Weeks 27–39	Weeks 40–52	Weeks 53–65	Weeks 66–78
Select consultant	▷					
Conduct ISO 9000 briefing	▷					
Conduct gap analysis	▷					
Form steering committee	▷					
Prep Q system procedures	▬▬▬▬					
Prep Q policy, objectives	▷					
Prep work instructions		▬▬▬▬				
Employee kickoff meeting		▷				
Evaluate registrars		▷				
Train internal auditors		▷		▷		
Implement QSPs			▬▬▬▬▬▬		▷	
Select, schedule registrar			▷			
Conduct internal audits				▬▬▬▬▬▬		▬▬
Prep quality system manual				▬▬▬		
Conduct audit behav. mtg.					▷	
Conduct preassessment				▷		
Take corr./preventive action						▬▬
Conduct final assessment						▷
Registration—celebrate						▷

Figure 10.8 Gantt chart.

Disadvantages of a Gantt chart are:

- It does not as clearly show interdependencies among project activities as does a network diagram.

- It cannot show the results or consequences of either an early or late start of project activities, thereby giving little or no clue as to the impact of slippage on the project completion date.

- It is unable to show uncertainty—that is, the effect of the longest, shortest, or most likely time estimates.

While a WBS depicts a project hierarchy and delineates the work to be done, the Gantt chart graphically indicates the time line for each significant piece of work or event and the current status of each. For smaller projects, the task dependencies may be sufficiently visible to obviate the need for time-dependency charting.

Activity Network Diagram (AND). This is a simple chart showing the dependencies of each task on other tasks in the project (what has to precede a given task and what has to follow). This chart is used in understanding and communicating task relationships within the project.

Critical Path Method (CPM). This chart is expanded *and* shows a time estimate for each activity. The sequence of interrelated activities that takes the longest is the *critical path*. CPM charts are commonly used for projects in which there are prior data or experience in documenting reasonably accurate time estimates. Computer software is usually employed for more complex projects.

Figures 10.9a and 10.9b follow the ISO 9001 Quality Management System Implementation Project, showing the development of a CPM chart. The critical path is the series of steps taking the longest time. No slack time exists on the critical path.

Program/Project Evaluation and Reporting Technique (PERT). A PERT chart expands the CPM concept by including three time estimates (optimistic, most likely, pessimistic) for each activity. From these data, comparative paths can be generated. Also, slack time may be computed for activities not on the critical path, thus providing decision information for reallocating resources and schedules. PERT is usually used where there is a paucity of estimated data and little to no prior experience with a similar project. Computer software is needed for complex projects. A significant feature of both the CPM and PERT methods is the ability to test the feasibility of different scenarios to find an optimum path.

Note that project management software often integrates the AND, CPM, and PERT concepts and computations into one tool—*network diagramming*. Examples of questions that can be answered with network diagramming are:

- What are the task dependencies?

- Where is slack or float apparent? Tasks with slack can be delayed without delaying the entire project. Tasks on the critical path have no slack. Float may be used to do certain tasks simultaneously or delay noncritical tasks and divert resources where needed so as not to affect the total critical path time.

- What task sequences can be overlapped and performed simultaneously?

ISO 9001 Quality Management System Project				
#	Tasks	Start in	After task #	Before task #	Weeks to complete
1	Select consultant	Wk 01		2	3
2	Conduct ISO 9000 briefing	Wk 04	1	3	1
3	Conduct gap analysis	Wk 05	2	4	1
4	Form steering committee	Wk 06	3	5	1
5	Prepare QSPs	Wk 07	4	16	57
6	Prepare quality policy and objectives	Wk 09	4	8	1
7	Prepare work instructions	Wk 14	4	16	39
8	Employee kickoff meeting	Wk 15	6	11	1
9	Evaluate registrars	Wk 26	4	12	1
10	Train internal auditors	Wk 26	6	13	2
11	Implement QSPs	Wk 29	5	16	35
12	Select and schedule registrar	Wk 33	9	16	1
13	Conduct internal audits	Wk 39	10	18	37
14	Prepare quality system manual	Wk 42	6	16	13
15	Conduct audit behavior meeting	Wk 64	11	16	1
16	Conduct pre-assessment	Wk 65	5	17	1
17	Take corrective/preventive action	Wk 66	16	18	12
18	Conduct final assessment	Wk 78	17	19	1
19	Registration notice—celebrate	Wk 79	18		1

Figure 10.9a CPM data table.

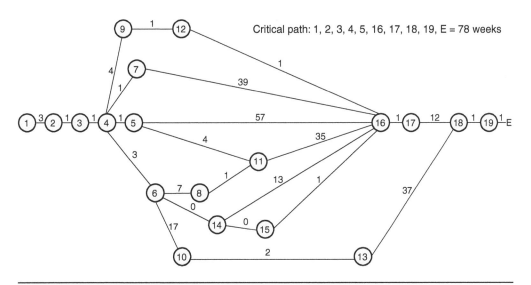

Figure 10.9b CPM chart.

- What tasks have to be *crashed*, meaning applying more resources to complete the task in a shorter time or on time?

- What is the cost effect of a late start or an early finish?

- What is the probability of completing the project on time and within budget?

- What is the cost effect of a project cancellation, an imposed temporary suspension of the project, or a mandated early completion of a rescoped project?

- What other alternatives are feasible? Subject the plans to *what-if* scenarios.

Resource Requirements Matrix (RRM). Requirements matrices are helpful for documenting resources required. A typical RRM may be prepared for each major resource, at any level of detail essential for managing the procurement and deployment of resources.

For example, an RRM spreadsheet for personnel could have left-column labels for the major categories of personnel needed and the columns to the right showing time periods (for example, weeks, months, quarters). The quantity posted in each applicable cell represents the number from each resource category needed in each time period. Column totals show the total number of personnel needed for each time period; the horizontal totals show the number of each category of personnel needed for the project. Similar RRMs can be compiled for facilities, equipment, materials, and contract/consulting personnel. A sample RRM for personnel is shown in Figure 10.10.

How resources are to be acquired, including special needs that might not have been considered in advance, should be determined as part of the project plan (for example, who has the authority to make such decisions?) and communicated to personnel responsible for allocating resources. Some resource questions to ask are:

- *What resources will be furnished, and by whom?* For example, if one resource is a work area within existing space, have arrangements been made and affected departments informed that they must provide such space? If the resources are people, what qualifications must they have?

- *When must these resources be available?* A piece of equipment might need to be available immediately or only during a particular phase of the project. Holidays and vacations might conflict with the project schedule.

- *How will the resource be delivered?* This factor can affect both cost and timing (for example, consider the arrival difference between shipboard freight, rail freight, truck freight, and airfreight).

- *How much will it cost, and when will payment be made?* The detailed costs and timing must be known in order to manage cash flow.

- *Who will pay?* This must be known in order for each direct stakeholder to budget and make decisions about the project's timing.

Linear Responsibility Matrix (LRM). For large projects with multiple responsibilities, an LRM is helpful for documenting a three-dimensional view of the project responsibilities. One way to construct an LRM follows: List tasks in the left column as row labels; identify the persons or functions responsible as labels for additional

Personnel Resource Requirements—Project #5
(Hypothetical)

Week ending ⟶

#	Talent required	Level	Equiv days	April		May		June		July		August	September
1	Project manager from quality function	5	62										
1	Engineering–laser-cutting machine specs and evaluation	4	14										
1	Machine installer	3	5										
1	Installer helper	1	5										
1	Production supervisior	4	47										
1	Cutting machine operator and trainer	2	32										
1	Work instruction documenter	4	10										

Figure 10.10 Personnel resource requirements matrix.

columns to the right. At the junction (cell) where a task relates to a person/function, a symbol is placed (the third dimension). Several types of symbols or codes may be used. Typical symbols denote the level of relationship—for example, primary, secondary, resource only, or need to know. Looking at a column, it is readily apparent for what tasks a person or function is responsible/involved, and to what extent.

Project Budget. A project budget sets financial expectations for project implementation. The budget plan details the magnitude and timing of projected financial resource inflows and outflows over the project's duration. Typically, management is concerned with the cash flow requirements and when the payback will be available.

A budgeted quality project is expected to be completed (1) within the time schedule approved, (2) within the approved costs and capital expenditures, and (3) within the approved scope and specifications. Typically, budgeting involves:

- Identifying the resource requirements for each of the defined project activities

- Estimating costs to complete the activities

- Communicating the requirements to top management for funding approval

Typical budget revenue estimating factors include:

- Increased sales

- Improved process capability

- Increased profits

- Increased equipment uptime

- Reduced defects

- Reduced spare parts inventory

- Reduced scrap

- Reduced customer cancellations

- Lowered warranty claims

- Fewer returned products

Quantifiable budget cost factors may include:

- Cost of money

- Energy costs

- Personnel costs

- Subcontracted work costs

- Overhead allocations

- Cost of materials

- Equipment costs—purchase, rentals, leases

- Fees—permits, licenses, and applications

- Consulting charges

- Reserve or contingency for unanticipated events

In general, a project budget should be:

- The mechanism for planning, authorizing, allocating, and controlling resources

- A basis for comparison of multiple projects (portfolio analysis)

- A baseline from which to measure the difference between the actual and planned uses of resources

A sample budget is shown in Figure 10.11.

Measurements and Reports. Developed and set in place early in the planning stage, a feedback system is designed to monitor the project to detect and report deviations from the plan so that corrections can be made as needed. Feedback is necessary to surmount communication barriers, which can include physical distances, priority conflicts within the company, language difficulties (for example, foreign, technical, and perceptual), work shift differences, interpretation of drawings and

Project: Improve Filler Cap Quality

Expected outcome: 50% reduction in returned products

Labor budget

Team	$/hr.	Planned hours per stage					Dollars of labor per stage				
		1	2	3	4	Total hrs	1	2	3	4	Total $
Beth Esda	20	10	15	15	25	65	200	300	300	500	$ 1,300
Anna Lyst	15	8	8	6	12	34	120	120	90	180	510
Ed Ifye	18	0	15	25	20	60	0	270	450	360	1,080
Jule Ly	9	0	20	20	25	65	0	180	180	225	585
Ali Ghator	10	10	5	10	15	40	100	50	100	150	400
Total		28	63	76	97	264	420	920	1,120	1,415	$ 3,875

Non-labor dollars budgeted per stage

Category	1	2	3	4	Total $
Facility rental	4,500	4,500	4,500	4,500	$ 18,000
Equipment rental	1,950	1,950	1,950	600	6,450
Materials	675	0	1,250	7,800	9,725
Consulting fees	20,000	0	5,000	18,000	43,000
Process changeover	0	0	0	235,000	235,000
Total	27,125	6,450	12,700	265,900	$ 312,175

Total budget per stage

Category	1	2	3	4	Total $
Labor	420	920	1,120	1,415	$ 3,875
Non-labor	27,125	6,450	12,700	265,900	312,175
Total	27,545	7,370	13,820	267,315	$ 316,050

Projected reduction in returned product—year one	$1,498,000
Estimated project costs	316,050
Projected net benefit from implementing project	$1,181,950

Figure 10.11 Sample project budget.

requirements, and rumors concerning the project status. Feedback is also useful for identifying learning opportunities for the current or future team.

The design of a tracking/monitoring system should consider:

- The objective for each type of feedback

- Providing data that can be used to initiate any corrective action needed

- How the data provided tie in with the planning documents, such as Gantt charts, network diagrams, and resource matrices

- The frequency and timing of data (for example, hourly, daily, weekly, or monthly)

Key measures should be selected by persons at each responsible level in the project team who can reliably see the status of both the whole project and their own part of the project. Factors to consider in planning these measures are:

- Time status (relative to plans/critical path, percentage completed)

- Resources expended status (relative to budgets, percentage expended)

- How future outcomes/impacts on the organization will be measured, when, and by whom

Care must be taken to ensure that project status reports are useful to those requiring them for decision-making purposes. Project planning must consider:

- What reports are needed by whom

- The frequency and timing of reports—for example, daily, weekly, or monthly

- Media by which data are reported

- How and from whom the project team is to request help when necessary

- How and by whom project plans and timetables will be updated

Project Funding Approval Request. For larger projects for which the funding has not been approved or allocated up front, a funding approval request is often required. The project-planning documents just described serve as backup for the funds requested. In some organizations this document may be called an *appropriation request.*

Project Plan Approval. Depending on the organization's policies and procedures, the scope of the project, the planned cost, the planned outputs and outcomes, and the requirements of stakeholders, the approval may take many forms, such as:

- A signature affixed to a project plan document (for example, funding request, project budget)

- A memo from an authorized person

- A sign-off sheet signed by key management

- Verbal approval from an authorized person for very small, short-duration projects

For larger projects, the documented project plan, represented by these documents, is packaged with an executive summary and presented to senior management for approval. If the team's work has been done well, the plan may be approved on first pass. Senior management, however, often has knowledge of pending situations that may have an impact on the timing or the potential effectiveness of the project's outcome. A project may be delayed, the plans sent back for revision, or the project canceled entirely. An example is a telecommunications equipment distributor that suddenly finds itself the target of a hostile takeover. Clearly, all available resources may have to be committed to challenging the takeover. The proposed project to implement an ISO 9001–based quality management system would likely be postponed, if not canceled.

3. MEASURE AND MONITOR PROJECT ACTIVITY

Use tools such as cost variance analysis, milestones, and actual versus planned budgets to monitor project activity against project plan. (Evaluate)

Body of Knowledge III.C.3

Tools for Monitoring and Controlling the Project

There are both measures of the ongoing project and measures of the results of the project. With an effective tracking/monitoring, measuring, and reporting system in place, the critical performance measures of an ongoing project follow.

Timeliness. Tracking includes overall progress (such as percentage complete), status of major stages or milestones, and completion of specific activities. It is important to track both late and early variances from the plan because they affect the probability of success, costs, and the status of other projects contending for the same resources.

In medium to larger projects, critical checkpoints are established in the planning stage (usually indicated on the Gantt chart). These milestones or stage gates are the points at which a check is made to ascertain progress. They are the points where key measures are taken to determine if the project is proceeding on target and, if not, decisions can be made to bring the project back on track. Adjustments may be made to increase or decrease resources and expenditures or shift resources to an activity or event on the critical path where needed. As a result of the ongoing monitoring of milestones, changes to plan may result—for example, recomputing of the critical path or revision to resource allocation plans. All changes must be documented.

While project monitoring continues at the milestone level throughout the implementation stage of the project life cycle, progress or stage/gate reviews may be targeted to key schedule dates or completion of major work packages (identified on the WBS). These reviews between the project manager, senior management, and key stakeholders evaluate the results of the project implementation to date. The reviews may include assessment of:

- Schedules against the critical path
- Expenditures against budget
- Resource utilization against plans
- Implementation results to date against plans
- Reevaluation of risks
- Major issues confronting project continuance

The outcome of the stage/gate review may be any one of these options:

- Continue on to the next stage at the approved level of funds and resources.
- Go to the next stage with new or changed objectives and plans.
- Hold off the next stage until more information is available and/or organizational conditions change.
- Postpone or cancel the project before entering the next stage.[21]

All such decisions must be documented.

Budget Variance. The project budget lays out the cash flow over the life of the project. Tracking expenditures and comparing to the budget, at critical project stages, provides a basis for appropriate financial control. A sample variance report for a partially completed project is shown in Figure 10.12.

The benefits/cost ratio should also be recomputed at critical stages of the project, inasmuch as more of the actual costs become known and the potential benefits clarified as the project progresses. A recomputation can signal a potential problem to address. Such changes must be documented.

Earned Value Analysis (EVA). EVA methodology consists of knowing the planned value of the work to be done, the earned value of the actual work completed, and

Work package	Labor hours and costs						Suppliers' charges			Equipment charges		
	Pld hrs	Act hrs	Var	Pld $	Act $	Var $	Pld $	Act $	Var $	Pld $	Act $	Var $
Project management (QE)	25	15	10	600	375	225						
Needs analysis (QE)	24	18	6	600	450	150						
Write calibration specs (PE)	32	26	6	960	780	180						
Select suppliers (QE)	8	10	-2	200	250	-50						
Order equipment (QE)	8	8	0	200	200	0				8200	8300	1000
Order computer program (QE)	1	1	0	25	25	0						
Train QE (supplier)	24	8	16	600	200	400	5000	2500	2500			
Set up system (QE, PS)	40			1000								
Calibrate tools, equip. (QE)	240			6000								
Set calibration schedule (QE)	16			400								
Write procedures (PE, PS)	30			735								
Close-out (QE, PE, PS)	24			680								
Contingency fund				1000								
Totals	472	86		13000	2280		5000	2500		8200	8300	1000

Figure 10.12   Calibration system project—sample variance report.

the actual costs to achieve the earned value. Two variances can then be determined: the difference between the planned and earned value of the work scheduled and the earned value of the work done compared with the actual costs to do the work. This method enables the project team to more closely monitor project performance against their scheduled plan. A scheduling system, such as CPM, is required.[22]

Resource Usage. The project plan specifies what resources (for example, facilities, human, equipment, funds, information) are required, as well as when they will be needed. Using resources owned or controlled by the organization can make the project easier to manage, but the need for special equipment or skills, or critical shortages in resources, often dictates that externally acquired resources will also be necessary. The usage of resources is reported and analyzed during the project life cycle to ensure that resources have been used wisely and that adequate resources will still be available to complete the project. Any changes must be documented.

Risk Analysis. Every project, large or small, involves some level of uncertainty. All projects that have an impact on organizational resources involve risk. Risk assessment is an important component of project management.

Proactively identifying and mitigating potential future events, risk management may include developing contingency plans when uncertainty is identified. Properly applied, risk management may avert an undesirable event, or at least minimize its impact.

For those risks having both a high probability of occurrence and a high level of negative consequences, a strategy should be developed for offsetting the risk (for example, through the purchase of insurance or through the development of a contingency plan).

Reassessment and analysis of potential risks should be performed at critical intervals. Schedule delays, resource shortages, financial developments, competitive influences, organizational leadership changes, and external events are examples of risks that can occur after a project is underway. Documentation of the risk management plan, including any changes, provides a guide for responding to adverse events that may occur during the project. (See Chapter 8, Section 6 for more on risk management.)

Methodologies for Evaluating and Closing Out the Project

Typical end-of-project evaluation measures include:

- Objectives accomplished
- Deliverables accepted
- Financial obligations completed
- Schedule met, early or late
- Budget performance favorable
- Return on project investment (ROPI) reasonable
- Payback period achieved
- Annualized cost savings realized
- Earned value analysis favorable

- Operational measures:
  - — Response time improvement
  - — Waste reduction
  - — Process capability improved
  - — Start-up efficiencies and rates

Project Closeout Actions

The time to close down the project occurs when:

- All planned deliverables have been completed
- All project documentation has been completed, including:
  - — A postproject summary review report presented to key stakeholders
  - — Assessment of key stakeholders' satisfaction, feedback shared, and necessary actions taken
  - — Project history (plans and decisions made) documented
  - — All outstanding accounts payable resolved
  - — Lessons learned have been discussed and documented (see section above)
  - — Appropriate project closeout document has been approved
  - — The project team has received appropriate recognition for their accomplishments, and the team has celebrated
  - — Project team is officially disbanded
- The project may also be terminated because:
  - — Project is no longer strategic or desirable
  - — Funds or other resources are no longer available
  - — Higher priorities prevail

Regardless of the project status, when closeout is to occur, the above actions must be taken. Failure to do so is one of the primary omissions in the project life cycle.

Postproject Audit. An important aspect of the project cash/capital budgeting process is the postaudit, which compares actual results to what was predicted in the project plans, requiring explanation of any differences. For example, many organizations require their operating divisions to send a monthly report for the first six months after a project is operating and a quarterly report thereafter until the project's results meet expectations. From then on, reports on the project are included with those of other operations.

Improved estimating can result when project managers know the results will be verified. Good decision-makers systematically compare their projections to actual results to identify and eliminate conscious or unconscious biases.

Because each element of the cash flow estimate is subject to uncertainty, a percentage of all projects undertaken by any reasonably venturesome organization will be off target. This fact must be considered when appraising the performances of the operating managers who submit capital expenditure requests. At times, projects fail to meet expectations for reasons beyond the control of the project managers and for reasons that could not be realistically anticipated. Separating the operating results of one investment from those of the larger system can often be difficult. While some projects stand alone and permit ready identification of costs and benefits, the actual cost benefit from some projects can be hard to measure because of the large number of variables.

Postproject Outcome Assessment. At some predetermined point or points in time, the ultimate outcomes of the project should be assessed and evaluated. This assessment should be both quantitative and qualitative in what it covers. Some of the areas addressed may include:

- Have the planned improvements from the project implementation been realized? For example, cycle time reduced, process capability improved, or mean time to failure increased?

- Have the planned organizational outcomes been achieved? For example, waste reduced, market penetrated, customers satisfied, employees retained, profitability increased, or organization restructured?

The assessment also typically probes the management of the project—the planning, implementation, and evaluation. Certain concepts, techniques, and tools may aid success for future projects. Identified, this information can be formulated as a guide for planning and managing projects. A goal is to not keep reinventing the project process but to enhance it through learning from each successive project—the plan-do-study-act cycle. Applying lessons learned may be one of the most valuable outcomes from examining the processes by which a project was successful, or the areas in which the project failed its objective.

4. PROJECT DOCUMENTATION

> Use written procedures and project summaries to document projects. (Apply)
>
> **Body of Knowledge III.C.4**

The job's not done until the paperwork is finished.

—Unknown

As emphasized earlier, one very important aspect in project management is documenting and sharing information with others outside of the project team to ensure that management and other stakeholders are aware of the project's status. Well-documented status reports will usually suffice.

Communicating and documenting lessons learned is important. Various channels are appropriate, including departmental meetings or time set aside specifically for shared learnings. Storing information and knowledge from projects, regardless of the degree of success, is vital to building a base for use in future project planning and estimating.

The details of each project should be documented utilizing the organization's preferred methodology. Such documentation will typically include:

- Project mission and/or charter statement
- Project scope
- Statement of work
- Project team members
- Stakeholder analysis
- Deliverables
- WBS
- Gantt charts
- Time and sequence dependency diagrams (AND, CPM, PERT)
- Resource allocation matrices
- LRMs
- Budget
- Request for funds
- Project plan approval
- Policies and procedures affected by the project outcomes (new or revised)
- Project plan updates or revisions
- Performance results and outcomes, including financial and final benefits/cost ratio
- Project implementation sign-offs
- All changes to plans and critical decisions made
- Lessons learned

The use of formal, written communications in project management helps ensure that records are timely and complete, that background materials exist for use in future projects, and that the concerns of all parties have been addressed. Informal communications are more likely to be incomplete or misinterpreted and do not allow transfer of the methodology. Knowledge is often lost when people transfer or leave. Many companies prefer to use a standardized project planning and management methodology. The rationale for any deviation from the standard should be documented.

The use of computer-based project management software is prevalent now that the cost and complexity in using the software have been reduced. Although a manual system has its own strengths (low cost and a hands-on feeling), a computer provides the ability to do what-if scenarios (for example, how will project timing and cost be affected by adding additional resources?) and makes it easier to create more-detailed Gantt and network charts. Computerization also permits integrating plans of multiple projects that utilize some of the same resources, making it easy to assess how a change in one project will affect others. However, it is suggested that new project planners and managers learn the basics by planning and managing a small project using manual methods.

Project Charter[23]

A formal project charter can help to clearly identify the team's purpose and goals. The charter could include:

- The purpose for the team and overall outcome anticipated
- The problem to be solved along with the scope of the project
- The sponsor
- Approval to launch the team (including release of funding)
- Criteria for team member selection
- Methodology and technology to be used
- Degree of autonomy granted and team member empowerment boundaries
- Any constraints pertinent to the team's work and conduct
- A start and complete time (as applicable), with appropriate milestones and dates
- Techniques and tools of project planning and management to be used
- Tracking, measuring, and reporting procedure to be implemented
- Risk assessment criteria to be established and contingency plans with periodic assessments conducted
- The means that will be put in place to recognize, reinforce, and reward the team for work done well
- List of team members, with their roles and responsibilities
- Potential project benefits, including impact to financials, such as increased revenues and reduced costs; impact on customer satisfaction, productivity, and quality

A sample project charter is shown in Figure 10.13 for a cross-functional Lean-Six Sigma project to reduce the patient length of stay in an emergency department of an acute-care hospital. The sample project charter includes the project overview, problem statement, goals, and scope. The project charter includes fields that help to define the project. The project charter is a "living" document that should be revised and enhanced as the project progresses, additional information is collected, and the problem is better understood.

Project Charter Fields

Project overview: Provides a summary of the project, with high-level information describing the purpose of the project.

Problem statement: Provides a description of the problem to be solved. This should be as descriptive as possible, with the information available when it is written. The problem statement can be further enhanced once additional information is collected as the project progresses.

Goals: The desired end state of the project to be achieved. The goal(s) should be SMART (specific, measurable, attainable, realistic, and time-based).

Project scope: The boundaries of the project, including the process to be improved, for process improvement projects. A description of what is in scope and out of scope of the project.

Project charter

Project overview, problem statement, & goals
Required

Provides a description of the problem to be solved. Be as descriptive as possible. Include improvement goals that are SMART (specific, measurable, attainable, realistic, and time-based).

Project overview: This project is focused on improving patient throughput in the ED. About 40% of the patients seen are admitted to the hospital, vs. 60% seen are discharged.

Problem statement: The emergency department is experiencing delays in moving the patient through the ED in a timely manner. For January through April, patients took an average of 5.8 hours for a patient to be seen, treated, tested and discharged and an average of 8.7 hours for a patient to be seen, treated, tested and admitted. There are excessive delays and an average 6.5% of the patients left without being seen. The total bypass hours for the past year were 341 hours.

Goal(s): Improve ED throughput time to 3 average hours for discharged patients and 5 average hours for admitted patients. There could be an improvement in patient satisfaction and quality of care due to the synergistic relationship between throughput, quality and satisfaction.

Project scope
Required

Identify what activities/functions will be included in your project. Include the beginning and ending steps of the process to be improved.

What are the boundaries of the process you're improving for your project? The scope includes the ED processes starting from patient entrance, to triage, treat, transport, test/diagnose, disposition and discharge/admit.

What does the project include/exclude? This project will include identifying the major constraints to throughputs, the root causes and improvement recommendations.

Figure 10.13 Sample emergency department patient length of stay improvement Lean–Six Sigma project charter.

Source: Reprinted from the *CQIA Handbook,* 4th ed.

Decision team members: A list of the members with their roles related to the project who will make decisions related to the project moving forward, approving the results of the project and the path forward at key gates or milestones.

Working team members: A list of the working team members who will be responsible for completing activities and deliverables of the project.

Stakeholder Analysis[24]

The stakeholder analysis is a tool used to define the people and their roles affected by the project and identify what team members should be on the team. A sample stakeholder analysis for the emergency department Lean-Six Sigma project is shown in Figure 10.14. The stakeholder analysis includes a listing of the stakeholders or functions that have a stake in the project. The role of each stakeholder group with respect to the project is identified. If there are a large number of stakeholders, they can be identified as primary, those who are directly affected by the process being improved or the project once it is implemented, and secondary, those who are affected not as directly as the primary stakeholders. The project sponsor or team leader should interview stakeholder representatives to understand their primary concerns regarding the project and/or the impact the project has on them. The project sponsor and team leader should assess how receptive the stakeholders are to the project as it is kicked off. They should also assess how receptive the stakeholders need to be when they begin implementing project changes. The receptivity is typically assessed based on a rating scale from *strongly support, moderately support, neutral, moderately against,* and *strongly against.* How do the project sponsor and the team leader assess the stakeholders' receptivity to the project? Assessing receptivity can be done in several ways: (1) talk to the stakeholders to assess their receptivity, (2) monitor body language and conversations of the stakeholders within and outside of meetings, and (3) talk with other employees who know the stakeholders. Supportive and engaged stakeholders, team members, and leaders:

- Attend meetings and are prompt and engaged
- Have a positive outlook and willingness to improve and change
- Push team for improvements with encouragement
- Exude genuine interest in change
- Share ideas in meetings and brainstorming sessions
- Perform tasks outside of meetings without being prompted
- Offer management perspectives to help the team with improvement ideas

Nonsupportive and nonengaged stakeholders, team members, and leaders:

- Complain within and outside of meetings
- Take confrontational tones in meetings
- Discourage most ideas
- May not provide ideas in meetings and brainstorming sessions
- Frown upon and discourage thinking outside of the box

- Display nonsupportive body language—crossed arms, eye rolling, always on phone, holding head in hands, putting hands out in front of body as if to stop someone from advancing

The team should consist of at least one representative from each primary stakeholder group. The project sponsor should decide whether there should be a representative from each secondary stakeholder group on the project team. If the team gets too

Stakeholder analysis   *Required*

Identify the internal and external customer roles and concerns to ensure their expectations are addressed. Define roles, impacts, concerns, and receptivity.

Stakeholder	Type	Primary role	Potential impacts/ concerns	Initial receptivity	Future receptivity
ED Patients	Primary	Patients that go through the emergency department. Includes patients who are seen and discharged, admitted, or who leave without being seen	Quality of care Low waiting time Patient satisfaction	Neutral	Neutral
ED Physicians	Primary	Physicians who provide care for ED patients	Efficient processes Patient satisfaction Patient throughput Patient capacity	Strongly support	Strongly support
Medical Staff	Primary	Nurses, technicians, transport, lab, radiology, pharmacy, other inpatient areas, who provide care for ED patients	Efficient processes Patient satisfaction	Moderate support	Strongly support
Administration	Primary	Administration of the hospital	Efficient use of resources Patient satisfaction Patient throughput	Strongly support	Strongly support
EMS	Secondary	Emergency medical services who transport patients to the ED from outside the hospital	Quality of care Low waiting time Patient satisfaction	Neutral	Neutral
Registration	Primary	Register the patient	Correct registration Accurate billing	Moderate support	Strongly support
Admitting Physicians and Consultant	Secondary	Physicians and specialty consultants who admit patients to the hospital, or provide care for the patients that go through the ED	Patient satisfaction Quality of care	Neutral	Strongly support
Regulatory Agencies	Secondary	Regulatory agencies who define regulatory criteria	Quality of care Revenue integrity	Neutral	Neutral
Ancillary Support	Secondary	Support staff, environmental services, central supply, dietary, insurance, payors	Efficient processes Patient satisfaction Patient throughput	Moderate support	Strongly support

Figure 10.14 Sample stakeholder analysis for the emergency department Lean-Six Sigma project.

Source: Reprinted from the *CQIA Handbook,* 4th ed.

Action plan

Means I.D./plan title:	Plan no.:	
Description:	Date initiated:	
	Date needed:	
	Approval:	
	Team (L):	
	Team (M):	
	Team (M):	
	Team (M):	
	Team (M):	

Major outcomes/objectives desired/required:

Scope (Where will the solution/implementation be applied? What limitations?):

By what criteria/measures will completion and success of project be measured?

Assumptions made that may impact project (resources, circumstances outside this project):

Describe the overall approach to be taken:

When should the project be started to meet the date needed/wanted?:

Estimate the resources required (time and money):

Outline the tentative *major* steps to be taken, a project *start and complete date* for each step, and the *person to be responsible* for each step. (Use the back to sketch your timeline.)

Figure 10.15a Action plan form (front).

Source: Reprinted with permission of R. T. Westcott & Associates.

Action plan implementation schedule

Step no.	Activity/event description	Depends on step	Start date	Finish date	Person responsible

Figure 10.15b Action plan form (back).
Source: Reprinted with permission of R. T. Westcott & Associates.

large, more than ten members or so, the project sponsor may consider reducing the team members to only the critical primary stakeholder team members.

Action Plans

The action plan is a convenient method for planning and documenting a small project. Figures 10.15a and 10.15b show a typical action plan form. Note that the back of the action plan form provides for an implementation schedule and is, essentially, an outline-type WBS.

REFERENCES

1. R. T. Westcott, *Simplified Project Management for the Quality Professional: Managing Small and Medium-Size Projects* (Milwaukee: ASQ Quality Press, 2004).
2. PMI Global Standard, *Project Management Body of Knowledge (PMBOK®) Guide*, 6th ed. (Newton Square, PA: Project Management Institute, 2017).
3. Ibid.
4. H. Kerzner, *Project Management: A Systems Approach to Planning, Scheduling, and Controlling*, 7th ed. (New York: Van Nostrand Reinhold, 2001).
5. SEBoK Editorial Board, *The Guide to the Systems Engineering Body of Knowledge (SEBoK)*, vol. 2.2, ed. R. J. Cloutier (Hoboken, NJ: Trustees of the Stevens Institute of Technology, 2020), accessed May 25, 2020, www.sebokwiki.org. BKCASE is managed and maintained by the Stevens Institute of Technology Systems Engineering Research Center, the International Council on Systems Engineering, and the Institute of Electrical and Electronics Engineers Computer Society.
6. Ibid.
7. SEBoK Editorial Board, *Guide to the Systems Engineering Body of Knowledge*.
8. PMI Global Standard, *Project Management Body of Knowledge*.
9. SEBoK Editorial Board, *Guide to the Systems Engineering Body of Knowledge*.
10. T. Lappi, T. Karvonen, L. E. Lwakatare, K. Aaltonen, and P. Kuvaja, "Toward an Improved Understanding of Agile Project Governance: A Systematic Literature Review," *Project Management Journal* 49, no. (2018): 39–63, doi:10.1177/8756972818803482.
11. E. C. Conforto, E. Rebentisch, and D. C. Amaral, *Project Management Agility Global Survey* (Cambridge, MA: Massachusetts Institute of Technology, Consortium for Engineering Program Excellence, 2014).
12. S. Nerur, R. Mahapatra, and G. Mangalaraj, "Challenges of Migrating to Agile Methodologies," *Communications of the ACM* 48, no. 5 (May 2005).
13. K. Beck, M. Beedle, A. Van Bennekum, A. Cockburn, W. Cunningham, M. Fowler, . . . D. Thomas, Agile Manifesto, 2001, http://agilemanifesto.org/.
14. Ibid.
15. Lappi et al., "Toward an Improved Understanding of Agile Project Governance."
16. K. Schwaber, and J. Sutherland, "The Scrum Guide, The Definitive Guide to Scrum: The Rules of the Game," 2017, Scrum.org.
17. Ibid.
18. "The Scrum Framework," accessed May 25, 2020, https://www.scrumalliance.org /why-scrum#why-its-called-scrum.
19. M. E. Porter, *Competitive Strategy: Techniques for Analyzing Industries and Competitors* (New York: Free Press, 1980).

20. Stage-gate (go/no-go) decision process is discussed in R. G. Cooper, *Winning at New Products: Accelerating the Process from Idea to Launch*, 3rd ed. (Cambridge, MA: Perseus, 2001).

21. Kerzner, *Project Management*.

22. W. Fleming, and J. M. Koppelman, *Earned Value Project Management*, 2nd ed. (Newtown Square, PA: Project Management Institute, 2000).

23. G. L. Duffy and S. L. Furterer, *The ASQ Certified Quality Improvement Associate Handbook*, 4th ed. (Milwaukee: ASQ Quality Press, 2020).

24. Ibid.

See Appendix A for additional references for this chapter.

Chapter 11
D. Quality System

Quality may be viewed from several perspectives:

- Various meanings of *quality*
- Various characteristics of quality
- Drivers of quality
- Quality of design versus quality of conformance
- Quality planning, control, and improvement
- Little q and Big Q
- Quality is strategic

Various Meanings of Quality

The meaning of quality differs depending on circumstances and perceptions. Quality is a different concept when tangible products are the focus versus the perception of a quality service. The meaning of quality is also time based, or situational. The new car bragged about yesterday is cursed this morning when it fails to start and an appointment is missed.

Quality is how the recipient of the product or service views it: before buying, upon delivery, and after the delivery—and use, of a product. Some of the common meanings for quality are:

Quality is conformance to requirements:

— Quality is keeping the promise made when an order is taken or a commitment is made.

— Quality means meeting the specifications.

— Quality means the product or service is free of deficiencies.

Quality is fitness for use:

— Quality means the product or service does what it is intended to do.

— Quality is what a product or service costs users if it does not do what it is supposed to do.

Quality is meeting customer expectations:

— Quality is satisfying the customer.

— Quality is whatever the customer says it is.

— Quality in a product or service is whatever the customer perceives it to be.

Quality is exceeding customer expectations:

— Quality is the extent to which the customers or users believe the product or service surpasses their needs and expectations.

— Quality is delighting the customer.

Quality is superiority to competitors:

— Quality is how a company's products and services compare to those of competitors or how they compare to those offered by the company in the past.

— Quality is perceived as the overall measure of goodness or excellence of a brand or supplier.

Of course, some customers may say, "Quality—I'll know it when I see it."

Examples of Quality Characteristics

Product:

- Performance
- Reasonable price
- Durability
- Availability
- Serviceability
- Ease of use
- Simplicity of design
- Safety
- Reliability
- Maintainability
- Aesthetics
- Ease of disposal

Service:

- Responsiveness
- Reliability
- Competence

- Accuracy

- Courtesy

- Credibility

- Security

- Understanding of customer

- Completeness

- Communication

- Availability

- Safety

- Accessibility

- Timeliness

Drivers of Quality

Customers. In a customer-driven organization, quality is established with a focus on satisfying or exceeding the requirements, expectations, needs, and preferences of customers. Customer-driven quality is a common culture within many organizations.

Products/Services. A culture of product-/service-driven quality was popular in the early stages of the quality movement. Conformance to requirements and zero-defect concepts have roots in producing a product/service that meets stated or documented requirements. In some cases, product/service requirements originate from customer requirements, thereby creating a common link to customer-driven quality, but the focus of the culture is on the quality of the product/service. If the customer requirement is accurately stated and designed into the production/service delivery process, then as long as the product/service meets requirements, the customer should be satisfied. This point of view is common in supporting the International Organization for Standardization (ISO) 9001–based quality management system (QMS).

Employee Satisfaction. This concept is that an organization takes care of employees' needs so they can be free to care only about the customer. Employee satisfaction is a primary measure of success for this type of organization.

Organizational Focus. Some organizations tend to focus on total organizational quality, while others are quite successful at using a segmented approach to implementing quality.

Competitors. While organizations typically strive to provide products and/or services that meet or exceed the customer's expectations, competitors can leverage quality of performance to their strategic benefit. Both short- and long-term performance may be compared by the customer in terms of reliability and cost of the product/service over its lifetime, thereby affecting the customer's selection of a supplier. This situation can cause an organization to ensure an aggressive and introspective review of its internal processes and product/service quality results.

Quality of Design versus Quality of Conformance

The organization's values, goals, mission, policies, and practices reinforce designing quality into the product or service rather than inspecting it in. Emphasis is placed on doing the right things right the first time. The organization's aim is to not only meet, to the letter, the customers' requirements but to exceed them wherever possible. This process is often called *Design for Six Sigma* (DFSS). Conformance is the norm; the organization's overriding purpose should be to excite the customers with extraordinary products and service.

Quality Planning, Control, and Improvement

The focus of this perspective is for organizations to continually improve their products, services, processes, and practices, with an emphasis on reducing variation and cycle time. This approach implies extensive use of the quality management tools, including cost of quality (COQ), process management approaches, and measurement techniques.

Little q and Big Q

Organizations focusing on quality control and inspection activities (little q) will fail to see that to be fully effective they must transform their thinking to quality across the organization (Big Q).

Quality Is Strategic

Quality, or the absence of it, has a strategic impact on the organization. Consumers buy certain products and request services based on their knowledge and perception of the organization and what it provides. Few buyers knowingly buy poor quality. Accumulated experiences and perceptions of customers ultimately make or break an organization. The Baldrige criteria do not mention the word *quality* because every activity and decision contained in the structure of the criteria must be a quality activity or decision. Under this assumption, quality is built into the very fiber of the organization—the preferred way to conduct the business of the organization.

1. QUALITY MISSION AND POLICY

> Develop and monitor the quality mission and policy and ensure that it is aligned with the organization's broader mission. (Create)
>
> **Body of Knowledge III.D.1**

Quality will be a focus of the organization's *strategic planning* and in its *mission statement*. The organization will have a *quality policy* to guide the organization to excellence.

Quality Function Mission

For most quality functions, the mission includes common elements to ensure that:

- Customer focus and quality are part of the organization's mission

- All suppliers understand fundamental principles of quality

- All employees understand how to apply the fundamental principles of quality

- All employees master the quality tools needed to carry out their mission within the organization

The quality function mission is both derived from and an input into the organization's mission. Upward and downward organizational collaboration is essential in quality planning. A quality function mission can be developed in several successive steps:

1. Identify one particular service or product provided by the quality function.

2. Determine the customer(s) of that service or product.

3. Discuss with the customer(s) whether they need this service or product.

   - What attributes are valuable?

   - Which are not valuable? (Consider such attributes as speed, accuracy, schedule, packaging, or formatting.)

4. If a need exists, agree on the standard and measures applicable; if the service or product is not needed, eliminate it.

5. Quantify the gap between current practice and customer needs.

6. Define the actions for improvement of that particular service or product on the basis of resources and relative priorities.

7. Make the improvement and track results.

8. Evaluate results and review lessons learned.

9. Maintain the gains.

10. Do it again.

The quality function mission statement should be clear and complete so that quantitative objectives and definite plans can be developed. The quality function mission statement must be linked to the organization's mission statement. For example, if the organization's mission statement emphasizes timeliness, then perhaps the quality function mission statement should emphasize that characteristic rather than cost.

Observations Related to the Quality Function Mission. The mission of the quality function cannot be developed in isolation from the overall mission of the organization. This problem occurs commonly in staff organizations. The mission of the quality function is not to produce quality in the organization's products and services and establish quality objectives; those are collaborative efforts whereby the quality function makes recommendations to and guides the operations function.

Compare the finance and quality functions. The finance function does not make the money, and it does not set the financial objectives; rather, it provides honest, trustworthy records of what is really happening so that others can make informed decisions. It also supplies various tools to enable others to meet their goals. Similarly, the quality function provides quality measures and supplies the tools needed to meet quality goals. Note: even if the quality function responsibilities are dispersed among functions producing the product, a process for understanding quality needs and tracking performance must still be defined.

Quality is an investment, not an expense. An investment is a current expenditure that is expected to produce benefits later, enabling recovery of the initial outlay and providing a surplus. Quality does cost money, but quality expenditures can be recovered. The problem with making this distinction is that usually the accounting is done department by department, function by function, so that outlays and income are separated both in time and in space. This makes it difficult to immediately spot the positive benefits-to-cost ratio.

Organizations that focus on quality enjoy many benefits. In a study commissioned by Congress, winners of the Baldrige Award, as a group, outperformed (on paper) Standard and Poor's index of five hundred leading companies in the stock market. In addition, data from Profit Impact of Market Strategy (PIMS) show that organizations that focus on quality and achieve it have higher returns on resources. They frequently are major players in their markets, and their products command a premium price.

Greater revenues and lower costs are potent inducements to consider quality. Companies that focus most on what customers need instead of what their rivals are doing enjoy higher growth rates.

Philip B. Crosby claims that quality is free. This is not to say that no costs are associated with achieving quality but rather that resources prudently allocated to quality have a positive yield that is greater than almost any other investment option the firm could explore.

If an organization strives for quality and X (whatever X might be), then it is likely to achieve both quality and X. Firms that have won the Deming Prize or the Baldrige Award report that the drive for quality is an enabler, as the struggle for quality often leads to the achievement of other business goals. However, if a firm has X for its primary goal and considers quality as an optional, secondary goal, then it is likely to achieve neither X nor quality over the long term.

Quality Function Policies, Principles, and Objectives

The formulation and deployment of quality policy, principles, and objectives is discussed in Chapter 7, as a subset of strategic plan deployment. Of primary importance is that quality policy, quality principles, and quality objectives support the organization's strategic goals and objectives.

The quality policy and the quality principles are guidelines and therefore not directly measurable. The effectiveness of the quality policy and quality principles is measured, indirectly, by the quality-related objectives that are linked to the policy and principles.

Quality policies may be found in a quality manual, framed and hanging on the wall, laminated into pocket-sized cards, or passed by word of mouth in smaller organizations. The key is whether or not the policy is followed and backed by management's support as well as by the actions of all employees.

Although a quality policy is not intended to be permanent, the need for revisions should be infrequent. A serious management problem is indicated when frequent changes are made.

2. QUALITY PLANNING, DEPLOYMENT, AND DOCUMENTATION

> Develop and deploy the quality plan and ensure that it is documented and accessible throughout the organization. (Create)
>
> **Body of Knowledge III.D.2**

Quality Plans

A quality plan is a document, or several documents, that together specify quality standards, practices, resources, specifications, and the sequence of activities relevant to a particular product, service, project, or contract. Quality plans should define:

- Objectives to be attained (for example, characteristics or specifications, uniformity, effectiveness, aesthetics, cycle time, cost, natural resources, utilization, yield, dependability, and so on)

- Steps in the processes that constitute the operating practice or procedures of the organization

- Allocation of responsibilities, authority, and resources during the different phases of the process or project

- Specific documented standards, practices, procedures, and instructions to be applied

- Suitable testing, inspection, examination, and audit programs at appropriate stages

- A documented procedure for changes and modifications to a quality plan as a process is improved

- A method for measuring the achievement of the quality objectives

- Other actions necessary to meet the objectives

At the highest level, quality goals and plans should be integrated with overall strategic plans of the organization. As organizational objectives and plans are deployed throughout the organization, each function defines its own best way for contributing to the top-level goals and objectives. At lower levels the quality plan (see earlier definition) assumes the role of an actionable plan. Such plans may take many different forms depending on the outcome they are to produce. Quality plans may also be represented by more than one type of document to produce a given outcome.

An example of this is a manufacturing company that machines metal parts. Its quality plan consists of applicable procedures (describing the production process and responsibilities), applicable workmanship standards, the measurement tolerances acceptable, the description of the material standards, and so forth. These may all be separate documents.

More variable information that pertains to a particular customer may be spelled out on individual work orders (sometimes called *travelers*). *Work orders* specify the machine setups and tolerances, operations to be performed, tests, inspections, handling, storing, packaging, and delivery steps to be followed. An operating-level quality plan translates the customer requirements (the what) into actions required to produce the desired outcome (the how) and couples this with applicable procedures, standards, practices, and protocols to specify precisely what is needed, who will do it, and how it will be done. A control plan may specify product tolerances, testing parameters, and acceptance criteria. While the terminology may differ, the basic approach is similar for service and other types of organizations.

Deployment and Documentation of Quality Plans

Quality plans result from both deployed strategic quality policies (which are linked to organizational strategic plans) and from the specific legal regulations, industry standards, organization policies and procedures, internal guidelines, and good practices needed to meet customers' requirements for products or services.

Strategic-level quality plans are developed and deployed through the strategic planning process. These broad-based quality plans become the guideline for each function's or department's supporting quality plan. Where appropriate, each function or department may develop and internally deploy operating-level quality plans.

Operating-level quality plans often are the resulting document(s) from a production-scheduling function. As such, this documentation often includes blueprints, a copy of the customer's order, references to applicable standards, practices, procedures, and work instructions, and details on how to produce the specific product or service.

When the product or service is produced, the planning documents may be augmented by inspection documentation, statistical process control (SPC) charts, and copies of shipping documents and customer-required certifications. In the process the plans are transformed from documents to records. In a fully computerized system, the documents mentioned may well be interactive computer screens, accessed at operators' workplaces and control points. These screens, internally, become records when operators, inspectors, shippers, and others make computer entries to the screens.

A completed set of matrices, developed by a quality function deployment (QFD) process, may fulfill a component of an organization's quality plan. The purpose of QFD is to capture and deploy the customers' needs and requirements throughout the organization.

Documenting the quality plan(s) has multiple uses, such as:

- Assuring conformance to customer requirements

- Assuring conformance to external and internal standards and procedures

- Facilitating traceability

- Providing objective evidence

- Furnishing a basis for training

- Together with multiple plans for the organization's products, services, and projects, providing a basis for evaluating the effectiveness and efficiency of the QMS

3. QUALITY SYSTEM EFFECTIVENESS

> Evaluate the effectiveness of the quality system using various tools: balanced scorecard, internal audits, feedback from internal and external stakeholders (including stakeholder complaints), warranty/return data analytics, product traceability and recall reports, and management reviews. (Evaluate)
>
> **Body of Knowledge III.D.3**

Tools and Metrics for Evaluating the Effectiveness of the Quality System

Balanced Scorecard. A popular method for tracking total organizational performance is to use the *balanced scorecard* (BSC) approach introduced by Kaplan and Norton.[1] This macrolevel evaluation is intended to move the organizational decision-makers away from considering only the financial factor. A basic approach defines metrics in four areas: customer, internal business process, learning and growth, and financial. Six common process metrics are cost, time, quality, agility (ability to adapt), capacity, and variability. The BSC approach considers metrics in multiple areas and recognizes that all are important to the organization's success.

Another method used is tracking leading indicators, which tend to be predictive of future performance, versus lagging indicators (easier to collect) that report on past successes or failures. Taking action to affect leading indicators is the secret to managing and understanding a process. Table 11.1 shows a partially completed matrix for a medium-size distributor of small household appliances. The * denotes those measures/indicators that are used as performance improvement drivers.

In Table 11.1, the shareholders should be financial shareholders per the BSC standard model, and it should include COQ as a key measure. Note: a BSC can be designed with virtually any choice of categories to track, as long as the categories chosen are critical to performance and kept to a minimum number.

Using one set of factors, following are examples of supporting metrics:

- Customer

  — Market share gains and losses

  — Customer retention

  — Satisfaction survey results

  — Complaints, product returns, product recalls, warranty costs

Table 11.1 Example of a partial, hypothetical balanced scorecard.

Category	Strategic objective	Action plan	Measures
Customers	1. Meet customers' requirements for just-in-time (JIT) delivery 2. Etc.	1. Establish regional warehouse operations 2. Etc.	1. # JIT deliveries by region 2. Average cost per delivery 3. % improvement in CSI (customer satisfaction index)* 4. Etc.
Employees	1. Develop a core competency to support a new service category 2. Etc.	1. Design and implement program to train service personnel 2. Etc.	1. % of service personnel qualified to provide new service* 2. CSI—new service* 3. ROTI—return on training investment 4. Etc.
Shareholders	1. Acquire new business 2. Etc.	1. Analyze acquisition alternatives, select investment, buy business 2. Etc.	1. ROA—return on assets 2. Dividend dollars 3. Etc.
Process	1. Reduce overall service cycle time 2. Etc.	1. Reengineer the service delivery process 2. Etc.	1. % on-time service* 2. ROPI—return on project investment 3. Cost of quality* 4. Etc.

*Leading indicators (performance drivers)

    — Field service performance

    — Certification by customers

    — Customer recognition

    — Favored supplier agreements

  • Internal business practices

    — COQ

    — Productivity

— Cost reductions

— Process cycle time

— Continual quality improvement

— Innovation

— Product/service development cycle time (from concept to market)

— Supplier performance

- Learning and growth

— Employee retention

— Competency level

— Employee development

— Knowledge management

- Financial

— Profitability or margin

— Cash flow

— Return on investments

— Return on assets

— Liquidity ratios

Self-Assessment. Documents are available from several sources to assess an organization against the Baldrige Award criteria and to assess an organization's QMS against the ISO 9001 standard. Such assessments are typically used prior to applying for the Baldrige Award or seeking certification to the ISO 9001 standard.

Quality Audits. On the microlevel, a quality audit is "a systematic and independent examination to determine whether quality activities and related results comply with planned arrangements and whether these arrangements are implemented effectively and are suitable to achieve objectives."[2]

Three principal parties are involved in a quality audit. By function, they are the:

- *Auditor:* the person(s) who plans and conducts an audit in accordance with an established standard

- *Client:* the person/organization that has been scheduled for an audit or that has requested that an audit be conducted

- *Auditee:* the organization to be audited

An audit may be classified as *internal* or *external*, depending on the interrelationships that exist among the participants. Internal audits are first-party audits, whereas external audits can be either second- or third-party audits:

- A *first-party audit* is performed within an organization to measure its strengths and weaknesses against its own procedures or methods and/or the external standards adopted by the auditee organization (voluntary) or imposed on the auditee organization (mandatory). A first-party audit is an internal audit conducted by auditors who are employed by the organization being audited but who have no vested interest in the audit results of the area being audited. The persons conducting these audits are referred to as *internal auditors*.

- A *second-party audit* is an external audit performed at a supplier's location by a customer or a contracted (consulting) organization on behalf of a customer. Typically, this is also called a *supplier audit.*

- A *third-party audit* is performed on a supplier or regulated entity by an external party other than a customer. The organization to be audited—or in some cases the client—compensates an independent party to perform an audit. For example, an auditor from the registrar for ISO 9001–based QMSs performs an audit of a client's QMS and recommends, or not, the QMS for certification to the standard. The auditor is compensated by the registrar. The registrar bills and collects its fees from the client.

Quality audits can be performed on a product/service, process, or system:

- A *product quality audit* is an in-depth examination of a particular product (or service) to evaluate whether it conforms to product specifications, performance standards, and customer requirements. A product audit should not be confused with inspection, although an auditor might use inspection techniques. Product audits have a broader scope and are a sporadic method of reinspecting or retesting a product to measure the effectiveness of the system in place for product acceptance. In contrast, inspection is a regular, continual method for product approval that verifies a product's conformance to standards as stipulated by certain product characteristics.[3]

- A *process quality audit* examines a single process or activity—such as marking, stamping, coating, soldering, or welding—to verify that the inputs, actions, and outputs are in accordance with requirements established by procedures, work instructions, or process specifications.

- A *quality system audit* is "a documented activity performed to verify, by examination and evaluations of objective evidence, that applicable elements of the quality system are appropriate and have been developed, documented, and effectively implemented in accordance and in conjunction with specified requirements."[4] A system audit examines processes, products, and services as well as all the supporting groups— for example, purchasing, customer service, design engineering, and order entry—that assist in providing an acceptable product or service.[5]

- Internal audits of a quality system are conducted to determine if:

  — The system is appropriate for the organization

  — The system design conforms to an established standard and/or accepted practices

  — The system is properly documented

— There is objective evidence available that the work performed is in accordance with the documented system

Auditing concerns the *check* and *act* stages of the plan-do-check-act (PDCA) cycle and consists of three stages: (1) audit preparation, (2) audit performance, and (3) audit reporting, corrective action, follow-up, and closure.

The following activities are performed during audit preparation:

- Prepare the audit plan

- Schedule activities

- Define the purpose of the audit

- Establish the scope of the audit

- Select the audit team

- Identify resources needed

- Identify authority for the audit

- Identify standard(s) to be used

- Conduct a technical review

- Secure and review quality-related documentation

- Develop checklists and other working papers (develop appropriate data collection methods)

- Contact auditee

Audit performance is the actual data-collection phase. The following activities occur during this phase:

- Hold the opening meeting

- Employ auditing strategies to collect data

- Verify documentation

- Analyze data and categorize results

- Present audit results (findings) at a closing meeting

Once the audit performance stage has been completed, the audit team must formally report audit results to the client and/or auditee. The appropriate corrective actions, follow-up, and closure must be performed for any problem areas noted:

- Distribute formal audit report

- Request corrective action

- Evaluate auditee's response to corrective action requests

- Assess the best mode for verifying corrective action

- Close out audit once corrective action has been verified

Figure 11.1 shows the sequence of steps performed in a typical audit.

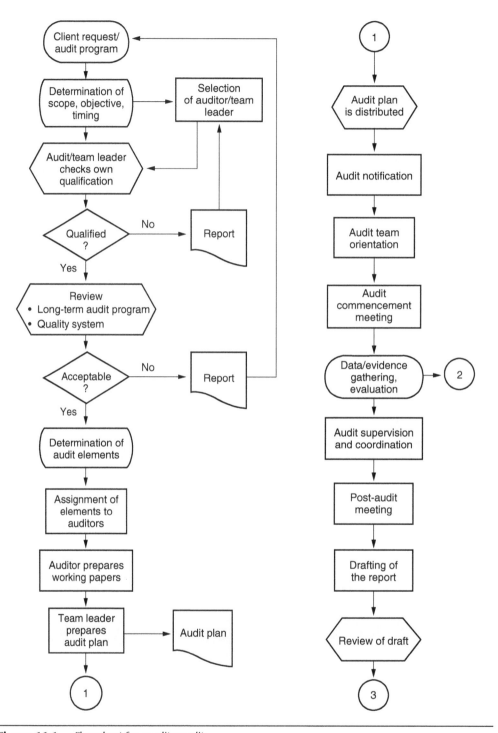

Figure 11.1   Flowchart for quality audit.

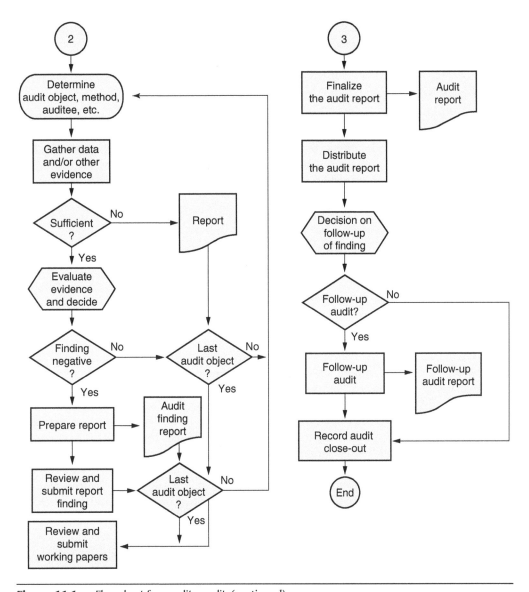

Figure 11.1   Flowchart for quality audit. *(continued)*

Management "Gemba" Walks. Senior management may, in addition to more formal means for evaluating, take a periodic walk through the production system, in its entirety or a part at a time. This may be done by following an order from receipt through to delivery. The observations from this informal approach may not be formally documented; however, the observations are shared with the responsible managers and are to be taken seriously. This kind of senior management involvement allows simple and direct evidence of their interest and active participation in the quality system.

Management Reviews. Considered microlevel, top management reviews, such as required by the ISO 9001 standard, are conducted on a schedule (bimonthly, quarterly, or annually). Key performance indicators, trends, and system problems may be reviewed, such as:

- The status of actions from previous management reviews

- Changes in external and internal issues

- The performance of the quality systems, including customer satisfaction and feedback; the meeting (or not) of quality objectives; process performance and conformity of products and services; nonconformities and corrective actions; measurement results; audit results; the performance of external providers

- Adequacy of resources

- Effectiveness of actions taken to address risks and opportunities

Usually, formal minutes are recorded and distributed to attendees. Action items are assigned, such as corrective actions, matters to research, external contacts to be made, or critical problems. Results of action items from the previous meeting are reviewed and closed out if the issue has been resolved. To meet current ISO 9001 requirements, full evidence of the activities listed above is required to be maintained and made available for audit review.

Skip-Level Meetings. A microlevel evaluation, skip-level meetings occur when a member of senior management meets with persons two or more organizational levels below, without in-between management being present. The purpose is to get a more grassroots perspective of the effectiveness of the quality system. Care must be taken to avoid appearing to be circumventing the in-between management levels. The intent is to give lower-level employees the opportunity to make higher management aware of system problems and needs. Skip-level meetings are often more for venting issues and concerns than for managing the operation. With the advent of internal electronic communication and a more open culture, one-to-one contact between various organizational levels is more prevalent and follows the chain of command less.

Collecting and Analyzing Customer Feedback. Using information to evaluate and improve customer service and satisfaction is implied in all QMSs and required in meeting certain standards—for example, ISO 9001. Inasmuch as the principal aim of a quality system is to be customer focused, assessing information derived from direct customer feedback is essential. Data should include feedback from both internal and external customers. This type of analysis is also considered a microlevel evaluation.

Among the quality system effectiveness data critical to review are trends relative to:

- Customer complaints

- Customer orders canceled

- Warranty returns

- Product recalls, including ease of traceability and percentage recalled

- Lost customers

Data may be categorized by:

- Product or service type
- Reason for complaint, return, recall, or loss
- Quantity
- Date or time of occurrence
- Frequency of occurrence
- Reported deficiency
- Risk level of deficiency
- Customer segment
- Response time to customer
- Ratio of resolutions to total reported
- Cost of resolution

Collecting and analyzing employee feedback—and using the information to evaluate and improve employee response to the quality mission, policies, and the quality system, as well as employee well-being and satisfaction—is implied in any effective quality system.

Typical employee-related trends reviewed are:

- Turnover rate
- Retention rate
- Grievances by type and frequency
- Lost time by type—accident, illness, disciplinary action, personal
- Mobility—promotions, lateral transfers, demotions
- Recognition and rewards by type, reason, and frequency

Tools and Metrics

The evaluator of quality systems has a number of tools and documents available:

- Accepted auditing protocols, auditor conduct standards, and codes of conduct
- Applicable standards and guidelines (external and internal)
- The organization's policies, procedures, work instructions, workmanship standards, and forms
- Process maps (detailed flowcharts depicting the steps and decision points in the system)
- Checklists (detailed questions to ask to get responses that can be verified by objective evidence)

- Sampling techniques (to enable an auditor to reduce the number of transactions/things checked, yet get a representative view of the operating effectiveness of the system)
- Copies of prior external assessments
- Copies of previous internal audits
- Quality system records

A variety of measurement approaches and metrics enable evaluation of the effectiveness of a quality system. Fundamental metrics include:

- COQ measure—for example, ratio of prevention costs to total quality costs increasing, with failure costs decreasing
- Return on quality investment (ROQI); rate of return equals or exceeds organizational norms for project investments
- Customer retention
- Supplier performance
- Process measurements
- Strategic goals, objectives, and plans
- Process benchmarking

REFERENCES

1. R. S. Kaplan, and D. Norton, "The Balanced Scorecard," *Harvard Business Review* 74 (November–December 1996): 86.
2. ANSI/ISO/ASQC A8402-1-1994, *Quality Management and Quality Assurance—Vocabulary* (Milwaukee: ASQC Quality Press, 1994).
3. J. P. Russell, ed., *The Quality Audit Handbook* (Milwaukee: ASQ Quality Press, 1997).
4. ASQ Certification Department.
5. Russell, *Quality Audit Handbook*.

See Appendix A for additional references for this chapter.

Chapter 12
E. Quality Models and Theories

Throughout this book, information is presented identifying central themes and principles of total quality that provide the foundation for achieving customer satisfaction. An organization needs a well-structured system that identifies, documents, coordinates, integrates, and maintains key quality-related activities throughout all operations. Armand V. Feigenbaum defined a total quality system as "the agreed companywide and plant-wide operating work structure, documented in effective, integrated technical and managerial procedures, for guiding the coordinated actions of the workforce, the machines, and the information of the company and plant in the best and most practical ways to assure customer quality and economical costs of quality."[1]

The process of implementing a system for quality is somewhat simplified if organizations have a model for guiding design and implementation of quality-related processes and a means of assessing how well actions are carried out. Awards and certification programs provide tested organizational models as well as a basis for assessing progress, achievement, and conformance. Widely used models for quality management are the United States' Baldrige Performance Excellence Program (BPEP), Japan's Deming Prize, and the worldwide International Organization for Standardization (ISO) 9000 series standards. In addition, many states, municipalities, industry groups, and even large corporations have developed significant quality awards, thereby widening the range of organizations eligible for recognition.

1. ISO QUALITY MANAGEMENT STANDARDS

> Describe and apply the requirements and basic principles of the ISO 9000–based standards used to support quality management systems. (Apply)
>
> **Body of Knowledge III.E.1**

International Quality Management—ISO 9000 Series of Standards

Since their inception in 1987, the ISO 9000 quality management standards have grown to become the most widely accepted international standard. The standard is currently the national standard in 178 countries around the world, and there are over one million registered organizations.

The ISO 9000 quality management system (QMS) standards and guidelines assist an organization in developing, implementing, registering, and sustaining an appropriate QMS that functions independently of the specific products and/or services. They are different from the traditional notion of a standard—for example, engineering standards for measurement, terminology, test methods, or product specifications; ISO 9000 standards are based on the premise that a well-designed and carefully managed QMS can provide confidence that the product or service produced by the QMS will meet customer expectations and requirements. Certification of the QMS, however, does not certify or guarantee the quality of the product or service produced.

The basic ISO 9000 series consists of three booklets. They are:

- ISO 9000:2015, *Quality Management Systems—Fundamentals and Vocabulary*, which covers fundamentals of QMSs and terminology and definitions.

- ISO 9001:2015, *Quality Management Systems—Requirements*, which specifies basic overall requirements for the QMS. Although it is permitted for an organization to self-declare its adherence to the standard's requirements, it is more common for the organization's QMS to be audited by a third party to obtain certification of the QMS. This booklet covers terms and definitions, general requirements, and a model for the QMS.

- ISO 9004:2018, *Quality Management—Quality of an Organization— Guidance to Achieve Sustained Success*, which describes and provides guidance on the principles of quality management to enhance performance improvements. It also includes a self-assessment to review the extent to which an organization has adopted QMS principles.

A fourth document that many find helpful is ISO/TS 9002, *Quality Management Systems—Guidelines for the Application of ISO 9001:2015*.

The ISO 9001:2015 standard defines requirements in broad, general terms. Each organization must interpret them within the context of its own business environment and develop its own QMS to support business success and achieve compliance with the standard's requirements. The ISO 9001:2015 QMS model is based on plan-do-check-act (PDCA) and addresses:[2]

Section 4 - Context of the Organization

- Understanding the context of the organization

- Understanding interested parties (stakeholders) and their needs

- Determining the scope of the QMS

- Defining the processes within the QMS that deliver products and services and support customer satisfaction

Section 5 - Leadership

- Follow the ten obligations for leadership, including promoting the process approach and risk-based thinking

- Demonstrate a customer-focused approach and promote that within the organization

- Establish and communicate an appropriate quality policy that includes continual improvement

- Effectively communicate the deployment of the responsibilities and authority granted within the organization to ensure employees have a clear understanding of their role in achieving customer satisfaction

- Ensure that the integrity of the QMS is maintained during times of change in the business

Section 6 - Planning

- Determining risks and opportunities that have an impact on customer satisfaction and taking appropriate actions to address them

- Creating quality objectives, which should determine what resources will be needed to achieve objectives and be SMART (specific, measurable, actionable, realistic/relevant, timely) and be deployed consistently throughout the organization (hoshin planning)

- Planning out any changes to the QMS, including defining the goal of the change(s), identifying risks associated with the change(s), and defining resources and responsibilities

Section 7 - Support

- Control any outsourced activities/processes that are required to achieve customer satisfaction

- Determine and provide appropriate human resources, infrastructure, and environmental resources to achieve required results

- Define and control monitoring and measuring resources (calibration)

- Define the knowledge required by the organization, what knowledge it possesses, and how it obtains and manages knowledge (this section points towards mentorship, succession planning, etc.)

- Determine the competency requirements for jobs that affect organizational performance and customer satisfaction; provide appropriate training and then evaluate the effectiveness of that training (note the PDCA approach here)

- Ensure that employees (and outside contractors as appropriate) understand the quality policy, their relevant quality objectives, how they contribute to the effectiveness of the QMS, and the implications of noncompliance with QMS requirements

- Determine how performance metrics will be communicated within (and outside of) the organization

- Determine requirements for documentation, including identification, format, and requirements for review and approval

- Define methods for document control, including change control, distribution, rights-of-access, retention, and disposition of records

Section 8 - Operations

- *Plan* the way operations are carried out (through defined processes and controls), *do* those processes under controlled conditions, *check* that outputs are being achieved efficiently and effectively, and *act* to get back on track when plans are not being met

- Ensure that customers' requirements are well defined and understood before accepting a product or service order or a contract

- Ensure that controls in an organization responsible for product/service design are established around such areas as design methodology, well-defined design inputs and design output goals, design reviews, verification and validation, and methods for ongoing design changes

- Define and exercise controls over suppliers, such as supplier selection, communication of requirements, and supplier controls (such as on-site inspections, audits, and ongoing evaluation of their performance)

- Implement controls over product manufacturing and/or service provisions, including work instructions and suitable equipment error proofing, et cetera

- Implement appropriate controls for product identification and traceability

- Implement packaging and delivery controls

- Exercise controls over changes in operations

- Define and exercise controls over final inspection

- Exercise controls over changes in operations

- Exercise controls over nonconforming outputs, including proper identification and segregation, correction, and the procurement of customer permissions for use/shipment where appropriate

Section 9 - Performance Evaluation

- Define what needs to be monitored and measured (based on the context of the organization, stakeholder needs, and the nature of operational processes)

- Evaluate the performance and effectiveness of the QMS, including seven mandatory aspects of the QMS

- Measure customer satisfaction

- Conduct internal audits, per a defined schedule, to evaluate the effectiveness of the QMS and its compliance to requirements (see ISO 19011 for guidance[3])

- Conduct management reviews at defined intervals to ensure the QMS's continuing suitability (to serve the organization's needs), adequacy, effectiveness, and alignment with the strategic direction of the organization

- Consider the changing business climate; the management review agenda will include twelve mandatory inputs to the meeting

- Include opportunities for improvement, the need for changes (including tasks to be performed and who will perform them), and resource needs in the management review meeting

Section 10 - Improvement

- Determine opportunities for improvement that lead to improving business and customer satisfaction

- Act on nonconformances, including customer complaints: correct the problem, determine the need to find root causes, take corrective actions at the system level to prevent recurrence of the problems, implement corrective actions, and verify the effectiveness of those actions

When using the ISO 9001 standard as a systems management model, remember the following:

- Seven quality management principles are the basis for the standard:[4] customer focus, leadership involvement, engagement of people at all levels, process management, continual improvement, fact-based decisions, and mutually beneficial supplier relationships.

- Recognize that customer requirements must drive transformation activities. This is important if an organization wants to retain customers. Management is responsible for identifying what the organization is going to do in the future and for establishing a policy for quality and the direction of the organization. Many organizations do this by creating a mission and vision statement and a quality policy.

- Organizations must obtain information from customers as to how well they have met their needs. It is essential to ensure that customer requirements are understood, agreed upon, and met prior to the delivery of the product or service. After the transaction, the organization can follow up with customers to see how well it met their expectations. Care must be taken to stay current with changing customer requirements.

- To create the capability to meet customers' needs, the organization must have resources available to perform the processes. This includes raw materials, skills, knowledge, talent, money, time, and space. Processes are developed and documented, delineating how resources are to be planned, allocated, and managed. Flowcharts are a very effective way of designing and operating business processes.

- After planning activities, ensure that resources are available for required activities, and production processes are identified and documented to ensure effective and efficient use of resources and product/service conformance to requirements. Contributing activities of suppliers and partners are included in the control of production activities. Although an ISO 9001 certification of the QMS does not guarantee that the quality system works as designed, there must be a feedback mechanism indicating the quality of the output. In process, final inspections and tests are conducted to determine the effectiveness of the inspection and test criteria, as well as to verify the conformance to customers' requirements of the product or service.

- Information from production output activities and feedback from customers provide indicators of whether the system for managing quality is working as planned. Management reviews the effectiveness and efficiency of the quality system by reviewing measurements, audits, analysis, and improvement information.

- The cycle repeats itself. Results from the management review are integrated into the management of resources, production activities, and measurement activities.

- The ISO 9001 standard is considered a foundation for an effective QMS. ISO 9004 provides guidelines to expand the potential to achieve maximum benefits (and return on investment) from the QMS implementation.

There are many benefits of implementation and certification of an ISO 9001–based QMS. Some common benefits are:

- Reduction in waste, rework, and redundancy

- Reduction in potential for external failures

- Cost reductions, increased productivity, and improved performance

- Improved customer satisfaction

- Reduction in number of on-site customer-ordered audits

- Marketing edge over suppliers that do not have a certified QMS

- Increased employee pride in the organization and the work they do

- Greater awareness and commitment to quality throughout the organization

Other Pertinent ISO-Related and International Standards

Following is a list of other important ISO-related standards:

ISO 19011:2018 *Guidelines for Auditing Management Systems*

ISO 10012:2003 *Measurement Management Systems—Requirements for Measurement Processes and Measuring Equipment*

ISO 14001:2015 *Environmental Management Systems—Requirements with Guidance for Use*

ISO 22000:2018 *Food Safety Management Systems—Requirements for Any Organization in the Food Chain*

ISO 26000:2010 *Guidance on Social Responsibility*

ISO 31000:2018 *Risk Management—Guidelines*

ISO 50001:2018 *Energy Management Systems—Requirements with Guidance for Use*

ISO 13485:2016 *Medical Devices—Quality Management Systems—Requirements for Regulatory Purposes*

ISO 45001:2018 *Occupational Health and Safety Management Systems—Requirements with Guidance for Use*

AS9100D *Quality Management Systems—Requirements for Aviation, Space, and Defense Organizations*

IATF 16949:2016 *Quality Management System Requirements for Automotive Production and Relevant Service Organizations*

ISO/IEC 27001:2013 *Information Technology—Security Techniques—Information Security Management Systems—Requirements*

TL 9000 R5.5 *Quality Management System Measurements Handbook* (telecommunications)

ISO 10001:2018 *Quality Management—Customer Satisfaction—Guidelines for Codes of Conduct for Organizations*

ISO 10002:2018 *Quality Management—Customer Satisfaction—Guidelines for Complaints Handling in Organizations*

ISO 10003:2018 *Quality Management—Customer Satisfaction—Guidelines for Dispute Resolution External to Organizations*

Examples of Other Standards

Other industries have issued standards, such as:

- *JC.* The Joint Commission was created to empower a formal accreditation process for ensuring the safety and integrity of healthcare. During the late 1990s, the commission realized the value in adapting the criteria outlined for the Baldrige Award. To date, each update of the Joint Commission standards has shown a closer linkage to the Baldrige criteria.

- *NCQA.* The National Committee for Quality Assurance (NCQA) is a not-for-profit organization that assesses and reports on the quality of managed care and health maintenance organizations. To earn this seal of approval, an organization must meet rigorous standards of confidentiality, access, customer service, and quality improvement. The mission of the NCQA is to provide information about managed healthcare organizations, enabling users to make better decisions about plans based on quality.

- *CE mark.* An abbreviation of a French phrase (*conformité Européenne*), the CE mark on a manufacturer's product asserts that the product complies with the essential/safety requirements of relevant European regulations.[5]

- *Good manufacturing practices (GMP).* There are variations in the requirements for GMP—for example, medical device manufacturing and pharmaceuticals in the United States, EU directives in Europe, and others. In the United States, the U.S. Food and Drug Administration (FDA) monitors medical device problem data and inspects the operations and records of device developers and manufacturers to determine compliance with GMP.

- There are quality-related guidance and certifications in the field of computer software development. *TickIT* is a certification of QMSs that conform to the requirements of the ISO 9001 standard.

- *CMMI capability maturity model.* This model is used to determine current process capabilities and identify critical software issues for improvement.

2. PERFORMANCE EXCELLENCE MODELS

Define and describe common elements and criteria of performance excellence models such as the European Excellence Award (EFQM), Excellence Canada, ASQ International Team Excellence Award (ITEA), or Malcolm Baldrige National Quality Award (MBNQA). Describe how their criteria are used as management models to improve processes at an organization level. (Understand)

Body of Knowledge III.E.2

In October 1982, recognizing that U.S. productivity was declining, President Ronald Reagan signed legislation mandating a national study/conference on productivity. The American Productivity Center (now the American Productivity and Quality Center) sponsored seven computer networking conferences in 1983 to prepare for a White House conference on productivity. The final report from these conferences recommended that "a National Quality Award, similar to the Deming Prize in Japan, be awarded annually to those firms that successfully challenge and meet the award requirements." The Malcolm Baldrige National Quality Award (MBNQA) was signed into law (Public Law 100-107) on August 20, 1987, and is named after President Reagan's secretary of commerce, who was killed in an accident shortly before the Senate acted on the legislation.

A *total quality management* (TQM) business approach is the basis for the MBNQA, an annual award to recognize U.S. organizations for performance excellence under the BPEP criteria. In 1999 the criteria for performance excellence expanded to create separate but parallel criteria for education and healthcare organizations. The BPEP promotes an understanding of the requirements for performance excellence and fosters sharing of information about successful performance strategies and the benefits derived from using these strategies. The

Here's what the Baldrige Excellence Framework can do for you.

Manufacturer
Grew return on investment at a 23% compound annual rate; increased annual orders from repeat and international customers 32% and nearly 400%, respectively

Small business
More than doubled in size over 6 years; created more than $26 million in revenue annually for 9 years

Government agency
Achieved $3.22 billion in cost avoidance over 5 years

Organizational profile

Strategy

Workforce

Leadership

Integration

Results

Customers

Operations

Measurement, analysis, and knowledge management

Core values and concepts

Hospital
Decreased the risk-adjusted mortality rate by 24%—better than the top-decile level in its six-county region

K-12 public school system
Over 10 years, tripled the number of advanced placement exams taken, with 66% of students taking at least one; more than doubled the number of AP exams with scores of 3 or higher

Nonprofit
Leads all local competitors in customer engagement and loyalty as measured by net promoter system scores

Figure 12.1 Baldrige criteria for performance excellence.

Baldrige criteria are presented from a systems perspective. Figure 12.1 shows the interrelationship of the seven categories.

Category Descriptions

An overview of the Baldrige Excellence Framework criteria categories follows.[6]

Preface: Organizational Profile. This is a snapshot of the applying organization, the key organizational characteristics, and the organization's strategic situation. The preface identifies the organization's product/service offerings, the vision and mission, a profile of its workforce, major physical assets, regulatory requirements, organizational structure, customers and stakeholders, and suppliers and partners.

    1. *Leadership.* This category examines how the organization's senior leaders guide and sustain the organization and communicate with the

workforce. Also examined are the organization's governance and how the organization addresses its ethical, legal, and societal responsibilities.

2. *Strategy.* This category examines how the organization develops strategic objectives and action plans. Also examined is how the chosen strategic objectives and action plans are deployed and changed if circumstances require and how progress is measured.

3. *Customers.* This category examines how the organization engages its customers for long-term marketplace success. Also examined is how the organization listens to the voice of its customers, builds customer relationships, and uses customer information to improve and identify opportunities for innovation.

4. *Measurement, Analysis, and Knowledge Management.* This category examines how the organization selects, gathers, analyzes, manages, and improves its data, information, and knowledge assets and how it manages its information technology. Also examined is how the organization reviews its performance in order to improve.

5. *Workforce.* This category examines the organization's ability to assess workforce capability and capacity needs and build a workforce environment conducive to high performance. Also examined is how the organization engages, manages, and develops the workforce to utilize its full potential in alignment with the organization's overall mission, strategy, and action plans.

6. *Operations.* This category examines how the organization designs, manages, and improves its work systems and work processes to deliver customer value and achieve organizational success and sustainability. Also examined is the organization's readiness for emergencies.

7. *Results.* This category examines the organization's performance and improvement in all key areas—product and process outcomes, customer-focused outcomes, leadership and governance outcomes, and financial and market outcomes. Performance levels are examined relative to those of competitors and other organizations with similar product offerings. *Results* is weighted higher (45%) than any of the other six to emphasize that business process performance must show high-performance outcomes.

The Baldrige program follows eleven core values.

Using the BPEP Criteria as a Management Model

The BPEP criteria are designed to help organizations improve the value of what they offer to their customers and market and improve their overall organizational performance. Criteria are specifically worded using nonprescriptive statements of requirements to allow for different interpretations. It is up to the organization to develop its approach to satisfy the criteria requirements that will best suit its needs. A QMS can be designed simply by using the seven categories, although for more complex systems, the criteria identify items within the seven categories and numerous areas within the items.

The Baldrige criteria can be used as a model for planning and implementing quality management. Figure 12.1 is the model:

- Senior leaders (category 1) identify the value of their products and services to their current customers and potential customers in their market.

- Key participants develop a strategy (category 2) to satisfy the requirements and expectations of customers and markets (category 3).

- Strategic objectives from planning are turned into action plans to track the movement of the organization from where it currently is in the market to where it wants to be.

- Measurement and analysis are accomplished to recognize achievement of planned activities or to stimulate improvement opportunities (category 4).

- Employees are trained, educated, and developed (category 5) to prepare for the organization's transition from where it is to where it needs to be relative to skills and knowledge of its products and services.

- Processes are managed (category 6) to ensure that performance expectations are effective and efficient and will satisfy the expectations and requirements of customers, markets, and regulatory agencies.

- Business results (category 7) are reported and analyzed (category 4) to determine the achievement and/or opportunity for improvement to expected outcomes as identified in strategy and action plans.

The BPEP criteria are designed to serve three purposes in building and strengthening U.S. competitiveness:

1. Helping improve organizations' performance practices, capabilities, and results

2. Facilitating communication and sharing of best practices information among U.S. organizations of all types

3. Serving as a tool for organizations' understanding and managing of performance, as well as for guiding organizational planning and opportunities for learning

As with any model for management of business, success is not a guarantee. Use of the Baldrige criteria as a management model will only increase the probability of achieving expected performance outcomes. Detailed examples of how the Baldrige criteria can be applied to an organization are available in the form of case studies used by examiners for the BPEP and many state quality award programs. Case studies can be obtained for a fee.

The Baldrige criteria booklets may be obtained from the BPEP (http://www.nist.gov/baldrige/) or from ASQ (http://www.asq.org).

Other Quality-Related Awards

Many states offer Baldrige criteria–type awards. A number of larger business entities have also established their own internal Baldrige-type awards.

The *European Quality Award* was initiated in 1991. This award is similar to the BPEP award in that it, too, is nonprescriptive. It is offered to four sectors: large business, operational units within companies, public sector organizations, and small and medium-size enterprises.

A Japanese award for excellence is the *Deming Prize*. It was established in 1951 to encourage and recognize quality improvement.

The *Shingo Prize for Excellence in Manufacturing* (Japan) was established in 1988 to promote lean manufacturing concepts and reduction of waste.

3. OTHER QUALITY METHODOLOGIES

Describe and differentiate methods such as total quality management (TQM), continuous improvement, and benchmarking. (Apply)

Body of Knowledge III.E.3

Total Quality Management

Total quality management (TQM) is a term that has been variously attributed to several sources. The U.S. Naval Air Systems Command used it in 1985 to describe its Japanese-style management approach to quality improvement. TQM is an umbrella methodology drawing on knowledge of the principles and practices of the behavioral sciences, the analysis of quantitative and nonquantitative data, economics theories, and process analysis to continually improve the quality of all processes.

The principles and tools of TQM were developed over a long period of time. Some of the first seeds of quality management were planted in the 1920s as the principles of scientific management swept through U.S. industry. At that time businesses clearly separated the processes of planning and carrying out the plan, and union opposition arose as workers were deprived of a voice in the conditions and functions of their work. The Hawthorne experiments in the late 1920s showed how worker productivity could be affected by participation.

In the 1930s Walter A. Shewhart developed the methods for statistical analysis and control of quality. In the 1950s W. Edwards Deming taught these methods to Japanese engineers and executives while Joseph M. Juran taught the concepts of controlling quality and managerial breakthrough.

Armand V. Feigenbaum's 1961 book *Total Quality Control* is a forerunner of the present understanding of TQM. Likewise, Philip B. Crosby's promotion of zero defects paved the way for quality improvement in many companies.

The Japanese approach to quality management, influenced by Deming, Juran, and Feigenbaum, was promoted under several names. In 1968 the Japanese named their approach to total quality *companywide quality control*. Kaoru Ishikawa's synthesis of the philosophy contributed to Japan's ascendancy as a quality leader.

TQM is the name for the philosophy of a broad and systemic approach to managing organizational quality. Quality standards such as the ISO 9000 series and quality award programs such as the Deming Prize and the BPEP specify principles and processes that compose TQM.

Primary Elements of TQM

The philosophy of TQM can be summarized as a management system for a customer-focused organization that engages all employees in continual improvement of the organization. It is an integrative system that uses strategy, data, and effective communications to integrate the quality discipline into the culture and activities of the organization.

• *Customer focused.* It is fundamental to understand that the customer ultimately determines the level of quality. No matter what an organization does to foster quality improvement—training employees, integrating quality into the design process, upgrading computers or software, or buying new measuring tools—the customer ultimately determines whether the efforts were worthwhile.

• *Total employee involvement.* Total employee involvement refers to participation of all employees in working toward common goals. Total employee commitment can only be obtained after fear has been driven from the workplace, when empowerment has occurred, and when management has provided a motivational environment. High-performance work systems integrate continuous improvement efforts with normal business operations. Self-managed work teams are one form of empowerment often used.

• *Process centered.* A fundamental part of TQM is a focus on process thinking. A process is a series of steps that take inputs from suppliers (internal or external) and transform them into outputs that are delivered to customers (again, either internal or external). The steps required to carry out the process are defined, and performance measures are continually monitored in order to detect unexpected variation.

• *Integrated system.* Although an organization may consist of many different functional specialties, often organized into vertically structured departments, it is the horizontal processes interconnecting these functions that are the focus of TQM. Microprocesses add up to larger processes, and all processes aggregate into the business processes required for defining and implementing strategy. Everyone must understand the vision, mission, and guiding principles, as well as the quality policies, objectives, and critical processes of the organization. Business performance must be monitored and communicated continuously. An integrated business system may be modeled after the BPEP criteria and/or incorporate the ISO 9000 or other standards. Every organization has a unique work culture, and it is virtually impossible to achieve excellence in its products and services unless a good quality culture has been fostered. Thus, an integrated system connects business improvement elements in an attempt to continually improve and exceed the expectations of customers, employees, and other stakeholders.

• *Strategic and systematic approach.* A critical part of the management of quality is the strategic and systematic approach to achieving an organization's vision, mission, and goals. This process, called *strategic planning* or *strategic management*, includes the formulation of a strategic plan that integrates quality as a core component.

• *Continual improvement.* A major thrust of TQM is continual process improvement. Continual improvement drives an organization to be both analytical and creative in finding ways to become more competitive and more effective in meeting stakeholders' expectations.

• *Fact-based decision-making.* In order to know how well an organization is performing, data on performance measures are necessary. TQM requires that an organization continually collect and analyze data in order to improve decision-making accuracy, achieve consensus, and allow prediction based on past history.

• *Communications.* During times of organizational change, as well as in day-to-day operations, effective communication plays a large part in maintaining morale and in motivating employees at all levels. Communications involve strategies, methods, and timeliness.

These elements are considered so essential to TQM that many organizations define them, in some format, as a set of core values and principles on which the organization is to operate. Therefore, even if the term itself is not in use, the concepts may be fundamental to operations in any organization. For example, the Baldrige criteria comprise core values and concepts that define behaviors in high-performing organizations.

Benefits of TQM

Following are some of the direct and indirect benefits that may result from TQM:

- Strengthened competitive position
- Adaptability to changing or emerging market conditions and to environmental and other government regulations
- Higher productivity
- Enhanced market image
- Elimination of defects and waste
- Reduced costs and better cost management
- Higher profitability
- Improved customer focus and satisfaction
- Increased customer loyalty and retention
- Increased job security
- Improved employee morale
- Enhanced shareholder and stakeholder value
- Improved and innovative processes
- Greater emphasis on and awareness of the value of producing quality products and services

TQM Implementation Approaches

No one solution is effective for planning and implementing TQM in all situations. Each organization is unique in terms of culture, management practices, its products and services, and the processes used to create and deliver them. The TQM strategy will then vary from organization to organization; however, the key elements just mentioned should be present. Following is a generic model for implementing TQM:

1. Top management learns about and decides to commit to TQM. TQM is identified as one of the organization's strategies.

2. The organization assesses current culture, customer satisfaction, and QMSs.

3. Top management identifies core values and principles to be used and communicates them.

4. A TQM master plan is developed on the basis of steps 1, 2, and 3.

5. The organization identifies and prioritizes customer demands and aligns products and services to meet those demands.

6. Management maps the critical processes through which the organization meets its customers' needs.

7. Management oversees the formation of teams for process improvement efforts.

8. The momentum of the TQM effort is managed by the steering committee.

9. Managers contribute individually to the effort through hoshin planning, training, coaching, or other methods.

10. Daily process management and standardization take place.

11. Progress is evaluated and the plan is revised as needed.

12. Constant employee awareness through feedback on status is provided, and a recognition/reward process is established.

Following are five different strategies that may be used to develop TQM:

• *Strategy 1: The TQM element approach.* This is a TQM element-by-element approach that uses the tools of TQM to foster improvements. This method was widely used in the early 1980s as companies tried to implement parts of TQM as they learned them. Examples of this approach include quality circles, statistical process control, Taguchi methods, and quality function deployment. Some gain is achieved, but overall effectiveness is lacking.

• *Strategy 2: The guru approach.* The guru approach uses the teachings and writings of one of the leading quality thinkers as a guide to determine where the organization has deficiencies, then make appropriate changes to remedy those deficiencies. For example, managers might study Deming's fourteen points and seven deadly diseases or other seminal (or derivative) works. They would then work on implementing the approach learned. This approach often ignores the values offered by gurus not selected and tends to lead to an elitist perspective (for example, "We follow Deming's teachings.")

• *Strategy 3: The organization model approach.* In this approach, individuals or teams visit organizations that have taken a leadership role in TQM and determine their processes and reasons for success. They then integrate these ideas with their own ideas to develop an organizational model adapted for their specific organization. This method was used widely in the late 1980s and is exemplified by the initial winners of the MBNQA. There is often a tendency to just copy what is learned.

• *Strategy 4: The Japanese total quality approach.* Organizations using the Japanese total quality approach examine the detailed implementation techniques and strategies employed by Deming Prize–winning companies and use this experience to develop a long-range master plan for in-house use. This approach was used by Florida Power and Light—among others—to implement TQM and to compete for and win the Deming Prize. If the approach is not integrated into the organization's culture and continually sustained, it fades away.

• *Strategy 5: The award criteria approach.* When using this model, an organization uses the criteria of a quality award—for example, the Deming Prize, the European Quality Award, or the BPEP—to identify areas for improvement. Under this approach, TQM implementation focuses on meeting specific award criteria. Although some argue that this is not an appropriate use of award criteria, some organizations do use this approach, and it can result in improvement.

What is the best approach? *The one that works best for the organization.* It is usually a mixture of various philosophies, theories, adaptations of successful techniques, and tools used by others, all combined to address the uniqueness of the organization.

Common TQM Implementation Problems

Difficulties in implementing TQM can include:

• *Lack of management commitment.* When management talks TQM but its actions fail to support the effort, it will ultimately fail to meet expectations. The result is cynicism and mistrust—and difficulty launching another attempt. For implementation to succeed, management must clearly and frequently communicate the reason for adopting TQM, be consistent in its application of TQM principles, and not present TQM as if it is another fad.

• *Changing organizational culture.* Changing an organization's culture is difficult and time-consuming, but it can be done. Fear of change must be addressed, labor-management conflicts must be resolved, and the organization's focus must change from maintaining the status quo. Most employees will need to be convinced of the benefits that a TQM program will provide for them to buy into the changes. This often means that employees need to change behaviors or perform tasks in a different way than before TQM. If motivation is lacking, frustration and stress are likely. And trust is a must!

• *Preparation.* Before implementing TQM, management should strive for an organization-wide commitment, clearly communicate the organization's vision, mission, goals, and strategies, and foster open communication about the organization's changed focus. Repeating the message is a requirement.

• *Use of data.* TQM relies on data-based decision-making. To succeed in building and sustaining a TQM environment, data must be accurate, timely, and reliable. The measurement process used must be valid and consistent, and data access should be efficient. Decision-makers must be trained in data analysis and interpretation.

Other problems, many of which fall under the four previous categories, include but are not limited to:

- Lack of strategic direction
- Lack of shared vision, mission, or guiding principles
- Lack of cooperation and teamwork among different work groups
- Focus on short-term profits rather than on long-term goals
- Failure to understand what teamwork entails
- Failure to focus on customers' needs and expectations
- Lack of mutual trust and respect among levels of employees
- Insufficient resources or lack of sustained commitment of those resources
- Lack of continual and effective training and education
- Management's failure to recognize and/or reward achievements

TQM, as a term, is not used as widely in the United States as it once was. Most of the concepts, principles, and methodology have been subsumed under the term *quality management*.

Continuous Quality Improvement (CQI)

The concept of company-wide continuous quality improvement originated with American companies (National Cash Register, Lincoln Electric) dating as far back as 1894. Gradually, the momentum changed from improving the workplace environment to an emphasis on productivity improvement and work simplification. Japanese companies began development of continuous quality improvement programs in the early 1950s (Toshiba, Matsushita Electric, and Toyota).

The ISO 9001:2008 standard requires continual quality improvement. The term changed from *continuous* (implying nonstop) to *continual* (meaning recurring often).

Lean and kaizen. *Kaizen* is a Japanese word meaning incremental and orderly continuous improvement and is often considered the single most significant contributor to Japanese success in the marketplace.[7] The kaizen philosophy embraces all business areas and processes. The focus is on improving the quality of people, which leads to quality of products and services.

Workers are given the quality improvement tools to expose opportunities for improvement and reduce waste. Top management supports the efforts, allocates resources, and provides reward programs that encourage improvement. Workers participate in suggestion systems and group activities. They receive training in problem-solving and quality tools. Japanese organizations expect and receive an extremely large quantity of suggestions per employee, most of them small, incremental improvements costing little to implement.

A *kaizen event* (also called a *kaizen blitz*) is typically a five-day, highly intensive activity that may target eliminating waste, improving the work environment (especially safety), and reducing costs. It involves a work team focused on a specific opportunity for increased effectiveness and efficiency. Importantly, the result is not only a process improvement but also the development of a new or revised work standard (without which the benefit of the improvement might soon dissipate). A structured approach is used for the five-day event.

A cycle time reduction team is a team comprising workers involved with a given process. They meet periodically—for example, once a week—to study the process and create innovative methods and/or use tools for shortening the process cycle time. Examples are single-minute exchange of die (SMED) and other ways to reduce setup time and cellular processing and incorporate single-piece flow.

Six Sigma. *Six Sigma*: A statistical term? A methodology? A breakthrough strategy? A philosophy? It is all of these. The overall objective of a Six Sigma approach is to reduce variation and produce the product or service outputs consistently within customers' requirements.

Benchmarking. *Benchmarking* is a process for identifying, comprehending, and adapting knowledge of exemplary practices and processes from organizations worldwide to assist an organization in improving its process or product performance. Best-in-class organizations use benchmarking as a key activity in setting goals as well as in determining how to meet them. Benchmarking assures management that chosen goals and objectives are competitive and attainable. *Benchmarks* are the measures of a best-in-class process.

Benchmarking involves identifying potential sources of best practices. First, however, it requires gaining a complete understanding of one's own process, as it is impossible to do an accurate comparison to others without such an understanding. This requires knowing the boundaries of the process to be studied, the steps involved (as identified through a process map), and the current performance level of the process. Benchmarking levels include:

1. *Internal benchmarking.* Comparing a process in one function with that of another function or comparing the same process across locations. Data are fairly easy to collect; however, focus is limited and possibly biased.

2. *Competitive benchmarking.* Comparing with direct competitors, either locally, nationally, or worldwide. The organization may not be viewed as a competitor when comparing with other organizations outside the local market area. In this case the data can be more relevant but difficult to collect. Typically, there will be resistance from a local direct competitor. Also, ethical and legal issues can be a concern.

3. *Functional benchmarking.* Comparing processes to other organizations with similar processes in the same function but outside of the industry.

4. *Generic benchmarking.* Finding organizations that have best-in-class processes and approaches from which one may learn and translate to improvements at one's own organization. When you think outside the box, there is a high potential for discovering innovative practices and usually little resistance to partnering with a noncompetitor (see

Table 12.1). There can be problems and high costs in translating practices learned to one's own work environment.

Many organizations conduct benchmarking studies at all four levels. Typical steps in benchmarking are:

1. Review, refine, and define existing process to be benchmarked

2. Determine what to benchmark

Table 12.1   Examples for benchmarking a process.

Industry	Area—process improvement	Possible partner
Airline	Service planes quickly	Auto racing pit crews
Bandage manufacturer	Convert material to product	Auto manufacturer
Education	Teach/train students	Industry trainers
Hospital	Bill and collect payments	Credit card companies
Pizza delivery	Deploy personnel rapidly	Military, hospital emergency room
Ammunition casing	Make smooth cylinders	Lipstick manufacturer
Municipal government	Pothole repairs—time and material	Electric or gas utility
Hotel	Maintenance of public spaces	Gambling casino
Professional association	Book and product sales	Internet-based book company
On-call TV repair service On-call plumber Cable TV service Public utility	Truck stock replenishment or selection of on-board tools and equipment	Fire department Ambulance service Police department
Urban transit company	Bus/trolley car maintenance	Interstate truck stop service center
Sports arena	Processing mailed-in ticket sales	Commercial mail-order company
Metal stamping manufacturer (job shop)	Time to changeover dies for new order	Aircraft carrier— mounting weapons/ ammunition on planes
Bank	Handling cash transactions	Sports arena
Assembly plant	Restocking parts just in time	Supermarket
Aerospace manufacturer	Large-project management	Major commercial building construction firm
Printer of continuous web paper products	Improving operating performance	Manufacturer of rolled metal products
Large hi-tech electronics manufacturing and assembly	Establishing customer/public tours and information center	NASA Large public utility

3. Form a benchmarking team

4. Identify benchmark partners

5. Collect and analyze benchmarking information

6. Evaluate organization's performance versus benchmark partner

7. Determine how upgrading practices will affect the organizations involved

8. Establish new strategic targets

9. Implement improvements and a system to monitor progress

10. Do it all over again

Sources of organizations with which to partner in a benchmarking study can be found by examining trade publications for listings of companies deemed best in their industries, perusing best-practices databases available from major consulting firms, or talking with award-winning companies or others from whom it is expected that significant learning can occur. The internet is a widely used resource for benchmarking, although the reliability of the information should be confirmed (see Figure 12.2 for a hierarchy of resources).

If process results or outcomes are all that are needed, then available performance figures might be sufficient and no further analysis necessary. If the process that achieves those results is to be benchmarked, however, then a visit to the benchmarking partner can be arranged. Once performance data have been analyzed, the project team can determine how the partner is achieving that performance and then develop objectives and an action plan to achieve similar or greater success.

The process of benchmarking can become so large that it becomes an entity in its own right. Before using it as a key decision-making tool, an organization should determine whether benchmarking is the best use of its resources. A benchmarking effort might initially be limited to discovering whether anyone has overcome the same or similar constraints as the organization is experiencing. If so, the benchmarking team can decide whether benchmarking is required in order to

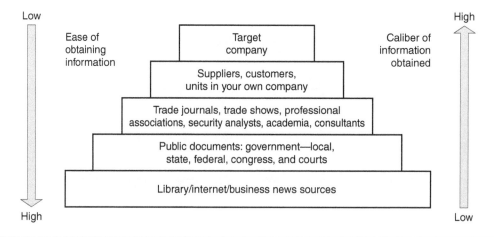

Figure 12.2 Sources of benchmarking information.

learn from the partner's success. Sponsorship and substantial support of management is mandatory when process benchmarking is to be done.

When done correctly, benchmarking offers many benefits. It allows the team to look beyond its own organization and even its industry. Looking beyond normal, everyday boundaries allows new ideas to emerge. In addition, a successful relationship with a benchmarking partner can create a mutually beneficial sales tool for both organizations. Significant research and development resources can be saved when mistakes are avoided. Finally, benchmarking can allow an organization to gain ground on the competition in a very short time.

Successful benchmarking includes:

- Having the right and best people on the team

- The ability to successfully break a process into its components

- Avoiding taking on too large a process for the resources available

- A long-term management commitment

- Focusing on a process rather than on just performance metrics

- Integrating the benchmarking initiative with broader goals

- Realizing that differences in culture, the portfolio of processes, and skill levels will likely make just copying a process from one organization into another ineffective

- Awareness of and diligent concern for proprietary and ethical issues

See Figure 12.3 for a benchmarking code of conduct.[8]

Organizations that already have effective quality systems in place and are among the high-level profit producers for their size and type of business will probably benefit most from benchmarking. Midlevel profit producers can gain valuable insights but may get a better return on their investment by first getting their own organization's processes in better shape. Lower-level profit producers, with few or no quality systems in place, may become frustrated with the gap between their practices and a best-in-class producer and have difficulty finding a benchmarking partner. (A benchmarking partner expects new partners to bring something to share and should not expect to be educated on basic knowledge.)

Examples of what to benchmark include systems, processes, or practices that:

- Incur the highest costs

- Have a major impact on customer satisfaction, quality, and process cycle time

- Strategically affect the business

- Have the potential for high impact on competitive position in the marketplace

- Present the most significant area for improvement

- Have the highest probability of support and resources if selected for improvement

Category	Item
1.0	Legality
1.1	If there is any potential question on the legality of an activity, then consult with your corporate counsel.
1.2	Avoid discussions or actions that could lead to or imply an interest in restraint of trade, market and/or customer allocation schemes, price fixing, dealing arrangements, bid rigging, or bribery. Do not discuss costs or prices with competitors.
1.3	Refrain from the acquisition of trade secrets from another by any means that could be interpreted as improper, including the breach or inducement of a breach of any duty to maintain secrecy. Do not disclose or use any trade secret that may have been obtained through improper means or that was disclosed by another in violation of duty to maintain its secrecy or limit its use.
1.4	Do not, as a consultant or client, extend benchmarking study findings to another company without first ensuring that the data are appropriately blinded and anonymous so that the participants' identities are protected.
2.0	Exchange
2.1	Be willing to provide to your benchmarking partner the same type and level of information that you request from your benchmarking partner.
2.2	Fully communicate early in the relationship to clarify expectations, avoid misunderstanding, and establish mutual interest in the benchmarking exchange.
2.3	Be honest and complete with the information submitted.
2.4	Provide information in a timely manner as outlined by the stated benchmarking schedule.
3.0	Confidentiality
3.1	Treat benchmarking interchange as confidential to the individuals and companies involved. Information must not be communicated outside the partnering organizations without the prior consent of the benchmarking partner who shared the information.
3.2	A company's participation is confidential and should not be communicated externally without their prior permission.
4.0	Use
4.1	Use information obtained through benchmarking only for purposes stated to the benchmarking partner.
4.2	The use or communication of a benchmarking partner's name with the data obtained or practices observed requires the prior permission of the benchmarking partner.
4.3	Contact lists or other contact information provided in any form may not be used for purposes other than benchmarking and networking.
5.0	Contact
5.1	Respect the corporate culture of partner companies and work within mutually agreed procedures.
5.2	Use benchmarking contacts designated by the partner company if that is its preferred procedure.
5.3	Obtain mutual agreement with the designated benchmarking contact on any handoff of communication or responsibility to other parties.
5.4	Obtain an individual's permission before providing his or her name in response to a contact request.

Figure 12.3 APQC *Benchmarking Code of Conduct.*

5.5	Avoid communicating a contact's name in an open forum without the contact's prior permission.
6.0	Preparation
6.1	Demonstrate commitment to the efficiency and effectiveness of benchmarking by being prepared prior to making an initial benchmarking contact.
6.2	Make the most of your benchmarking partner's time by being fully prepared for each exchange.
6.3	Help your benchmarking partners prepare by providing them with a questionnaire and agenda prior to benchmarking visits.
7.0	Completion
7.1	Follow through with each commitment made to your benchmarking partner in a timely manner.
7.2	Complete a benchmarking effort to the satisfaction of all benchmarking partners as mutually agreed.
8.0	Understanding and Action
8.1	Understand how your benchmarking partner would like to be treated.
8.2	Treat your benchmarking partner in the way that your benchmarking partner would want to be treated.
8.3	Understand how your benchmarking partner would like to have the information he or she provides handled and used. Handle and use it in that manner.

Figure 12.3 APQC *Benchmarking Code of Conduct. (continued)*

Source: APQC, 123 N. Post Oak Ln., Houston, TX 77024. Reproduced with permission.

Examples of some of the areas for which benchmarking studies have been done include:

- Accounting systems
- Compensation systems
- Purchasing practices—for example, supplier selection
- Manufacturing and distribution processes
- Customer service practices
- Customer database design
- Cost of quality
- Capital investments—for example, selection criteria
- Techniques and tools
- Facility size, layout, decor
- Staffing practices—for example, size of departments, hiring criteria, training programs
- Employee involvement, empowerment, and recognition

- Marketing and promotion practices
- Knowledge management approaches
- Innovative usage of information technology
- Services and products offered
- Customer acquisition and retention approaches
- Customer satisfaction practices
- Overall operation—for example, building the organization's image, hours of operation
- Special practices and incentives

It is crucial to understand that benchmarking *is not*:

- Industrial spying
- Competitive analysis
- Industrial tourism
- Focused only on numbers but mostly on the processes that produce the numbers
- Effectively planned and initiated unless there are significant potential gains expected
- A quick or inexpensive process when properly executed
- For organizations that are unwilling to make the effort to learn and measure what they are presently doing
- Appropriate without proper protocol and legal considerations
- Worth initiating unless your organization is prepared to make changes resulting from what is learned
- Easily accomplished if you have nothing to trade in your partnering arrangement
- Usually a one-shot process

In a 1944 interview, Juran told a story about German generals in the early 1900s who came to the United States to follow an American circus around.[9] The circus performed in tents, monstrous things to set up and take down. The circus moved from city to city on very short notice, which was a complicated process involving animals, people, equipment, food, and housing. To do this they had special railway cars designed. They were very proficient at handling every little detail.

The generals had a situation that seemed to be far from that of a circus, or so they thought until they looked at the similarities. They had people, horses, ammunition, food for both humans and animals, and tons of equipment. And they, too, were faced with the need for setting up and dismantling their camps on very short notice. These generals learned about deployment from observing a circus, which, at first, appeared to have no relation to their army. This was a classic case of functional benchmarking.

4. QUALITY PHILOSOPHIES

> Describe and apply basic methodologies and theories proposed by quality leaders such as Shewhart, Deming, Juran, Crosby, Feigenbaum, and Ishikawa. (Apply)
>
> **Body of Knowledge III.E.4**

Theories of Major Contributors to Quality

Many theorists contributed to the philosophies and methods supporting TQM. Following are brief summaries of some of the work of the more widely known quality gurus.

Walter A. Shewhart. Shewhart is referred to as the father of statistical quality control because he brought together the disciplines of statistics, engineering, and economics. Shewhart worked at Bell Laboratories, who pioneered the quality discipline and gave the profession some of its most capable experts. A mentor of both Juran and Deming, Shewhart did extensive research in statistics and probability. He described the basic principles of the new discipline in his book *Economic Control of Quality of Manufactured Product*, the first statistics text focused on quality.

In his book he first proposed that there are two types of variation in a process—*chance causes* and *assignable causes*—and pointed out that assignable causes can be searched out and removed. He then presented a theory of charting data from the process using statistically based control limits as a means of differentiating between the two types of causes. The use of lot-by-lot inspection and understanding the relationship between process variation and specifications were also spelled out. Shewhart's focus was on finding economic ways to reduce costs by identifying problems sooner in the process and by reducing the cost of inspection. Shewhart created the concept of PDCA, which Deming later adapted.

W. Edwards Deming. Deming saw quality as the primary driver for business and societal success and communicated the philosophy as a chain reaction. The premise is that if one improves quality, then costs will be lowered and resources better utilized. This increase in productivity will then allow the company to capture market share due to both higher quality and lower price, which will allow the organization to stay in business and to provide more jobs (known as the *Deming chain reaction*).

Deming's best-known contribution was his fourteen points for transformation of Western management:

1. Create constancy of purpose for improving products and services.

2. Adopt the new philosophy.

3. Cease dependence on inspection to achieve quality.

4. End the practice of awarding business on price alone; instead, minimize total cost by working with a single supplier.

5. Improve constantly and forever every process for planning, production, and service.

6. Institute training on the job.

7. Adopt and institute leadership.

8. Drive out fear.

9. Break down barriers between staff areas.

10. Eliminate slogans, exhortations, and targets for the workforce.

11a. Eliminate numerical quotas for the workforce.

11b. Eliminate numerical goals for management.

12. Remove barriers that rob people of pride of workmanship and eliminate the annual rating or merit system.

13. Institute a vigorous program of education and self-improvement for everyone.

14. Put everybody in the company to work accomplishing the transformation.

Deming also defined *seven deadly diseases* that he believed to be the major barriers to business success:

1. *Lack of constancy of purpose.* A company without constancy of purpose has no long-range plans for staying in business. Management is insecure and so are employees.

2. *Emphasis on short-term profits.* Looking to increase the quarterly dividend undermines quality and productivity.

3. *Evaluation by performance, merit rating, or annual review of performance.* The effects of these are devastating—teamwork is destroyed; rivalry is nurtured. Performance ratings build fear and leave people bitter, despondent, and beaten. They also encourage defection in the ranks of management.

4. *Mobility of management.* Job-hopping managers never understand the companies they work for and are never there long enough to follow through on long-term changes that are necessary for quality and productivity.

5. *Running a company on visible figures alone.* The most important figures are unknown and unknowable—the multiplier effect of a happy customer, for example.

6. *Excessive medical costs for employee healthcare.* These increase the final costs for goods and services.

7. *Excessive costs of warranty.* These are often fueled by lawyers who work on the basis of contingency fees.

Deming emphasized that transformation of organizations begins with the individual and that this comes from gaining a different understanding of self and the world in which he or she lives. This will require understanding the *system of profound knowledge*, which consists of four major components:

1. *Appreciation for a system.* An organization is a system of interrelated components with a common purpose. Changing one part of the system affects other parts.

2. *Knowledge about variation.* Everything varies, but understanding whether the variation is due to chance cause or random cause will determine what action should be taken, if any.

3. *Theory of knowledge.* No learning has occurred if there is no theory that allows prediction. Operational definitions are necessary in order to allow theories to be useful to many.

4. *Psychology.* We all want to be appreciated. People have different needs, however, and what will make one happy might negatively affect another.[10]

Deming adapted Shewhart's plan-do-check-act cycle to plan-do-study-act (with proper attribution to Shewhart) to better reflect the actions of this process. *PDCA* is the term more often used and is often incorrectly attributed to Deming.

Joseph M. Juran. Juran pursued a varied career as an engineer, executive, government administrator, university professor, labor arbitrator, corporate director, and consultant. Specializing in managing for quality, his *Juran's Quality Handbook* is now in the seventh edition, edited by Joseph A. Defeo.[11]

Juran defines quality as consisting of two different but related concepts:

1. One form of quality is income oriented and consists of those features of the product that meet customer needs and thereby produce income. In this sense, higher quality usually costs more.

2. A second form of quality is cost oriented and consists of freedom from failures and deficiencies. In this sense, higher quality usually costs less.

He defined three basic managerial processes required for quality, called the *Juran trilogy*. The processes are quality planning, quality control, and quality improvement, which, he noted, parallel the processes traditionally used to manage finance.

Juran's quality-planning road map consists of the following steps:

- Determine quality goals

- Identify customers

- Discover customers' needs

- Translate customer language into products having desired features

- Develop processes able to produce the product

- Transfer the process, with appropriate controls, to operations

Quality control takes place at all levels, from the CEO down to the workers, and all use the same feedback loop, which is the following:

- Measure performance of the process
- Compare performance to the goal
- Take action if there is a gap

Quality improvement occurs when the current system is suspected of being inadequate:

- Prove the need
- Establish the infrastructure
- Identify the improvement projects
- Establish project teams
- Provide the teams with resources, training, and motivation to diagnose the causes and stimulate remedies
- Establish controls to hold the gains

The goal of management should be to achieve what Juran calls *self-control* in all processes, wherein the person performing the process is capable of making all adjustments necessary to maintain control. Planning for control is part of the function of designing the process.

Juran presented a structured approach for improvement in his book *Managerial Breakthrough* (1964) and included a list of responsibilities that upper managers should not delegate:

- Creating awareness of the need and opportunity for improvement
- Making quality improvement a part of every job description
- Creating an infrastructure—a quality council that selects projects for improvement and establishes teams
- Providing training in quality improvement methods
- Regularly reviewing improvement progress
- Giving recognition to improvement teams
- Using the results to spread the word on the power of the efforts
- Revising the reward system to enforce the rate of improvement
- Maintaining momentum by enlarging the business plan to include goals for quality improvement

Juran also defines three levels of quality management:

1. *Strategic quality management*, which concerns itself mostly with policies
2. *Operational quality management*, which concerns itself with process management
3. *The workforce*, which concerns itself with specifications and work procedures

Juran defines TQM as a collection of certain quality-related activities:

- Quality becomes a part of each upper management agenda.

- Quality goals enter the business plan.

- Stretch goals are derived from benchmarking; focus is on the customer and on meeting competition, and there are goals for annual quality improvement.

- Goals are deployed to the action levels.

- Training is done at all levels.

- Measurement is established throughout.

- Upper managers regularly review progress against goals.

- Recognition is given for superior performance.

- The reward system is revised.

Juran expressed what he termed a *universal sequence*, described in two journeys. A *diagnostic journey* goes from symptom to cause. This includes analyzing symptoms, theorizing causes, testing theories, and establishing causes. A *remedial journey* moves from causes to remedy. The activities included are developing remedies, testing remedies, proving remedies under operating conditions, dealing with resistance to change, and establishing controls to maintain the gains.

Other Juran concepts include big Q and little q and the Pareto principle. Prior to 1980, *little q* meant quality control of products. Often accomplished via sampling and sorting, this technique was expensive and only prevented defects from flowing, not from occurring. Juran's *big Q* meant design, control, and improvement for all processes.[12]

Philip B. Crosby. Crosby defines quality as conformance to requirements; therefore, quality is measured by the cost of nonconformance. Using this approach means that one arrives at a performance goal of zero defects. Quality management means prevention, so inspection, testing, checking, and other nonpreventive techniques have no place in quality management. Crosby believed that statistical levels of compliance set people up for failure.

Crosby defined what he called *absolutes of quality management*:

1. Quality means conformance, not elegance.

2. There is no such thing as a quality problem.

3. There is no such thing as the economics of quality; it is always cheaper to do the job right the first time.

4. The only performance measurement is the cost of quality.

5. The only performance standard is zero defects.[13]

Crosby maintains that absolutely no reason exists for having errors or defects in any product or service and that companies should adopt a quality "vaccine" to prevent nonconformance. The three ingredients of this vaccine are determination, education, and implementation. Quality improvement is a process, not a program;

it should be permanent and lasting. He also has fourteen steps he believes necessary for improvement:

1. Make it clear that management is committed to quality.

2. Form quality improvement teams with representatives from each department.

3. Determine how to measure where current and potential quality problems lie.

4. Evaluate the cost of quality and explain its use as a management tool.

5. Raise the quality awareness and personal concern of all employees.

6. Take formal actions to correct problems identified through previous steps.

7. Establish a committee for the zero defects program.

8. Train all employees to actively carry out their part of the quality improvement program.

9. Hold a zero defects day to let all employees realize that there has been a change.

10. Encourage individuals to establish improvement goals for themselves and their groups

11. Encourage employees to communicate to management the obstacles they face in attaining their improvement goals.

12. Recognize and appreciate those who participate.

13. Establish quality councils to communicate on a regular basis.

14. Do it all over again to emphasize that the quality improvement program never ends.

Armand V. Feigenbaum. Total quality control uses quality as a strategic business tool that requires awareness by everyone in the organization (just as cost and schedule are regarded in most organizations). Quality reaches far beyond defect management on the shop floor: it is a philosophy and commitment to excellence.

Quality is a way of corporate life—a way of managing. Total quality control has an organization-wide impact that involves implementation of customer-oriented quality activities. This is a prime responsibility of general management as well as marketing, engineering, production, industrial relations, finance, and service and of the quality function itself. Feigenbaum defines total quality control as excellence driven rather than defect driven and suggests that the quest consists of three elements: quality leadership, quality technology, and organizational commitment. Continuous leadership emphasis must be placed on quality, which must be thoroughly planned in specific terms. The establishment of a quality circle program or a corrective action team is not sufficient for ongoing success.

The traditional quality department cannot resolve 80% to 90% of quality problems. In a modern setting, all members of the organization must be responsible for the quality of their product or service. This means integrating office staff into the process, as well as engineers and shop floor workers. Error-free performance should be the objective. New techniques must be evaluated and implemented as appropriate. What might be an acceptable level of quality to a customer today might be unacceptable tomorrow.

For quality to be achieved, continuous motivation is required. Training that is specifically related to the task at hand is of paramount importance. Quality should be considered a strategic element of business planning.

Feigenbaum defined four management fundamentals of total quality:

1. Competition means there is no such thing as a permanent quality level. Continuous improvement is necessary if one is to stay competitive.

2. Good management involves personally leading the effort by mobilizing the organization's quality knowledge, skill, and attitudes such that everyone realizes that improvement in quality makes everything better.

3. Successful innovation requires high quality to support it, especially where it enables new products to be designed and launched more quickly and effectively.

4. Cost and quality are complementary rather than conflicting objectives.[14]

Kaoru Ishikawa. Ishikawa was an early student of Deming and a member of the Union of Japanese Scientists and Engineers (JUSE). He authored the *Guide to Quality Control* to help in the training of foremen and middle managers in Japan for the operation of quality circles. In his book *What Is Total Quality Control? The Japanese Way*, he discusses the following aspects of total quality control:

- *Quality control* (QC) is the responsibility of all workers and all divisions.

- *Total quality control* (TQC) is a group activity and cannot be done by individuals. It calls for teamwork.

- TQC will not fail if all members cooperate, from the president down to line workers and sales personnel.

- In TQC, middle management will be frequently talked about and criticized—be prepared.

- QC circle activities are a part of TQC.

- Do not confuse objectives with the means to attain them.

- TQC is not a miracle drug; its properties are more like those of Chinese herbal medicine.

To achieve TQC, a thought revolution must occur:

- Quality first—not short-term profit first

- Consumer orientation—not producer orientation; think from the standpoint of the other party

- The next process is your customer—break down the barrier of sectionalism

- Use facts and data to make presentations—utilize statistical methods

• Respect for humanity as a management philosophy—full participatory management

• Cross-functional management

Ishikawa advocated four types of audits:

1. Audit by the president

2. Audit by the head of the unit (for example, division head or branch office manager)

3. QC audit by the QC staff

4. Mutual QC audit

The concept of quality circles is attributed to Ishikawa. He also introduced the cause-and-effect diagram (sometimes called the Ishikawa diagram or the fishbone diagram) and variations of the check sheet.[15]

Genichi Taguchi. Taguchi is best known in the United States for the *Taguchi methods*, which involve the efficient use of design of experiments for identifying the major contributors to variation (parameter design), for setting tolerances based on inherent statistical variation (tolerance design), and for designing robust products and processes. Taguchi maintains that the goal is the most robust combination of product and process—that is, the product that best meets the customers' requirements by being most consistently produced by the process.

He defines quality of a product as "the (minimum) loss imparted by the product to society from the time the product is shipped." From this, he designed the *Taguchi loss function*, which translates any deviation of a product from its target parameter into a financial measure (see Figure 12.4). The Taguchi loss function is a driver for continuous improvement.

Figure 12.4 The Taguchi loss function.

REFERENCES

1. A. V. Feigenbaum, *Total Quality Control*, 3rd ed. (New York: McGraw-Hill, 1991).

2. ISO 9001:2015, *Quality Management Systems—Requirements* (Geneva: International Organization for Standardization [ISO], 2015).

3. ISO 19011:2018, *Guidelines for Auditing Management Systems* (Geneva: ISO, 2018).

4. ISO 9000:2015, *Quality Management Systems—Fundamentals and Vocabulary* (Geneva: ISO, 2015).

5. P. Brooks, "The Global Marketplace and CE Marking: If You Want to Sell in Europe, Here's What You Need to Know," *Quality Digest* (July 2002): 44–47.

6. NIST/BPEP, Baldrige Excellence Framework, accessed July 5, 2019, www.nist.gov /baldrige.

7. M. Imai, *Kaizen: The Key to Japan's Competitive Success* (New York: Random House Business Division, 1986).

8. Benchmarking Code of Conduct, January 19, 2014, accessed April 24, 2019, https:// www.apqc.org/knowledge-base/documents/benchmarking-code-conduct-0.

9. J. M. Juran, ed., *A History of Managing for Quality* (Milwaukee: ASQC Quality Press, 1995).

10. W. Edwards Deming, *The New Economics*, 2nd ed. (Cambridge, MA: MIT Center for Advanced Educational Studies, 1994).

11. J. A. Defeo, ed., *Juran's Quality Handbook*, 7th ed. (New York: McGraw-Hill, 2017).

12. J. A. Defeo, "From Little q to Big Q—and Back Again," *Six Sigma Forum Magazine*, Guest Editorial, May 2, 2015, 5–7.

13. P. B. Crosby, *Quality Is Free* (New York: Mentor Books, 1979).

14. Feigenbaum, *Total Quality Control*.

15. K. Ishikawa, *Guide to Quality Control* (Tokyo: Asian Productivity Organization, 1982).

See Appendix A for additional references for this chapter.

Part IV
Quality Management Tools

Chapter 13   A. Problem-Solving Tools
              Contributors: Eileen Serrano, Douglas C.
              Wood, and Sandra L. Furterer
Chapter 14   B. Process Management
              Contributors: Eileen Serrano and
              Jd Marhevko
Chapter 15   C. Measurement: Assessment and Metrics
              Contributor: Eileen Serrano

The significant problems we face cannot be solved at the same level of thinking we were at when we created them.

—Albert Einstein

The systems perspective tells us that we must look beyond individual mistakes or bad luck to understand important problems.

—Peter Senge

Defects are not free. Somebody makes them, and gets paid for making them.

—W. Edwards Deming

Chapter 13
A. Problem-Solving Tools

Regardless of the current level of organizational performance, room for improvement always exists. Project-by-project problem-solving and process improvement has become a basic practice for managing any organization. In order for improvement efforts to be effective, however, a systematic approach must be used to identify, understand, and address the opportunities.

Analyzing a process in order to identify factors needing to be changed involves the use of data or ideas. Such information needs to be presented in a way that allows ease of interpretation. Visual representation of processes and information is one way of accomplishing this, and tools such as flowcharts and Pareto charts have therefore become widespread in their use. Since solutions often call for outside-the-box thinking, additional tools have been developed to help increase creativity.

Often, what is initially determined to be causing a problem or defect (for example, a specific machine, department, component, or person) may simply be a symptom of a much larger difficulty. Problems are also often caused by a combination of factors that require in-depth searches for root causes. In addition, what may appear to be a problem may just be the result of random variation of a process. Punishing or rewarding people for random swings in a process is a sure way for management to lose credibility.

Just as auto mechanics need to accurately diagnose and quickly fix engine problems (rather than simply replacing components until the problem part is found—a lengthy and costly method), process improvement efforts need to follow a systematic approach. A systematic approach, carried out on a project-by-project basis, works for several reasons:

- Focused allocation of resources improves the chances of success by preventing spreading those resources too thinly.

- The use of facts and data improves problem-solving efficiency and effectiveness by ensuring that improvement efforts are objective and focus on the proper causes.

- A system-wide view may allow other areas of the organization to benefit.

Some reasons a problem-solving process often fails are:

- Jumping from analysis to a solution too quickly

- Using data that are inaccurate or biased

- Failing to test a solution before implementing it

- Mistaking a symptom for the root cause of the problem

- Failing to include the right people in the problem-solving process

- Failing to evaluate the potential benefits and costs of the chosen solution

Many methods and associated tools can be used to improve organizational processes. The focus of this chapter is on the tools typically used to reduce process variation.

Finally, it is important that improvement efforts not simply be a hodgepodge of seemingly random projects. Organizations need to have a process for identifying the most significant improvement opportunities and must also track the progress of efforts. *Cost of quality* (COQ) is a tool that can be used to look at an organization's financial information in such a way as to highlight opportunities for quality improvement.

1. THE SEVEN CLASSIC QUALITY TOOLS

> Select, interpret, and evaluate output from these tools: Pareto charts, cause-and-effect diagrams, flowcharts, control charts, check sheets, scatter diagrams, and histograms. (Evaluate)
>
> **Body of Knowledge IV.A.1**

Flowchart (1)

A *flowchart* is a map of the sequence of steps and decision points in a process. An example of a flowchart is shown in Figure 13.1. Flowcharting a process is a good starting point for a team, as it helps the group gain a common understanding of the process flow. Each team member typically has a perspective based on his/her own role but may not have a full understanding of the entire process. A flowchart can also reveal missing, redundant, or erroneous steps.

In addition to providing basic information, flowcharts may contain additional items depending on the purpose of the project, such as times, tools, and responsibilities. For example, a *deployment flowchart*, sometimes called a *swim-lane chart* (Figure 13.2), is likely to be used for a larger process in which multiple departments have responsibility.

A flowchart may be used to:

- Document the as-is condition of a process

- Reflect changes that are to be made to a process

- Design an entirely new process

- Fulfill the International Organization for Standardization (ISO) 9001 standard's requirements to identify and document the organization's processes and the sequence and interaction of these processes

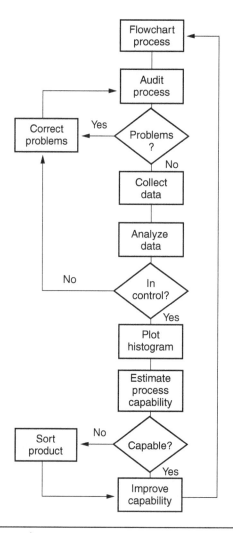

Figure 13.1   Flowchart example.

Check Sheet (2)

The *check sheet* (sometimes called a *tally sheet*) is used for gathering information to analyze. As with most of the tools, it facilitates the use of facts, rather than just opinions, in talking about and solving problems. Check sheets are used to gather data on frequency of occurrence (see Figure 13.3). Data from several check sheets can be organized into a Pareto chart for final analysis.

In some applications a more visually oriented data collection device may be desired. For example, in order to record the location of defects in a printing process, a sample of the product being printed could be given to individuals who are to collect the data. They could then simply mark on the printout where each of the defects is located on the inspected products. Clusters indicating the biggest problem areas would quickly become apparent. (This type of check sheet is sometimes called a *measles chart* or a *defect data check sheet*.)

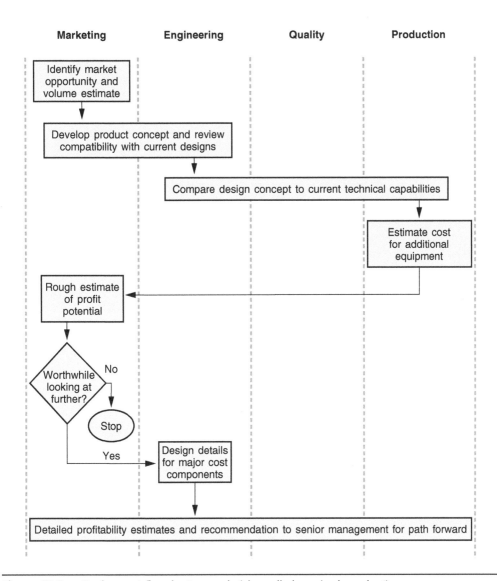

Figure 13.2   Deployment flowchart example (also called a swim-lane chart).

Cause-and-Effect Diagram (3)

The *cause-and-effect* (C-E) diagram (also called an *Ishikawa diagram* after its developer Kaoru Ishikawa, or alternatively called a *fishbone diagram*) provides a way of collecting and organizing what may be a long list of potential causes that might contribute to a particular problem. In a C-E diagram, the problem (the effect) is stated in a box at the right side of the chart, and likely causes are listed under major categories that can lead to the effect. The *four Ms* (manpower, machinery, methods, and materials) are categories of problem sources typically used for manufacturing problems, although other headings such as *environment* and *measurements* are sometimes added. For service processes, the *four Ps* (people, policies, procedures, and plant) are often used. Figure 13.4 shows a C-E diagram of some of

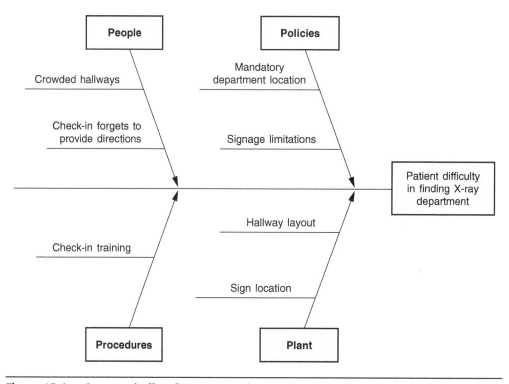

Switch Assembly Op 236 Plastic footer Operator_____

Chart began July 12, 2013

	Week 1						Totals
Burns	III	JHt					
Misrun		III	II				
Bad finish	JHt						
Porosity		I					
Flash	JHt JHt I	IIII I					
Color							

Figure 13.3 Check sheet example.

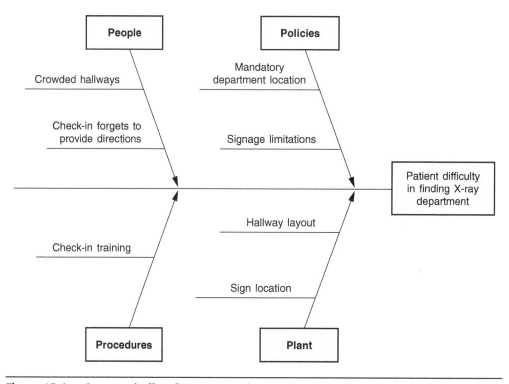

Figure 13.4 Cause-and-effect diagram example.

the reasons that outpatient clients may not be able to locate the X-ray department in a hospital.

The items for the diagram may be created through a brainstorming session or by a review of the relevant process flowchart to explore what can go wrong at each step. Once the C-E diagram is completed, the potential causes should be organized and ordered so that internal and external relationships are clear. The *affinity diagram* is one way to do this. Data must be gathered to determine which of the causes or groups of causes are most likely to be acting on the problem being studied.

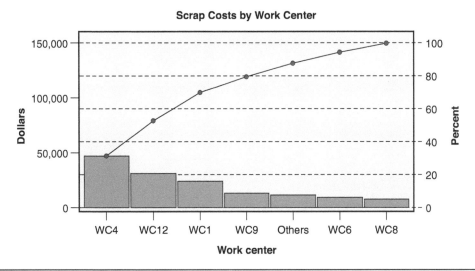

Figure 13.5   Pareto chart example.

Pareto Chart (4)

Vilfredo Pareto, an 1800s Italian economist, noted that 80% of the wealth in Italy was held by 20% of the population. Juran later applied the Pareto principle for other applications, pointing out that 80% of the variation in a process is caused by roughly 20% of the variables; he labeled these variables the *vital few*, as opposed to the *trivial many* (changed later to *useful many*), which had much less overall impact.

Figure 13.5 is an example of a *Pareto chart* that indicates how much each work center contributes to quality costs. Pareto analysis could also be used by a supervisor within each of the higher-cost work centers to pinpoint the particular machines that are the primary sources of trouble. Note that although the *y*-axis of a Pareto chart often represents the frequency of a problem, it is also important to do a similar analysis based on costs since not all problems have equal financial impact. The right side of Figure 13.5 includes another feature, cumulative percentage.

Pareto charts may be used to drill down into a situation. The major left-hand bars represent categories of issues, and those individual bars may be sliced into other categories, showing more detail about the relationships between various aspects of a situation.

Control Charts (5)

Control charts are a refinement of the original *run chart*, which does not include control limits. A control chart serves several vital purposes as a data-gathering tool: (1) it shows when a process is being influenced by special causes, creating an out-of-control condition; and (2) it indicates how a process behaves over time and/or whether a corrective action taken in a process has been effective.

Control charts should be examined for nonrandom patterns of data points; such an analysis of patterns can indicate what source of variation is most likely creating the condition (for example, which of the causes in the C-E diagram is most likely influencing the process). Patterns could reflect wildly fluctuating values, sudden

Figure 13.6   Control chart example.

process jumps or shifts, a gradual trend, or increased variation. Each of the causes in the C-E diagram is likely to create only a particular type of pattern, making the control chart a valuable diagnostic tool. The pattern might also reveal improvement in a process, indicated by decreased variation. Investigating this change to find the cause may provide deeper learning.

A control chart is shown in Figure 13.6. See Chapter 15 for more on control charts.

Histograms (6)

While control charts allow seeing how a process performs over time, a *histogram* provides a graphical picture of the frequency distribution of the data. The histogram allows detection of distributions that do not demonstrate a typical bell-shaped curve and shows how the process spread and central tendency relate to process specifications. A histogram is shown in Figure 13.7.

For a normal (bell-shaped) distribution, the most frequently appearing value (mode) is centered, with data appearing equally on either side. If data extend beyond the specification limits, the process or product is out of tolerance. Additionally, the histogram may also point out that there are actually two different distributions at work (as shown in Figure 13.7) in the process (for example, differing impact of the same raw material purchased from two different suppliers).

Scatter Diagrams (7)

A *scatter diagram* shows whether or not there is a relationship between two variables. A relationship between two variables does not necessarily mean a direct cause-and-effect association, however. If it appears that values for one of the variables can be predicted based on the value of another variable, there is correlation.

In the example in Figure 13.8, the curing temperature of a glue joint has been plotted along the x-axis and the shear strength along the y-axis. In this example the shear strength of the joint increases with an increase in cure temperature, within the normal processing limits. If the data points were to fall along a single, straight line, the variation in glue strength would be fully explained by the value of the cure temperature. In most cases there is deviation from a straight line, indicating the existence of other sources of variation in the process.

Figure 13.7   Histogram example.

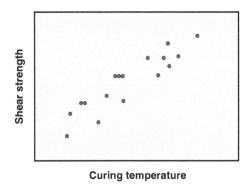

Figure 13.8   Scatter diagram example.

If the slope of the plots is generally upward, as in this example, it is said that a *positive correlation* exists between the variables. That is, as one increases, the other also increases. Other possible measures of correlation are negative, weak, or none. A *negative correlation* exists if the line slopes downward, meaning that as one variable increases in value, the second decreases. If no visible pattern appears to exist in the plotted points, the two variables are not correlated. A numeric value called the correlation coefficient (r) can also be calculated, with values approaching +1 or −1 indicating high positive or negative correlation, respectively, and a value near zero indicating no correlation.

Some additional factors should be considered when using the scatter diagram. First, not all relationships between variables are linear. If the range of temperatures were extended in Figure 13.8, it is likely that a peak strength in the glue joint would be reached, after which increasing the cure temperature would damage the joint and reduce its strength. Therefore, the relationship between the two variables is not really a straight line but rather a curve that climbs upward, peaks, and then descends.

A second consideration is that the visual slope of the line does not provide any information about the strength of correlation since the scales of the graph can be expanded or compressed on either axis. The third consideration, and probably the most important, is that a direct and strong correlation does not necessarily imply a cause-and-effect relationship. An example is that the volume of ice cream sold per day is strongly correlated to the daily number of fatalities by drowning. Obviously, neither of these variables is the cause of the other, and the most likely explanation is that each of these variables is a result of and is therefore strongly correlated to a third variable, such as the outside temperature.

While correlation does not prove causality, the lack of correlation may indicate that no cause-and-effect relationship exists.

2. BASIC MANAGEMENT AND PLANNING TOOLS

> Select, interpret, and evaluate output from these tools: affinity diagrams, tree diagrams, process decision program charts (PDPCs), matrix diagrams, prioritization matrices, interrelationship digraphs, and activity network diagrams. (Evaluate)
>
> **Body of Knowledge IV.A.2**

While the quality control (QC) tools in the previous section are typically used by employee teams to analyze and improve processes, the tools presented in this section are more often used by managers or knowledge workers to organize concepts, ideas, and words. These tools are also known as the *new QC tools* and are oriented more toward facilitating management and planning activities. The seven tools are the activity network diagram, affinity diagram, interrelationship digraph, matrix diagram, priorities matrix, process decision program chart (PDPC), and tree diagram.

Activity Network Diagram (1)

The *activity network diagram* (AND) is an umbrella term that includes the *critical path method* (CPM) and the *program evaluation and review technique* (PERT). The AND is used when a task is complex and/or lengthy and, because of schedule constraints, it is desirable to determine which activities can be done in parallel. The AND is used often as a planning aid for construction projects and for large manufacturing contracts that are best handled as projects. The AND shows who is going to do what and when, and arrows are drawn to show what must be done in series and what can be done in parallel so that action can be taken if the overall time estimate is too high to meet goals.

In the AND shown in Figure 13.9, each numbered node represents one task that must be completed as a part of a project. The numbers shown between nodes are estimates of the number of weeks to complete the work in a given activity. The critical path can then be computed. The *critical path* is the longest path in the series of activities—those activities that must be completed on time to meet the planned

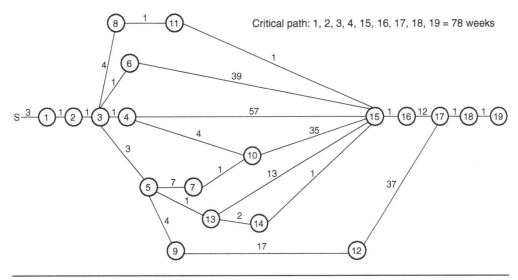

Critical path: 1, 2, 3, 4, 15, 16, 17, 18, 19 = 78 weeks

Figure 13.9   Network diagram example (activity on node).

project completion date. This diagram is often created via a project management software package. For control of scheduling simpler projects or where clarity of monitoring and communication of status is desired, the Gantt chart may be used.

Affinity Diagram (2)

The *affinity diagram* is a method used to organize a large group of items into smaller chunks that are easier to understand and deal with. It is often used after a brainstorming process (discussed later in this chapter) to organize the ideas that were listed. It can be done by first creating categories into which ideas will be placed, or all ideas can first be grouped into what appear to be similar categories that will be named after all grouping is completed. The process can be aided by writing each idea on a sticky note and having members of the group move the notes around until they are satisfied with the groupings. Some items may also be placed in multiple groups when deemed useful.

A major benefit of the affinity diagram is that it creates a discussion on what the various ideas mean to each individual, and the resulting diagram is a jointly created mental model of the situation being analyzed. Figure 13.10 is an example of a completed simple affinity diagram.

Interrelationship Digraph (3)

While the affinity diagram organizes and makes visible various ideas about a project, the *interrelationship digraph* (or *relationship diagram*) pinpoints logical cause-and-effect relationships between ideas. The interrelationship digraph is often constructed using the components of an affinity diagram by asking, "If this category were changed, would it have an impact on each of the other categories?"

Team success factors

Demonstrated commitment
- Assign management sponsors
- Assign a facilitator to each team
- All team members to volunteer

Team process knowledge

Technical process
- Better data analysis skills
- Training for team leaders
- Simpler process improvement model

Meeting process
- Improved use of meeting time
- Reduced conflict between team members
- More listening, less talking, in meetings

Support tools
- Access to a computer
- Standardized forms for agendas and minutes
- Better meeting facilities

Figure 13.10 Affinity diagram of "methods to improve team performance."

When the answer is yes for any pair of categories, an arrow is drawn from the first to the second, showing the cause-and-effect relationship.

A completed interrelationship digraph is shown in Figure 13.11. It shows the various issues that can affect the results of a team-based continual improvement effort and how they are interconnected. This diagram could be used to identify which components of the team process in an organization may not be working sufficiently well or how there may be a lack of alignment between them. It may also be used to distinguish processes that are primarily drivers from processes that are primarily driven.

If there are many ideas or the relations are complex, counting the arrows in and out of each idea and making a ratio of "arrows in" versus "arrows out" allows a single number to represent the degree that each idea is a driver or is driven.

Matrix Diagram (4)

The *matrix diagram* answers two important questions when sets of data are compared: Are the data related, and if so, how strong is the relationship? A matrix diagram can be used to analyze the relationships between variables in an affinity diagram as part of the process in creating an interrelationship digraph. In this way the matrix diagram promotes systems thinking.

Another use of the matrix diagram is when an organization is faced with a large and complex project requiring the integration of activities carried out by resources from multiple departments. The horizontal axis of the matrix diagram

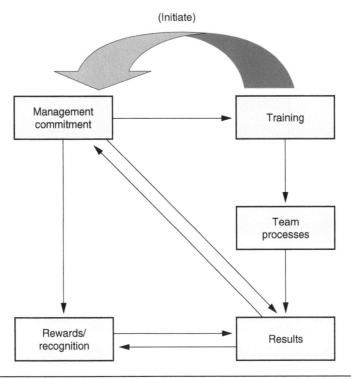

Figure 13.11   Interrelationship diagraph example.

would represent the tasks required and the vertical axis the departments available to perform the work. For each of the required tasks, the matrix diagram shows which departments are in charge, which have some involvement, and which have no involvement in the performance of the tasks. Figure 13.12 shows different ways to show relationships between up to three variables in a matrix diagram.

Priorities Matrix (5)

The *priorities matrix* assists in choosing between several options that have many useful benefits but are not all of equal value. The relative merit of each available course of action and the related effects create a complicated picture that is difficult to prioritize in one's mind. For example, how does a person choose between two automobiles, one of which offers average gas mileage, four-wheel drive, and a fully automated set of window and seat controls and another that has a superior sound system, a significantly smoother ride, and better fuel economy? For one driver, four-wheel drive might be a must-have option that dominates all other considerations, but another driver might value fuel economy above all other options.

A priorities matrix is created and used according to the following steps:

- A matrix is created to compare all criteria to be used in making the choice (see Figure 13.13a). All criteria are listed on both the horizontal and vertical axes and are then compared and assigned a weighted score (relative row percentage) on the basis of the perceived importance of each criterion relative to each other.

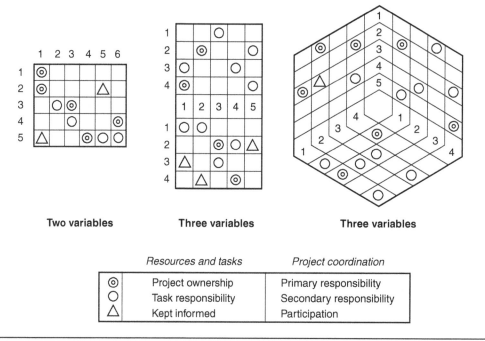

Two variables   Three variables   Three variables

	Resources and tasks	*Project coordination*
⊙	Project ownership	Primary responsibility
○	Task responsibility	Secondary responsibility
△	Kept informed	Participation

Figure 13.12   Matrix diagrams at various stages of completion.

- Once criteria have been weighted, then all possible choices (items from which selection will be made) are rated on how well they compare based on each criterion. A new matrix is required to evaluate the options against each criterion (for example, Figure 13.13b only evaluates the choices based on one of the four criteria that are to be used).

- A final matrix compares the possible choices on the left axis and the decision criteria along the top. The appropriate weighted scores from the other matrices are inserted and multiplied to get a score for each option for each criterion. Figure 13.13c shows the beginning of this matrix based on information gained from Figures 13.13a and 13.13b. The option achieving the highest row total is then considered the best overall choice.

The priorities matrix can add objectivity to what might otherwise be an emotional decision. When numerous possibilities exist and the selection criteria are many and complicated, this tool permits a group to systematically discuss, identify, and prioritize the criteria that should have the most influence on the decision and to then evaluate all of the possibilities while keeping a complete picture in mind.

Process Decision Program Chart (6)

No matter how well planned an activity is, things do not always turn out as expected. The PDPC, similar to fault tree analysis, can be used to identify contingency plans for several situations that might contribute to failure of a particular

	Handling	Acceleration	Comfort	Price	Row total	Row %
Handling		1	10	5	16.0	42.3
Acceleration	1		10	5	16.0	42.3
Comfort	1/10	1/10		1/5	.4	1.1
Price	1/5	1/5	5		5.4	14.3

10	Overwhelmingly more important
5	More important
1	Equal
1/5	Less important
1/10	Overwhelmingly less important

Total   37.8

Figure 13.13a   Priorities matrix—evaluating relative importance of criteria.

	Auto 1	Auto 2	Auto 3	Auto 4	Row total	Row %
Auto 1		5	1/10	1/10	5.2	10.2
Auto 2	1/5		1/5	1/10	.5	1.0
Auto 3	10	5		1/10	15.1	29.7
Auto 4	10	10	10		30	59.1

10	Overwhelmingly better
5	Somewhat better
1	Same
1/5	Somewhat less good
1/10	Overwhelmingly less good

Total   50.8

Figure 13.13b   Priorities matrix—comparing objects based on one criterion (acceleration).

	Handling	Acceleration	Comfort	Price	Row total	Row %
Auto 1	(Criteria row total × Option row total)	(42.3 × 10.2) 431				
Auto 2		(42.3 × 1.0) 42				
Auto 3		(42.3 × 29.7) 1256				
Auto 4		(42.3 × 59.1) 2500				

Figure 13.13c   Priorities matrix (partial)—evaluating all objects against criteria.

project. The tasks to be completed for the project are listed, followed by a list of problems that could occur. For each problem, a decision can be made in advance as to what will be done if each problem does occur. The contingency plan should also include ensuring availability of the resources needed to take the action. Figure 13.14 shows a PDPC, a tool that is especially useful when a process is new, meaning there are no previous data on types and frequencies of failure.

Tree Diagram (7)

The *tree diagram* breaks down an objective into the more detailed steps that must be carried out in order to achieve the objective. It begins with the broad objective and becomes more specific at each level. A tree diagram, shown in Figure 13.15, is similar to the work breakdown structure used in project management.

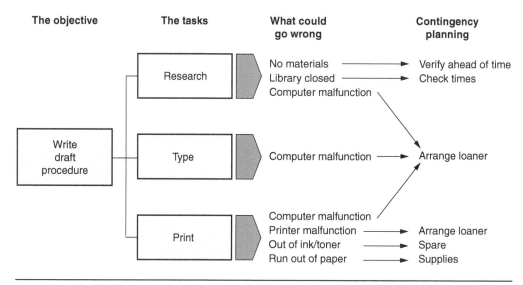

Figure 13.14 Process decision program chart example.

Figure 13.15 Tree diagram example.

3. PROCESS IMPROVEMENT TOOLS

> Select, interpret, and evaluate tools such as root cause analysis, Kepner-Tregoe, PDCA, Six Sigma DMAIC (define, measure, analyze, improve, control), and failure mode and effects analysis (FMEA). (Evaluate)
>
> **Body of Knowledge IV.A.3**

Root Cause Analysis

Problem-solving efforts are often focused on remedying a situation that has developed in which a process is not operating at its normal level. Much of continual improvement, however, involves improving a process that may be performing as expected but where a higher level of performance is desired. Although an effort to solve a problem may utilize many of the tools, involve the appropriate people, and result in changes to the process, if the order in which the problem-solving actions occur is not logically organized and methodical, much of the effort is likely to be wasted. In order to ensure that efforts are properly guided, many organizations create or adopt one or more models—a series of steps to be followed—for all such projects. Note that if a situation is not occurring at present, but rather there is a desire to avoid potential issues, the better tool is *failure mode and effects analysis* (FMEA; see below) either for product or for process.

Seven-Step Problem-Solving Model. Problem-solving is about identifying root causes of the problem and taking actions to alleviate those causes. Following is a typical problem-solving process model and some possible activities and rationale for each step:

1. *Identify the problem and the process.* This step involves making sure that everyone is focused on the same issue. It may involve analysis of data to determine which problem should be worked on and writing a problem statement that clearly defines the exact problem to be addressed and where and when it occurred. A flowchart might be used to ensure that everyone understands the process in which the problem occurs.

2. *List possible root causes.* Before jumping to conclusions about what to do about the problem, it is useful to look at a wide range of possibilities. Brainstorming and cause-and-effect analysis are often used.

3. *Search out the most likely root cause.* This stage of the process requires looking for patterns in failure of the process. Check sheets might be used to record each failure and supporting information, or control charts may be used to monitor the process in order to detect trends or special causes.

4. *Identify potential solutions.* Once it is fairly certain that the particular root cause has been found, a list of possible actions to remedy it should be developed. This is a creative part of the problem-solving process and

may rely on brainstorming as well as input from specialists who may have a more complete understanding of the technology involved.

5. *Select and implement a solution.* After identifying several possible solutions, each should be evaluated as to its potential for success, cost and timing to implement, and other important criteria. Simple processes such as ranking or multivoting, or more scientific analysis using a matrix, are likely to be used in the selection process.

6. *Follow up to evaluate the effect.* All too often, problem-solving efforts stop after remedial action has been taken. As with any good corrective action process, however, it is necessary that the process be monitored after the solution has been implemented. Control charts or Pareto diagrams are tools used to determine whether the problem has been solved. Possible findings might be that there was no effect (which may mean the solution was not properly implemented, the solution is not appropriate for the root cause, or the real root cause was not found), a partial effect, or full resolution of the problem. If there was no effect, then the actions taken during the previous steps of the problem-solving model need to be reviewed in order to see where an error might have occurred.

7. *Standardize the process.* Even if the problem has been resolved, there is one final step that needs to occur. The solution needs to be built into the process (for example, poka-yoke, training for new employees, updating procedures) so that it will continue to work once focused attention on the problem is gone. A review to see what was learned from the project is also sometimes useful.

Kepner-Tregoe

Kepner-Tregoe is a fact-based approach to systematically eliminate possible causes and identify the true cause of a problem or situation. This methodology was developed in the 1950s by Dr. Charles Kepner and Dr. Benjamin Tregoe while working at Rand Corporation. They conducted research on successful decision-making and found that successful decisions depend on the logical process used by individuals to collect, organize, and analyze information before taking action. Together, Kepner and Tregoe wrote the book *The Rational Manager*, first published in 1965.[1]

The Kepner-Tregoe consists of four basic steps:

- Situation appraisal—identifying concerns and outlining priorities for the work environment. It helps managers to see:

  — Where to begin

  — How to recognize situations that require action

  — How to break apart issues that are overlapping and confusing

  — How to set priorities

  — How to manage a number of simultaneous activities efficiently

- Problem analysis—describes the problem, identification, evaluation, and confirmation of causes. This is used when an immediate, visible concern must be resolved.

- Decision analysis—clarifying the purpose, identifying and evaluating alternatives by performing a risk analysis for each of them, and then making a final decision. This explains techniques to refine the elements in thinking patterns:

  — Appreciate that a choice must be made

  — Consider the specific factors that must be satisfied for success

  — Decide what kind of action will best satisfy these factors

  — Consider what risks may be attached to choices

- Potential problem analysis (opportunity)—identify potential problems, establish priorities, take preventive measures, and prepare contingency actions. This is used when needed to avoid potential problems and anticipate and improve future situations.

The Kepner-Tregoe approach reinforces disciplined analysis and decision-making by establishing a problem or situation with a high level of specificity while ensuring that the necessary results or decisions are taken into account. It emphasizes defining a problem in depth before steps are taken to try to solve it. This approach generates a robust problem description that allows ideas, hypotheses, and potential solutions to be tested.

PDCA/PDSA Cycle

The seven-step problem-solving model presented above is actually nothing more than a more detailed version of a general process improvement model originally developed by Walter A. Shewhart, the *plan-do-check-act* (PDCA) *cycle*, which was adapted by W. Edwards Deming as the *plan-do-study-act* (PDSA) *cycle*, emphasizing the importance of learning from improvement. In both cases action is initiated by developing a plan for improvement, followed by putting the plan into action.

In the next stage, the results of the action are examined critically. Did the action produce the desired results? Were any new problems created? Was the action worthwhile in terms of cost and other impacts? The knowledge gained in the third step is acted on. Possible actions include changing the plan, adopting the procedure, abandoning the idea, modifying the process, amplifying or reducing the scope, and then beginning the cycle all over again. Shown in Figure 13.16, the PDCA/PDSA cycle captures the core philosophy of continual improvement.

Six Sigma and the DMAIC Model

Six Sigma is a quality management philosophy and methodology that focuses on reducing variation, measuring defects (per million output/opportunities), and improving the quality of products, processes, and services. The concept of Six Sigma was developed in the early 1980s at Motorola. Six Sigma became popularized in the late 1990s by General Electric and its former CEO Jack Welch.

The Six Sigma DMAIC (define, measure, analyze, improve, control) problem-solving methodology is used to improve processes. The phases of the DMAIC are well defined and standardized, but the steps performed in each phase can vary based on the reference used. The *Define* phase is where the scope of the project charter is developed. The goal of the *Measure* phase is to understand and baseline

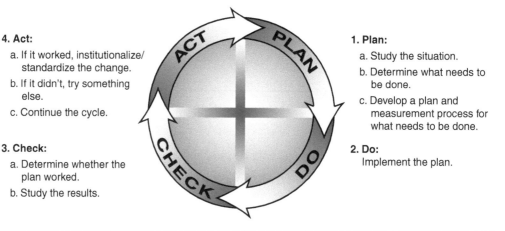

4. Act:

   a. If it worked, institutionalize/
      standardize the change.

   b. If it didn't, try something
      else.

   c. Continue the cycle.

3. Check:

   a. Determine whether the
      plan worked.

   b. Study the results.

1. Plan:

   a. Study the situation.

   b. Determine what needs to
      be done.

   c. Develop a plan and
      measurement process for
      what needs to be done.

2. Do:

   Implement the plan.

Figure 13.16   PDCA/PDSA cycle.

the current process. In the *Analyze* phase, we analyze the data collected in the Measure phase to identify the root causes of the problems identified. In the *Improve* phase, the improvement recommendations are developed and implemented. The goal of the *Control* phase is to ensure that the improvements had a positive impact and that they will be sustained and controlled. In Figure 13.17 is a description of the activities that can be performed within each phase of the DMAIC problem-solving methodology.[2]

There are many tools that are part of the Six Sigma tool kit, which are selected based on the problem to be solved. Figure 13.18 shows the most common tools applied within each DMAIC phase.[3]

In statistical analysis, the term *sigma* refers to a calculated measure of variability called *standard deviation of the sample*. In process improvement language, *sigma* is a term that refers to what extent a process varies from its target condition or perfection. The quantity of units processed divided into the number of defects actually occurring, multiplied by one million, results in defects per million. Adding a 1.5 sigma shift in the mean results in the following number of defects per million:

   1 sigma = 690,000 defects per million

   2 sigma = 308,000 defects per million

   3 sigma = 66,800 defects per million

   4 sigma = 6210 defects per million

   5 sigma = 230 defects per million

   6 sigma = 3.4 defects per million

Six Sigma, as a philosophy, translates to the organizational belief that it is possible to produce totally defect-free products or services—albeit more a dream than a reality for many organizations. For organizations operating at about three sigma or below, getting to perfection leaves much work to be done. Six Sigma constitutes an evolving set of principles, fundamental practices, and tools—a breakthrough strategy.

Phase	Step
Define	1. Create project charter, plan, and stakeholder analysis
	2. Perform initial voice of customer (VOC) and identify critical to satisfaction (CTS)
	3. Select team and launch project
Measure	4. Define the current process and voice of process (VOP) performance
	5. Define detailed VOC
	6. Validate measurement system
Analyze	7. Develop cause-and-effect relationships
	8. Determine and validate root causes
	9. Develop process capability
Improve	10. Design future state with costs and benefits
	11. Establish performance targets and project scorecard
	12. Gain approval, train, and pilot
Control	13. Implement improvement recommendations and manage change
	14 Incorporate process control plans and scorecard
	14. Implement continuous improvement cycle and plan-do-check-act (PDCA)

Figure 13.17 DMAIC phase and activities.
Source: Sandra L. Furterer.

The evolving Six Sigma principles are:

1. Committed and strong leadership is absolutely essential—often, this is a major cultural change.

2. Six Sigma approach and other existing initiatives, strategies, measures, and practices must be integrated—Six Sigma must be an integral part of how the organization conducts its business.

3. Quantitative analysis and statistical thinking are key concepts—it is data-based managing.

4. Constant effort must be applied to learning everything possible about customers and the marketplace—intelligence gathering and analysis is critical.

5. The Six Sigma approach must produce a significant payoff in a reasonable time period—real, validated dollar savings is required.

6. A hierarchy of highly trained individuals with verified successes to their credit, often referred to as Master Black Belts, oversee the Black Belts and Green Belts needed to extend the leadership to all organizational levels.

Define	Measure	Analyze	Improve	Control
• Project charter	• Process map	• Cause-and-effect diagrams	• Quality function deployment	• Hypothesis testing dashboards
• Stakeholder analysis	• Critical to quality characteristics	• Cause-and-effect matrix	• Recommen- dations for improvement	• Statistical analysis
• SIPOC	• Data collection plan with opera- tional definitions	• Why-why diagram	• Action plan	• Graphic analysis
• Process map (high level)	• Pareto chart	• Process analysis, histograms and graphic analysis, waste analysis, value analysis, FMEA	• Cost-benefit analysis	• Sampling
• Communication plan	• Measurement system analysis	• Statistical analysis	• Future state pro- cess map	• Mistake proofing
• Change plan	• Metrics with baseline	• Analysis of vari- ance (ANOVA)	• Affinity diagram	• FMEA
• Project plan	• Benchmarking	• Defective parts per million (DPPM) / Defects per mil- lion opportunities (DPMO), process capability	• Dashboards/ scorecards	• Control plan
• Responsibilities matrix	• Check sheets		• Training plan and materials	• Process capability
• Items for resolu- tion (IFR)	• Histograms		• Procedures	• DPPM/DPMO
• Ground rules	• Surveys, inter- views, focus groups, affinity diagrams		• Policies	• Statistical process control
	• Descriptive statistics			• Standard work
				• Prioritization matrices

Figure 13.18   Six Sigma tools by DMAIC phase.
Source: Sandra L. Furterer.

7. Performance tracking, measuring, and reporting systems are needed to monitor progress, allow for course corrections as needed, and link the Six Sigma approach to the organizational goals, objectives, and plans. Very often, existing performance tracking, measuring, and reporting systems fail to address the level where they are meaningful to the people involved.

8. The organization's reward and recognition systems must support continual reinforcement of the people, at every level, who make the Six Sigma approach viable and successful. Compensation systems, especially, need to be reengineered.

9. The successful organization should internally celebrate successes frequently—success breeds success.

10. To further enhance its image, and the self-esteem of its people, the successful organization should widely publicize its Six Sigma accom- plishments and, to the extent feasible, share its principles and prac- tices with other organizations—it should be a member of a world-class group of organizations that have committed their efforts to achieving perfection.

Failure Mode and Effects Analysis

FMEA has been in use for many years. FMEA is a systematic tool used for analyzing systems, designs, or processes to identify potential failure and its causes. Its aim is to identify and reduce risk of failure by focusing actions on areas of greatest risk. There are two types in general use: the *design* FMEA (DFMEA) for analyzing potential design failures and the *process* FMEA (PFMEA) for analyzing potential process failures. FMEA is discussed in Chapter 6 in relation to strategic planning and business environment analysis. In this chapter, it is covered as a tool for risk management in processes and designs.

FMEA is for potential failures and is less useful for current problems. Should a situation be occurring, the root cause analysis tool is preferred. See above for the discussion of root cause analysis. For example, a small organization engaged in bidding on military contracts for high-tech devices successfully used a DFMEA to identify and assess risks for a product never made before. The DFMEA aided in evaluating design inputs, assured that potential failure modes were identified and addressed, provided for the identification of the failure modes' root cause(s), determined the actions necessary to eliminate or reduce the potential failure mode, and added a high degree of objectivity to the design review process. The DFMEA also directed attention to design features that required additional testing or development, documented risk-reduction efforts, provided lessons-learned documentation to aid future FMEAs, and assured that the design was performed with a customer focus.

The basic FMEA methodology is:

1. Define the device design inputs or process functions and requirements.

2. Identify a failure mode (what could go wrong) and the potential effects of the failure.

3. Rank the severity of the effects using a 1–10 scale, where 1 is minor and 10 is major (and without warning).

4. Establish what the root cause(s) could be.

5. Rate the likelihood of occurrence for the failure using a 1–10 scale.

6. Document the present design or present process controls regarding prevention and detection.

7. Rate the likelihood of these controls detecting the failure using a 1–10 scale.

8. Compute the risk priority number (RPN = Severity × Occurrence × Detection). Using the RPN, rank order items, the worst at the top.

9. Recommend preventive/corrective action (what action, who will do it, when). Note that preventive action is listed first when dealing with the design stage and corrective action first if analyzing potential process failures.

10. Return to number 2 if other potential failures exist.

11. Build and test a prototype.

12. Redo the FMEA after test results are obtained and any necessary or desired changes are made.

13. Retest and, if acceptable, place in production.

14. Document the FMEA process for the knowledge base.

The collaboration of employees who have been involved in design, development, production, and customer service activities is critical because their knowledge, ideas, and questions about a new product design will be based on their experience at different stages of product realization. Furthermore, if your employees are also some of your customers (end users), obtaining and documenting the employees' experience is most useful.

This experiential input, along with examinations of similar designs (and their FMEAs, nonconforming product and corrective action records, and customer feedback reports), is often the best source for analysis input. Figure 13.19 shows a sample PFMEA.

Process Improvement Model

As not all improvement projects involve root cause analysis, a more general model for continual process improvement is also useful. Following is one example:

1. *Select the process to improve.* This is done through analysis of feedback from customers (external or internal), as well as identifying those processes that are critical to improvement.

2. *Review current performance.* Current performance measures are reviewed to ensure that they are adequate and appropriate and compared to expectations or needs.

3. *Identify improvement needs or opportunities.* Areas of the process where improvement would be most beneficial are selected and the process analyzed to determine what could be changed to improve it.

4. *Implement process changes.* A plan is developed and communicated regarding changes in the process steps and may be piloted on a small scale before full implementation.

5. *Evaluate progress.* Process performance is again reviewed to see whether the desired impact was achieved. If so, the change is standardized, and a new process or opportunity for improvement is selected. Many organizations also include celebrations and sharing of learning as part of wrapping up each improvement effort.

Although using the appropriate steps for problem-solving and process improvement will enhance the probability of success, a set of guiding principles used to shape all such efforts is often useful. These principles can be used by the steering committee, a process improvement team, or a team facilitator as a tool for helping identify barriers to improvement progress. The steps are:

- *Leadership.* Senior executives should oversee the process of continual improvement.

- *Strategic.* Improvements should be targeted primarily at those processes that will provide a strategic gain or advantage; they should have an impact on the bottom line.

- *Customer.* Process changes should be based on and/or take into account customer feedback, needs, and potential impact.

Item/change level _____ EVN-7823/C _____ Process responsibility _____ Housing assembly _____

Team members _____ J. White, S. Burns, C. Smith _____

FMEA no. _____ 10554 _____

Page _____ 1 _____ of _____ 1 _____

Prepared by _____ J. White _____

Date _____ 4/3/13 _____

Operation no. Process function and/or requirements	Potential failure mode	Severity	Class	Potential cause(s) of failure	Occurrence	Current controls prevention	Current controls detection	Detection	RPN	Recommended actions	Responsible and target completion date	Action results Actions taken	Action results S	Action results O	Action results D	Action results R P N
40 Press bearing into housing	Bearing not fully seated	7		Improper setup of press	5	First-piece approval Machine setup training	Depth check by operator	7	2 4 5	Add auto depth check to force electronics	J. White 5/10/13		7	5	2	70
	Assemble wrong bearing	9	X	Operator loaded wrong bearing to chute	8	Push-in force measurement	Daily inventory balance of bill of materials	2	1 0 8	None						

Figure 13.19 Process FMEA example.

Source: Used with permission of APLOMET.

- *Involvement.* Because of their knowledge and responsibility, people who actually carry out the process to be improved should be the ones who are involved in making the decisions and implementing change.

- *Process.* Approach all projects from the view that what is to be improved is a process that transforms inputs (from suppliers) into outputs (for customers).

- *Data.* Decisions such as what processes to improve and what to change to make them better should be based on data, when possible.

- *Prevention.* Because the idea is to create processes that are able to meet or exceed requirements, actions taken should keep process problems from occurring or recurring.

4. INNOVATION AND CREATIVITY TOOLS

Use various techniques and exercises for creative decision-making and problem-solving, including brainstorming, mind mapping, lateral thinking, critical thinking, the five whys, and Design for Six Sigma (DFSS). (Apply)

Body of Knowledge IV.A.4

Creative Thinking versus Analytical Thinking

The process of improvement often requires analysis of the process, breaking it down into discrete parts and understanding how each part contributes to the overall process. Many of the tools presented in this chapter provide a means of performing this analysis, either by representing the process (for example, through a flowchart or C-E diagram) or showing how it is currently performing (for example, through a Pareto chart of the problem or a control chart of trends). Therefore, analytical thinking is an important part of process improvement.

Equally important is the part of improvement that requires identifying new ideas and deciding which of those ideas will be used to take action. For example, brainstorming possible causes of a problem before determining what is actually the cause or identifying potential solutions to a problem before settling on one to try is not an analytical process; it uses creativity and openness.

Analytical and creative thinking are sometimes seen as opposites because a person cannot do both at the same time. Because an individual usually has a dominant way of thinking, it is sometimes a challenge to get both the analytical and creative processes to work within the same group. There are, however, tools designed specifically to help facilitate the creative and group decision-making processes.

As with analytical thinking, creativity also has stages that can be followed in order to improve outcomes. One model is:

- *Generate.* Create a list of as many ideas as possible, regardless of how wild some of them may be.

- *Percolate.* Allow time to think over these and other ideas. A few days away from the problem allows the subconscious mind to continue working, and often many new ideas will occur.

- *Illuminate.* Return to the list and discuss what has been discovered since the last meeting. Add, delete, combine, or otherwise modify items on the list.

- *Substantiate.* Test out and verify some of the ideas that appear more feasible.

Brainstorming

Brainstorming is a simple way for a group to generate multiple ideas, such as possible solutions to a known problem. A brainstorming session proceeds as follows:

- The brainstorming topic is agreed on and written in clear terms in view of the group.

- The leader/facilitator asks for ideas from the group.

- Each idea is written down without discussion, analysis, or criticism.

- The process is continued until the flow of ideas stops or time runs out.

The list of ideas is then reviewed to ensure that everyone understands the ideas and is then processed by combining similar ideas, eliminating some, or adding something forgotten to produce a smaller set from which a final selection will be made.

Brainstorming can also be more structured. A *round-robin* approach involves asking each person in the group to state one idea. If someone has none, that individual simply passes. The next person is asked for one idea, then the next, and so on. When everyone has passed on a final round, the brainstorming session is complete. A similar process can be used where several sheets of paper (for example, flip charts) are posted around the room, with a particular topic or problem written at the top of each one. Team members simply move from sheet to sheet, writing down ideas that come to mind. Other groups have simply rotated sheets of paper around the table to accomplish the same result.

A final method of brainstorming is especially useful when the topic with which the team is dealing is particularly sensitive or when the team may not yet have a high level of trust. This method, called *Crawford slip*, asks each person to create his or her own list of ideas on a slip of paper, and the slips are subsequently given to a trusted individual who compiles them into a single list. The anonymous nature of this method allows people to feel freer to provide their ideas, and the team will often find that several people have the same idea, which begins to build common ground.

Mind Mapping

When trying to improve a process, an individual or group must think through many different issues, and keeping them all in mind simultaneously is difficult. A mind map creates a visual representation of many issues and can help a group get a more complete and common understanding of a situation.

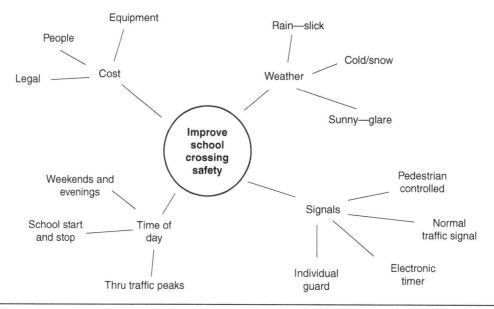

Figure 13.20 Mind map example.

A mind map is created by first listing the primary objective or topic in the center, then listing major related issues around it. Each of these issues will then bring other issues to mind, which are added to the map wherever logical. As a creative process, it can be useful to use symbols or photos rather than words in creating the map.

Figure 13.20 is a mind map created by a school board that was trying to decide how to improve the safety of a specific school crossing. The map helped the board look at the wide range of issues to consider, which meant members were more likely to make a decision to which all agreed and would be willing to express to the public, and decide which was best for the situation.

Analogies

Innovation is about coming up with new ideas that do not fit the norm. One way to help accomplish this is to come at a problem or situation from a completely different viewpoint. Using words or ideas that are seemingly unrelated to the problem can help an individual or group to develop a perspective from which they are likely to see the situation differently.

Consider the example of an organization that wants to make and sell a new gardening tool used to remove weeds. In order to come up with a unique perspective to guide the design and marketing processes, the group randomly selects the phrase "soaring like an eagle" to help. Group members then list ideas that come to mind when they think of this phrase and ask, "How do these ideas apply to a gardening tool?" Figure 13.21 shows the results, which can be used to help ensure that the new tool will be designed and marketed based on what customers would perceive as being as pleasurable as soaring like an eagle.

The words or phrases used for this process can be completely randomly selected. For example, simply opening a newspaper or looking at an object nearby might work. If a particular selection does not help, then the group simply selects another word or phrase.

Eagle description	Would equate to
Sharp eyes	Seeing ways to reduce the time required to weed
Weightless	Wouldn't be tired after weeding
Automatic, air does the work	Very easy to use, doesn't require bending/stooping
Wide view	Can cover a lot of ground
Kills rodents	Gets weeds out by the roots so they don't come back

Figure 13.21 Use of analogies for a gardening tool.

Nominal Group Technique

One popular way of processing brainstormed ideas is the *nominal group technique* (NGT), which consists of applying the following steps to a list of ideas from which a small number is to be selected:

1. Discuss the ideas and simplify/combine those where it makes sense in order to make the list complete and clear, but not repetitive.

2. Ask each participant to rank the items in numerical order (for example, 1 is best to 8 is worst in a list of eight items).

3. Record the ranks of all participants beside each item.

4. Total the rankings for each item. Those with the lowest totals are the preferred options.

Figure 13.22 shows a simple example of the nominal group technique applied by a group of course participants to decide where they wanted to go for lunch. Out of four choices, Marlow's received the lowest total (highest priority), becoming the first choice.

Multivoting

Another way to reduce a long list of items or ideas generated through brainstorming to a fewer number of items is to have the group members select those that they prefer. The number they select is often approximately one-half of the beginning number. After all participants have made their selections, the facilitator goes down the list and asks how many participants have voted for each option. The Pareto principle will most likely apply, with several of the options getting none or a very few votes, and they are dropped from the list. The process of voting is then repeated (for example, vote for approximately one-half of the number left on the list) until a workable number of items are left. Figure 13.23 shows repetitive multivoting for a larger number of possible selections.

Lateral and Parallel Thinking

The concept here is that the mind acts as a system of patterns. When these patterns are continually reinforced, mainstream patterns form. As these patterns grow deeper (like a rut), these perceptions are harder to ignore or discard. *Lateral*

Restaurant	Individuals and rankings					
	Tom	Joe	Mary	Sue	Terry	**Total**
Marlow's	1	2	3	1	2	9
Grunge Café	3	1	1	2	3	10
Stew & Brew	2	4	2	4	4	16
Fancaé	4	3	4	3	1	15

Figure 13.22 Nominal group technique ranking table.

Restaurant	First vote (Select 4)	Second vote (Select 3)	Third vote (Select 1)
~~Pizza R Us~~	2		
~~Marlow's~~	4	3	
~~Alice's Restaurant~~	1		
Grunge Café	5	5	④
~~Mom's Diner~~	0		
~~Stew & Brew~~	3	2	
~~Fancaé~~	5	5	1

Figure 13.23 Multivoting example.

thinking is a process that includes recognizing the patterns and becoming unencumbered with old ideas while creating new ones. Or, as Dr. deBono, the originator of the term, described it, "pattern switching in an asymmetric patterning system."[4] Dr. deBono asserts that one can get only so much from the traditional tools and approaches. There comes a time when creativity is needed to go further.

With *parallel thinking*, Dr. deBono proposes a concept that is more constructive than traditional argument-type thinking. He uses the *six thinking hats* to enable participants to try one role at a time and to ultimately map a preferred style of thinking. The six roles he calls *hats* are:

Color	Characteristics
White	Just the facts, figures, or information. Neutral
Red	Emotions and feelings predominant. Intuitive
Black	Brings out the negative viewpoint
Yellow	Optimistic, proactive, and constructive—makes it happen
Green	Creative. Looks for alternatives. Moves forward
Blue	Controlled. Focused. Summarizes. Ensures rules are followed

Critical Thinking

Critical thinking relies on careful analysis, evaluation, and reasoning (both deductive and inductive) and clear thinking (analytical as well as systems thinking).

Critical cognitive skills for critical thinkers are:

- Interpret
- Analyze
- Evaluate
- Infer
- Explain
- Self-regulate

Critical thinkers are:

- Inquisitive
- Judicious
- Truth seeking
- Confident in reasoning
- Open-minded
- Analytical
- Systematic

Five Whys

Throughout most problem-solving activities, there is usually a significant amount of effort expended in trying to understand why things happen the way they do. Root cause analysis requires understanding how a system or process works and the many complex contributors, both technical and human.

One method for getting to root causes is to repeatedly ask, "Why?" For example, if a car does not start when the key is turned, ask, "Why?" Is it because the engine does not turn over or because when it does turn over, it does not begin running on its own? If it does not turn over, ask, "Why?" Is it because the battery is too weak or because the starter is seized up? If it is because the battery is too weak, ask, "Why?" Is it because the temperature outside is extremely cold, the battery cables are loose, or an interior light was left on the previous evening and drained the battery? Although this is a simple example, it demonstrates the process of asking *why* until the actual root cause is found. It is called the *five whys* tool since it will often require asking *why* five times or more before the actual root cause has been identified. The use of data or trials can help determine answers at each level. Figure 13.24 is adapted from a healthcare facility application.

Design for Manufacturing Ability and Design for Six Sigma

Design for manufacturing ability (DFMA), also called *design for manufacture/manufacturing and assembly*, sometimes aims to create a design at its utmost

5 Whys

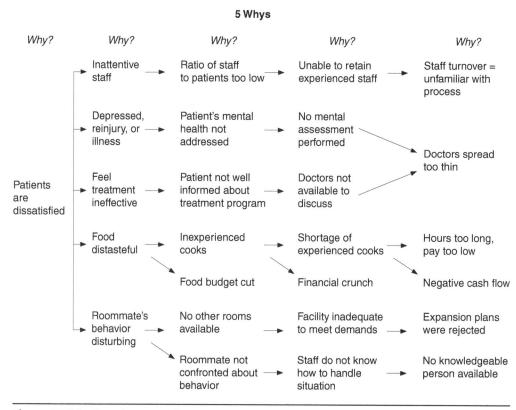

Figure 13.24   Five whys example.

level of simplicity. Intended to develop an awareness of the need for con-current product/process development, DFMA focuses on preventing design changes during production. It also emphasizes decreasing the number of parts required and the specification of new but similar parts. DFMA standardizes and simplifies—for example, setting design tolerances based on previous pro-cess capability instead of engineering's frequent emphasis on close tolerance for every part.

Design for Six Sigma (DFSS) adds statistical techniques to the DFMA princi-ples, including analysis of tolerances, mapping of processes, development of a product scorecard, design to unit production costs (DTUPC), and design of exper-iments (DOE). DFSS aims to design products and services so that they can be produced and delivered with Six Sigma quality. Focused on new product develop-ment, DFSS provides additional structure and better methods for managing the deliverables.

DFSS is a strategy that uses tools that are not always new. The strength of DFSS is the organization of the tools and their integration with and alignment to the new product design process. A key to the effective use of DFSS is the selection process used to determine the probability of commercial and technical success of the ultimate product. Mader outlines a twelve-step method.[5]

Table 13.1 TRIZ principles.

Segmentation	Partial or excessive action
Extraction	Transition into a new dimension
Local quality	Mechanical vibration
Asymmetry	Periodic action
Consolidation	Continuity of useful action
Universality	Rushing through
Nesting	Convert harm into benefit
Counterweight	Replacement of mechanical systems
Prior counteraction	Pneumatic or hydraulic construction
Prior action	Flexible membranes or thin films
Cushion in advance	Porous material
Equipotentiality	Changing the color
Do it in reverse	Homogeneity
Feedback	Rejecting or regenerating parts
Mediator	Transformation of properties
Self-service	Phase transition
Copying	Thermal expansion
Dispose	Accelerated oxidation
Spheroidality	Inert environment
Dynamicity	Composite materials

TRIZ

TRIZ is a Russian acronym. Translated, it is *the theory of the solution of inventive problems.*[6] Under development and testing for over fifty years, TRIZ evolved into a structure for the deployment of innovative and creative problem-solving.

TRIZ comprises a set of analytical and knowledge-based tools that are typically hidden, subconsciously, in the minds of creative inventors. Ask an inventor what process he or she uses and the answer is vague or "Don't really know." Genrich Altshuller (the inventor of TRIZ) has succeeded in identifying the mystifying process of invention. Using TRIZ, persons of average intelligence can access a huge quantity of inventive knowledge. With that knowledge, they can, using analogic analysis, produce outside-the-box solutions.

TRIZ has been refined from the output of some of the world's best inventors. The result is a large collection of knowledge-based tools and forty principles. The principles are shown in Table 13.1.

SCAMPER

Using this method, seven questions are used by a team to stimulate creativity:

- What can be used as a *substitute*?
- What can be *combined* with _____?
- How can _____ be *adapted*?
- How can _____ be *modified*?
- How can _____ be *put* to other uses?
- How can _____ be *eliminated*?
- What if _____ were *reversed* (or *rearranged*)?

Storyboard

The *storyboard* technique is used in a team context to build the key ideas and the relationship of those ideas to the problem. It is a visual display of thoughts. As scriptwriters for a film would do, a storyboard introduces the physical setting and a two-dimensional view of the product, process, or action being discussed, usually in step-by-step or scene-by-scene views, as the team progresses through the problem-solving process. Ideas are generated through brainstorming and captured in words and pictures on sticky notes and posted under major topical headings. Ideas are added and deleted, and the notes are moved around to relate the ideas in various configurations in search of the best alignment. When the ideas (pictures) finally appear to fit together, the storyboard displays the problem solution in a desired sequence for further action. Nancy Tague, in *The Quality Toolbox*, provides more detailed process steps for this tool.[7]

Other Creativity Tools

Other tools for stimulating creativity include:

- Brainwriting—same as Crawford slip method
- Imaginary brainstorming—breaks traditional thinking patterns
- Knowledge mapping—visual thinking, similar to mind mapping
- Morphological box—developing the anatomy of a solution
- Picture association—using pictures to generate new perspectives
- Purpose hierarchy—identifies all potential purposes of an improvement intervention
- TILMAG (Transformation of Ideal Solution Elements with a Common Association Matrix)—stimulates ideal solutions using associations and analogies
- Who, what, where, when, why, and how questions
- Is-is not question

5. COST OF QUALITY (COQ)

> Define and distinguish between prevention, appraisal, internal, and external failure cost categories and evaluate the impact that changes in one category will have on the others. (Evaluate)
>
> **Body of Knowledge IV.A.5**

COQ is a method used by organizations to show the financial impact of quality activities. Attaching a dollar amount to quality-related activities clarifies where there may be significant opportunities for quality improvement. Once recognized, process improvement efforts can be focused on those with the higher potential payoff.

In the 1950s Armand V. Feigenbaum saw value in a management reporting system focusing on quality costs, their causes, and their effects. During this time it was recognized that costs buried in standards and buried in overhead rates were not addressed. During the same period, Joseph M. Juran wrote of the importance of measuring quality in terms best understood by upper management: dollars. These concepts were the basis of what has evolved into cost-of-quality programs. No one method exists for collecting and reporting an entity's quality cost drivers because each company's accounting system collects and reports costs differently. By applying the concept of COQ, however, any accounting or quality manager can design a meaningful measurement tool that can be used to report on and highlight quality issues and that will help the company undertake meaningful quality improvement activities.

By the 1980s the costs of quality were categorized: failure costs (internal and external), prevention costs, and appraisal costs. In the efforts to learn more about and attempt to control the true costs of quality, certain facts became evident:

- Most quality costs are not identified in the financial records and statements of the organization.

- Most organizations were not aware of the cost to produce poor quality.

- Increasing sales does not decrease the cost of poor quality.

- The focus should really be on cost of poor quality and its impact on the organization (financial, competitiveness, customer retention and satisfaction, employee motivation).

Because it is measuring dollars, COQ reporting is one of the best tools available to raise an organization's awareness of quality issues. Some basic education on the concept and methods of COQ must be done, with an initial focus on top management. The educational process might also be deployed to other levels, however, as workers who understand how costs are collected and reported are more likely to understand how their work influences the company's performance.[8]

Categorizing Quality Costs

There are three major categories of quality costs: *appraisal, prevention*, and *failure*. In his book *Quality Is Free*, Philip B. Crosby asserts that quality does not cost money; rather, it is the absence of quality (the nonconformances and failures) that increases total costs. Crosby popularized the terms *cost of poor quality*, or *cost of nonquality*, emphasizing that to avoid these bad costs, money would have to be spent up front on prevention and appraisal.

When designing a COQ program and setting up accounts to track the elements, attention must be given to the three categories of quality cost typically used: prevention, appraisal, and failure (internal and external). Because the total COQ can often be 10% to 15% of sales, these dollars must be traced to their sources to understand their cause-and-effect relationships:

- *Internal failure costs* occur before the product is delivered to the customer. Examples are costs of rework and repair, reinspecting and retesting of product, material downgrading, inventory shrinkage, unscheduled downtime, and internal miscommunications that result in delays. In today's language this may be called *waste*.

- *External failure costs* occur after the delivery of product or while furnishing a service to the customer. Examples include the costs of processing customer complaints, field service, customer returns, warranty claims, product recalls, and product liability lawsuits. In today's language this may be described as *downstream consequences*.

- *Appraisal costs* are costs associated with measuring, evaluating, or auditing products or services to ensure conformance to quality standards and performance requirements. They include the costs of incoming and source inspection/test of purchased materials; validation, verification, and checking activities; in process and final inspection/test; product, service, or process audits; and calibration of measuring and testing equipment, including associated supplies, materials, and external services. In today's language this may be called *monitoring*.

- *Prevention costs* are costs incurred in minimizing failure and appraisal costs throughout the entire organization's processes. Examples include new-product design reviews, quality planning, supplier quality surveys, process capability evaluations, quality improvement team meetings, and quality education and training. In today's language this may be called *process improvement investments*.

- *Total COQ* is the sum of all failure costs + appraisal costs + prevention costs.

Following is an example of quality cost categorization: The total COQ, before improvement, was 15% of sales, broken down into internal failures at 45% of total COQ, external failures at 30%, appraisal costs at 20%, and prevention costs at 5%. Once known, these were unacceptable. The organization's objective is to reduce the total costs by decreasing failure costs, minimizing appraisal costs, and increasing prevention costs only to the extent necessary to achieve the failure and appraisal cost decreases. The objective for the COQ improvement initiative is total costs of quality reduced to 3% of sales, broken down into internal failures at 20%, external failures at 5%, appraisal costs at 25%, and prevention costs at 50%.

Quality costs apply to all departments and should not be confined to just those associated with production. The costs generated within support functions often represent a significant portion of total quality costs and may be hidden within standard costs. Lack of good prevention in support processes often results in higher waste in production areas. In addition, labor expenses might be reported with an overhead allocation that includes benefits and other indirect expenses. These issues require care in properly determining true and comparable costs.

The COQ categories also apply equally well to nonmanufacturing situations. Consider the training conducted in a restaurant to help ensure that food and service quality are maintained (prevention), as well as the sampling done by the cook, and customer feedback cards used to measure quality (appraisal). Internal failure costs are incurred if food must be returned to the kitchen due to inadequate preparation or if the customer refuses to tip based on poor service. In this case, as is true with many service processes, direct external failure costs are absorbed by the customer, who ends up with indigestion or food poisoning, but the loss of future business (and perhaps litigation) is incurred by the restaurant.

Other service examples include:

- *Prevention costs.* Time and expenses related to an accounting firm learning about changes in tax laws

- *Appraisal costs.* Screening of baggage by an airline

- *Internal failure costs.* Incurred when a technician in a hospital must repeat a chest X-ray because the first one was not clear

- *External failure costs.* Correction of an error found by a customer in a bank statement

Initiating a COQ Program. For an organization that has not used COQ measurement before, education of senior management in the methods for and benefits of such a program must be done first. Once management has agreed to implement COQ, a pilot program can then be used to help demonstrate the process and benefits without fully involving the entire organization and extensive resources. For example, a product line where there are obvious opportunities for improvement, but where the improvements are not expected to be overly complex, might be a good place to start.

Key management/supervisory personnel from the pilot area should be involved in estimating the COQ and working with accounting and quality personnel. A rough estimate may be all that is required to show the opportunities, which can then be addressed through either a process improvement team or other organized methods for improvement.

Establishing and Tracking Measurements. Once the organization is convinced and committed to using COQ, a more detailed COQ baseline should be established that allows the organization to know its current status and will allow tracking of overall improvement. In developing the details of the quality cost system, there are two important criteria to follow: (1) recognize that quality cost is a tool to justify improvement actions and measure their effectiveness and (2) realize that including insignificant activities is not essential. Indeed, including insignificant activities may actually be harmful to acceptance of the quality cost system.

Several methods are available for measuring COQ. One method often used in manufacturing organizations is to analyze the company's chart of financial accounts. If the accounting manager and quality manager were to review the accounts on the expense side, they would quickly find that some contain expenses obviously related to quality (for example, salary of the quality manager and metrology technicians, scrap of nonconforming material, travel expenses to visit customers when problems occur), while others have no or very few quality-related expenses (for example, tooling and accountant's salary).

The accounts that do contain quality expenses can then be pulled out separately and categorized as to whether they contain prevention, appraisal, internal failure, or external failure costs. The proportion of each account that should be allocated to each COQ category can then be estimated and a rough estimate of COQ obtained by totaling the actual expenses for the last year as indicated by the allocations.

The total then needs to be normalized to adjust for changes in volume of business. Reporting COQ as a percentage of a commonly used internal volume measure is typical. Care must be exercised not to relate COQ to a volume metric occurring at a time distant from the cost-of-quality expenditure. This will result in a highly variable measure.

Another method is simply to do an activity assessment of the organization. By listing the activities that fit into the COQ categories and estimating the amount of time invested in each activity, a rough calculation of COQ can be obtained. This process could be used more accurately at the department level, although it must be understood that failures may be created in one part of the organization but found in another.

Some organizations also elect to measure only failure costs. Depending on where they are in their quality journey, this may be enough to provide the incentive to move forward with improvement and to see the benefits. For organizations that are using activity-based costing/management (ABC/M), quality cost dollar amounts are more easily obtained. Activity-based costing allocates overhead expenses to the activities based on the proportion of use rather than proportion of costs.

Institutionalizing COQ. Once an organization is comfortable with the concept and usefulness of COQ, a formal reporting process needs to be developed. Quality costs should be a performance measure used for decision-making for continuous improvement and strategic planning. Responsibilities for and the format for collecting and reporting the information must be defined, as well as the frequency and agenda where it will be used for decision-making.

Education of the workforce—whether just before beginning a COQ-driven improvement project in a particular area or having everyone learn about COQ—can help the organization to make a permanent connection between quality performance and cost performance.

Activity-Based Costing. The objective of *activity-based costing* (ABC) is to improve the organization's effectiveness through the identification of quality costs associated with specific activities, analysis of those costs, and implementation of means to lower total costs. Under the ABC approach, costs of resources used are allocated in proportion to the use of the resource for given activities.

ABC contrasts with traditional cost accounting whereby costs were allocated based on some arbitrary percentage of direct labor. With direct labor becoming a smaller portion of the cost of producing a specific product or service, this approach is no longer viable for many organizations.

Employing ABC, some organizations have identified and discontinued producing unprofitable products. Before ABC, they had not realized the extent to which such products were eating their profits.

REFERENCES

1. C. H. Kepner, and B. B. Tregoe, *The New Rational Manager: An Updated Edition for the New World* (Princeton, NJ: Kepner-Tregoe, 2013).

2. S. L. Furterer, *Lean Six Sigma Case Studies in the Healthcare Enterprise* (New York: Springer, 2013).

3. Ibid.

4. E. DeBono, *Six Thinking Hats* (Boston: Little, Brown, 1985), 141.

5. D. P. Mader, "Selecting Design for Six Sigma Projects," *Quality Progress* (July 2004): 65–70.

6. S. F. Ungvari, "TRIZ," in *Manufacturing Handbook of Best Practices: An Innovation, Productivity, and Quality Focus*, ed. J. B. ReVelle (Boca Raton, FL: CRC Press, 2016), 399–425.

7. N. R. Tague, *The Quality Toolbox*, 2nd ed. (Milwaukee: ASQ Quality Press, 2005).

8. ASQ Quality Management Division, *Principles of Quality Costs: Financial Measures for Strategic Implementation of Quality Management*, 4th ed., ed. D. C. Wood (Milwaukee: ASQ Quality Press, 2013).

See Appendix A for additional references for this chapter.

Chapter 14

B. Process Management

A process is a series of interrelated actions taken to transform a concept, a request, or an order into a delivered product or service. A process is an activity or group of activities that takes an input, adds value to it, and provides an output to an internal or external customer.

A fundamental step to improving a process is to understand how it functions from a process management perspective. This can be seen through an analysis of the process to identify the supplier-input-process-output-customer (SIPOC) linkages (see Figure 14.1). It begins with defining the process of interest and listing on the right side the outputs that the process creates that go to customers, who are also listed. Suppliers and what they provide to enable the process (the inputs) are similarly shown on the left side. Once this fundamental process diagram is developed, two additional items can be discussed—measures that can be used to evaluate performance of the inputs and outputs and the information and methods necessary to control the process.

The terms *process* and *system* are often used interchangeably, causing some confusion (for example, is a process part of a system, or is a system part of a process?). A *system* may be defined as a network of connecting processes that work together to accomplish the aim of the system. When viewing the total organization as a system:

- There will be subsystems (for example, a payroll system, accounting system, management information system).

- There will be processes (for example, manufacturing process, accounting process).

- There will be subprocesses (for example, design process, field service process).

- There may be supporting systems (for example, calibration system, activity-based costing system, inventory management system, fleet-scheduling system, production-scheduling system).

- Within these supporting systems there will be processes (for example, data entry process, data analysis process, report generation process, error alert process).

The distinction appears to be that a system has its own self-serving objective. A process aims at transforming inputs into outputs to achieve (ultimately) the strategic objectives of the organization. Thus, an accounting system might achieve its

Figure 14.1 SIPOC diagram example.

own purpose of processing numbers in accordance with the parameters set for the system but could fail to meet the needs of management in managing the entire organization.

Process management is using a collection of practices, techniques, and tools to implement, sustain, and improve process effectiveness. Process management includes planning and setting goals, establishing controls, monitoring and measuring performance, documenting, improving cycle time, eliminating waste, removing constraints, eliminating special causes of variation, maintaining gains, and continually improving. Figure 14.2 is a *process management maturity assessment* tool for assessing an organization's process management maturity level relative to six criteria.

The American Productivity and Quality Center (APQC), Houston, Texas, is a member-based nonprofit serving organizations in all sectors of business, education, and government. As an aid to their members and the public, the APQC has created the *APQC Process Classification Framework* (PCF) as an open standard to facilitate improvement through process management and benchmarking regardless of industry, size, or geography. The PCF is available for download at http://www.apqc.org /process-classification-framework. Readers will find the PCF helpful in visualizing the processes and activities that may compose an organization. The PCF is updated periodically.

1. PROCESS GOALS

Describe how process goals are established, monitored, and measured and evaluate their impact on product or service quality. (Evaluate)

Body of Knowledge IV.B.1

To begin, let us look at how process goals and process objectives are related:

- Process goals are aims, intents, targets, or ends.[1]

- Process goals are supported by measurable objectives.

- Process goals are linked to the strategic plan of the organization.

- Process objectives represent the intended actions that are needed to achieve the process goals.

Assessment criteria

Level		Activities	Metrics	Ownership	Interconnections	Improvement	Changes
Improved	5	Process activities are continually improved.	Metrics are altered as necessary to identify new opportunities. Leading metrics are used where feasible.	Process owners place high value on ensuring that all employees have ownership of processes.	Internal customers and suppliers work together on improvement projects.	Processes have been continually improved in line with business objectives and desired outcomes.	The method for changing processes is continually upgraded to provide rapid and effective response to changing needs.
Managed	4	Process activities are reviewed for acceptable performance.	Metrics are reviewed regularly to provide feedback and improve.	Process owners regularly discuss process performance with team members.	Discussions between internal customers and suppliers have resulted in process changes.	Process improvement is regularly carried out, but may not impact business performance.	Process changes are evaluated, validated, and documented.
Standardized	3	Process is documented and personnel trained to follow it.	Standard metrics are in place for most processes, but do not impact performance.	An owner has been identified for most processes.	Regular feedback exists between internal customers and suppliers.	A standard process improvement methodology exists.	A process for reviewing and approving process changes exists.
Repeated	2	Personnel try to replicate actions each time.	Processes are measured when there are problems.	Individuals are responsible for certain portions of processes.	Discussions occur between members of related processes when there are problems.	Attempts are made to improve processes when there are significant problems.	Sketchy records are kept of process changes.
Unmanaged	1	Processes are carried out as each person sees fit.	Performance of processes is not measured.	Anyone or no one may claim to own a process.	Interconnection of processes has not been discussed.	Processes are seldom improved.	Anyone can make a process change.

Figure 14.2 Process management maturity assessment.

Source: Adapted from the Capability Maturity Model Integration (CMMI), Reprinted with permission of APLOMET.

- Process objectives are measurable.

- Process objectives may be supported by product or service specifications, work orders, and so on.

- Process objectives may also be based on maintaining the gains in a stable process, or the objectives may support the resolution of a previous performance problem or deficiency.

Figure 14.3 is an example of the deployment of strategic goals and objectives to process goals and objectives.

Process goals, derived from strategic goals, interpret and expand the top-level goals and objectives for use at the operational level. Each organization, no matter the industry, will have its own set of process goals; however, some generic topical areas may be addressed, such as:

- Meeting or exceeding customers' requirements for the product/service

- Ensuring that the process makes a contribution to the organization's profits (or cost containment)

- Ensuring that the product or service design and execution follow good practices to ensure users' safety, including unintended use

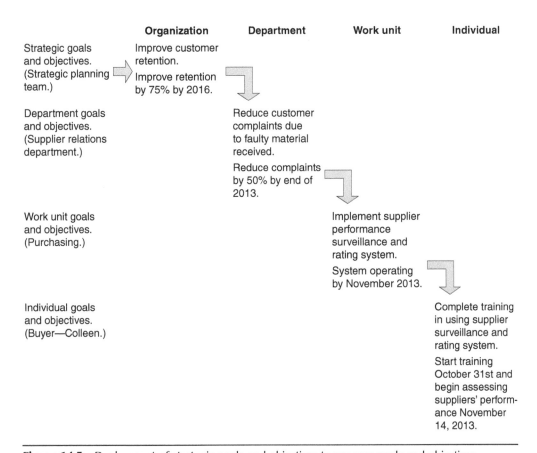

Figure 14.3 Deployment of strategic goals and objectives to process goals and objectives.

- Ensuring that the product or service produced does not present a hazard to users or the environment for the life of the product or service

- Ensuring the safety, security, and well-being of employees

- Meeting or exceeding industry-accepted practices for a good working environment

- Continually improving the process through elimination of non-value-added product/service features, process steps, and materials

- Continuing the quest to reduce cycle time

Goals may involve making changes or maintaining a specific target level. How the process goal is defined depends on the strategic direction of the organization and the level of the process being addressed (for example, from order entry through design, production, and shipping or just the subprocess of accepting and entering a customer's order).

For example, a process goal for Family Cleaners, which handles an average of 158 customer orders per day, is "Family Cleaners will ensure that all customers receive high-quality cleaning services." This goal is then translated into a process objective: decrease disputes and rework due to receiving errors from twelve per week to one per week within six months. The objective is supported by a procedure, which outlines the receiving clerk's responsibilities:

1. Before accepting customer items, examine each with the customer and determine the type of cleaning service required, level of warranty (standard or premium), price, and delivery date.

2. Determine, based on training, experience, or approval of the manager, whether any questionable item can be properly cleaned by Family Cleaners. If not, provide the customer with an explanation and return the item to the customer. Should the customer opt to waive the information provided, prepare a waiver form and obtain the customer's signature.

3. Prepare and present to the customer a claim check (yellow copy of cleaning order) identifying the items received for cleaning, warranty level, the price for each, and the agreed date available for pickup.

4. Bundle the items received with the cleaning order (white original) in a receiving basket and place basket on conveyor.

How Are Process Objectives Monitored, Measured, and Reported?

Process objectives are monitored, measured, and reported for decisions as to actions needed. In the previous example, when the customer picks up the cleaning, any disputes and rework due to receiving errors are recorded by the pickup clerk on the original work order. The completed work orders are processed weekly. The total of disputes and rework are measured against the standard (no more than one occurrence). If more than one, the manager reviews the case(s) with the receiving clerk to determine the cause and any corrective or preventive action necessary.

Guidelines for monitoring, measuring, and reporting include:

- It must be known what value is desired, what to measure, how to measure it, unit of measure, device/method to be used, frequency of measure/analysis, and priority of the objective.

- How objectives are monitored is a function of who does it, how often it is to be done, and to whom information is distributed for analysis.

- Objectives are monitored through minute-to-minute, day-to-day, month-to-month, and year-to-year analysis by individuals, teams, departments, the management group, and executive staff.

In more complex situations, a more extensive system for monitoring, measuring, analyzing, and reporting results versus objectives would be necessary, but the principles remain the same.

2. PROCESS ANALYSIS

> Use various tools to analyze a process and evaluate its effectiveness on the basis of procedures, work instructions, and other documents. Evaluate the process to identify and relieve bottlenecks, increase capacity, improve throughput, reduce cycle time, and eliminate waste. (Evaluate)
>
> **Body of Knowledge IV.B.2**

There are many reasons for examining and documenting the steps in a process. Several examples are:

- When designing a new process or a change to a process

- To prepare for an audit/assessment of a process or system

- As part of the building project plans for a new facility

- To aid in planning a preventive action

- As a diagnostic technique for locating possible problem areas

- As a tool for identifying non-value-added steps and bottlenecks in an effort to increase capacity, improve throughput, reduce cycle time, and eliminate waste

- As a technique for comparing before and after changes to a process

- To aid in developing a quality system's documentation (often including both text and process maps)

- As a technique for helping quality improvement teams to understand a process

- As a training aid for understanding the process for which training is being given

- As a technique to help strategic planners understand the interrelationships of existing processes

While there are a number of tools and techniques used in understanding and analyzing processes, the basic flowchart/process map is the predominant tool used.

Flowcharting/Process Mapping

Flowcharting is briefly discussed in Chapter 13 as one of the seven classic quality tools. A *process map* is a more detailed process flowchart. Process mapping is a technique for designing, analyzing, and communicating work processes. A process map may often show the tasks, activities, functions, and/or decisions that must be performed in a particular process and, where applicable, by whom (participants).

Process mapping is used:

- To communicate and create understanding of a process flow

- To identify non-value-added steps for potential elimination or modification

- To serve as a procedure on how to perform a task or job

- To serve as part of the instructional material used in training a new performer

- To envision the flow of a new or redesigned process

- To support a planning exercise for a team to map what members perceive the process flow to be

- To serve as a simulation tool for a hypothetical walk-through of a process (for example, to look for possible redundancies, disconnects, dead ends, and other anomalies)

Depending on needs identified from the previous list, process mapping may be done by a:

- Current process owner

- Potential process owner

- Quality/process improvement team

- Reengineering team

- Strategic planning team

- Trainer

- Trainee

- Technical writer

Process mapping is usually iterative because to get it right may take a number of PDCA-type cycles. The methodology depends on the purpose and style of the map, where in the sequence of mapping steps the map is being created, and the competency of the mapper. A generic sequence of mapping steps is:

1. Select the process to be mapped

2. Define the purpose for the map

3. Select the style of map to be produced

4. Define the process to be mapped:

   • Inputs and outputs

   • Users/customers to whom outputs are directed

   • Requirements of users/customers

   • Titles of persons involved in the process

   • Title of process owner

   • Titles of other stakeholders (not including suppliers)

   • First and last step in the process

   • Suppliers and their inputs

   • Constraints (for example, standards and regulations)

5. Map out the principal flow (main flow without exceptions)

6. Add the decision points and alternative paths

7. Add the check/inspection points and alternative paths

8. Do a desktop walk-through with persons who know the process

9. Modify the map as needed (and as it will be)

10. Review changes and obtain approval

11. Use map for purpose intended[2]

Whether the process mapper uses pencil and paper or a computer software product to produce the process map depends on the stage in the mapping process and the desired end result. Unless the mapper is also the process owner, one or more persons usually have to be queried as to what they do and how they do it. The approach can be as simple as taking pencil and paper notes in a one-to-one off-site interview to collecting data on-site from the work unit performers, using notetaking, or videotaping the performers. The mapper, unless very experienced, will probably sketch, free-form, the process steps using paper and pencil. When reasonably satisfied that the process sketched is correct, it may be more formally drawn in pen and ink, or with a software product.

Process-Mapping Methods. Traditional process-mapping symbols are shown in Figure 14.4. A sample process map (incomplete) is shown in Figure 14.5.

Organizational processes usually involve two or more participants (individuals and/or groups, such as a department or organizational unit). There is then an advantage if the process map indicates who is responsible for actions depicted in the process. Figure 14.6 shows the process flow in a grid format (also called a

Symbol	Descriptor	Comments
⬭	Terminal symbol	Shows beginning and ending points. Usually labeled *start* or *begin* or *stop* or *end*.
▭	Activity symbol	Shows any single step in the process. A brief description of the activity appears inside the rectangle.
◇	Decision symbol	Shows the decision point at which the process branches into two or more paths. A question appears within the diamond, and the path taken depends on the answer to the question.
↑→↓←	Flow line	Connects steps and shows the direction of process flow from one activity to the next in a sequence. The arrowhead on a flow line shows the direction of the process flow.
⯈	Delay or wait symbol	Shows a bottleneck or holding point, which is an opportunity for time reduction. A brief description of the delay appears inside the symbol.
◯	Link symbol	Used to show the beginning and the end of a page or column break in the drawing of the process flow. Usually the *from* and *to* circles are labeled with a letter.
▱	Input or output symbol	Identifies either current or expected inputs and outputs within the process flow. A brief description of the item appears inside the symbol.
▢	Document symbol	Identifies either the input or the output as a document. The title of the document may appear inside the symbol.

Figure 14.4 Traditional process-mapping symbols.

swim-lane chart) that lays out the map in columns representing each department. This type of chart is also called a *cross-functional flowchart* or *deployment chart*.

What to Look for in the Process Map. The mere action of process mapping will often surface situations that may be the cause of current problems or identify potential areas for improvement. Some of these situations are:

- Branching steps exceed the number of steps in the main flow.
- Checking/inspection steps are missing or excessive.
- Steps take the process flow back and forth between different work units.
- Important steps are missing.
- There are steps that add no value to the end product or service.
- There are redundant steps.
- Steps may need to be decomposed into several steps.
- There are dead ends.

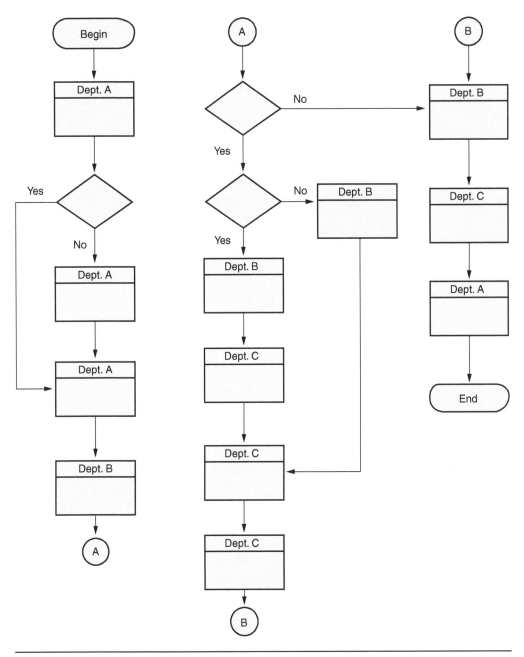

Figure 14.5 Process map—nongrid format.

- There are disconnects (for example, a *go to* but no *from* circle).
- Flow is difficult to understand and confuses performers.
- Too much detail is shown:
  — Map appears to be overdone.
  — Map is a jumbled mass of data.

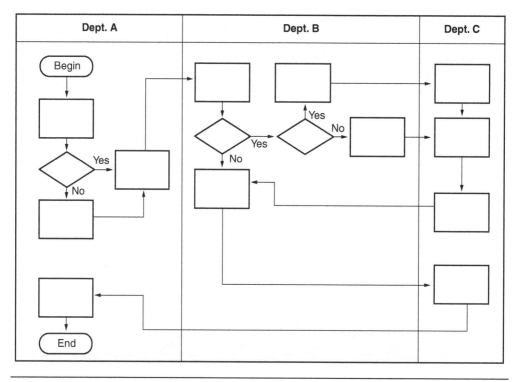

Figure 14.6 Process map—grid format.

- Too little detail is shown:
  - — Map is too skimpy for purpose intended.
  - — Complexities are masked by macrolevel steps.
  - — The detail expected is omitted—for example, duration of steps, responsibility, and number of operatives.
- The point of the purpose for mapping the process is missed.
- The process map is not presented in the most advantageous style or format wanted.

Common problems with developing effective process maps include the following:

- Difficulty in identifying processes and subprocesses from beginning to end; often lacking is a common understanding of what a process consists of and what the parameters of the processes are in the context of the work environment
- Difficulty in identifying alternative paths, inspection points, and ways to improve a process
- Difficulty in applying principles and techniques for effective communication regarding quantity of information, formats, styles, layout, wording, and titles to the process map

Procedures and Work Instructions

Many organizations have been in existence for decades, managing their processes without much, if any, formal documentation and yet continuing to ship products that meet customers' specifications. Today, however, major changes are having an impact on all organizations—for example, global marketing, mergers and sellouts, cultural norms, population movement, and time pressures. These types of changes are causing organizations to document their systems, processes, and practices. In many cases they may be forced to do so to remain competitive. In formally documenting processes, organizations are realizing the following internal advantages. The documentation:

- Identifies the preferred/required approach to be followed
- Provides a basis for measuring/assessing performance
- Emphasizes a consistent method of doing work
- Supports training
- Captures the one best way as a synthesis of methods used by experienced people
- Serves as a job aid guiding/refreshing the trained performer
- Provides a baseline for assessment and improvement

One model for structuring the quality management system documentation is shown in Figure 14.7. As implied by the pyramidal structure, each level in the structure interlocks with and supports a higher level. For example, the description of the system in level 1 references the supporting procedures in level 2, level 2 procedures reference work instructions, and records are referenced in both level 2 and 3 documents.

In documenting procedures and work instructions, ensure that the following questions are addressed:

- If the documentation is to conform to a standard, does it?
- Is the documentation appropriately deployed and kept up to date?
- Is the documented system being followed by the people who produce the work?
- Are the required records kept?
- Is the documentation system periodically assessed for effectiveness?

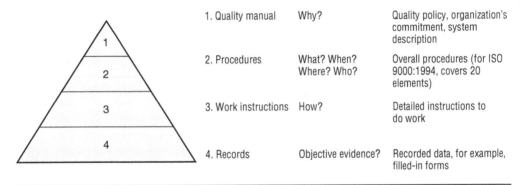

1. Quality manual	Why?	Quality policy, organization's commitment, system description
2. Procedures	What? When? Where? Who?	Overall procedures (for ISO 9000:1994, covers 20 elements)
3. Work instructions	How?	Detailed instructions to do work
4. Records	Objective evidence?	Recorded data, for example, filled-in forms

Figure 14.7 A quality management system documentation hierarchy.

Excepting standards that an organization may self-impose, there are no prescribed standards for composing or formatting a documented system. Variations include:

- Outline with bulleted text
- Process map with annotations
- Process map with adjacent outline text
- Photographs depicting different stages in the process with outline text
- Checklists

Organizations choose their own approach to documentation unless they are required to conform to a specific standard. Some examples of the media on which procedures and work instructions may be presented are:

- Hard copy (paper or like material)
- Computer screen at workstation
- Video (stream or clips)
- Instructions embedded in a work order/traveler
- Process map displayed in work area
- Handheld electronic display
- Intranet (internal organization's own internet)
- Job aids:
  - Samples or photos of product in various stages of manufacture
  - Painted color-coded work areas and tool boards (for placement of tools)
  - Signage to designate specific areas for materials and scrap
  - Forms annotated with brief instructions for completion
  - Laminated cards/tags displayed at workstation

Control Plans

Control plans typically address product/service plans: identifying, classifying, and weighting the characteristics for quality, as well as tolerances, applicable measurements, and methods of control.

A control plan does not replace the details required in specific operator instructions. Typically, each item in the control plan is supported by procedures and/or work instructions. For example, the overall standard for packaging and delivery may be supported by a shipping manual giving specifications for packaging different types, sizes, and weights of product and the type of carrier to use. In the case of a project-oriented organization where every project is unique, the control plan is specific to each project. (Note: Specific customer requirements could, in case of conflict, override the organization's control plan when mutual agreement has been obtained up front.) Figure 14.8 shows a partial sample of one type of detailed control plan.

Control Plan

Control Plan Number	10233	Key Contact/Phone	John White/423-555-1212	Date (orig)	01/09/13	Date (rev)	07/13/14
Part Number/Latest Change Level	EVN-7823/C	Core Team	JWhite, SBurris, CSmith	Customer Engineering Approval/Date (if req'd)			
Part Name/Description	Outer Housing Assembly	Supplier/Plant Approval/Date	03/05/13	Customer Quality Approval/Date (if req'd)			
Supplier/Plant	XYZ Company, Anywhere USA	Other Approval/Date (if req'd)		Other Approval/Date (if req'd)			

Part/ process number	Process name/ operation description	Machine, device, jig, tools for mfg.	Characteristics			Special char. class	Specification/ tolerance	Methods				Reaction plan
			No	Product	Process			Evaluation measurement technique	Size	Freq.	Control method	
10	Receive and verify	N/A	A	Chemistry			Spec 0143	Compare COA	1	Lot	Accept/reject, lot acceptance report	Return to vendor
20	Machine complete	Mazak	B	Bearing diameter		X	23.00 ± .01mm	CMM	3	2 hrs	x-bar/R chart	Change tool, scrap bin
		BV-120.1 bore tool										
30	Impregnate	Vacufill tank			Temperature		90–100 C	Temp chart	1	Batch	Batch signoff sheet	Reprocess once, then return to vendor
					Vacuum		12 mm	Vacuum chart	1	Batch	Batch signoff sheet	Reprocess once, then return to vendor
					Viscosity		100–120 mpoise	Viscon meter	1	Batch	Batch signoff sheet	Reprocess once, then return to vendor
			C	Leakage		X	2cc/min max @ 60 PSI	Aircheck M/C	5	Batch	Batch signoff sheet	Reprocess once, then return to vendor
40	Assemble bearing	Bearing press			Force required	X	150–220 N	Load cell	100%	100%	Machine accept/reject, production log	Scrap part
			D	Flush to surface			.2 mm max above	Caliper	2	Hour	Production log	Scrap part

Figure 14.8 Portion of a sample control plan.

Source: Used with permission of APLOMET

Industry-Specific Documentation

The automotive industry standard (International Organization for Standardization [ISO]/TS 16949) requires the following from its suppliers:

- Advanced Product Quality Planning (APQP) and control plan are used to guide the process of developing and launching a new product and/or process.

- Production part approval process (PPAP) is used to document the findings of the new process.

- Failure mode and effects analysis (FMEA) is used to evaluate risks related to product and process design.

- Measurement systems analysis (MSA) and statistical process control (SPC) are used to evaluate the ability of measurement devices and processing equipment to meet capability requirements.

Other industries may require specific instructional documentation.

Eliminating Waste

Waste is anything that does not add value. Waste is frequently a result of how the system is designed. The Japanese word for waste is *muda*. *Waste or muda is the opposite of value, which is simply what the customer is willing to pay for.*

The seven types of waste, with examples, are:

1. Overproduction—producing too much at a particular point in time

    - Enlarging the number of requirements beyond customers' needs

    - Including too much detail or too many options in designs

    - Specifying materials that require sole-source procurement or that call for seeking economy-of-scale-oriented procurement

    - Requiring batch processing, lengthy and costly setups, or low-yield processes

2. Waiting—or when a worker has to wait

    - Holdups due to people, information, tools, and equipment not being ready

    - Delays waiting for test results to know if a part is made correctly

    - Unrealistic schedules resulting in backups in manufacturing flow

    - Part improperly designed for manufacture, design changes

3. Transportation—waste caused by inefficient workplace layout; all forms of transportation are muda

    - Non-value-added transport of work in process

    - Inefficient layout of plant, causing multiple transports

- Specifying materials from suppliers geographically located a great distance from manufacturing facility, resulting in higher shipping costs

4. Overprocessing—when extra effort is expended than would be normal

   - Non-value-added effort expended
   - Designers failed to consider production process capabilities (constraints, plant capacities, tolerances that can be attained, process yield rate, setup time and complexity, worker skills and knowledge, storage constraints, material handling constraints)
   - Designs too complex
   - Pulse (takt time) of production flow too high or too low in relation to customer demand

5. Excess inventory—keeping unnecessary raw materials, parts, et cetera

   - Stockpiling more materials than are needed to fulfill customer orders
   - Material handling to store, retrieve, store as part proceeds in the process
   - Unreliable production equipment, necessitating safety stock

6. Motion—extra or unneeded operator motions

   - Non-value-added movements, such as reaching, walking, bending, searching, sorting
   - Product designs that are not manufacturing-friendly
   - Requirements for lifting cumbersome and/or heavy parts
   - Manufacturing steps that require frequent repositioning

7. Rejects or defective parts—involves scrapping or reworking parts

   - Corrective actions, looking for root cause
   - Scrap
   - Downgrading defectives (reducing price, seeking a buyer) in order to recover some of the cost of manufacture
   - Faulty design, causing defects
   - Excessive tolerances, creating more defectives

Inventories (buffer stock and batch and queue processing) can be a huge waste. Consider this example: The order is for 200 pieces. The process consists of three operations of 10 seconds each. If the 200 pieces are processed as a batch, the total cycle time is 6000 seconds (200×30 seconds). However, in a single-piece flow mode, there is no accumulation of material between steps. Cycle time is 30 seconds for a single piece and approximately 2000 seconds total for the lot of 200 (each completed piece is coming off the line at 10-second intervals $\times$ 200 pieces). The reduction in total cycle time (6000 seconds – 2000 seconds) = 4000 seconds/6000 = 67% reduction. Work in process (WIP) has also been reduced to 3 pieces, from all 200 waiting at step 2 and then again at step 3. Aside from reducing the cycle time by single-piece flow, if any problem occurs during processing, it is more likely to be detected early in the process, reducing scrap and the potential for shipping defective product.

Analyses of processes for waste usually involve diagrams that show the flow of materials and people and document how much time is spent on value-added versus non-value-added activity. Cycle time is affected by both visible and invisible waste.

Examples of *visible waste* are:

- *Out-of-spec incoming material.* For example, an invoice from a supplier has incorrect pricing, or aluminum sheets are the wrong size.

- *Scrap.* For example, holes are drilled in the wrong place, or shoe soles are improperly attached.

- *Downtime.* For example, a school bus is not operable, or process 4 cannot begin because of a backlog at process 3.

- *Product rework.* For example, an electrical continuity test is failed, or a customer number is not coded on the invoice.

Examples of *invisible waste* are:

- *Inefficient setups.* For example, a jig requires frequent retightening, or incoming orders are not sorted correctly for data entry

- *Queue times of work in process.* For example, an assembly line is not balanced to eliminate bottlenecks (constraints), or an inefficient loading zone protocol slows school bus unloading, causing late classes

- *Unnecessary motion.* For example, materials for assembly are located out of easy reach, or workers need to bring each completed order to the dispatch desk

- *Wait time of people and machines.* For example, a utility crew (three workers and truck) waiting until a parked auto can be removed from the work area, or planes are late in arriving due to inadequate scheduling of available terminal gates

- *Inventory.* For example, obsolete material returned from a distributor's annual clean out is placed in inventory, anticipating the possibility of a future sale, or, to take advantage of quantity discounts, a year's supply of paper bags is ordered and stored

- *Movement of material, work in process, and finished goods.* For example, in a function-oriented plant layout, WIP has to be moved from 15 to 950 feet to the next operation, or stacks of files are constantly being moved about to gain access to filing cabinets and machines

- *Overproduction.* For example, because customers usually order the same item again, an overrun is produced to place in inventory just in case, or extras are made at earlier operations in case they are needed in subsequent operations

- *Engineering changes.* For example, problems in production necessitate engineering changes, or failure to clearly review customer requirements causes unnecessary changes

- *Unneeded reports.* For example, a report initiated five years ago is still produced each week even though the need was eliminated four years ago, or a hard copy report duplicates the same information available on a computer screen

- *Meetings that add no value.* For example, a morning production meeting is held each day whether or not there is a need (coffee and Danish are served), or fifteen people attend a staff meeting each week where one of the two hours is used to solve a problem usually involving less than one-fifth of the attendees

- *Management processes that take too long or have no value.* For example, all requisitions (even for paper clips) must be signed by a manager, or a memo to file must be prepared for every decision made between one department and another

3. LEAN TOOLS

> Identify and use lean tools such as 5S, just-in-time (JIT), kanban, value stream mapping (VSM), quick changeover (single-minute exchange of die), poka-yoke, kaizen, standard work (training within industry), and productivity (OEE). (Apply)
>
> **Body of Knowledge IV.B.3**

Lean tools are used to identify non-value-added steps and bottlenecks in an effort to increase capacity, improve throughput, reduce cycle time, and eliminate waste. Today, lean goes by many different names. Some common terms include: continuous improvement (CI), process excellence (PEX), performance excellence (also PEX), operational excellence (OpEx), organizational excellence, and so on. Many of these disciplines have extensive systems and tools around them with reams of supporting literature. Depending on the organization, the breadth and scope of each of these systems can vary widely. This intent of this section is not to delve into the various naming conventions but to provide some traditional definitions of some of the most commonly used forms of lean tools that may be used to help improve upon a process or system.

Many often apply the acronym LEAN (less employees are needed) when leveraging lean systems and tools. Via the application of common lean tools, transformational improvements are often observed. As such, the acronym is true; fewer personnel will be needed, thereby incurring less cost. What physically changes are the types of work that are being performed as non-value-added (NVA) activities are evolved to the execution of more value-added (VA) activities. Therefore, as NVA wastes are eliminated, more units per hour and/or efficiencies can be attained. (Keep in mind that this applies to both direct and indirect processes.) As business growth and natural attrition occur, a calculated execution of lean systems and tools should be affected to minimize the negative impact of job loss to a dedicated employee. If personnel view LEAN as a system of elimination of personnel, then they simply will not participate, and anticipated benefits will not likely be attained or sustained. As such, the organization's cultural approach to the application of lean (not capitalized) tools is critical.

Cycle Time Reduction

Cycle time is the total amount of time required to complete a process, from the first step to the last. Today's methods for cycle time reduction came about through Henry Ford's early focus on minimizing waste, traditional industrial engineering techniques (for example, time and motion studies), and the Japanese adaptation of these methods (often called the Toyota Production System [TPS]) to smaller production-run applications. Although cycle time reduction is best known for its application to production operations, it is equally useful in nonmanufacturing environments, where person-to-person handoffs, queues of jobs, and facility layout affect the productivity of knowledge workers.

To be able to select where best to implement cycle time reduction requires a high-level system analysis of the organization to determine where current performance deficits or bottlenecks are located. The organization's overall system has a *critical path* (the series of steps that must occur in sequence and that take the longest time to complete). Clearly, improving a process that is not on the critical path will have no real impact on cycle time.

Typical actions to shorten the cycle time of processes include:

1. Removing non-value-adding steps.

2. Speeding up value-adding steps.

3. Integrating several steps of the process into a single step; this often requires expanding the skill level of employees responsible for the new process and/or providing technical support such as a computer database.

4. Breaking the process into several smaller processes that focus on a narrower or special product. This *work cell* or *small business unit* concept allows employees to develop customer product-focused skills and usually requires colocating equipment and personnel responsible for the cell.

5. Shifting responsibility to suppliers or customers or taking back some of the responsibility currently being performed by suppliers or customers. The practice of modular assembly is a typical example of this process.

6. Standardizing the product/service until as late as possible in the process, then creating variations when orders are received; this allows the product to be partially processed, requiring only completion before shipment (for example, the practice of producing only white sweaters then dyeing them just prior to shipment).

Other ways of improving cycle times include improving equipment reliability (thereby reducing non-value-added maintenance downtime), reducing defects (that use up valuable resource time), and reducing unnecessary inventory. Another fundamental process for improving cycle time is that of simply better organizing the workplace (see the 5S tools discussed later).

Reducing cycle time can reduce WIP and finished goods inventories, allow smaller production lot sizes, decrease lead times for production, and increase throughput (decrease overall time from start to finish). Also, when process steps are eliminated or streamlined, overall quality tends to improve. Because many opportunities might be identified when beginning the effort to reduce cycle time, a Pareto analysis can be performed to decide which factors demand immediate attention. Some problems might be fixed in minutes, whereas others might require the establishment of a process improvement team and take months to complete.

A *work cell* is a self-contained unit dedicated to performing all of the operations to complete a product or a major portion of a production run. Equipment is configured to accomplish:

- Sequential processing

- Counterclockwise flow to enable operators to optimize use of their right hands as operators move through the cell (moving the part to each subsequent operation)

- Shorter movements by close proximity of machines

- Positioning of the last operation close to the first operation for the next part

- Adaptability of the cell to accommodate customers' varying demands

The most prevalent layout is a U shape (see Figure 14.9), although L, S, and V shapes have been used. Product demand, product mix, and constraints (such as that management just will not dispose of) are all considerations in designing a work cell.

Although lean production is based on basic industrial engineering concepts, it has been primarily visible to U.S. companies as the TPS. The basic premise is that only what is needed should be produced, and it should only be produced

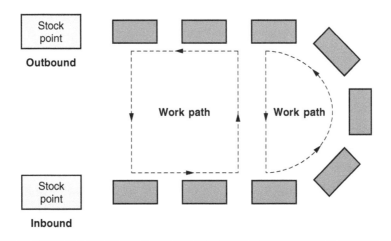

Figure 14.9 Typical U-shaped cell layout.

when it is actually needed. Due to the amount of time, energy, and other resources wasted by the way processes and organizations are designed, however, organizations tend to produce what they think they might need (for example, based on forecasts) rather than what they actually need (for example, based on customer orders).

5S

5S is a method to improve and sustain workplace organization. It is generally meant to be applied to shared work spaces. 5S represents the five disciplines for maintaining a visual workplace where visual controls and/or information systems are used. 5S is foundational to continual improvement and positively lessens several forms of waste such as waiting, inventory, defects, overproduction, et cetera. A common acronym associated with 5S is PEEP, where there is a *place for everything and everything is in its place*. 5S is not a "housekeeping regime." It is a form of standard work that is expected to be sustained each and every time. Taiichi Ohno created the original concept of "4S" for workplace organization at Toyota in the early 1950s. It further evolved into 5S during the 1960s and 1970s. Many organizations add a sixth S for safety.[3] The Japanese use the term *5S* for five practices for maintaining a clean and efficient workplace:

1. *Seiri* (sort). Separate needed tools, parts, and instructions from unneeded materials and remove the latter.

   During this phase, "red tags" are often used to remove materials that are not thought to be needed. The format of a red tag is organization dependent, or they can be purchased from a variety of lean system suppliers. A mantra of "when in doubt, move it out" is often applied. Team members have an opportunity across a specified time period to evaluate the items and then identify anything that is critical or necessary. Necessary items are moved to their proper locations, and remaining items are disposed of or potentially sold. This is one area where lean may be "self-funding."

2. *Seiton* (set in order). Neatly arrange and identify parts and tools for ease of use. This is the act of identifying where things should go. During this phase, the items are placed where the team thinks they will work best. However, all users of the area should have an opportunity to evaluate placement as well; this includes personnel from other shifts or users from other departments. Visual signals are implemented such as lines, labels, signs, and so on to show both users and nonusers where materials should be stored.

3. *Seiso* (shine). Conduct a cleanup campaign. This is the act of cleaning everything. Include the insides of drawers and cabinets and from "floor to ceiling."

4. *Seiketsu* (standardize). Conduct *seiri, seiton,* and *seiso* at frequent intervals to maintain a workplace in perfect condition. This phase is the finalization of where things should go. The PEEP is now in effect. When refinements occur, personnel that utilize the area must all be

informed and/or retrained as necessary. It is often helpful to take a photo of the area and post it nearby to help personnel to remember the operating condition of the area. Standards developed for the area may include how frequently items should be moved in or out or how often surfaces should be cleaned and/or wiped down.

5. *Shitsuke* (sustain). Form the habit of always following the first four Ss. This is the standard work that is performed to maintain the area. Checklists may frequently be employed with a minimal time set aside to tend to the area. Typically, the area would then be included in some form of regular audit. Training and cross-communication to affected personnel is necessary.

Far more than just good things to do, 5S can:

- Build awareness of the concept and principles of improvement
- Set the stage to begin serious waste reduction initiatives
- Break down barriers to improvement, at low cost
- Empower the workers to control their work environment

In step 2 (*seiton*), visual management is used to arrange the workplace—all tools, parts, and material and the production process itself—so that the status of the process can be understood at a glance by everyone. Further, the intent is to furnish visual clues to aid the performer in correctly processing a step or series of steps, reduce cycle time, cut costs, smooth workflow, and improve quality. By seeing the status of the process, both the performer and management have an up-to-the-second picture of what has happened, what is presently happening, and what is to be done. Advantages of visual management are:

- It catches errors and defects before they can occur.
- Quick detection enables rapid correction.
- It identifies and removes safety hazards.
- It improves communications.
- It improves workplace efficiency.
- It cuts costs.

Examples of visible management include:

- Color-coded sectors on meter faces to indicate reading acceptance range and low and high unacceptable readings
- Electronic counters mounted over a work area to indicate the rate of accepted finished product
- Work orders printed on colored paper where the color denotes the grade and type of metal to be used
- Lights atop enclosed equipment indicating the status of product being processed

- Slots at the dispatch station for pending work orders, indicating work to be scheduled (and backlog) and when the work unit(s) will become idle

- Painted floor and/or wall space with shadow images of the tool, die, or pallet that usually occupies the space when not in use

Just-in-Time

Just-in-time (JIT) is a material requirement planning system that provides for the delivery of material or product at the exact time and place where the material or product will be used. Highly coordinated delivery and production systems are required to match delivery to use times. The aim is to eliminate or reduce on-hand inventory (excessive buffer stock) and deliver material or product that requires no or little incoming inspection.

The main intent of JIT is to reduce the consumption of working capital (monetary outlay) and lead time. There are a variety of visual signals or kanban cues (not to be confused with queues) to indicate when to trigger the next part. While JIT is largely applied in production operations, it can also be used in transactional processes. JIT can lead to significant improvements in return on investment (ROI), quality, and efficiency.

JIT was first used by Ford Motor as a part of "dock to the factory floor," initiating what many now call "point of use," or POU. Toyota then adopted it as a part of its TPS. Taiichi Ohno further recognized the potential of JIT and further adapted it into reducing lot sizes so that a smaller warehouse footprint could be leveraged. For JIT to be successful, changeovers needed to be aggressively reduced and managed. An outcome of this partnering was the single-minute exchange of die (SMED) developed by Shigeo Shingo. As SMED was executed, lot size could be reduced, and JIT could be optimized.[4] This enabled less capital outlay as capacity was already inherent in the existing equipment.

JIT enabled the evolution from push to pull scheduling. Pull scheduling relies on the extensive use of visual cues (such as kanban cards) and is driven by demand. This reduces later symptoms of excess inventory, handling, and other wastes. As a management philosophy, JIT forces continuous problem-solving, with the constant intent of eliminating inventory.[5] Supplies and components are pulled through the system to arrive where they are needed when they are needed in the quantity and quality they are needed in. The goal is to achieve the minimal level of resources required to add the necessary value to the production system.[6] Quality at the source of each of the various process steps is key to avoid disruption to the flow. Key benefits include: smaller inventories, shorter lead time, improved quality, smaller footprints, lower production costs, increased productivity and agility, et cetera. A key challenge to many organizations is that most material requirement planning (MRP) software was developed decades ago, prior to the understanding of the power of JIT. It can be challenging to effectively deploy JIT in a business where the MRP is unable to be adapted accordingly.

The elements of JIT in a manufacturing environment are:[7]

- Inventory reduction

- Kanbans and pull production systems

- Small lots and quick setups
- Uniform production loading
- Flexible resources
- Efficient facility layout

The principles of JIT are:[8]

- Produce only the product that the customer wants
- Produce product only at the rate that the customer wants
- Produce with perfect quality
- Produce with minimum lead time
- Produce products with only those features that the customer wants
- Produce with no waste of labor, material, or equipment
- Produce in a way that enables the development of people
- Create a flow of production in the most practical manner
- Establish takt time (takt is the rate of customer demand)
- Use kanban to pull product

The system of JIT is accomplished via the execution of multiple tactics. Different organizations manage the types of tactics based on their business needs. A few of these tactics may include: SMED, statistical process control (SPC), usage of takt time, 5S, visual management, total productive maintenance (TPM) and others.

Understanding WIP and throughput are also key in establishing JIT. In 1954, John Little authored what is known today as Little's law. The formula is:[9]

$$\text{Average WIP} = \text{Throughput rate} \times \text{Average production lead time}$$

In order to reduce the WIP, the throughput rate and lead time must be constantly evaluated for opportunities to reduce them.

Per the Gemba Academy,[10] expected JIT results may be:

- 50–90% reduction in throughput time
- 50–90% reduction in WIP
- 60–80% reduction in scrap and rework
- 50–90% reduction in setup times
- 30–60% reduction in space requirements

Much of the above was also validated in the business case study by Accuride,[11] where they observed a 50% reduction in lead time, a 50% improvement in productivity, and a 20% reduction in cost per unit.

JIT is only effective with some form of visual cue system. Typically, that format is in the use of kanban cards. These are discussed in the next section.

Kanban

This method is used in a process to signal an upstream supplier (internal or external) that more material or product is needed downstream. Originally, it was just a manual card system but has evolved to more sophisticated signaling methods in some organizations. It is referred to as a *pull* system because it serves to pull material or product from a supplier (or previous work unit) rather than relying on a scheduling system to push the material or product forward at predetermined intervals. It is said that the kanban method was inspired by Toyota executive Taiichi Ohno's visit to a U.S. supermarket.

Kanban is the Japanese word for card. It is used to authorize or pull production from downstream operations based on existing physical consumption. While the signal used does not have to be a physical card, kanbans today can be used to mean an empty space, a bin, a light, a sound, or any means in which to cue the personnel to build the next product based on consumptive demand. Kanban quantities are calculated based on lead time and the rate of consumption. There is usually a minimum quantity determined for a market. As that market is consumed, triggers are created to replace the items. If the market is full, there are no triggers, and production does not occur. This is often at odds with the common financial key process indicator (KPI) of absorption, which rewards a facility for making as many units as possible. The quantity that a market needs can be calculated. While formulas may vary by organizations as they optimize their processes, the general formula for a minimum kanban quantity is:

$$\text{Minimum quantity} = (\text{Demand during lead time} + \text{Safety stock})/\text{Container quantity}$$

The inputs to the formula must be evaluated regularly to address changes that may happen in the business environment. Kanban cards are used to convey information. While formats will vary, some basic pieces of information will include:[12]

- Part number

- Part description

- Quantity of units in the kanban

- Where to find the part when the bin is empty (stock location)

- Where to return the kanban when it is filled

A few key notes on kanban cards:

- There should only be the exact amount of cards needed to create the planned market.

- The cards should all be accounted for and audited for quantity.

- The cards should be of a size or shape to not fit into a pocket where they may be forgotten and inadvertently taken out of the production cycle.

Ultimately, kanban is meant to get to an optimum level of one-piece flow. This is often not practical or feasible depending upon the processes at hand. Therefore, all effort should be made to identify what that movement quantity should be and focus on working to attain the smallest increment.

Value Stream Mapping

Value stream mapping (VSM) is charting the sequence of movements of information, materials, and production activities in the value stream (all activities involving the designing, ordering, producing, and delivering of products and services to the organization's customers). An advantage to this is that a "before action is taken" value stream map depicts the current state of the organization and enables identification of how value is created and where waste occurs. Plus, employees see the whole value stream rather than just the one part in which they are involved. This improves understanding and communication and facilitates waste elimination.

A VSM is used to identify areas for improvement. At the macrolevel, a VSM identifies waste along the value stream and helps strengthen supplier and customer partnerships and alliances. At the microlevel, a VSM identifies waste—non-value-added activities—and identifies opportunities that can be addressed with a *kaizen blitz*.

At least three distinctive types of VSM have evolved:

1. Material flow: Typically, in manufacturing, this type of VSM tracks raw material transformation into consumer goods. It links the material and information flows together and provides a common language. Takt time, or the rate of customer demand, must be understood. Takt is the "beat you need to meet." It is calculated as:

$$\text{Takt} = \text{Available work time per day}/\\ \text{Daily required demand in parts per day}$$

For example, if a customer needed one hundred units/day and the facility ran ten hours/day, the takt would be ten hours/one hundred units or one hour for every ten units. It is critical to note that takt is not the same thing as cycle time. It may be impossible for the organization to make ten units in an hour, or they might be able to make one thousand units in an hour. The takt is independent of the cycle time. The opportunity is to balance and optimize the work flow to meet the takt time.

2. Transactional or business process VSM (TVSM) for information flow: TVSMs can typically be applied to any type of movement of data and information upon which decisions and actions are taken. Examples include engineering new product development, human resource hiring of new employees, supply chain development of a new supplier, strategic planning, financial order entry to cash collection, and more. Generally, all of the various types of TVSMs can have an impact on the efficacy of material flow.

3. Enterprise VSM flow (EVSM). This is a specialized form of TVSM that evaluates and improves the movement of products or processes across the business enterprise—typically, outside of the four walls of a facility and across multiple locales and/or geographies. The assessment is of what types of markets should be kept where to minimize inventory and logistical costs. In Accuride's case study,[13] they were able to further reduce lead time by 5% to 8%.

Regardless of the type of VSM, there are usually two states: current state and future state. Each of the three types of VSMs above would be drafted to reflect the current state (C-VSM, C-TVSM, C-EVSM) and their matching future state (F-VSM, V-TVSM, F-EVSM). The timing of the future state is often a business cultural decision. Timing can range from three months to years.

A VSM is a process map that leverages flowcharting techniques. The key steps to creating a VSM are:

- Identify and define the process to be mapped. It is critical to identify the scope of the process to avoid scope creep, or worse, scope avalanche.

- Map the current state. This can be time-consumptive as data will be needed for each step of the flow. If the data do not exist, then they must be obtained. Depending upon the type of VSM being evaluated, the data will differ.

- Analyze the flow for opportunities for improvement. Creating a VSM in an office is often not effective. It should be done in the work environment where the work is being performed. Consider "stapling yourself to an order" and following it through. Evaluate the process and data for the various forms of waste. Create plans of action to bridge the current state into the desired future state.

- Develop the future state map.

For a material flow VSM, some common forms of data input at each stage of a process might include:

- Cycle time

- Changeover time

- Process uptime

- Scrap/rework rate

- Quantity of product variations

- Number of operators

- Number of shifts

- Lot sizes

- Time available

- Packing size

- Efficiency

While VSM symbols are now largely standardized, many companies have created their own formats. Rother and Shook's book, *Learning to See*,[14] demonstrates the most common symbols now in use on material flow VSMs. Figures 14.10 and 14.11 are sample value stream maps (macrolevel and microlevel).

VSMs are effective if the changes are enabled to occur. There are several critical success factors:[15]

- Management must be supportive of the process and enable the sufficient resources for execution.

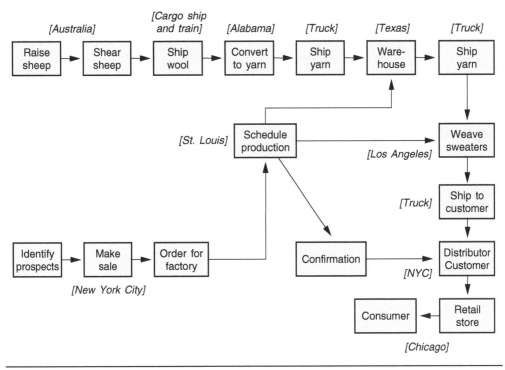

Figure 14.10 Value stream map—macro level (partial).

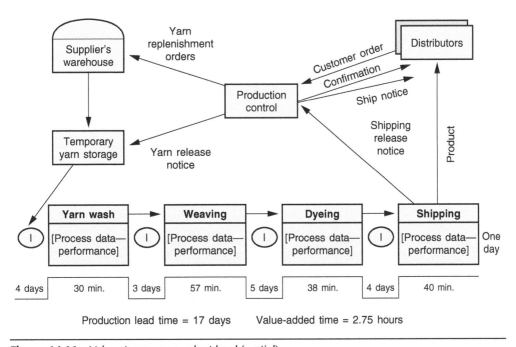

Figure 14.11 Value stream map—plant level (partial).

- Value stream managers must be empowered to enable the changes.

- Training and knowledge of the basic lean and quality improvement tools are needed to understand what the opportunities are and how to execute them.

- The financial impact needs to be understood.

Single-Minute Exchange of Die

The long time required to change a die in a stamping operation meant that a longer production run would be required to absorb the downtime caused by the change-over. To address this, the Japanese created a method for reducing setup times called *single-minute exchange of die* (SMED), also referred to as *rapid exchange of tooling and dies* (RETAD). Times required for a die change were dramatically reduced, often reducing changeover time from several hours to minutes.

To improve setup/changeover times, initiate a plan-do-check-act approach:

1. Map the processes to be addressed. (Video recording the setup/change-over process is a useful means for identifying areas for improvement.)

2. Collect setup data times for each process.

3. Establish setup time reduction objectives.

4. Identify which process is the primary overall constraint (bottleneck). Prioritize remaining processes by magnitude of setup times and target next process by longest time.

5. Remove non-value-adding activities from the targeted process (for example, looking for tools required for the changeover). Trischler lists dozens of non-value-added activities,[16] most of which are applicable in a variety of industries and processes. Note that there are some steps that fit the non-value-added category that cannot actually be removed but can be speeded up.

6. Identify setup steps that are internal (steps the machine operator must perform when the machine is idle) versus steps that are external (steps that can be performed while the machine is still running the previous part. For example, removing the fixture or materials for the next part from storage and locating them near the machine).

7. Focus on moving internal steps to external steps where possible.

8. Identify setup activities that can be done simultaneously while the machine is down (the concept of an auto racing pit crew).

9. Speed up required activities.

10. Standardize changeover parts (for example, all dies have a standard height, all fasteners require the same size wrench to tighten).

11. Store setup parts (dies and jigs) on portable carts in a position and at the height where they can be readily wheeled into place at the machine and the switchover accomplished with minimum movement and effort.

12. Store all setup tools to be used in a designated place within easy reach (for example, visual shadow areas on a portable tool cart).

13. Error proof the setup process.

14. Evaluate the setup/changeover process and make any modifications needed.

15. Return to step 4 and repeat the sequence until all setup times have been improved.

16. Fully implement setup/changeover procedures.

17. Evaluate effectiveness of setup/changeover time reduction efforts against objectives set in step 3.

18. Collect setup time data periodically and initiate improvement effort again; return to step 1.

While SMED is most commonly applied to manufacturing or equipment scenarios, these concepts can also be applied in transactional settings. There has been success in call centers, material picking, order entry, et cetera.

Poka-Yoke or Mistake Proofing

Mistake proofing originated in Japan as an approach applied to factory processes. It was perfected by Shigeo Shingo as *poka-yoke*. It is also applicable to virtually any process in any context. For example, the use of a spell checker in composing text on a computer is an attempt to prevent the writer from making spelling errors (although we have all realized it does not catch every mistake).

This analytical approach involves probing a process to determine where human errors could occur. Then each potential error is traced back to its source. From these data, consider ways to prevent the potential error. Eliminating the step is the preferred alternative. If a way to prevent the error cannot be identified, then look for ways to lessen the potential for error. Finally, choose the best approach possible, test it, make any needed modifications, and fully implement the approach. Mistakes may be classified into four categories:

- Information errors:

  — Information is ambiguous.

  — Information is incorrect.

  — Information is misread, misinterpreted, or mismeasured.

  — Information is omitted.

  — There is inadequate warning.

- Misalignment:

  — Parts are misaligned.

  — A part is misadjusted.

  — A machine or process is mistimed or rushed.

- Omission or commission:

    — A material or part is added.

    — A prohibited and/or harmful action is performed.

    — An operation is omitted.

    — Parts are omitted so there is a counting error.

- Selection errors:

    — A wrong part is used.

    — There is a wrong destination or location.

    — There is a wrong operation.

    — There is a wrong orientation.

Mistake-proofing actions are intended to:

- Eliminate the opportunity for error
- Detect potential for error
- Prevent an error

Effective poka-yoke systems can combat the errors discussed above. People do not typically wish to make mistakes and often cannot help it when they happen. Reprimanding and retraining are not effective countermeasures. Management needs to respect the intelligence of operators by taking over repetitive tasks or actions that depend on vigilance or memory. Below are seven guidelines to poka-yoke attainment:[17]

1. Quality processes: design "robust" quality processes to achieve zero defects

2. Utilize a team environment: leverage the team's knowledge and SME expertise to enhance the improvement efforts

3. Elimination of errors: utilize a robust problem-solving methodology to drive defects toward zero

4. Eliminate the "root cause" of the errors: use the five whys and two hows approach

5. Do it right the first time: utilize resources to perform functions correctly the "first" time

6. Eliminate non-value-added decisions: do not make excuses—just do it!

7. Implement an incremental continual improvement approach: implement improvement actions immediately and focus on incremental improvements; efforts do not have to result in a 100% improvement immediately

Two poka-yoke system approaches are commonly utilized in manufacturing that lead to successful zero defect systems:

1. Control approach: this takes the human element out of the equation and has a high capability of achieving zero defects.

— It shuts down the process when an error occurs.

— It keeps the "suspect" part in place when an operation is incomplete.

2. Warning approach: signals the operator to stop the process and correct the problem via some form of alarm (light/sound). This may be used when an automatic shutoff is not an option.

There are multiple types of poka-yoke devices available with today's technology. New forms are being developed regularly. Poka-yoke devices generally consist of three primary methods that can be used via a control or a warning approach:

- Contact: uses some form of sensing to detect for presence or lack of presence of a desired feature

- Counting: uses some form of sensing device to count a fixed number of operations required within a process and/or the number of times a part is used

- Motion sequence: uses sensors to verify if a motion or step has occurred as desired

When proactive poka-yoke systems are not yet developed (those that prevent the creation of the defect), a reactive poka-yoke approach with informative inspection can be developed. This is where the check occurs immediately after the process. While it does not eliminate the defect, it does prevent the defect from being advanced and is more effective than statistical sampling.

Let us look at some examples. In the first situation, a patient is required to fill out forms at various stages of diagnosis and treatment (the ubiquitous "clipboard treatment"). The patient is prone to making errors due to the frustration and added anxiety of filling out multiple forms.

After analyzing the situation, the solution is to enter initial patient data into a computer at the first point of the patient's arrival, adding to the computer record as the patient passes through the different stages with different doctors and services. When referrals are made to doctors outside the initial facility, send an electronic copy of the patient's record (e-mail) to the referred doctor. Except to correct a previous entry, the intent is to never require the patient to furnish the same data more than once.

Considering the four types of mistakes, we can see that information was omitted or incorrectly entered at subsequent steps. The solution eliminates resubmitting redundant data.

In the second example, a low-cost but critical part is stored in an open bin for access by any operator in the work unit. While there is a minimum on-hand quantity posted and a reorder card is kept in the bin, the bin frequently is empty before anyone takes notice. The mistake is that there is inadequate warning in receiving vital information.

The solution is to design and install a spring-loaded bin bottom that is calibrated to trigger an alarm buzzer and flashing light when the minimum stock level is reached. The alarm and light will correct the mistake.

In the final example, there is a potential to incur injury from the rotating blades when operators of small tractor-mowers dismount from a running tractor. The solution is to install a spring-actuated tractor seat that shuts off the tractor motor as soon as weight is removed. Using this tractor seat will prevent a harmful action.

Careful elimination, detection, and prevention actions can result in near 100% quality. Unintended use, ignorance, or willful misuse or neglect by humans may still circumvent safeguards, however. For example, until operating a motor vehicle is prevented before all seatbelts are securely fastened, warning lights and strict law enforcement alone will not achieve 100% effectiveness. Continually improve processes and mistake-proofing efforts to strive for 100%.

Kaizen

Kaizen is a Japanese word (*kai* means *change* or *school*; *zen* means *good* or *wisdom*). It has come to mean a continual and incremental improvement (as opposed to reengineering, which is a breakthrough, quantum-leap approach). A *kaizen blitz*, or *kaizen event*, is an intense process often lasting three to five consecutive days. It introduces rapid change into an organization by using the ideas and motivation of the people who do the work. It has also been called *zero investment improvement* (ZII).

In a kaizen event/blitz, a cross-functional team focuses on a target process, studies it, collects and analyzes data, discusses improvement alternatives, and implements changes. The emphasis is on making the process better, not necessarily perfect. Subprocesses that have an impact on cycle time are a prime target on which to put the synergy of a kaizen team to work. The typical stages of a kaizen event are:[18]

- Week before blitz:

  — *Wednesday.* Train three or four facilitators in kaizen blitz techniques and tools and enhance their facilitation skill level.

  — *Thursday.* Target the process to be addressed.

  — *Friday.* Gather initial data on the present targeted process.

- Blitz week:

  — *Monday.* Train the participants in kaizen blitz techniques and tools.

  — *Tuesday.* Train (a.m.), create process map of present state (p.m.).

  — *Wednesday.* Create process map of future state. Eliminate non-value-added steps and other waste. Eliminate bottlenecks. Design new process flow.

  — *Thursday.* Test changes, modify as needed.

  — *Friday.* Implement the new work flow, tweak the process, document the changes, and be ready for full-scale production on Monday. Prepare follow-up plan.

- Postblitz:

  — Conduct follow-up evaluation of change (at an appropriate interval).

  — Plan the next blitz.

Overall Equipment Effectiveness

Overall equipment effectiveness (OEE) is a method for measuring the efficiency and effectiveness of a process by breaking it down into three constituent components:

availability, performance, and quality. *Availability* takes into account *downtime loss*, or events that stop planned production for an appropriate amount of time, such as setups, adjustments, and breakdowns. *Performance* takes into account *speed loss*, or factors that cause the process to operate at less than the minimum possible speed, when running. *Quality* takes into account *quality loss*, or parts that do not meet quality requirements, such as start-up rejects or production rejects. The three components are calculated as:

- Availability = Operating time/Planned production time

- Performance = Actual run rate/Ideal run rate

- Quality = Good pieces/Total pieces

- OEE = Availability × Performance × Quality

See the OEE website for more information at http://www.oee.com.[19]

Pitfalls to Avoid in Achieving Cycle Time Reduction

Any time an organization applies lean tools, there can be problems. Common pitfalls include:

- Creating a bottleneck.

- Focusing on a portion of the system that is not on the critical path. Bottleneck operations in a production process must be recognized and addressed first.

- Failing to attend to the social aspects of any change.

- Failing to give attention to other issues. For example, in and of itself, cycle time reduction might not result in an improved product or service. It must be studied to ensure that it does not adversely affect quality or other processes or resources. Also, expectations need to be examined to determine whether they are realistic. Finally, remember that absence or misinterpretation of data can lead to unexpected results. Establishing times for and determining the true sequence of events are important to the improvement process. (Video recording of activities for review by the cycle time improvement team is an excellent technique for doing this.)

4. THEORY OF CONSTRAINTS (TOC)

Define key concepts of TOC: systems as chains, local versus system optimization, physical versus policy constraints, undesirable effects versus core problems, and solution deterioration. Classify constraints in terms of resources and expectations as defined by measures of inventory and operating expense. (Understand)

Body of Knowledge IV.B.4

Most organizations have strategies, goals, objectives, and plans to do more with less. They usually have finite resources available, which tends to conflict with ever-increasing expectations from stakeholders. Traditional process improvement methods—for example, to reduce cycle time and get more done with less—have focused on Pareto analysis to pinpoint what process or problem area to tackle first. The resulting fragmented approach has often led to improving the target processes at the expense of the whole organization (suboptimization).

Among a new group of thinkers promulgating the concept of thinking of organizations as systems is Eliyahu Goldratt. Goldratt's principles in the *theory of constraints* (TOC) are:[20]

- The whole organization must be treated as a system.

- Systems thinking is favored over analytical thinking for managing change and problem-solving.

- Over a period of time, the optimal system solution degenerates as changes occur in the environment. Continual improvement is necessary to refresh and sustain the system's effectiveness.

- Optimum performance of a system means that only one part of the system is performing as well as it can. Optimum system performance is not the aggregate of all of the local optima.

- Success or failure is dictated by how well the several processes within the system affect one another.

- The system, much like a chain with individual links connecting the whole, is only as strong as its weakest link.

- Little improvement occurs until the improvement of the weakest link is addressed.

- The weakest link is the system's *constraint*.

- A few core problems constitute the majority of the unwanted effects within a system.

- Linking *undesirable effects* (UDEs) by cause and effect helps surface core problems that are not apparent.

- Solving individual UDEs and neglecting the core problems leads to short-duration solutions.

- Obscure underlying conflict tends to perpetuate core problems. Solutions involve addressing the conflicts and abolishing at least one such conflict.

- The system's current reality must be understood, as well as the difference between it and the goal, including the magnitude and direction.

- To improve the overall system, increase throughput and decrease inventory and operating expenses (terms are modified for the not-for-profit sector).

- Continual improvement can be thwarted by inertia. Solutions may appear to reject further change.

- Coming up with an idea is not coming up with a solution.

How the TOC Treats the Flow of Money

Let us begin with some definitions:

- *Throughput* (T) is the rate at which the entire system generates money through sales of product or service (money coming in).

- *Inventory* (I) is all the money the system invests in things it intends to sell (money tied up inside the organization).

- *Operating expense* (OE) is all the money the system spends turning inventory into throughput (money going out).

So, to figure out key measures, use these equations:

$$\text{Profit} = T - OE$$

$$ROI = \frac{T - OE}{I}$$

$$\text{Productivity} = \frac{T}{OE}$$

$$\text{Inventory turns} = \frac{T}{I}$$

To focus improvement on the part of the process most capable of producing a positive impact on the system:

1. Locate the weakest link in the system and identify whether it is physical or a matter of policy constraint

2. Determine what can be done to squeeze more capability from the constraint without having to undergo expensive changes

3. Unless step 2 eliminated the constraint, adjust the system so that the constraint can function at its greatest effectiveness

4. If steps 2 and 3 were not sufficient, consider making major changes to eliminate the constraint.

5. When either step 3 or 4 has eliminated the constraint, the steps must be repeated in order to deal with the next constraint; this is a never-ending cycle.[21]

Tools Used in the TOC

There are a variety of diagrams used in TOC. They are:

- *Current reality tree.* A root cause analysis method to identify undesirable effects by working backward from the undesirable effect to identify the core problem.

- *Future reality tree.* A picture of the changed process identifying the desirable effects (used to show what to change and to identify any new unfavorable aspects to be addressed before implementing change).

- *Prerequisite tree.* Identifies obstacles to implementation by creating a sequence of events and potential obstacles.

- *Transition tree.* Details for implementing change, including a step-by-step action plan.

- *Conflict resolution diagram.* Described by Goldratt as an "evaporating cloud." As the name implies, this method aids in the resolution of conflicts. This includes identifying assumptions that appear valid but are suspect and can be eliminated as a conflict.[22]

Constraints are categorized as *physical* or *policy* constraints. Physical constraints are the easiest to identify and eliminate. Policy constraints are more difficult, but their elimination usually means a higher degree of system improvement.

All resources (raw material availability, equipment capacity, workforce, number of hours in the day, cash) are finite or limited. Exceeding the limit causes a constraint. What often drives these resources to the limit are increased expectations of the marketplace, customers, and management.

Table 14.1 includes some of the techniques and tools that are used in process management. Note: the table mentions tools that are not discussed in the chapter.

Table 14.1 Techniques, methodologies, and tools applicable to process management.

Techniques/methodology/tool	Explanation/purpose
Action plan	A miniproject plan. Describes action to be taken, responsibility, start and end dates, applicable standards and constraints, resources, and steps to be taken.
Activity-based costing (ABC)	Accounting system that allocates cost to products based on resources used to produce the product
Activity network diagram (AND)	Diagram showing the flow of activities in a process/project and the dependencies among activities
Advanced Product Quality Planning (APQP)	Methodology used to guide the process of developing and launching a new product/process (automotive industry). Defines the phases: conceptualize, design, develop, validate, and launch new product and process designs.
Affinity diagram	A method to organize a large number of items into smaller chunks/clusters
Andon board	Electronic device to display status alerts to operators
Autonomation (*jidoka*)	Specially equipped automated machines capable of detecting a defect in a single part
Batch-and-queue	Scheduling large batches of product that must wait in a queue between each step in the process
Brainstorming	Team technique to generate ideas, for example, on how to reduce cycle time

Table 14.1   Techniques, methodologies, and tools applicable to process management. *(continued)*

Techniques/methodology/tool	Explanation/purpose
Cause-and-effect (fishbone) diagram	Diagramming technique to identify causes and subcauses leading to an effect. Aids in analyzing the root causes of how a situation came to be.
Cell (typically U-shaped)	Configuration of machines of varying types, arranged so that operations occur in sequence, permitting single-piece flow and flexible use of cross-trained operators
Chaku-chaku (load-load in Japanese)	Within a cell, operator removes a part from one machine and loads it into the next machine, continuing the sequence until the part has been through all the steps needed for completion. As one part is removed from a machine, another is started through, thus enabling one-piece scheduling.
Changeover	Changing machine from one part number (for example, product) to another
Check sheet	Tool for tallying frequency of occurrences, over time, for several items being tracked
Control charts (or statistical process control)	Charts used to identify special cause variation, or that a process is out of control
Control plan	The control plan is a document that describes the actions (measurements, inspections, quality checks, or monitoring of process parameters) required at each phase of a process to ensure the process outputs will conform to predetermined requirements.
Cost of quality (COQ)	A method used by organizations to show the financial impact of quality activities
Cycle time	The total time to complete one cycle in an operation
Design for Six Sigma (DFSS)	DFSS is used to design products and services so that they can be produced and delivered with Six Sigma quality.
DMAIC	DMAIC stands for define, measure, analyze, improve, and control. The DMAIC is the problem-solving approach using the Six Sigma methodology. These are the five phases of the approach.
	Define the customer and organizational requirements
	Measure what is critical to quality, map the process, establish measurement system, and determine what is unacceptable (defects)
	Analyze to develop a baseline (process capability), pinpoint opportunities and set objectives, identify root causes of defects

(continued)

Table 14.1 Techniques, methodologies, and tools applicable to process management. *(continued)*

Techniques/methodology/tool	Explanation/purpose
	Improve the process
	Establish a system to *control* the process
Eliminate non-value-added steps in the process	Reduce waste and cut costs
Eliminate or reduce buffer stocks and inventories	Smooth process flow, reduce costs, improve quality, and increase customer satisfaction
Failure mode and effects analysis (FMEA)	Used to develop a preventive strategy, based on risk analysis, with identification of corrective or preventive actions to be taken. Applicable to designs, processes, support services, suppliers, etc. Encourages the development of control mechanisms to control the process. These control mechanisms can be used in the control plan.
5S	(Japanese) methods to make everything about the workplace orderly and clean and keep it so. Conveys the message that a clean and orderly workplace enhances quality, which can result in less waste, lower costs, increased customer satisfaction, and pride in work.
Five whys	Probing method of repeatedly asking "Why?" until reaching the root cause of a situation or problem
Flexibility/agility	Concept and practice of configuring facilities, equipment, people, and support services to cope with inevitable change. Enables organization to reduce costs, respond more effectively to reduce costs, respond more effectively to marketplace demands, withstand economic fluctuations, and facilitate continual improvement.
Flowchart	Step-by-step diagram of a process flow. Helps in understanding the process, identifying bottlenecks, and eliminating non-value-added steps.
Gemba (Japanese for *workplace*)	Management is urged to go to *gemba*, to get out to where the work is being done to better understand a problem and appreciate the process involved in making the product or delivering the service. The management concept, which started in Japan, encourages managers to visit the place where the work happens to better understand the process.
Histogram	Diagram showing the frequency distribution of data
Interrelationship digraph	Tool to examine the relationships of a category/item to each of the other categories being examined
Just-in-time (JIT)	An approach that allows the matching of material deliveries to the right time and place in the manufacturing process. Concepts are applicable elsewhere—for example, JIT training (training delivered in the exact time and place needed).

Table 14.1 Techniques, methodologies, and tools applicable to process management. *(continued)*

Techniques/methodology/tool	Explanation/purpose
Kaizen	A Japanese term that means incremental and unending improvement by doing little things better and setting and achieving increasingly higher standards. The term was made famous by Masaaki Imai in his book *Kaizen: The Key to Japan's Competitive Success.*
Kaizen blitz/event	In a kaizen event, a cross-functional team focuses on a target process, studies it, collects and analyzes data, discusses improvement alternatives, and implements changes. The intense event may consume three to five consecutive days.
Kanban	Signaling method to alert an upstream process that more material/product is required; the pull method. Signal may be a card, ticket, empty bin, and so on.
Line balancing	The process of distributing work and performers evenly to meet takt time and smooth workflow
Matrix diagram	Diagram showing relationships between variables
Mind mapping	A mind map creates a visual representation of many issues and can help a group get a more complete and common understanding of a situation.
Monument	The point in a process that necessitates a product waiting in a queue before processing further; a barrier to continuous flow—for example, a large, expensive machine purchased with the aim of achieving economies of scale
Muda (Japanese for *waste*) (seven classes of waste)	Non-value-added activity that consumes resources: • Overproduction • Delays • Transportation • Processing • Excess inventory • Wasted motion • Defective parts
Objectives, setting of, S.M.A.R.T.W.A.Y.	A template for setting objectives—*specific, measurable, achievable, realistic, time, worth, assign, yield*
Overall equipment effectiveness (OEE)	Method for measuring effectiveness and efficiency of processes
Pareto chart	A basic tool used to graphically rank causes from most significant (or frequent) to least significant (or frequent). It utilizes a vertical bar graph in which the bar height reflects the frequency or impact of causes.

(continued)

Techniques/methodology/tool	Explanation/purpose
PDCA cycle	A tool for planning and analyzing a continual improvement: P plan D do C check (or study) A act
Poka-yoke (error proofing)	Methods for mistake proofing a process to prevent a defect from occurring, cut costs, improve/decrease cycle time, improve quality, and improve safety
Priorities matrix	A tool to compare all criteria to be used in making a choice, assigning weights to the choices, and scoring to identify the priorities of the choices
Problem-solving model—seven steps	1. Identify the problem 2. List possible root causes 3. Search out the most likely root causes 4. Identify potential solutions 5. Select and implement a solution 6. Follow up to evaluate the effect 7. Standardize the process
Procedures, work instructions	Documentation for the quality management system
Process decision program chart	A tool for breaking down a decision into tasks with outcomes and contingency plans
Process map	A more detailed process flowchart used for designing, analyzing, and communicating information about work processes
Process reengineering	A "start from scratch" breakthrough strategy aimed at eliminating non-value-added operations, reducing cycle time, cutting costs, and so on. May be applied to an organization as a system or to specific processes.
Process village	Machines grouped in one area by the type of operation/function they are used for; a batch-and-queue arrangement
Production part approval process (PPAP)	Documents used to demonstrate to the customer that the new product/process is ready for full-blown production and to obtain approval to release it for production. Started in the automotive industry and is now moving into usage in other industries.
Quality manual	A document that may include descriptions of the organization's policies, practices, procedures, responsibilities, and so on, pertaining to the quality management system
Root cause analysis	Use of one or more tools to locate the real cause of a problem or situation

Techniques/methodology/tool	Explanation/purpose
Sales leveling	Establishing long-term relationships with customers that lead to fixed-amount, fixed-delivery-date contracts to enable smoothing the production flow and eliminate surges
Scatter diagram	Tool used to show if there is a correlation between two variables
Single-minute exchange of die (SMED)	A term used to indicate rapid setup changeovers to the next type of product
Single-piece flow	Product proceeds through the sequence of operations, one piece at a time, without interruption, backflows, or scrap
SIPOC analysis	S suppliers I inputs P process A tool for analyzing a process O outputs C customer
Six Sigma approach	A process improvement initiative that uses a variety of techniques and tools all focused on producing defect-free products and services
Takt time	Available production time divided by the rate of customer demand. Takt time sets the production pace to match the rate of customer demand—the lean system's heartbeat.
Theory of constraints (TOC)	A methodology aimed at improving system performance by eliminating the constraint (weakest link in the process)
Throughput time	Total time required (processing + queue) from concept to launch, order to delivery, raw material to customer
Total productive maintenance (TPM)	Methodologies for reducing and eventually eliminating equipment failure, setup and adjustment, minor stops, reduced speed, product rework, and scrap; preventive maintenance
Tree diagram	Tool for breaking down an objective into more detailed steps
TRIZ	Russian acronym. Translated, it is the theory of the solution of inventive problems
Value stream map	A map of all process activities needed to provide specific products/services to the customer. The map shows metrics related to each process step (for example, cycle time, equipment downtime, quality performance, number of operators, WIP).
Visual control	Positioning all tools, parts, production activities, and performance indicators so that the status of a process can be seen at a glance. Purpose is to provide visual clues to aid the performer in correctly processing a step or series of steps, reduce cycle time, cut costs, smooth workflow, and improve quality.

REFERENCES

1. GembaAcademy.com.
2. N. R. Tague, *The Quality Toolbox*, 2nd ed. (Milwaukee: ASQ Quality Press, 2005).
3. GembaAcademy.com.
4. Ibid.
5. M. Imai, *Gemba Kaizen* (New York: McGraw Hill, 1997).
6. R. Harris, C. Harris, and E. Wilson, *Making Materials Flow* (Cambridge, MA: Lean Enterprise Institute, 2003).
7. Ibid.
8. Ibid.
9. GembaAcademy.com.
10. Ibid.
11. J. Marhevko, A. Srivastava, and M. Blair, *Lean Management 50-50-20* (Seattle: Amazon, 2017).
12. GembaAcademy.com.
13. Marhevko, Srivastava, and Blair, *Lean Management 50-50-20*.
14. M. Rother, and J. Shook, *Learning to See* (Cambridge, MA: Lean Enterprise Institute, 1999).
15. GembaAcademy.com.
16. W. R. Trischler, *Understanding and Applying Value-Added Assessment: Eliminating Business Process Waste* (Milwaukee: ASQC Quality Press, 1996).
17. D. Galloway, *Mapping Work Processes* (Milwaukee: ASQC Quality Press, 1994).
18. D. Lynch, course material, "Implementing Kaizen Events," University of Michigan, 2018.
19. "What Is Overall Equipment Effectiveness?," accessed June 8, 2019, https://www.oee.com/.
20. E. Goldratt, and J. Cox, *The Goal: A Process of Ongoing Improvement*, 2nd rev. ed. (Croton-on-Hudson, NY: North River Press, 1992).
21. H. W. Dettmer, *Goldratt's Theory of Constraints: A Systems Approach to Continuous Improvement* (Milwaukee: ASQ Quality Press, 1997).
22. Goldratt and Cox, *Goal*.

See Appendix A for additional references for this chapter.

Chapter 15
C. Measurement: Assessment and Metrics

E ffective management of an organization depends on defining, gathering, and analyzing information that provides feedback on current performance as well as projects' future needs. This concept is embodied in *management by fact*, a core value of the Baldrige Performance Excellence Program.

Most organizations have massive amounts of data available. Much of it, however, may have little value or may even pose a risk if it is not accurate, timely, and properly analyzed, or is measuring the wrong things. Deming's famous red bead experiment demonstrated how improper responses to data could undermine employee morale while resulting in no improvement to the system.[1]

Statistics is the science of turning data into information. Many statistical techniques are simple yet powerful, such as looking at how data from a process vary over time. For example, a change could consist of a gradual increase or decrease in the relative value or average or could involve rapid but short-term changes in the range or variance of the data.

Ensuring that the data measure what is intended requires understanding the purpose of the data (for example, what decisions are to be made based on them?) and making sure that the measurement system will repeatedly produce the same data in increments appropriate for the purpose. This involves calibrating and verifying the capability of the data source. It is also possible that the process being measured was not properly designed to be able to produce the desired results and will, therefore, require more than monitoring to meet requirements.

Data can be past or future oriented. They can indicate what has happened and help project what may happen. Much of the data used by organizations is *quantitative*, meaning that it comes from simply counting something (for example, the number of customers who complain) or a physical measurement (for example, temperature of a heat-treat oven). Sometimes, however, the most useful information is *qualitative*, for which special methods for gathering and analysis have been developed.

1. BASIC STATISTICAL USE

> Use statistical techniques to identify when, what, and how to measure projects and processes. Describe how metrics and data-gathering methods affect resources and vice versa. (Apply)
>
> **Body of Knowledge IV.C.1**

Techniques and Tools to Measure Processes

To begin, go over a checklist for developing measures. Ask:

- Are measures simple to understand and easy to use?
- Do they have adequate and appropriate meaning to stakeholders?
- Is the definition clear?
- Are the data economical to gather and analyze?
- Are the data verifiable and repeatable?
- Does the measure make sense to those who must use it?
- Is the message conveyed by the measure consistent with the organization's values, vision, mission, strategy, goals, and objectives?
- Does the measure indicate trends?
- Will the use of the measure cause the correct actions?
- Does the measure achieve the stated purpose?

Goal-question-metric (GQM) is a method used to define measurement of the project, process, and product in such a way that:

- Resulting metrics are tailored to the organization and its goal
- Resulting measurement data play a constructive and instructive role in the organization
- Metrics and their interpretation reflect the values and the viewpoints of the different groups affected (for example, developers, users, and operators)

GQM defines a measurement model on three levels:

- *Conceptual level (goal).* A goal is defined for an object—for a variety of reasons—with respect to various models of quality, from various points of view, and relative to a particular environment
- *Operational level (question).* A set of questions is used to define models of the object of study and then focuses on that object to characterize the assessment or achievement of a specific goal
- *Quantitative level (metric).* A set of metrics, based on the models, is associated with every question in order to answer it in a measurable way

Although originally used to define and evaluate a particular project in a particular environment, GQM can also be used for control and improvement of a single project within an organization running several projects.

The development of metrics can vary from one organization to another and depends on the project or process involved. An example of the steps in development is:

- Determine how to plan a good measurement program
- Determine how to define goals, questions, metrics, and hypotheses for related processes

- Collect data

- Analyze and interpret the results and present the results

Using the GQM technique benefits the organization because writing goals, defining questions, and showing the relationships between goals and metrics help it focus on important issues. Plus, GQM techniques provide the organization with flexible means to focus the measurement system on its particular need. Another advantage of using GQM is that it aids in reducing costs and cycle time, increasing efficiency, understanding risk, and improving overall quality.

Measuring Independent Process Variables

It is important to determine the process parameters that are the real drivers of process performance. Most process output measures cannot be directly changed because they respond to other variables within the process. In this case, the independent variables must be changed before the response-type variables. Consider an example.

A hospital pharmacy's management wants to improve the time from receipt of the paper script (order for medicine) to delivery of the prescribed medicine to the nurses' station where the medicine will be dispensed. A simple cycle time measure would record the time elapsed in filling and delivering the order (response-type measure) but would shed little light on the process delays. These are independent variables such as availability of requested medicine in proper strength and quantity, adequacy of pharmacy staffing to meet the demand, delivery schedule, and communication-related questions that arise, for example, from incorrect patient identification, illegible writing, and questionable dosage instructions. Measures would be needed for all of the independent variables, or a Pareto analysis could be used to select one or two of the independent variables that incur the largest number of problems.

In the realm of Six Sigma methodology, there is a tool for displaying the causal relationship between the key business indicators (labeled Y), the *critical-to-quality* (CTQ) process outputs (labeled y) that directly affect the Ys, and the causal factors that affect the process outputs (labeled x). For example, one key business indicator (an outcome, a dependent variable) is *customer retention* (Y). CTQ outputs are *services delivered on time* (y), *services delivered correctly* (y), and *customer satisfied* (y). Factors affecting outputs (independent variables) are scheduling/dispatch system (x); training of service personnel (x); supplies, vehicles, tools, and equipment (x); and time to complete service properly (x). See the relationship of x to y and y to Y in Figure 15.1.

The selecting of the key metrics to be included in the balanced scorecard is illustrative of how key indicators are established. The top-level metrics of the scorecard (typically four) are the ones executives use to make their decisions. Each of these top-level metrics (dependent variables) is backed up by metrics on independent variables. Thus, if the marketing vice president wants to know the cause for a negative trend in the customer metric of the scorecard, the vice president can drill down to the variable affecting the negative trend.

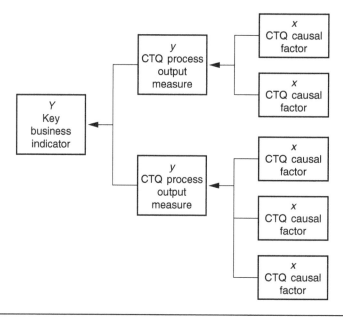

Figure 15.1   Causal relationship in developing key process measurements.

Establishing Process Measures

Four steps are needed to establish process measures:

1. Identifying and defining the critical factors affecting the customers, such as:

   • Timing

   • Availability

   • Cost to purchase

   • Product quality

   • Product reliability and usability

   • Life cycle of product

   • Safety and environmental safeguards

2. Mapping the process across all applicable functions

3. Identifying and defining the critical tasks and resources (including competencies) required

4. Establishing the measures that will be used to track and manage the required tasks and resources

Techniques and Tools for Measuring Projects

It is important to remember that there is a minimum of two processes involved: the *project planning and management* process and the *deliverables* process for which the project is initiated. Within the context of the project planning and managing process, measurements are applied during all phases of the project implementation as well as after the project is completed. Measuring the deliverables process commences when there are outputs delivered and for some reasonable period thereafter.

Project planning and management measurements may include:

- Schedules met

- Resources used

- Costs versus budget

- Earned value analysis (EVA)

- Risks identified and eliminated or mitigated

- Project objectives met

- Safety and environmental performance

- Project team effectiveness

Project deliverables measurements may include:

- Targeted outcomes achieved

- Additional unplanned benefits obtained

- Return on investment

- Customer satisfaction (internal and/or external)

How Metrics and Data-Gathering Methods Affect Some People

Some negatives to managing projects can be:

- Performers often perceive excessive data collection and creation of a plethora of metrics as management's obsession with the numbers rather than as being helpful in producing a better product or service. A major concern in many organizations is the number of measures it is attempting to monitor. In extreme cases this can result in rooms displaying wall-to-wall and ceiling-to-floor charts. This presents a problem of keeping the charts up to date and keeping the data flow accurate, as well as how effectively the charts can be used.

- Performers doing the work often do not understand the connection between what they produce and the metrics by which management assesses their performance. Without seeing the connection, the performers may feel unappreciated, unmotivated, and unfairly treated.

- When performers receive criticism or a disciplinary action because they are considered the cause of a negative event or trend in the metrics, they are likely to perceive the metrics as the cause of their discomfort. The performer's resulting reaction may be adopting a "don't care" attitude, finding a way to fudge the numbers, bad-mouthing management, initiating a grievance, purposely causing defects, or quitting the job.

- Performers are asked to do A, but recognition and reward (and measurement) relate to doing B.

- If management views the use of metrics primarily as a means for controlling those beneath them in the hierarchy, management demonstrates a misguided strategy. Metrics should be focused on surfacing areas for continual improvement.

- People, especially skilled workers, tend to resent the paperwork (or computer data entry work) usually required for their job positions. They often feel that the systems in which they work put greater emphasis on gathering data than on performing their tasks. They feel particularly resentful when they can see no logical reason for the data collected and/ or how or whether they are used.

Well-intended and well-designed metrics can positively affect performers when the metrics:

- Provide a means for the performer to measure her or his own performance against a standard, objective, or customers' requirements. How effective this feedback is depends on:

  — The performer being aware of the basis for measurement

  — How meaningful and understandable the metric is to the performer prior to the work being performed

  — The frequency of the feedback

  — The presentation of the feedback (simple graphics usually preferred)

  — Whether the performer participated in the development of the metric

  — Whether oral discussion with the boss accompanies the visual feedback and whether the oral feedback is constructive and reinforces positive actions of the performer

  — Whether the metrics presented clearly indicate a linkage with the higher-level organizational metrics (the strategic plan, the big picture)

  — Whether the metrics are generally perceived as beneficial and the basis for improvement rather than just another management effort to control

  — Whether the metrics support or conflict with delivered rewards and formulated strategy

- Create a work environment in which the performer feels motivated to improve, including:

  — Feeling good about achieving the objectives and meeting the expectations, or feeling good about the progress made since the last feedback

  — Making suggestions for improving the process being measured

  — Making suggestions for improving the metric(s) by which the process is measured

Measurement data also must be reliable, accurate, and accessible to the right people at the right time in order to be useful in detecting a need for corrections. Personnel who are responsible for analyzing data and taking action should be trained to do so to reduce the likelihood of human errors in judgment. "Quality control is greatly simplified when operating people are in a state of self-control. . . . Ideally, the quality planning for any job should put the employee into a state of self-control. When work is organized in a way that enables a person to have full mastery over the attainment of planned results, that person is said to be in a state of self-control and can therefore properly be held responsible for the results. . . . To put people into a state of self-control, several fundamental criteria must be met. People must be provided with:

- Knowledge of what they are supposed to do (for example, the budgeted profit, the schedule, and the specification).

- Knowledge of what they are doing (for example, the actual profit, the delivery rate, the extent of conformance to specification)

- Means for regulating what they are doing in the event that they are failing to meet the goals. These means must always include the authority to regulate and the ability to regulate by varying either (a) the process under the person's authority or (b) the person's own conduct."[2]

Three Timely Tenets

Whether you are measuring a process or a project, remember these tenets:

1. Never design and institute a measurement without first knowing:

   - What data you need

   - Who will supply the data

   - How the data will be transformed into information

   - How the information will be used and for what purpose

   - How you will communicate this information to all applicable stakeholders

   - How cost-effective taking the measurement will be

     These questions may not come up automatically, and they may not be asked in this order. Answers to one may affect the others: how the information will be used may change what data you need or how you will communicate this information to all applicable stakeholders, for example.

2. Always involve the people doing the work in helping in the design of the measurement

3. Establish a rule that the primary reason for the measurement is to improve the process, project, or product. There may be other secondary reasons.

2. SAMPLING

> Define and describe basic sampling techniques such as random and stratified. Identify when and why sampling is an appropriate technique to use. (Understand)
>
> **Body of Knowledge IV.C.2**

Determining the process for acquiring data is an important part of any measurement process. Whether it is selecting the number of customers to survey or the process of taking samples from a moving conveyor, the sampling process will depend on the purpose, desired statistical confidence, and economics.

Whether or not sampling is needed is an important determination. Some of the reasons for not using sampling include:

- The customer's requirement is for 100% inspection of the entire shipment.

- The number of items or services is small enough to inspect the entire quantity produced/delivered.

- The cost of sampling is too high relative to the advantages gained from sampling.

- Self-inspection by trained operators is sufficient for the nature of the product produced.

- The inspection method is built in, or the process is mistake proofed so that no defectives can be shipped.

- Product is low cost and/or noncritical (wide or no specification range) to the customer so the producer can risk not sampling. (For example, delivering the fill to bring a building lot up to grade level to meet town height requirements.)

Sampling Methods

Assuming sampling is needed, the intended purpose helps in deciding whether the sample should be randomly selected or stratified. *Random sample* selection is similar to pulling a number out of a hat (although a random sample number generator or table of random numbers is more likely used) and helps ensure that data will not be biased toward one particular portion of the population. It is expected that the sample will truly represent the range and relative distribution of characteristics of the population. In some cases, however, it may be desired that only a particular portion of the population be evaluated, which means that a *stratified sample* will be set up to create the desired distribution within the sample.

Sample size is dependent on the desired level of statistical confidence and the amount of difference between samples that one is trying to detect. For a given difference (for example, between means of two groups of data), testing at a statistical probability of .01 (a 1% chance the result will be labeled as significant when it is not), a larger sample size will be needed than if a probability of .05 is acceptable. The cost of selecting the samples and collecting the information also enters into this decision.

An additional sampling issue, *rational subgrouping*, must be considered for control charts. A chart meant to detect a shift in the mean will be more sensitive if variability within subgroups is minimized. This means that all samples within a subgroup should consist of parts taken within a relatively short time as compared to the time between subgroups. In addition, a subgroup should consist of a single process stream rather than mixing products from different streams (for example, two cavities in the same mold).

Systematic sampling is where every *n*th item is selected—for example, every tenth item. *Cluster sampling* is when a random sample is taken from within a selected subgroup. *Best judgment sampling* is when an expert's opinion is used to determine the best location and characteristics of the sample group.

Acceptance sampling is the process of sampling a batch of material to evaluate the level of nonconformance relative to a specified quality level. It is most frequently applied to decide whether to move material from one process to another or to accept material received from a supplier. Many sampling processes are based on the work of Dodge and Romig and standards such as ANSI/ASQ Z1.4 and ANSI/ASQ Z1.9.

Sampling assumes that nonconformances randomly occur throughout a lot and that a random sample can determine whether a given level of nonconformance is exceeded. Whether sampling is the best technique for assessing a product depends on the lot size, frequency of production/receipt, typical level of nonconformance, and acceptable level of risk. For example, pencils received from an office supply house are normally not sampled because the risk associated with defective pencils is minimal. In contrast, medical devices might be subjected to extensive sampling or even 100% inspection because of the consequences of failure.

When properly applied over time, sampling can keep nonconformances below a predetermined level called the *average outgoing quality limit* (AOQL). Compared with 100% inspection, sampling is more economical, requires less handling of the product, and is often more accurate since there is less fatigue. Sampling plans do have drawbacks: they may be used to avoid adequate process control, they are less economical than process control, and they yield less information on the true state of nonconformance than do 100% inspection or statistical analysis. *No sampling plan yields 100% detection of nonconformances.* Because of this and possible legal or political issues, some industries do not use sampling. For example, a U.S. population census conducted by sampling might be believed to result in misleading allocation of tax funds.

Besides missing some defectives, 100% sampling may inflate the number of false negatives, or good items sorted as bad. Most inspectors will be choosier if they are told to do 100% sampling, and the good parts set aside as bad will add to the costs of inspection and control.[3]

Risks in Sampling

Two types of errors can occur in sampling. The alpha (α) or *producer's risk* refers to the possibility that good product will be rejected (a *type 1 error*). The beta (β) or *consumer's risk* refers to the possibility that bad product will be accepted (a *type 2 error*). The *operating characteristic* (OC) curve for a particular sampling plan indicates the probability of accepting a lot based on the sample size to be taken and the fraction defective in the batch. Producer's risk is often set at .05 (acceptance probability of .95) and consumer's risk at .10. Consumer's risk is also frequently called *lot tolerance percent defective* (LTPD). Figure 15.2 shows the OC curve for two sampling plans with different sample sizes. In both cases the acceptance number is zero ($c = 0$).

When sampling is to be used, the decision must be made as to which family of sampling plans and which table within that family will be applied. The *acceptable quality limit* (AQL) must be determined and is often spelled out in a specification or contract. The AQL is associated with the point on the curve correlated to the producer's risk. ANSI/ASQ Z1.4 (2008) perceives the AQL as the worst tolerable process average when a continuing series of lots is submitted for acceptance sampling. Inasmuch as the AQL goes against the philosophy of zero defects, it is useful to ensure that all parties involved understand why a particular AQL has been chosen.

Sampling can also be done based on a single sample or multiple samples. In *single sampling*, lots are inspected, and the decision to accept or reject is based on the acceptance number c for the sample size n. In *double sampling* (see Figure 15.3), lots are inspected, and the decision to accept or reject is based on the acceptance number c for the combined sample size ($n1 + n2$). In double sampling plans, the first sample will have an acceptance number, a zone of continuing sampling, and a reject number. If process quality is good, most lots will be accepted on the first sample, thereby reducing sampling cost. The inspector also can feel that the lot is being given a second chance if a second sample must be drawn.

Figure 15.2   OC curves.

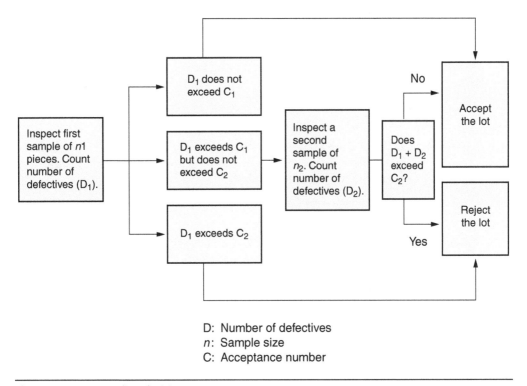

D: Number of defectives
n: Sample size
C: Acceptance number

Figure 15.3   Sampling decisions.

In *multiple sampling,* lots are inspected, and the decision to accept or reject is based on a maximum of seven samples of *n.* Multiple plans work the same as double plans but use as many as seven draws before a final decision is made. This is the most discriminating of plans but also the most susceptible to inspector abuse.

3. STATISTICAL ANALYSIS

Calculate basic statistics: measures of central tendency (mean, median, mode), and measures of dispersion (range, standard deviation, and variance). Identify basic distribution types (normal, bimodal, skewed) and evaluate run charts, statistical process control (SPC) reports, and other control charts to make data-based decisions. (Evaluate)

Body of Knowledge IV.C.3

Simple Statistics Used to Analyze Groups of Data

Descriptive statistics are used to provide information about a set of data. There are two types of measures: central tendency and measures of dispersion or spread. Some measures of central tendency are:

- *Average.* Also called the *arithmetic mean*, it is the sum of the individual data values (Σx) divided by the number of samples (n).

- *Median.* If data are arranged in numeric order, the median is the center number. If there is an even number of data points, the median is the average of the two middle numbers.

- *Mode.* Another measure of central tendency, mode is the number in the data set that occurs most often.

The *spread* of a sample group of data (also called *dispersion* or *variation*) is:

- *Range (R).* The arithmetic difference between the largest and smallest number in the data—a measure of spread, dispersion, or variation.

- *Standard deviation.* The standard deviation of a sample of data is given as:

$$s = \sqrt{\frac{\Sigma\left(X - \bar{X}\right)^2}{n - 1}}$$

- *Variance.* Another measure of dispersion, it is the standard deviation squared.

If variance is the same as the standard deviation squared, why does it exist? The standard deviation is in the same units as the mean or average, the units of the measurement. This allows a clear representation of both the central tendency and the variability. If there are multiple sources of variability (such as tool choice and material choice), there would be several components of variability that are added to make the total. Standard deviations from multiple sources cannot be added, but the square of the standard deviation components (that is, the variances) may be added.

Two sets of data could be analyzed simply by comparing their central tendencies and spread. For example, standardized test scores for groups of students who attend two different schools could be compared to try to determine whether the scores are higher (average, median, or mode) or more consistent (range or standard deviation) at one school versus the other. (Note: Making decisions based solely on these rough comparisons would of course be dangerous due to the large number and the interactive nature of the variables that could contribute to differences.)

Another way to analyze two comparable data sets is to create a histogram to see how their distributions compare. (Care must be taken to use the same *x*- and *y*-axis scales).

Probability Distributions. Comparisons that take into account statistical probability can be done using tests for significance such as the *F*-test to compare standard deviations and the *t*-test to compare means. *Juran's Quality Handbook* contains a table to help in selecting these and other test statistics. Advantages of this approach include compensating for sample size differences (by adjusting based on the degrees of freedom) and basing the decision on whether observed differences are actually statistically significant.

Although the normal distribution may be more common, there are several different shapes that probability distributions can take, depending on the type of data (for example, discrete versus continuous data) and characteristics of the process that produces the data. Following are some of the more widely used distributions; Figure 15.4 depicts them graphically.

- *Normal.* This is a bell-shaped distribution for continuous data where most of the data are concentrated around the average (approximately two-thirds are within ±1 standard deviation), and it is equally likely that an observation will occur above or below the average. This distribution especially applies to processes where there are usually many variables that contribute to the variation. This is one of the most common distributions.

- *Exponential.* This is a continuous distribution where data are more likely to occur below the average than above it (63.2% and 36.8%, respectively, compared to 50%/50% for the normal distribution). Typically, it is used to describe the break-in portion of the failure bathtub curve.

Juran's Quality Handbook discusses the *bathtub curve* for predicting reliability of a product over its lifetime. There would be a high incidence of failures during the product's "infant mortality" phase, random failures during the period of normal use, and an increase in wear-out failures toward the end of the product's life cycle. The chart of the distribution appears to resemble a bathtub.

- *Weibull.* This is a distribution of continuous data that can take on many different shapes and is therefore used to describe a variety of patterns, including distributions similar to but slightly different from the normal and exponential.

- *Binomial.* This defines the probability for discrete data of r occurrences in n trials of an event that has a probability of occurrence of p for each trial. It is used when the sample size is small compared to the population size and when proportion defective is greater than 0.10.

- *Poisson.* This is also used for discrete data and resembles the binomial. It is especially applicable when there are many opportunities for occurrence of an event but a low probability (less than 0.10) on each trial.

- *Hypergeometric.* This is a discrete distribution defining the probability of r occurrences in n trials of an event when there are a total of d occurrences in a population of N. It is most applicable when the sample size is a large proportion of the population.

Advanced Statistical Methods

More complex analysis of process variables can be done with advanced statistical methods such as *regression, analysis of variance* (ANOVA), and *response surface methodology*. Such experimental design techniques are used for two primary purposes: (1) screening, or trying to find which independent variables have the greatest impact on results, and (2) optimization, or finding the level and combination for each independent variable that will provide the best overall performance.

Design of experiments (DOE) looks at interrelationships between many variables at one time. Replication of runs at particular levels is used to reduce the amount of experimental error, and designs include techniques such as blocking,

Distribution	Form	Probability Function	Comments on Application
Normal		$$y = \frac{1}{s\sqrt{2p}}e^{-\frac{(X-m)^2}{2s^2}}$$ m = Mean s = Standard deviation	Applicable when there is a concentration of observations about the average and it is equally likely that observations will occur above and below the average. Variation in observations is usually the result of many small causes.
Exponential		$$y = \frac{1}{m}e^{-\frac{X}{M}}$$	Applicable when it is likely that more observations will occur below the average than above.
Weibull		$$y = ab(X-g)^{b-1}e^{-a(X-g)^b}$$ a = Scale parameter b = Shape parameter g = Location parameter	Applicable in describing a wide variety of patterns of variation, including departures from the normal and exponential.
Poisson		$$y = \frac{(np)^r e^{-np}}{r!}$$ n = Number of trials r = Number of occurrences p = Probability of occurrence	Same as binomial but particularly applicable when there are many opportunities for occurrence of an event, but a low probability (less than 0.10) on each trial.
Binomial		$$y = \frac{n!}{r!(n-r)!}p^r q^{n-r}$$ n = Number of trials r = Number of occurrences p = Probability of occurrence $q = 1-p$	Applicable in defining the probability of r occurrences in n trials of an event which has a probability of occurrence of p on each trial.
Negative binomial		$$y = \frac{(r+s-1)!}{(r-1)!(s!)}p^r q^3$$ r = Number of occurrences s = Difference between number of trials and number of occurrences p = Probability of occurrence $q = 1-p$	Applicable in defining the probability that r occurrences will require a total of $r+s$ trials of an event that has a probability of occurrence of p on each trial. (Note that the total number of trials n is $r+s$.)
Hypergeometric		$$y = \frac{\binom{d}{r}\binom{N-d}{n-r}}{\binom{N}{n}}$$	Applicable in defining the probability of r occurrences in n trials of an event when there are a total of d occurrences in a population of N.

Figure 15.4   Probability distributions.

nesting, and fractional factorials to gain maximum useful information with a minimum amount of testing.

Linear regression is a mathematical application of the concept of a scatter diagram but where the correlation is actually a cause-and-effect relationship. The analysis provides an equation describing the mathematical relationship between the two variables, as well as the statistical confidence intervals for the relationship and the proportion of the variation in the dependent variable that is due to the independent variable. Regression can also be applied to nonlinear relationships by transforming the data (for example, performing a mathematical conversion such as squaring each value of the independent variable), as well as to situations in which there are multiple independent variables (called *multiple regression*).

ANOVA is a hypothesis test used to determine if there is a difference between groups. If you had three or more sets of measurements from processes you expect to be similar, ANOVA can tell if any of them are different from the others. It looks at the means of each group and the overall average of all groups. The ANOVA table provides an *f* value for which statistical significance can be determined.

Response surface methodology is the process of graphically representing the relationship between two or more independent variables and a dependent variable. A response surface often looks similar to a topographic map, which uses lines to indicate changes in altitude at various latitudes and longitudes. *Evolutionary operation* (EVOP) is the process of adjusting variables in small increments in a search for a more optimal point on the response surface.

Statistical Process Control (SPC)

Simply comparing the results of a process to itself over time is not sufficient in an environment where external competitive pressures and an internal desire for continual improvement exist. The focus of this section is on how to effectively analyze information to enable the organization to manage and improve processes—whether at the strategic or operational level. Let us look at a simple example: Three people—a manager, a computer technician, and a staff analyst—each review the same data on downtime of a particular computer (see Table 15.1). What conclusions might each make?

The manager might total up the amount of lost time and convert it to average daily dollars in lost productivity. The technician might notice times when the downtime appeared excessive compared to other machines for which she is also responsible and that the last six days have been better than any other period, indicating improvement. The analyst (the user of the machine) might point out that problems occur with the computer nearly every day.

Another way to look at the data is to use a control chart (see Figure 15.5). If these same three individuals understand this simple statistical tool, they are likely to agree that (1) the computer is down an average of ten minutes per day, (2) there were four days where downtime was, statistically, significantly higher, and (3) there is insufficient data to confirm a trend at the end of the month.

Other questions could be asked about the raw data themselves, such as:

- Was the computer being used the full twenty-four hours of each day, or might days when downtime was lower have been during periods when it was not used on all shifts?

Table 15.1 Computer downtime log.

Date	Downtime (minutes)	Causes	Date	Downtime (minutes)	Causes
4/1	0	—	4/16	12	Printer
4/2	2	—	4/17	33	Backup
4/3	18	Backup	4/18	6	Locked up
4/4	11	Cable damaged	4/19	6	Printer
4/5	7	Power failure	4/20	17	Cable damaged
4/6	4	Locked up	4/21	1	—
4/7	4	Locked up	4/22	0	—
4/8	5	—	4/23	13	Upgrading software
4/9	10	Unknown	4/24	22	Backup
4/10	25	Backup	4/25	8	Locked up two times
4/11	8	Locked up two times	4/26	6	Swap out display
4/12	12	Printer	4/27	2	—
4/13	3	Locked up	4/28	0	—
4/14	0	—	4/29	4	—
4/15	63	Unknown, reload TCP/IP	4/30	2	Locked up

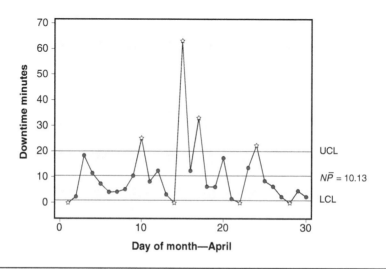

Figure 15.5 Control chart for computer downtime.

- Who recorded the data (for example, one person or several), and was the same definition of downtime used by all? Did they measure the downtime in the same way? For example, if the computer went down five minutes before midnight and was down a total of twelve minutes, did this count as five minutes one day and seven the next, or were all twelve minutes recorded for the first day or for the second day?

- What other information might be necessary in order to make sense of the data? For example, if the day of the week was also included in the log, it would be more readily apparent that there is a pattern of high downtime every seven days, when the system backup is done.

- Should the data be separated into groups by cause of downtime (for example, backups, printer, and cable, or an actual failure versus intentional downtime) in order to more easily identify and remedy root causes?

- Is one month's data sufficient for making a decision, or might there have been something different about this month versus previous months?

- How much downtime can be incurred before the quality or output of the process for which the computer is used is affected?

- How does downtime for this computer compare to other computers used within the same location, to similar computers used at other locations, and to different brands of computers?

As the previous example shows, tabular data do not as easily lend themselves to consistent interpretation. The power of statistics is that it can reduce the amount of data to be interpreted and also help to point out specific issues that may be more important. Simple statistics used to analyze groups of data are discussed earlier in this section.

Types of Control Charts. A control chart is used to determine whether or not a process is *stable*, which means that it has predictable performance. By monitoring the output of a process over time, a control chart can be used to assess whether the application of process changes or other adjustments has resulted in improvements. If the process produces measurable parts, the average of a small sample of measurements, not individual measurements, should be plotted.

There are several software packages that assist in control chart creation and maintenance. Care should be taken in using these that the fundamental process of control charts is understood. For example, most of these software packages allow the instant recalculation of the control limits as new data are added to the chart. This is a feature to aid in the creation of the control system. If this feature is not disabled after the control limits have been set from an in-control data set, the process will never leave the control region. Thus, the purpose of the control chart will be lost.

There are many different types of control chart, each of which applies to either variables data (continuous or measured) or attributes data (discrete or counted).

Variables-type control charts include:

- Charts for average and range (x-bar and R chart)

- Charts for averages and standard deviation (x-bar and s chart)

- Chart used to detect very small changes that occur over time (CUSUM chart)

Attributes-type control charts include:

- Chart used to chart number of defective units where sample size is constant (*np*-chart)

- Chart used for tracking fraction of units defective, where sample size is not constant (*p*-chart)

- Chart used to chart number of defects in a constant sample size (*c*-chart)

- Chart for number of defects where sample size is changing (*u*-chart)

There are other less common charts; however, understanding those above should suffice for managing operations. Additional detail can be found in the references for this chapter in Appendix A.

Although control limits are usually set at ±3 sigma using data from when the process is in control, in some applications they may be set tighter (for example, ±2.5 sigma) if one desires a quicker response to an out-of-control situation; however, this increases the probability of reacting when the process is actually in control. The inverse is also true: control limits can be loosened in order to reduce the frequency of looking for a change in variation, but this also means there is an increased chance of not reacting when the process has actually changed.

Four guidelines are used as a basic test for randomness in control charts:

- The points should have no visible pattern.

- Approximately two-thirds of the points should be close to the centerline (within ±1 standard deviation).

- Some points should be close to the outer limit (called *control limits* in statistical process control).

- An approximately equal number of points should fall above and below the centerline.

If all four criteria are met, then the process is likely to be in control.

Control charts are based on the concept of statistical probability but are used for time-ordered data. The theory is that if the process from which the data are collected is a stable one (in control), then future values of data from the process should follow a predictable pattern. The probability limits (control limits) are based on the distribution for the type of data being analyzed. For example, the control limits for an *x*-bar and *R* chart are based on the normal distribution since it is known that averages will tend to create a normal distribution regardless of the shape of the underlying distribution from which the individual values were taken. (Note: There is a test for normality called the chi-square test. See references for this chapter in Appendix A.)

Control charts can be used for both analysis of a process (for example, for improvement purposes) and for maintaining control of a process. For process control purposes, an alternative to control charts, precontrol, can sometimes be used.

Precontrol

Precontrol is an alternative to statistically based control charts and involves dividing the specification range into four equal zones. The center two zones are the green (good) zone, the two areas on the outside of the green zone (which are still within spec) are considered the yellow (caution) zone, and the area outside specification is considered the red (defect) zone.

Decisions about the process are made according to the particular zone into which process output falls. For example, the red zone indicates that the process has probably shifted, while the green zone indicates that everything is okay. If output falls into the yellow zone, another reading is taken. If both readings are in the same yellow zone, it is assumed that the process has shifted, while if they are in opposite yellow zones, it is assumed that there is abnormal variation in the process that must be investigated. An example from one organization uses the same concept with the four bands but in a slightly different manner:

- The green zone is set to $\pm 50\%$ of the tolerance (to simulate 95.4% within ± 2 sigma).

- The yellow zone is within the 2 to 3 sigma range or the 50%–75% range of the tolerance (to simulate 99.7% within ± 3 sigma).

- The red zone is just *before* the spec limit at the 75%–100% range of the tolerance (to simulate 4 sigma for a coverage of 99.997).

Following the same reaction plans for points in the yellow and red zones and utilizing proper sampling and operator responsiveness can usually enable a process to achieve a 1.33 C_{pk}. In this case if a point occurs within the red zone, the product would be in specification, but the process is likely out of control. Containment/rework should not be necessary, but preventive process adjustment would be. In the original definition, if the red zone were set beyond the specification limit, then a C_{pk} of 1 could likely be enabled, and defective process results could inadvertently be passed on to the customer. See section 7 in this chapter.

Precontrol is often used when a process is just being started and can be especially useful when there is not yet sufficient data to develop statistically based control limits. The rules for precontrol include both sampling frequency and actions to take, with the sample frequency being varied according to how well the process appears to be working.

4. MEASUREMENT SYSTEMS ANALYSIS

> Understand basic measurement terms such as accuracy, precision, bias, and linearity. Understand the difference between repeatability and reproducibility in gage R&R studies. (Understand)
>
> **Body of Knowledge IV.C.4**

Another measurement validation process is that of *gage repeatability and reproducibility* (gage R&R) studies. The purpose of a gage R&R study is to determine how much variation exists in the measurement system, which includes variation in the product, the gage, and the individuals using the gage. The desire is to have a measurement system whose error does not take up a large proportion of the product tolerance. *Repeatability* is the variation in results on a single gage when the same parts are measured repeatedly by the same person, while *reproducibility* is the variation from person to person using the same gage.

Calibration is a process used to maintain the performance of a measurement system. For physical measurement devices, this involves determining whether, under a predefined set of conditions, the values indicated by the instrument agree with the results obtained for a standard that has been independently tested. The standards used for calibration are typically traceable back to an organization such as the National Institute of Standards and Technology (NIST) in the United States.

The terms *accuracy* and *precision* are most often used to discuss physical measurement devices, where accuracy is equivalent to *validity* (the correct value), and precision is how well the device can reproduce the same results when measurements are taken repeatedly (*reliability*). Bias is a characteristic of measurement that refers to a systematic difference between the observed average measurement and a reference value. Linearity assesses how accurate your measurements are, through the expected range of the measurements. Linearity considers whether the gage has the same accuracy across all reference values.[4]

Calibration programs typically consist of the following general requirements:

- Identify all equipment that is used for measuring product quality or controlling important process variables

- Ensure that the equipment is capable of the accuracy and precision necessary for the tolerance to be measured

- Give each piece of equipment a specific identification number and establish a frequency and method for calibration

- Calibrate the equipment using traceable or otherwise documented standards

- Perform the calibrations under known environmental conditions

- Record the calibration findings, including as-found and after-correction data

- Investigate any possible problems that may have been created by an out-of-calibration device

- Identify or otherwise control any devices that have not been calibrated or are otherwise not for use

The principle of calibration can also be applied to nonphysical measurement applications. For example, if several people are to conduct separate interviews on the same subject, then in order to calibrate all of the interviewers a set of definitions is usually developed and documented, and interviewers are trained to ensure consistent understanding and use of the terms.

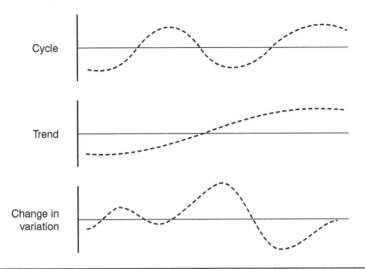

Figure 15.6   Run chart patterns.

5. TREND AND PATTERN ANALYSIS

> Interpret graphs and charts to identify cyclical, seasonal, and environmental data trends. Evaluate control chart patterns to determine shifts and other trend indicators in a process. (Evaluate)
>
> **Body of Knowledge IV.C.5**

Trend analysis is the process of looking at data over time in order to identify, interpret, and respond to patterns. A desired trend may be a continuous upward movement (for example, in gross sales or net margin), a continuous downward movement (for example, in customer complaints), or a sustained level of performance (for example, holding nominal specification).

Before conducting trend analysis, one must ensure that the correct things are being measured and that the measurements are accurate and able to discriminate at the desired level. Trend data must also sometimes be normalized to compensate for changes in other parameters that have an impact on the measure being tracked. For example, tracking scrap dollars in absolute terms is not the same as tracking them as a percentage of cost of goods sold.

By themselves, measurement data do not result in continual improvement, but having data organized in a manner that supports analysis is vital.[5] Analytical tools that organize data and are helpful in trend analysis include Pareto charts, check sheets, histograms, control charts, and run charts that simply show data arranged chronologically. In analyzing a trend, it is important to distinguish a trend from a cyclic pattern and from changes in variation. Figure 15.6 portrays the distinction.

Having a clear understanding of the purpose of the data being used for trend analysis is most necessary. "A further distinction in controls is whether they provide information before, during, or after operations."[6] Leading indicators are measures that can be used to predict the outcome of future events on the basis of analysis of past and current results. For example, market research to ascertain customer wants and needs, as well as what competitors are doing, might precede the determination to develop a new product. Lagging indicators depict actual trends versus expected performance levels, such as warranty claims. "A well-balanced system of executive reports makes use of leading indicators as well as indicators that lag behind operations."[7]

Long-Term versus Short-Term Trend Analysis

Long-term trend analysis is the examination and projection of company-level data over an extended period of time. It is used primarily for planning and managing strategic progress to achieve organization-wide performance goals.[8] At the organization level, data—including corporate summaries of financial and nonfinancial measures—are analyzed to help management understand the company's performance and prioritize improvement actions. Performance trends can also be compared to those of competitors.

Various forms of trend charts are used to trigger process adjustments or systems improvements when conducting short-range trend analysis at the process level or the work unit level.[9] At the process level, analysis of measurement data provides both departmental and cross-functional understanding of the system's performance over time. Often, company policy defines the frequency for the trending and reporting of performance results, along with criteria that define what are considered adverse trends and the appropriate actions to take to establish or regain control.

At the work unit level, the process operator analyzes measurement data and adjusts the process to eliminate special causes of variation. To accomplish this, the operator might use a control chart to help determine what constitutes a trend. This type of trending is based on the interpretation of a series of events that are closely related in time, with the objective of sustaining process control.

Through the use of quality control tools incorporated into work processes, process operators are able to monitor the performance of key process characteristics. Work instructions for measuring data, analyzing trends in data, and making and recording process adjustments are documented as part of the quality system.

Patterns in Trend Analysis

As previously mentioned, it is typically expected that trended data will show a continual increase or decrease or will maintain a consistent level. Some data, however, will exhibit other particular patterns that indicate that the process being measured is working as desired or has encountered an unexpected factor. Two other patterns that may be superimposed on the three basic trends are:

- *Cyclical.* Some businesses or processes are affected by seasonal or other factors that cause the output to gradually increase (or decrease) and then gradually return to approximately the original level. For example, the quality of product produced in a plant that is not temperature controlled might be affected by seasonal changes in outdoor temperatures.

- *Shifts.* An abrupt change in an important variable (for example, a new sales initiative or change in raw material suppliers) may cause an output measure to suddenly increase or decrease. For example, facilities that operate three work shifts and do not have adequate standardization of operational methods often see significant differences in process performance at shift changeovers.

Tabular Data

Although run charts and other graphic displays of information are preferable, data are sometimes organized in tables for presentation. When tables are used, the following are a few simple rules that can help make interpretation of the data easier and more accurate:

- Organize the data so that they flow down, then across; it is generally easier to compare numbers in a column than across rows.

- Keep the number of digits to the right of the decimal point constant so that numbers are properly aligned; this helps highlight differences in magnitude of numbers.

- Use clear column titles and row headings, and keep the groupings consistent throughout the table.

- Ensure the length of a column before beginning a new one on the same page encompasses a logical block of data (for example, all data for a particular week or state should be in the same column if comparison of weeks or states is of interest).

Tabular data are more likely to be analyzed correctly if analysis is done using statistical methods. However, visual scanning of tables can sometimes identify patterns that might be investigated by simply circling the larger and/or smaller numbers.

Data Mining

Data mining began as a marketing process used to surface previously unknown linkages between variables in mammoth data sets—for example, mining the data collected by computerized checkout registers in retail stores. Its advantage is that it brings to light patterns of influence on quality that heretofore would have appeared impossible to detect.

Data-mining technologies include:

- *Neural networks.* A computer with its architecture patterned after the neurons of a human brain uses its web of electronic neurons to send signals over thousands of connections. A neural network is capable of simple learning.

- *Decision trees.* This technology uses a tree-shaped structure representing sets of decisions used to predict which records in an uncategorized data set will yield a stated outcome.

- *Rule induction.* This method is the finding of useful if/then rules within the data, based on statistical significance.

- *Genetic algorithms.* This method applies optimization techniques derived from the concepts of genetic combination, mutation, and natural selection.

- *Nearest neighbor.* This technique classifies each record based on other records that are most similar.

- Other pattern recognition techniques:

  — Linear models

  — Principal component analysis

  — Factor analysis

  — Linear regression

- Other methods:

  — Hotelling's *t*-squared statistic

  — Forecasting

  — Clustering

One of data mining's strengths is the capability to uncover an optimum combination of factors that can be used for *design of experiments* (DOE). Another advantage is that data mining and a geographic information system can be combined to produce smart maps.

Geographic Information System

A *geographic information system* (GIS) is especially useful in looking at markets, customer clusters, and social/economic/political data—before change and after change. GIS is a specialized type of software that depicts patterns and runs on personal computers. It resembles a database program in that it analyzes and relates stored records, with some major differences—the GIS database contains information used to draw a geometric shape. That shape represents a unique place on Earth to which the data correspond. Fields of special data enable the program to draw the shape of the information.

A GIS is more than a program for drawing maps; it is a system for mapping and analyzing the geographical distribution of data. There is a big difference between viewing data in tabular form and seeing it presented as a map. Because of the human ability of *pattern recognition*, the way one sees the data has a huge effect on the connections and conclusions one derives from the mapped data. GIS is an extremely useful tool for trend analysis, providing "before" and "after" maps of data from a targeted population or area of investigation.

Barriers to Successful Trend Analysis

Some common barriers to successful trend analysis include lack of:

- Timely access to data required in order to maintain a state of control or to prevent nonconformances

- Knowledge of how to interpret the data

- Knowledge or authority to respond to trends

- Understanding of the theory of variation (see Section 6), leading to poor decisions when evaluating alternatives and projecting results

In *The Fifth Discipline*, Senge discusses the difficulties corporations have related to trend analysis and how this threatens their survival. He believes that managers often are so concerned with individual events that they are precluded from recognizing longer-term patterns (or trends) of change that lie behind the events and from understanding the causes of the patterns. Senge uses the parable of the boiled frog to illustrate this lack of managerial self-control in being able to recognize and respond to gradual changes that often pose the greatest threats to survival.[10]

Senge then describes how the U.S. automobile industry succumbed to this phenomenon when it did not view Japanese automakers as a threat when the Japanese had less than 4% of the market. It was not until the 1980s that attention was given to the trend, which by then had reached a 20% market share—and the trend continued to increase, spreading to other Asian countries.

Another difficulty in trend analysis is that attempts to fix one problem often trigger another one. It is often difficult to identify this sort of pattern since consequences of an action are not immediately apparent and may only be visible in another part of the system.

Organizations should constantly be on the watch for both short- and long-term trends. Responses should be made according to company policy, objectives, and strategic plans. When the plan-do-check-act (PDCA) cycle is not executed at all levels within a company, nonsystemic and non-fact-based decision-making occurs.

6. PROCESS VARIATION

> Analyze data to distinguish between common and special cause variation. (Analyze)
>
> **Body of Knowledge IV.C.6**

Variation is inherent; it exists in all things. No two entities in the world have exactly the same measurable characteristics. The variation might be small and unnoticeable without the aid of precise and discriminative measuring instruments, or it might be quite large and easily noticeable. Two entities might appear to have the same measurement because of the limitations of the measuring device.

Factors Affecting Variation

Everything is the result of some process, so the chance for some variation in output is built into every process. Because material inputs are the outputs of some prior process, they are subject to variation, and that variation is transferred to the outputs. Variation will exist even in apparently identical processes using seemingly identical resources. Even though a task is defined and performed in the same manner repeatedly, different operators performing the same task or the same operator performing the same task repeatedly introduce variation. The precision and resolution of the measuring devices and techniques used to collect data also introduce variation into the output data.

Variation can result from changes in various factors, normally classified as follows:

1. People (worker) influences

2. Machinery influences

3. Environmental factors

4. Material influences

5. Measurement influences

6. Method influences

The resulting total variation present in any product is a result of the variations in these six main sources. Because the ramifications of variation in quality are enormous for managers, knowing a process's capabilities prior to production provides for better utilization of resources. Operating costs are reduced when inspection, rework, safety stock storage, and troubleshooting are eliminated. Proper management requires a deep appreciation of the existence of variation, as well as an understanding of its causes and how they can be corrected.

Types of Variation

Walter A. Shewhart, the father of modern quality control, was concerned with the low-cost reduction of variation. Shewhart distinguished two kinds of processes: (1) a stable process with "inevitable chance variation" and (2) an unstable process with "assignable cause variation." If the limits of process variation are well within the range of customer tolerance (specification), then the product can be made and shipped with reasonable assurance that the customer will be satisfied. If the limits of process variation just match the range of customer tolerance, then the process should be monitored closely and adjusted when necessary to maximize the amount of satisfactory output. If the limits of process variation extend beyond the range of customer tolerance, output should be inspected to determine whether it meets customer requirements.

When the amount of variation can be predicted with confidence, the process is said to be in a state of *statistical control* (*stable*). Although a singular value cannot be predicted exactly, it can be anticipated to fall within certain limits. Similarly, the long-term average value can be predicted.

In an unstable process, every batch of product is a source of excitement. It is impossible to predict how much, if any, of the product will fall within the range of customer tolerance. The costs necessary to produce satisfactory product are unknown because the organization is forced to carry large quantities of safety stock, and bids for new work must include a safety factor.

Shewhart developed simple statistical and graphic tools to inform operators and managers about their processes and to detect promptly when a stable process becomes unstable and vice versa. These tools, called *control charts*, come in various forms depending on whether measures are attributes or variables and whether samples are of constant size or not. Deming also recognized Shewhart's two sources of variation, calling them *common causes* and *special causes*. He also distinguished between the duties of those who work in the process and the managers who work on the process.

Common Causes. Variation that is always present or inherent in a process is called *common cause variation*. It occurs when one or more of the six previously mentioned factors fluctuate within the normal or expected manner, and the process can be improved only by changing a factor. Common causes of variation occur continually and result in controlled variation. They ensue, for example, from the choice of supplier, quality of inputs, worker hiring and training practices, equipment selection, machinery maintenance, and working conditions. If the process variation is excessive, then the process must be changed.

Eradicating these stable and predictable causes of variation is the responsibility of the managers of the process. Common causes are beyond the control of workers, as was demonstrated by Deming's famous red bead experiment.[11] In that experiment, volunteers were told to produce only white beads from a bowl containing a mixture of white and red beads. Monitoring or criticizing worker performance had no effect on the output. No matter what the workers did, they got some red beads (representing common cause variation)—sometimes more, sometimes less—but always some because the red beads were in the system.

Deming estimated that common causes account for 80% to 95% of workforce variation. This is not the fault of the workers, who normally do their best even in less than ideal circumstances. Rather, this is the responsibility of the managers, who work on, not in, the process.

Management decides how much money and time are to be spent on designing processes, which affects the resources and methods that can be used. It is the design of the process that has an impact on the amount of common cause variation.

Special Causes. When variation of one or more factors is abnormal or unexpected, the resultant variation is known as *special cause variation*, or *assignable cause variation*. This unexpected level of variation that is observed in an unstable process is due to special causes that are not inherent in the process. Special causes of variation are usually local in time and space—for example, specific to a change in a particular machine or a difference in shift, operator, or weather condition. They appear in a detectable pattern and cause uncontrolled variation. Special causes of variation often result in sudden and extreme departures from the normal but can also occur in the form of gradual shifts (or drifts) in a characteristic of a process. When a control chart shows a lack of control, skilled investigation should reveal what special causes are affecting the output. The workers in the process often have the detailed knowledge necessary to guide this investigation.

Structural Variation. Structural variation is inherent in the process;[12] however, when plotted on a control chart, structural variation looks like a special cause (blip), even though it is predictable. For example, a restaurant experiences a high number of errors in diners' orders taken on Saturday nights. The number of diners increases by 50% or more on every Saturday night, but they are served by the same number of waitpersons and chefs as on other nights.

Achieving Breakthrough Improvement

Building on Shewhart's notions of developing a systematic method for improvement, Juran distinguished between sporadic and chronic problems in *quality improvement projects* (QIPs). Starting from a state of chaos, a QIP should first seek to control variation by eliminating sporadic problems. When a state of controlled variation is reached, the QIP should then break through to higher levels of quality by eliminating chronic problems, thereby reducing the controlled variation. The notions of control and breakthrough are critical to Juran's thinking.

The following scenario demonstrates this concept: A dart player throws darts at two different targets. The darts on the first target are all fairly close to the bull's-eye, but the darts are scattered all over the target. It is difficult for the player to determine whether changing stance (or any other variable) will result in an improved score. The darts thrown at the second target are well off target from the bull's-eye, but the location of the darts is clustered and therefore predictable. When the player determines what variable is causing the darts to miss the bull's-eye, immediate and obvious improvement should result.

The impetus behind Juran's work was to achieve repeatable and predictable results. Until that happens, it will be almost impossible to determine whether a quality improvement effort has had any effect. Once a process is in control, breakthroughs are possible because they are detectable.

The following points are essential to an understanding of variation:

- Everything is the result or outcome of some process.

- Variation always exists, although it is sometimes too small to notice.

- Variation can be controlled if its causes are known. The causes should be determined through the practical experience of workers in the process as well as by the expertise of managers.

- Variation can result from special causes, common causes, or structural variation. Corrective action cannot be taken unless the variation has been assigned to the proper type of cause. For example, in Deming's bead experiment (white beads = good product, red beads = bad product) the workers who deliver the red beads should not be blamed; the problem is the fault of the system that contains the red beads.

- Tampering by taking actions to compensate for variation within the control limits of a stable process increases rather than decreases variation. Think of this as patting on the surface of a pond to eliminate ripples.

- Practical tools exist to detect variation and to distinguish controlled from uncontrolled variation.

Variation exists everywhere (even the earth wobbles a bit in its daily rotation on its axis). So, too, variation exists at an organizational level—within management's sphere of influence. The organization as a system is subject to common cause variation and special cause variation. Unfortunately, members of management in many organizations do not know about or understand the theory of variation. As a result of this, management tends to treat all anomalies as special causes and therefore treats actual common causes with continual tampering. Three examples follow:

- A donut shop, among its variety of products, produces jelly donuts. The fruit mix used to fill the jelly donuts is purchased from a longtime, reliable supplier. From time to time, a consumer complains about the tartness of the donut filling (nature produces berries of varying degrees of sweetness). The shop owner complains to the jelly supplier, who adds more sugar to the next batch (tampering). Several consumers complain about the overly sweet donut filling. The shop owner complains to the supplier, who reduces the amount of sugar in the next batch (tampering). More consumers complain about tartness, and so it goes. (Then there is the common example of an office building's occupants and their ongoing up-and-down interaction with the air conditioning and heating system.)

- Susan, a normally average salesperson, produces 10% fewer sales (number of sales, not dollar value) this month. The sales manager criticizes Susan for low sales production and threatens her with compensation loss. Susan responds with an extra effort to sell to anyone who will buy the service, regardless of the dollar volume of the sale (tampering). The sales manager criticizes Susan again, pointing out that dollar volume is more important than number of sales made. Susan concentrates on large-dollar buyers, which take several months to bring to fruition. Susan's monthly figures show a drastic drop, and she is severely criticized for lack of productivity. Susan leaves the company and takes the large-dollar prospects with her to a competitor. The system failed due to tampering, but the worker was blamed.

- A vice president of finance of a widely known charity continually tinkers with the organization's portfolio of investments, selling or buying whenever a slight deviation is noted, resulting in suboptimal yield from the portfolio.

An organization must focus its attempts at reducing variation. Variation does not need to be eliminated from everything; rather, the organization should focus on reducing variation in those areas most critical to meeting customers' requirements.

7. PROCESS CAPABILITY

> Recognize process capability (C_p and C_{pk}) and performance indices (P_p and P_{pk}). (Understand)
>
> **Body of Knowledge IV.C.7**

Stability or statistical control is an essential requirement to assess process capability. Process capability is the range within which a process is normally able to operate given the inherent variation due to design and selection of materials, equipment, people, and process steps. Knowing the capability of a process means knowing whether a particular specification can be held if the process is in control.

If a process is in control (see "Types of Control Charts," Section 3), one can then calculate the process capability index. Several formulas are used to describe the capability of a process by comparing it to the specification limits; the two most popular indexes are C_p and C_{pk}. C_p measures the spread of the specifications relative to the Six Sigma spread in the process. C_p does not take into account where the process mean is located relative to the specifications. C_{pk} takes process centering into consideration, and it represents the shortest distance for the specification limit nearest to the process average. Following are the formulas:

$$C_p = \frac{\text{Specification range}}{\text{Process range}} = \frac{\text{Upper spec} - \text{Lower spec}}{6\sigma}$$

$$C_{pk} = \frac{|\text{Upper spec} - \text{Average}|}{3\sigma} \text{ (or) } \frac{|\text{Lower spec} - \text{Average}|}{3\sigma}, \text{ whichever is smaller.}$$

Note that the sigma used for this calculation is not the standard deviation of a sample. It is the process sigma based on time-ordered data, such as given by the formula $R\text{-bar}/d_2$.

Following are the rules often used to determine whether a process is considered capable:

$$C_{pk} > 1.33 \text{ (capable)}$$
$$C_{pk} = 1.00 - 1.33 \text{ (capable with tight control)}$$
$$C_{pk} < 1.00 \text{ (not capable)}$$

A C_{pk} of 2 corresponds to approximately 6 sigma for short-term performance or 4.5 sigma for long-term performance, when applying a shift of 1.5 sigma.[13]

Initial process capability studies are often performed as part of the process validation stage of a new-product launch. Since this is usually a run of only a few hundred parts, it does not include the normal variability that will be seen in full production, such as small differences from batch to batch of raw material. In this case the study is called *potential process capability*, with the symbol P_{pk} used instead of C_{pk}. To compensate for the reduced variability, the decision points are typically set at:

$$P_{pk} > 1.67 \text{ (capable)}$$
$$P_{pk} = 1.33 - 1.67 \text{ (capable with tight control)}$$
$$P_{pk} < 1.33 \text{ (not capable)}$$

Capability is then studied soon after production release and on an as-needed basis during normal production. Changes to the process due to engineering changes or as part of continuous improvement should also be evaluated for their impact on process capability.

If process capability is found to be unsatisfactory, the following may be considered:

- Ensure that the process is centered

- Initiate process improvement projects to decrease variation

- Determine if the specifications can be changed

- Do nothing but realize that a percentage of output will be outside acceptable variation

When using statistical software programs to evaluate process capability, it is important that the user understand the specific terminology used by the programmers. Although the same concepts may be used, different symbols or formulas may be used.

8. RELIABILITY TERMINOLOGY

> Define and describe basic reliability measures such as infant mortality, end of life (e.g., bathtub curve), mean time between failures (MTBF), and mean time to repair (MTTR). Understand the value of estimating reliability to meet requirements or specifications. NOTE: Reliability calculations will <u>not</u> be tested. (Understand)
>
> **Body of Knowledge IV.C.8**

Product Reliability

Reliability refers to the probability that a product can perform its required functions for a specified period of time under stated conditions. Consistent repeatability during the useful life of the product is the objective. Important concepts are:

- A product's failure conditions must be clearly stated, including its decreasing degree of performance over time.

- A time interval is specified using metrics such as hours, cycles, miles, and so on, in defining the life cycle of the product.

- Some products are for one-time use, such as the ignition device for a rocket. Such devices operate only when initiated or triggered and are measured as *worked as planned* or *failed*.

Reliability engineers are concerned with how a product fails so they can compute, predict, and improve the product's reliability. One reliability model is referred to as the *bathtub curve* (also called *life-history curve* or *Weibull curve*) because graphically it resembles a bathtub (see Figure 15.7). Plotting the failure rate over the life cycle of a product (*left to right*), the stages are:

- *Infant mortality* (burn-in period). The failure rate decreases as the next stage is reached.

- *Random failure* (useful life period). Stable failure rate during normal use.

- *Wear out (end of life).* The failure rate increases until the product is no longer useful as intended.

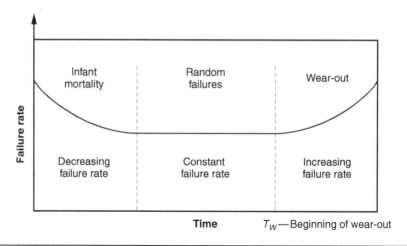

Figure 15.7 Bathtub curve.

Some methods for consideration to reduce the burn-in period are:

- Stringent supplier certification
- Production and quality engineers participating in design reviews
- Appropriate acceptance sampling
- Application of process failure mode and effects analysis (PFMEA)
- Use of statistical process control methodology
- Application of design for manufacturability and assembly (DFMA)

A key point to consider is that the life cycle of the entire product is dependent on the failure of the weakest (most failure-prone) element or part within the product—for example, the material used, the process used, the robustness of the design, the unexpected, unintended improper use of the product by the buyer, the environment in which the product is used, or even regulatory restrictions not anticipated.

Mean Time to Failure (MTTF)

This is a basic measure of reliability for nonrepairable product and is computed as the total number of delivered products divided by the total number of failures within a population receiving the product during a discrete measurement interval and under stated conditions. MTTF should not be confused with MTBF.

Mean Time between Failures (MTBF)

This is a basic measure of reliability for repairable product and refers to the mean (average) number of products in which all elements or parts of the product perform within their specification limits during a discrete measurement interval under stated conditions.

Other Measures of Reliability

Maintainability is the ability of a product to be retained in, or restored to, a state in which it can meet the service or intent for which it was designed. The focus is on reducing the duration of downtime. Maintainability would be a factor to consider during the early stages of product development.

Mean time between maintenance actions (MTBMA) is a measure related to demand for maintenance personnel. It is computed as the total number of system product units divided by the total number of preventive and corrective maintenance actions during a stated time period.

Mean time to repair (MTTR) is another basic reliability measure. It is calculated by dividing the sum of corrective maintenance actions at any specific level of repair by the total number of failures within an item repaired at that level during a specific time interval under stated conditions.

Availability is the probability that a unit will be ready for use at a stated time, or over a stated time period, based on the combined aspects of reliability and maintainability. Three types of availability are identified:

1. *Inherent availability* is a function of reliability (MTBF) and maintainability (MTTR). To calculate inherent availability:

$$(A_I) = \text{MTBF}/(\text{MTBF} + \text{MTTR})$$

2. *Achieved availability* includes the measure of preventive and corrective maintenance. To calculate achieved availability:

$$(A_A) = \text{MTBMA}/(\text{MTBMA} + \text{MMT})$$

   where MMT = mean maintenance time = the sum of preventive and corrective maintenance times divided by the sum of scheduled and unscheduled maintenance events during a stated period of time.

3. *Operational availability* includes both the inherent and achieved availability and also logistics and administrative downtime. To calculate operational availability:

$$(A_O) = \text{MTBMA}/(\text{MBTMA} + \text{MDT})$$

   where MDT = mean maintenance downtime, which includes supply time, logistics time, administrative delays, active maintenance time, and so on.

Effective process management and continual improvement rely on data to help ensure that decisions are made based on facts rather than just opinions. Data on customer satisfaction, cost of quality, product quality levels, process capability, and many other performance measures are continually being gathered, analyzed, and reported in order to support quality planning, control, and improvement. Another level of quality is then also important—quality of the data being used to make decisions. Two specific measures of data quality are typically used: reliability and validity.

Reliability is a measure of the repeatability of the data. That is, if the same measurements were made over and over, would the same results be obtained? In the field of instrumentation, this is called *precision* and reflects the amount of spread in the data if the same measurement is repeatedly made.

Validity is the accuracy of the data—how close it is, on average, to the real value? In instrumentation this is known as *accuracy*, or amount of inherent bias in the device. Figure 15.8 visually demonstrates the concepts of reliability and validity.

Reliability and validity can be affected by the design of the measurement device (for example, how a survey question is written, what training is provided for interviewers, or how a piece of equipment used for physical measurement is handled), how the sample is chosen, and how the data are interpreted. For example, if an incorrect word is used in a questionnaire, the answers may be invalid. If a word is correct but does not mean the same thing to all respondents (or to different researchers), reliability will be affected.

When measuring validity, consider these issues:

• *Face.* An instrument may be said to have face validity to the extent that the distinctions it provides correspond with those that would be made by most observers without the aid of the instrument.

• *Criterion.* A criterion-related strategy looks at how well the performance of one measure can predict performance of a particular variable to be affected. For example, if a written test on troubleshooting techniques is given to people who are studying to learn computer repair, how well do the results predict who is more likely to be able to solve real computer problems quickly? In this case the criterion for success is the ability to solve real problems, and if the written test is able to predict success, then it is considered a valid test.

• *Construct.* Construct-related validity also uses one variable to predict another but does so using a pseudovariable (a construct one believes to be related) as the predictable variable. If a company wants to measure the level of customer satisfaction by simply observing customers as they are shopping, it might choose to use how much customers smile as they look at products as a predictive measure of satisfaction. If it finds that those who smiled more were, in fact, more satisfied with their shopping experiences (for example, based on a sample of shoppers who were both observed and interviewed), then *smiling* has construct validity. If, however, it was found to not be a good predictor, then it is not valid.

• *Content.* Content-related validity is concerned with how well a measure predicts the full range of performance measures for which it might be used. For example, the written troubleshooting test might be a valid predictor of whether an

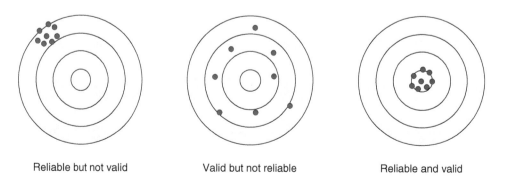

Reliable but not valid   Valid but not reliable   Reliable and valid

Figure 15.8   Reliability and validity.

individual would be a good hardware troubleshooter but not a valid predictor of the person's ability to correct software problems.

Reliability and validity are often controlled by using data collection devices that have already been proven instead of designing new ones. Contract test labs and firms that specialize in customer satisfaction measurement attest to the costs that can be incurred in developing new measurement systems. When it is necessary to develop a new measurement device, it must first be calibrated by comparing it to one of known reliability and validity.

REFERENCES

1. W. E. Deming, *The New Economics*, 3rd ed. (Cambridge, MA: MIT Center for Advanced Educational Services, 2018), chap. 7.

2. J. A. DeFeo, ed., *Juran's Quality Control Handbook*, 7th ed. (New York: McGraw-Hill, 2017), 53.

3. ASQ Statistics Division, *Improving Performance through Statistical Thinking* (Milwaukee: ASQ Quality Press, 2000).

4. "What Are Bias and Linearity?," *Minitab*, 2018.

5. ASQ Quality Management Division, *Principles of Quality Costs: Financial Measures for Strategic Implementation of Quality Management*, 4th ed., ed. D. Wood (Milwaukee: ASQ Quality Press, 2013).

6. Ibid., 28.

7. Ibid.

8. Ibid.

9. Ibid.

10. P. Senge, *The Fifth Discipline: The Art and Practice of the Learning Organization* (New York: Doubleday, 1990), 22.

11. W. E. Deming, *Out of the Crisis* (Cambridge, MA: MIT Center for Advanced Educational Services, 1986).

12. Six Sigma Material, Process Capability Index, Cpk, accessed January 9, 2020, https://www.six-sigma-material.com/Cpk.html.

13. Ibid.

See Appendix A for additional references for this chapter.

Part V

Customer-Focused Organizations

Chapter 16   A. Customer Identification and
                   Segmentation
                   Contributor: Jeff Israel
Chapter 17   B. Customer Relationship Management
                   Contributor: Jeff Israel

There is only one boss—the customer. And he can fire everybody in the company— from the chairman on down—simply by spending his money somewhere else.

—Sam Walton

Marketing and customer service research studies have shown that it is more cost-effective to win and keep a customer than to move through a customer life cycle of acquiring, losing, and reacquiring a customer. Hence, the emphasis here on the importance of becoming a customer-focused organization.

—ASQ's Certified Manager of Quality/Organizational Excellence Program

Real profits are generated by loyal customers—not just satisfied customers.

—Rafael Aguayo

When a customer complains, consider getting down on your knees to offer profuse gratitude because that person has just provided you with priceless advice—free of charge.

—Owen Harari

Chapter 16
A. Customer Identification and Segmentation

Virtually all quality management approaches focus on the customer. The first step in all quality planning is the identification of customers. Correctly identifying customers is essential because all activities are based on the fulfillment of customers' needs or requirements. Today, most quality professionals consider the customer to be any individual or group that receives and must be satisfied with the service, work product, or output of a process. In other words, the customer is the individual or group whose requirements a process is intended to fulfill. This, however, is a fairly narrow definition of the term. Gryna broadly describes a customer as "anyone who is affected by the product or process."[1] Clearly, this definition includes more than just those who receive the output of a process.

The quality professional must realize that a process and its output touch many people both within and beyond organizational boundaries. Whether or not an organization's definition of *customer* encompasses all stakeholder groups, it is important to recognize that each group might have requirements that need to be satisfied.

Overview of Customer Types

Harrington, in *Business Process Improvement*, discussed five types of customers.[2] Other types have also been identified. Customers can be in more than one of these categories:

• *Primary customer.* A primary customer is the individual or group who directly receives the output of a process. For a bank loan officer, the primary customer is the individual or organization that is requesting a loan. For a test laboratory, it is the individual or department who needs the requested test results in order to make a decision. The primary customer is a major source of product and process requirements and is sometimes referred to as a *direct customer*.

• *Secondary customer.* Secondary customers are those individuals or groups from outside of the process boundaries who also receive process output but who are not the reason for the process's existence. For example, a business process that produces invoices for an organization's primary customer might also send copies of those invoices to an internal department for sales analysis and reporting. In this case, the internal department is a secondary customer.

• *Indirect customer.* Like secondary customers, indirect customers are within the organizational boundaries. They do not receive process outputs directly but are affected if the process output is incorrect or late. The output passes through other steps before leaving the organization. For example, the delivery function of a wholesale grocery distributor is not the final user of the grocery order but is still affected if the packed order is late in arriving on the shipping dock and delivery is delayed.

- *External customer.* External customers are located outside of the organizational boundaries and receive the end product or service but might not be the actual user. For example, an award-winning company makes power supplies for computers, copiers, and other business machines. The company's external customers are companies such as computer equipment, camera manufacturers, or other original equipment manufacturers (OEMs); however, these customers are not the final users of the power supplies.

- *Consumer/end user.* Consumers, also called *end users*, are the final users of a product or service. This term describes where a product or service is finally used or consumed. Sometimes the external customer and the end user are the same, but more often products and/or services are delivered to a distributor, representative, or retailer that sells the product to the consumer.

- *Intermediary.* An intermediary may exist to perform tasks not always visible to the consumer/end user—for example, the owner of the boxcar containing the consumer's product and the several different rail carriers that handle the boxcar during shipment.

- *False customer.* A false customer is an individual or group within a process that performs activities that do not add value to the product or service. Obviously, an objective of process improvement projects is to identify and eliminate as many false customers as possible. Examples of false customers include an inspector who monitors 100% of process output because of poor up-front quality planning, a manager who edits all memos written by all of his or her employees before they can be distributed, and a process or business function that cannot identify its customer. "If a function or process does not seem to have a real customer, then that function should be reevaluated. The function may be unnecessary, or it may simply be part of a larger process."[3] When a function does not add value, it should be eliminated unless mandated by a regulation or some other necessary requirement.

- *Internal customer.* The term *internal customer* has come into popular use to generally refer to individuals or groups within a process who are inside the organizational boundaries. It is used to refer to the idea that everyone who works in a process has a customer and that their objective is to identify and meet their internal customer's requirements. This concept has value in process management; however, some companies have discovered that the term often lessens the focus on the external customer and consumer. To avoid confusion and ensure a customer focus, one company refers to these individuals or groups as *process partners*. Others refer to *service providers* and *service receivers*. A company that chooses to use the internal customer label must be sure that all employees recognize that the company's ultimate responsibility and the intent of the process is to serve the external customer.

Importance of Identifying Customer Types

There are a number of reasons for knowing an organization's customer types:

1. Identifying and defining customer types is an important part of service and process management and improvement:

   - Defining a process through documentation and process mapping requires that process owners and improvement teams identify every customer type and source of process and service/product requirements.

   - Measuring service/process effectiveness also requires customer input.

2. Generally, customer satisfaction research is performed among the end users of an organization's products or services.

3. When an organization performs market research, it should not only look at its current customers but also look beyond them. Surveying lost customers, prospective customers, and competitors' customers can also provide useful insights as to what satisfies customers. Such research can also provide information as to what new or improved products, services, or processes might fulfill the customers' requirements and result in satisfaction. Methods used to gather customer satisfaction data are discussed in this chapter.

Figure 16.1 depicts a greatly simplified hypothetical product/service flow, through several types of customers, for a consumer product sold via an internet web page:

- Consumer (external customer) accesses the web via an external provider

- Consumer searches for desired product, accessing various product sellers

- Consumer places the order electronically through selected seller's website

- Seller places/forwards the order to the publisher (seller is external customer of publisher)

- Publisher notifies seller, who notifies consumer that order is confirmed

- Publisher transmits pick order to warehouse (not shown), which picks product from shelf and sends to shipper (warehouse is internal customer of order service)

- Shipper delivers product to consumer (shipper is an intermediate customer of warehouse; consumer is an external customer of shipper)

- Warehouse notifies billing (billing is an internal customer of warehouse)

- Billing bills consumer (consumer is external customer of billing)

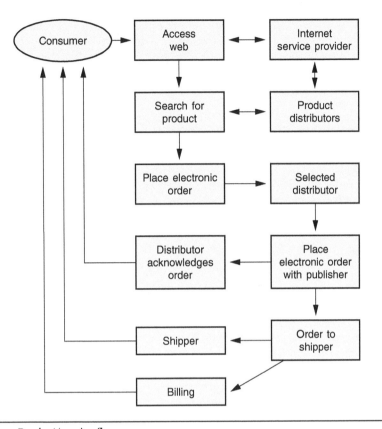

Figure 16.1   Product/service flow.

1. INTERNAL CUSTOMERS

Define internal customers and describe the impact an organization's treatment of internal customers will have on external customers. Evaluate methods for influencing internal customers to improve products, processes, and services and evaluate the results. (Evaluate)

Body of Knowledge V.A.1

Internal customers are found within an organization. Who are they? How can an organization work with internal customers to effectively improve processes and services? How does an organization's treatment of its internal customers influence its processes for external customers?

Bhote discusses the term *next operation as customer*.[4] Every function and work group in an organization is both a receiver of services and/or products from internal and/or external sources as well as a provider of services and/or products to internal and/or external customers. These interfaces between provider and receiver may be one to one, one to many, many to one, or many to many. Each receiver has needs and requirements. Whether the delivered service or product meets these needs/requirements has an impact on the customer's effectiveness and the quality of service/product to its customers, and so on. Examples include:

• If A delivers part X to B one hour late, B may have to apply extra effort and cost to make up the time or else perpetuate the lateness in delivering to the next customer.

• Engineering designs a product based on the salesperson's understanding of the external customer's need. Production produces the product, expending material, personnel, and other costs. The external customer rejects the product because it fails to meet its needs. The provider reengineers the product; production makes a new one that the customer accepts, late. This could possibly be the last order from this customer.

• Computer services delivers copies of a production cost report (average of fifty pages of fine print per week) to six internal customers. Computer services has established elaborate quality control of the accuracy, timeliness, and physical quality of the report. Of the six report receivers, however, only two need information of this type any longer. Neither of these two finds the report directly usable for its current needs. Each has assigned clerical people to manually extract pertinent data for its specific use. All six receivers admit diligently storing the reports for the prescribed retention period.

• Production tickets, computer printed on light card stock, are attached by removable tape to each module. When the module reaches the paint shop, it is given an acid bath, a rinse, high-temperature drying, painting, and high-temperature baking. Very few tickets survive intact and readable. The operation following the paint shop requires attaching other parts to the painted modules, depending on information contained on the ticket. Operators depend on their experience to guess which goes with what. Ninety-five percent emerge from this process correctly, a lower percentage when variations go down the line or when an experienced operator is absent.

In order to improve internal processes and services, the approach is to:

1. Identify internal customer interfaces (providers of services/products and receivers of their services/products).

2. Establish internal customers' service/product needs/requirements.

3. Perform a gap assessment to identify areas for improvement.

4. Set improvement objectives and measurements.

5. Modify processes where needed.

6. Implement systems for tracking and reporting performance and for supporting the continual improvement of the process.

7. Document *quality-level agreements* between provider and receiver.

Quality-Level Agreements

Quality-level agreements (QLAs), also called *service-level agreements (SLAs)*, can be implemented on a gradual basis, starting with the most critical deliverables first.[5] QLAs aid employees' understanding and recognition of the importance of internal customer/receiver requirements, from the receiver's perspective. Employees can also gain insights into the potential impact of their contribution on the business process in which they play a part. QLAs and the documented performance achieved show the objective evidence that providers comply with their receiver/customer requirements, thus linking internal product/service quality with the quality management system and ultimately with external customers' requirements. QLAs provide a natural extension of documented quality management systems by providing the basis for working-level performance measurement and review, leading to continuous improvement. QLA content data will vary according to the needs of the providers and receivers of the products/services and their organization.

Initiating QLAs increases understanding and collaboration between providers and receivers. A QLA should remove all doubt as to what a receiver expects from a service or product received from its provider. It should eliminate needless controversy and confusion if expectations are not met. The QLA can offer a sound basis for performance measurement, evaluation, and continual improvement. A QLA deploys the voice of the internal customer. Figure 16.2 is a sample QLA.

Three Timely Tenets

1. Valid requirements for the service/product to be delivered by the providers are the requirements the receivers have provided, have agreed to, and that meet the receivers' needs.

2. A valid measurement of the quality of the service/product delivered is the level of the receiver's satisfaction.

3. All internal customer requirements must be consistent with the external customers' requirements.

How Treatment of Internal Customers Influences Processes for External Customers

Careless behavior of management (and management's systems) toward internal customers (for example, poor tools and equipment, defective and late material input from previous operations, incorrect/incomplete instructions, ineligible work orders or prints, circumvention of worker safety procedures and practices, unhealthy work environment, disinterest in internal complaints, disregard for external customer feedback) may engender careless or indifferent treatment of external customers. Continued, this indifference could generate a downward spiral that can adversely affect an organization's outcomes. Ignoring regard for the needs of internal customers makes it very difficult to instill employees' intent to care for the needs of external customers.

So many organizations fail to learn, or may ignore, the internal customers' needs and wonder why their management's exhortations fail to stimulate internal

Panacea, Inc. Quality-Level Agreement	
Services/product receiver: Dept./function	QLA no.:
Contact name:	Original issue date:
Title: Contact no.	Date last revision:
	Current date:
Description of service/product:	Identifiers: Part nos.: External customer:
Specific requirements: 1 2 3 4	Measurements: 1 2 3 4
Conditions that may impact achieving agreed quality level:	Relative to requirement no.:
Report quality level agreement failure to: Name: Title: Contact no.:	Comments:
Agreed for receiver/customer: Name: Title: Contact no.:	Date: Signature: _____
Agreed for provider: Name: Title: Contact no.:	Date: Signature: _____
Approval (if required) for receiver/customer: Name: Title: Contact no.:	Date: Signature: _____
Approval (if required) for provider: Name: Title: Contact no.:	Date: Signature: _____
This agreement relates to:	Procedure nos.: Work instruction nos.:

Figure 16.2   Quality-level agreement.

Source: Reprinted with permission of R. T. Westcott & Associates.

customers to care about how and what they do for external customers. The surly and uncooperative sales representative, waitperson, housekeeping employee, delivery person, and customer service representative usually reflect lack of caring for internal customers behind the scenes.

Organizations must work constantly to eliminate the internal customers' lament: "How do you expect me to care about the next operator, or external customer, when no one cares whether I get what I need to do my job right?" Hal Rosenbluth in *The Customer Comes Second* believes organizations must behave as though their people come first. Supporting and caring for employees is a core value and the primary responsibility of all of Rosenbluth's managers.

The culture of an organization and the treatment of its employees directly affect the treatment of its external customers. The model presented in *Putting the Service Profit Chain to Work* underscores the importance of facilitating employee satisfaction by providing high-quality support services and policies that enable employees to deliver results to customers. The service profit chain suggests that improved employee (internal customer) satisfaction leads directly to improvements in employee productivity and retention, which in turn affects the value delivered to external customers, ultimately resulting in higher levels of customer satisfaction, loyalty, goodwill, and profitability. Perhaps the best indicator that an organization has attained a true culture of customer focus is the extent to which the following statement is true for the organization: "If you're not serving the customer, you'd better be serving someone who is."[6] This statement implies the notion of servant leadership and caring for those who provide care for the customer.

Methods to Energize Internal Customers

The organization should consider all or several of the following methods to energize internal customers to improve products, processes, and services:

- Ensure that all employees understand who the external customers are and what the customers need and want.

- Ensure that employees know what the organization expects of them and what boundaries pertain to what they can do to satisfy the external customer.

- Involve employees in designing and implementing strategies, procedures, and tools that will facilitate customer satisfaction.

- Ensure that employees have the information, training, time, and support they need to meet external customer needs, wants, and satisfaction.

- Ensure that employees have the tangible things they need to serve customers well—for example, supplies, tools, working equipment, clean workspace, safe work place, and appropriate policies and procedures.

- Demonstrate through words and actions the commitment the organization has to serving its customer to the best extent possible.

- Ensure that the recognition and reward systems are supportive of the internal customer satisfaction focus.

- Provide positive reinforcement to employees who are, or are trying, to do their best to satisfy external customers.

- Provide employees with substantive performance feedback and assist in continual improvement.

2. EXTERNAL CUSTOMERS

> Define external customers and describe their impact on products and services. Evaluate strategies for working with them and integrating their requirements and needs to improve products, services, and processes. (Evaluate)
>
> **Body of Knowledge V.A.2**

Types of External Customers

The following is a list of many types of external customers and some of the influences these customers have on the products and services provided.

- *Wholesale buyer.* Wholesalers buy what they expect they can sell. They typically buy in large quantities. They may have little direct influence on the product design and manufacture but do influence the providers' production schedules, pricing policies, warehousing and delivery arrangements, and return policies for unsold merchandise.

- *Distributor.* A distributor is similar to a wholesaler in some ways but differs in the fact that they may stock a wider variety of products from a wide range of producers. What they stock is directly influenced by their consumers' demands and needs. Their customers' order quantities may often be small and for diverse products. The distributor's forte is stocking thousands of catalog items that can be picked and shipped on short notice at an attractive price. Distributors stocking commodity-type items (for example, sheet metal, construction materials, mineral products, stationery items, and so on) are mainly influenced by customers seeking an industry level of quality, at a good price and immediately available. For example, to reduce the buyer's cost and enable the supplier's efficiency, orders for some types of materials might be for a yearly quantity delivered in partial shipments throughout the year (called *blanket orders*).

- *Retail chain buyer.* Buyers for large retail chains, because of the size of their orders, place major demands on their providers—for example, pricing concessions, very flexible deliveries, requirements that the provider assume warehousing costs for already purchased product, special packaging requirements, no-cost return policy, or a requirement that the provider be able to accept electronically sent orders.

- *Other volume buyers.* Government entities, educational institutions, healthcare organizations, transportation companies, cruise lines, hotel chains, and restaurant chains all represent large-volume buyers who provide services to customers. Each of these organizations has regulations governing its services. Each requires a wide range of products, material, and external services in delivering its services, much of which is transparent to the consumer. Each requires high quality, and each has tight limitations on what it can pay (for example, based on appropriations, cost-control mandates, tariffs, heavy competition). Each such buyer demands much for its dollar but may offer long-term contracts for fixed quantities. The influences on products required are frequently generated by the buyer organizations' internal customers. Inasmuch as price and delivery are often the prevailing considerations, feedback to the providers relative to end-user satisfaction with the products or services delivered, if feedback is available at all, travels a slow and convoluted path.

• *Service providers.* The diversity of service providers buying products and services from other providers is mind-boggling. These buyers include the plumber, public accountant, dentist, doctor, building contractor, cleaning service, computer programmer, website designer, consultant, manufacturer's rep, actor, and taxi driver. This type of buyer, often self-employed, buys very small quantities, shops for value, buys only when a product or service is needed, and relies on high quality of purchases to maintain its customer's satisfaction. Influences on products or services from providers to this type of buyer range from being able to furnish service and/or replacement parts for old or obsolete equipment, or being able to supply extremely small quantities of an extremely large number of products (for example, such as supplied by a hardware store, construction materials depot, medical products supply house, and so on), to having product knowledge that extends to knowing how the product is best used.

• *Retail buyer.* The retail buyer influences the design and usability of product features and accessories based on volume purchased. Consumer product watch organizations warn purchasers of potential problems. (For example, in the late 1990s a fake fat substance was introduced in a number of food products as a boon to health-conscious people. These products did not taste good and were found to have harmful side effects. Many buyers stopped buying those products.) Features important to these buyers, depending on type of product, are reasonable price, ease of use, performance, safety, aesthetics, and durability. Other influences on product offerings include installation, instructions for use, post-purchase service, warranty period, packaging, and brand name.

• *Discount buyer.* The discount buyer shops primarily for price, is more willing to accept less well-known brands, and is willing to buy quantities in excess of immediate needs. These buyers have relatively little influence on the products, except for, perhaps, creating a market for off-brand items, production surpluses, and discontinued items.

• *Employee buyer.* The employee buyer purchases their employer's products, usually at a deep discount. Often being familiar with, or actually a contributor to the products bought, this buyer can provide valuable feedback to the employer (directly through surveys, indirectly through volume and items purchased). A useful question is "Would the salespersons who sell an organization's product buy and use it themselves?"

• *Service buyer.* The buyer of services (for example, TV repair, dental work, tax preparation) often buys by word of mouth. Word of good or poor service spreads rapidly and influences the continuance of the service provider's business. Organizations have created lists, accessed through a website, to furnish feedback from former service buyers to prospective service buyers to help guide them in their selection of a service provider.

• *Service user.* A captive service user (electricity, gas, water, municipal services, schools) generally has little influence as to from whom it receives services. In recent times, more choices are available, but customers are still limited to a small number of providers. Until more competition is introduced, there is little incentive to providers to vary their services.

• *Organization buyer.* Buyers for organizations that use a product or service in the course of their business or activity can have a significant influence on the types of products offered them, as well as the organization from which they buy. Raw materials or devices that become a part of a manufactured product are especially critical in sustaining quality and competitiveness for the buyer's organization (for example, performance, serviceability, price, ease of use, durability, simplicity of design, safety, and ease of disposal). Other factors include flexibility in delivery, discounts, allowances for returned material, and extraordinary guarantees. Factors that particularly pertain to purchased services typically include reputation and credibility of provider, range of services offered, degree of customization offered, timeliness, and fee structure.

In addition to the above descriptions of external customer types, it is useful to examine the nature of the provider and customer relationship. For example, does the provider market and sell to consumers (business-to-consumer, or B2C) or to businesses (business-to-business, or B2B)? In B2C, often the purchaser and end user are the same. As such, it is relatively straightforward to determine customer requirements and the best approaches to meet their needs and improve their customer experience. In the case where the provider serves B2B customers, the definition of who the "real customer" is becomes unclear. It will not suffice to consider that the "company" is the customer. In reality, customers in B2B markets have a number of stakeholders who are involved in the totality of the customer relationship. Typically for B2B the provider will be serving purchasing, manufacturing, and likely other customer stakeholders. The key point is that each stakeholder group has unique requirements, so it is important to consider which stakeholders are most important and to determine their key requirements.

3. CUSTOMER SEGMENTATION

> Describe and assess the process of customer segmentation and its impact on aligning service and delivery to meet customer needs. (Evaluate)
>
> **Body of Knowledge V.A.3**

The Shift to Customer Segmentation

One key legacy of the industrial age was the trend of mass production. Henry Ford said the following about the people waiting to buy his company's Model Ts: "Any customer can have a car painted any color that he wants so long as it is black." In reality, not every customer would have wanted to purchase a black car, but this was the only choice, given Ford's initial concept of mass production (and the fact that black paint was the only color that would dry fast enough). For many decades the idea of mass production was associated with the concept of mass markets.

Market segmentation has its roots in the marketing concept, generally attributed to Philip Kotler. The basic premise of the marketing concept is that a company should determine what consumers need and want and then try to satisfy those wants and needs, provided that (1) doing so is consistent with the company's, strategy, and (2) the expected rate of return meets company objectives.[7] By encouraging organizations to structure products and services around customers' needs and wants rather than being driven strictly by technological capability, organizations move from a product-driven approach toward a market- or customer-driven emphasis.

Alvin and Heidi Toffler offer clues on trends relating to mass production, mass markets, and the changing workplace. They used the term *demassification* to describe these changes, including a trend in which organizations' homogeneous customer groups begin to splinter into many groups with unique needs and expectations.[8] In his keynote address at the Fiftieth Annual Quality Congress in 1996, Alvin Toffler used the term *mass customization* to further characterize this trend, suggesting that nearly every customer has unique requirements that product and service providers need to address on a customer-by-customer basis.

The implication of such a trend is staggering for many organizations, especially in view of their current practices used to serve their customers. Organizations that surpass competitors in serving key market segments should find themselves in a commanding position in the marketplace. The challenge to an organization is to clearly know its customers and their unique requirements and expectations. This new way of thinking has come to be known as *customer relationship management* (CRM), or *one-to-one marketing*.

"The biggest single barrier to the development of an effective corporate strategy is the strongly held belief that a company has to appeal to the entire market."[9] Organizations can often realize more efficient returns on their marketing resources when they narrow the scope of their focus. This section discusses some of the ways to identify and segment particular customers or markets.

Customer Segmentation

The identification of customers is straightforward for some organizations and very difficult in others. When the supplier and customer have a direct relationship, identifying customers and their requirements is a relatively simple task. For example, new car dealers have detailed information on the purchasers of new cars and frequently provide postpurchase service and support. When the supplier and end user never come into direct contact, however, it is much more difficult for the product or service provider to identify the customer and his or her unique needs. For example, manufacturers of consumer products distributed through various retail outlets rarely have detailed information about end users unless these customers return warranty registration cards, submit complaints, or respond to special offers. In any case the product or service provider might speculate on the requirements of the key customer segment(s) served, but knowing the actual identity of the customer (as in the case of the automobile dealership) enables the provider to collect information and make special offers to that customer or customer segment.

An organization must be able to meet or exceed the needs of key customers to remain in business. An organization that neglects to explore the ways in which customer needs and wants vary across market and customer segments misses an opportunity to maximize customer satisfaction in segments vital to the organization's well-being. Scarce service delivery resources can be better allocated to maximize satisfaction among the most critical customer segments.

Core customers/key customers typically are those customers most vital to the organization's economic success. These can be high-volume customers, customers from selected industries, customers with the greatest impact on the organization's profitability, or customers most likely to have an impact on the firm's future viability. A company can identify its core customers by doing a detailed analysis of their financial performance, such as the 20% of customers accounting for 80% of the operating profit.

Noncore customers may or may not have unique requirements from core customers. If possible, companies look for lower-cost service and support solutions for noncore customers (such as self-service web support). It is generally beneficial to serve noncore customers, as long as the cost of service is less than the economic benefit.

Sometimes core customers are referred to as the *Vital Few* and the noncore customers as the *Useful Many*. This is a great definition to explore the concept of segmentation. In the early days of customer focus, many subscribed to the ideal that all customers are equally important, and organizations should be committed to meeting and exceeding the expectations of all customers. Operating under that assumption, a company could undertake to understand customer requirements for all customers. The peril in this example is that, typically, core customers have higher expectations than noncore customers. If we were to only consider our customers as having the same (homogeneous) requirements, we'd no doubt set the bar too low for performance. As a result, our most critical (core) customers would be the ones most likely to experience failed expectations and the most likely customers to switch to the competition. In an ideal world, we would like to know customer expectations for both core and noncore customer segments, as well as perceptions of performance for each segment. However, most organizations have limited resources to evaluate customer requirements and measure customer satisfaction. In this case, better to be clear about core customer requirements and how well you are doing, rather than to lump all customers into one group and pretend they are all equally important.

Potential customers are not currently on the customer list but could be in the market for the product or service offered. A strategy to reach appropriate segments of potential customers needs to be developed and implemented as the business grows.

The Process of Segmenting Customers

The term *market segments* refers to the concept that there are groups of potential customers sharing particular wants or needs (rather than simply one large homogeneous market) and that these groups are objectively identifiable.[10]

Segmentation differentiating factors can be considered in creating customer or market segments. Examples of some commonly used differentiators are:

- *Purchase volume.* Some organizations split their customer base into two or more groupings on the basis of volume. High-volume customers are often thought of as core customers and might account for only 10% of the customer base but as much as 90% of the total business volume.

- *Profitability.* Profitability segmentation can yield different results than volume segmentation. The key distinction is that the criteria would be based on the profit from customer segments rather than on purchase volume.

- *Industry.* One common basis of segmentation in business-to-business markets is identifying that customers from different industries have unique requirements that determine the value they receive from products and services. For example, customers in the energy utility industry may have different key requirements than those customers offering internet and wireless services.

- *Type of organization.* Segments could include OEM, distributor, retailer, wholesaler, repackager, and so on.

- *Purchasing organizations' size.* Size of the buyers may be a useful segmentation strategy for some organizations.

- *Type of purchases made.* Segmentation could include raw materials for conversion into product, facility maintenance supplies, calibration services, hazardous waste disposal services, and so on.

- *Buyers' organizational structure.* Differentiating by type of organizational structure, such as sole proprietorship, partnership, corporation, and joint venture, may constitute a useful segmentation strategy.

- *Geographic.* Customers and markets are often segmented geographically, but usually this is a method of allocating resources (for example, sales and field support) to a region rather than being driven by unique customer requirements. An exception would be when buying habits for certain types of products or services differ by geographic region (for example, due to a predominant culture).

- *Demographic.* Examples of demographic-based segments include groupings based on any combination of factors such as age, income, marital status, education, and gender. Sometimes, demographic characteristics are combined. For example, family life cycle usually combines head-of-household age, marital status, and a factor indicating both the presence and the ages of children living at home to determine a resulting segment. Some of the unique resulting segments include single adult head of household, young married couples with no children, households with young children, households with teenagers, same-sex partners, empty nest (working age, but children have left home), and retired. Marketers have long used these kinds of segments to identify and characterize key target markets. Certain products/services (for example, diapers and educational software) appeal to or are best suited for one or more demographic segments.

- *Psychographic.* Segmentation leads to groupings based on values, attitudes, and beliefs. Insurance marketers might want to target consumers with a balanced, healthy lifestyle as manifested by attitudes. For example, a key target segment might include individuals who believe that smoking is unhealthy and that a good diet, a regular exercise regimen, and getting plenty of rest are all important. Strong religious beliefs of a group could identify a segment.

- *Language spoken.* Segmentation groups customers into clusters based on the buyers' language in common use. Care must be taken that the data for making this determination are factual. For example, it would not be useful to presume that every customer with a Spanish-sounding or -spelled name speaks Spanish and others do not.

- *Decision-maker.* Segmentation requires factual data that identify the decision-maker in a purchase. This means that other data that are pertinent are correctly linked with the decision-maker.

- *Occasion for purchase.* Segmenting customers by the event or reason for the purchase and for whom the purchased product or service is intended.

- *Potential or past customers.* This can constitute a segment, providing the data are available. Data for the potential customers would be drawn from outside the organization's customer database. Data for past customers may still reside in the customer database or in archived files.

Segmentation Concepts

Key segmentation concepts are depicted in Figure 16.3.[11] These concepts are:

- *No segmentation.* In Figure 16.3a customers are completely undifferentiated; all customers are perceived as having the same expectations. Uniform quality is the goal, and mass marketing is used.

- *Complete market segmentation.* Each customer in Figure 16.3b has a unique set of requirements. The quality requirements are set by each customer's individual demands, and customized marketing is used.

- *Segmentation by a single criterion.* Figures 16.3c and 16.3d show segmentation based on a single differentiating factor (income or age). Each distinct class requires a different marketing approach, and quality requirements may differ for each class.

- *Segmentation by multiple criteria.* Two differentiating factors (income and age) are used in Figure 16.3e. Customers are classified according to both factors. Marketing strategy and quality requirements can vary for each class identified.

- *Patterns of segmentation.* Customers are often segmented by demographic (for example, age and income) or psychographic (lifestyle and attitudes) criteria, but segmentation by product attributes is especially helpful to quality managers. Customers' likes and dislikes indicate their preferences. Three broad preference patterns are shown in Figure 16.4.

- *Homogeneous preferences.* Customers with homogeneous preferences have roughly the same preferences. In Figure 16.4 (*left*) the two product attributes (quality and price) graphed do not appear to cause a natural segmentation. Competing brands are likely to be similar and located near the center.

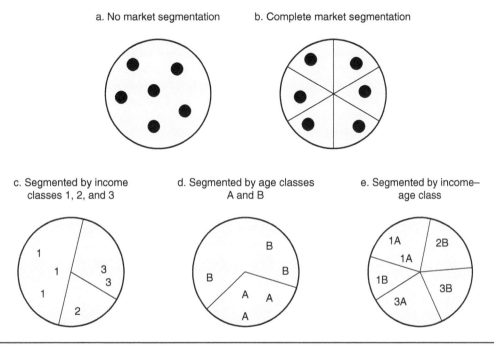

Figure 16.3   Preference segment patterns.

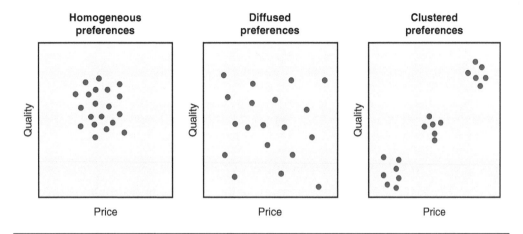

Figure 16.4   Segmentation concepts.

- *Diffused preferences.* In Figure 16.4 (*middle*) no natural segments exist, but customer preferences vary greatly. Competitors would be expected to offer dissimilar products in response to customer preferences.

- *Clustered preferences.* Natural market segmentation occurs in Figure 16.4 (*right*). Distinct preference clusters exist, and competing products are expected to be dissimilar between clusters and similar within clusters.

Market segmentation must be based on sound statistical techniques that ensure that samples taken represent the market as a whole, as well as the individual segment being studied. This aids in the identification of key segments of potential customers. *Cluster analysis* is a multivariate technique that creates groupings on the basis of minimizing variation within groups and maximizing variation between groups, according to a list of variables or criteria. *Factor analysis* is sometimes used to map the perceptual space of customer needs and wants for a market for a particular good or service. Used together, the resulting perceptual maps identify both the location of segments and the market perceptions of competitors in meeting key needs and wants. For example, creation of multiple fragrances of cleaning products was based on research that identified market segments with the requirement of something other than lemon or pine fragrances for cleaning products. As none of the existing brands were positioned to meet these requirements, fragrances such as Sea Breeze, Spring Rain, and Mountain Fresh were created and marketed specifically to meet those needs.

To aid in discerning discrete customer patterns, population mapping using geographic information systems (GIS) is frequently used. Uncovering relationships from a vast amount of customer data is the aim of data mining the customer database.

Choosing a Segmentation Strategy

Identifying customers and providing benefits targeted to meet or exceed their unique requirements is a prescription leading to extraordinary levels of customer satisfaction, loyalty, and profitability. The principal reasoning behind this axiom is that a market includes individuals and organizations from all circumstances. If all individuals and organizations had the same needs and expectations, it would be easy to standardize product features and service delivery processes to maximize the value that each desired.

In reality, however, the marketplace is far more complex. Many subsets of customer needs and requirements (segments) exist. An organization attempting to appeal to the needs of everyone in the market might actually fail to deliver the value expected by any of its segments. The key is to identify the segment(s) that should be the strategic focus of the organization. High rates of market segment penetration are likely when product features and service processes are in alignment with customers' requirements.

Best practices in customer identification and segmentation include the following:

- Creating and maintaining a customer information system to provide data on customer identity, potential segmentation criteria, and, if possible, data on customer needs and requirements. If a comprehensive customer database is not feasible, market and customer research can be used to characterize segments.

- Using SWOT analysis as a preliminary indication of competitive position. Segmentation strategies that offer the most leverage for building on current strengths and minimizing current weaknesses should be explored.

- Using customer and market surveys to evaluate customer and market perceptions of the organization and comparing these perceptions to those held toward competitors. This information can be used to identify current position (in the minds of both customers and noncustomers) relative to current and potential market opportunities.

- Choosing a segmentation strategy that fits the organization's strategic intent in the context of opportunity. Segmentation can be integrated into strategic planning, marketing planning, and quality and service process improvement plans.

An organization's marketing strategy must take into consideration whether the organization is interested most in pursuing more customers or in targeting the right customers. Effectively targeting a market requires a clear understanding of the current customer strata and how each contributes to revenue and profit. Anthony suggests a focused approach for developing the right customers:

- Direct the marketing efforts precisely (focus to avoid undisciplined expansion).

- Tailor marketing plans/campaigns (and service delivery processes) to meet the needs of core customer segments. This translates into properly allocating marketing resources across segments, as underfunding efforts directed at core segments could result in lost opportunities.

- Use appropriate marketing performance indicators to monitor and guide the relative success of segmentation initiatives. Move away from indicators such as number of customers and gross sales in favor of cost of sales, cost of retention (a cost-of-quality component), potential for expansion, and customer profit contribution.[12]

Considerations for effective customer identification and segmentation are:

- Make the effort to identify customers.

- If an organization sells through wholesalers and retailers and has no idea of the identity of its customers, it can build a segmented customer database through product registrations and warranty work or conducting market research.

- When an organization believes it knows its customers, the evidence might be anecdotal and unsupported by hard data. Effective segmentation requires metrics to classify customers into groups, as well as to evaluate their value to the organization (for example, sales revenue and profit contribution).

- A segmentation initiative generally emanates from the marketing side of the organization, supported by the organization's strategy. However, stakeholders in quality and operations planning need to integrate the thinking and systems of the organization to align service delivery processes and quality with the customers' requirements dictated by the segmentation strategy.

There are some cautions when following a segmentation strategy. For example, be careful that the segmentation strategy is not actually a ruse or can be misinterpreted as such—for example, charging a higher late-payment fee to delinquent buyers from low-income families. And, if using segmentation concepts and practices with internal customers, be mindful of any potential for violating a management-labor contract in effect—for example, arbitrarily tailoring employee benefits according to employee gender, age, or other demographic or psychographic factor.

When an organization adopts a segmentation strategy, it is tempting to optimize the service delivery system to maximize customer satisfaction for the core customers or the strategically most significant segment. Sometimes a separate service delivery process is created to serve noncore segments. This may entail duplication of whole systems internally—for example, call centers, distribution facilities, and staff functions such as sales, technical support, and installation and repair personnel.

Process for Working with External Customers

The following process is an approach to working with external customers to improve products, services, and internal processes:

1. Identify who the customers are:

   • Define and prioritize the customer segments the organization serves.

   • Determine whether the types of customers served represent the right segment mix to support the organization's strategic objectives.

   • Conduct a gap analysis to highlight types of customer segments that should be added, phased out, or realigned to meet strategic objectives.

2. What do the customers in the key segments to be served need/want?

   • Use techniques and tools to capture the voices of the key customer segments.

   • Conduct a gap analysis to identify opportunities for adding to, discontinuing, or modifying the present product and service portfolio.

3. What internal processes would need to be changed?

   • Examine internal processes for their capability to meet the new needs resulting from the two gap analyses.

   • Perform a feasibility study of each recommended change.

   • Perform a risk analysis of each recommended change.

4. Establish action plans and implement the feasible changes to internal processes.

5. Test market the changes and make necessary corrections.

6. Roll out the full-scale changes.

7. Evaluate the effectiveness of implemented changes.

4. QUALITATIVE ASSESSMENT

> Identify subjective information such as verbatim comments from customers, observation records, and focus group output. Describe how the subjective information differs from objective measures and determine when data should be captured in categories rather than numeric value. (Analyze)
>
> **Body of Knowledge V.A.4**

Much of the information used by organizations to measure and track performance consists of quantitative data. Figures such as sales of a particular product, on-time delivery of suppliers, average length of stay in a hospital, or percentage of college entrants who graduate are easily measured or counted.

Qualitative information is also important for organizational decision-making. Examples could be customer requirements for a new product, employee opinion about the value of a new benefits package, or consistency of leadership practices with stated organizational principles. Qualitative data are expressed using words (opinions, beliefs, feelings, attitudes)—things that are not really measurable per se.

Qualitative data add complexity to the assessment process due to the subjectivity of what is being studied. What information can be gathered that will reflect the parameter(s) of interest? This is usually addressed by creating a series of questions to be answered or by gathering information that is already available and grouping the findings into categories believed to be related to a question of interest.

Qualitative assessments are frequently conducted using one of the following techniques:

- One-on-one interviews (in person or by phone) or group interviews (focus groups)

- Observation of actual behaviors (for example, mystery shoppers who study how they are treated during transactions)

- Content analysis conducted by reviewing memos or other normal business processes to determine what events occur (or do not occur)

- Surveys or questionnaires with mostly open-ended questions that are mailed (or e-mailed) to target groups or are available as part of a business interaction (for example, a comment card at a restaurant table)

Qualitative surveys use mostly open-ended questions and usually in-person phone interviews or focus groups to gather the data. This allows in-depth exploration for each question as an interviewer is able to ask respondents to elaborate on and to clarify their comments. While qualitative investigations help identify key constructs (i.e., customer requirements), quantitative surveys allow us to objectively measure how well we are delivering for those things that are important to customers.

It is highly appropriate to ask a limited number of qualitative questions when conducting a quantitative investigation. It is extremely valuable to know the reasons why customers say they are either delighted or disappointed with their customer experience, for example.

In order for qualitative data to be analyzed, they are usually converted to categories (nominal data), so frequencies of occurrence may be tabulated. If the information is narrative, it can be analyzed by looking for particular words, phrases, or contexts that occur repeatedly. The information can also be organized into an affinity diagram to help indicate common areas, themes, or categories.

Qualitative data, when transformed through analysis into information, are used to examine the depth of motivations, values, attitudes, perceptions, and emotions. Quantitative data, in contrast, are better used for developing information regarding statistical estimation, such as about the breadth of information—how many and how much.

Survey Analysis and Use

Surveys typically require a significant investment of time and resources but if effectively analyzed and used, can drive and monitor continual improvement efforts. Following are suggested actions:

1. Analyze the raw data:

   - It is helpful to review frequency distributions of responses for each question to understand the data.

   - Rank the findings (answers to questions) in order of high to low outcomes. What does this say about particular topics?

   - Look for correlation between questions. Do multiple questions designed to assess the same topic agree or disagree?

   - Segregate the data based on demographic, market, or other groups within the study population. Look for differences based on product line, geographic location, and so on.

2. Compare the data to other information:

   - Compare findings to those of previous surveys. Do they show expected/desired changes? If not, why? Are changes over time statistically significant?

   - Compare findings to other internal and external data. Do they agree or do anomalies exist that should be further investigated?

3. Communicate the information to decision-makers:

   - Give the data to those who had originally planned to use it. Also consider openly sharing the findings with others who may be able to learn from them and improve. (Caution: This sharing may exclude competitors.)

   - Do not be selective in communicating the information. Do not hide findings where results were undesired or are uncomfortable to deal with.

4. Use the information and verify results:

- Where significant needs or opportunities for improvement are indicated, find ways to confirm understanding or get more detailed information to guide changes.

- Do a follow-up survey after improvements have been implemented to determine how effective they have been.

REFERENCES

1. F. M. Gryna, "Market Research and Marketing," in *Juran's Quality Handbook*, 5th ed., ed. J. M. Juran and A. B. Godfrey (New York: McGraw-Hill, 1999), 18.11.

2. H. J. Harrington, *Business Process Improvement: The Breakthrough Strategy for Total Quality, Productivity, and Competitiveness* (New York: McGraw-Hill, 1991).

3. J. L. Hradesky, *Total Quality Management Handbook* (New York: McGraw-Hill, 1995), 29.

4. K. R. Bhote, *Strategic Supply Management* (New York: AMACOM, 1989).

5. R. T. Westcott, "Quality-Level Agreements for Clarity of Expectations," *Informed Outlook* (December 1999): 13–15.

6. K. Albrecht, and R. Zemke, *Service America!* (New York: Dow Jones-Irwin, Warner Books ed., 1990), 96.

7. T. Levitt, *The Marketing Imagination* (New York: Free Press, 1983), 216–17.

8. A. Toffler, and H. Toffler, *Powershift: Knowledge, Wealth, and Violence at the Edge of the 21st Century* (New York: Bantam, 1990).

9. A. Ries, *Focus: The Future of Your Company Depends on It* (New York: HarperCollins, 1996), 128.

10. Levitt, *Marketing Imagination*, 217.

11. T. J. Pyzdek, *The Complete Guide to the CQM* (Tucson: Quality, 1996), 299–302.

12. M. Anthony, "More Customers or Right Customers: Your Choice," *Marketing News*, August 31, 1998, 13.

See Appendix A for additional references for this chapter.

Chapter 17
B. Customer Relationship Management

Chapter 16 defined types of customers. This chapter focuses on the most important customer type, the primary customers. The *primary customer* is almost always an external customer and is frequently the consumer, or end user, of the organization's product or service.

Defining Customer Focus

Organizations that recognize the importance of customers and focus on their wants and needs are commonly referred to as being *customer focused* or *customer driven*. In business literature, the terms *customer driven* and *market driven* are often used interchangeably; however, a customer-driven organization focuses more on the care and retention of existing customers, whereas the market-driven organization is more attuned to attracting new customers.

In best-in-class organizations, virtually every activity is undertaken with the customers' interests in mind. Note that this does not imply that an organization should do so at a financial loss. Organizations that are not profitable ultimately cease to do business.

Many customers express requirements in value terms—the components that influence the buy decision—for example, price, product quality, innovation, service quality, provider's image, and reputation.

Managing Customer Relationships

Customer relationships, in their most advanced form, become supplier-customer partnerships or alliances. Although partnerships or alliances are not always the ultimate objective of a customer relationship, an effective relationship exists when a customer has a strong preference for a particular supplier. This may be based on any number of factors, such as performance history or experience, responsiveness, flexibility, trust, and other aspects that lead to value for the customer. The practice of *customer relationship management* (CRM) is most appropriate with those customers who can most affect a company's future.

A relationship strategy may not be possible, or even desirable, with all customers. Relationship strategies may vary considerably from one customer or customer segment to another. A company's CRM strategy aims to learn, in depth, about the customers' needs, values, and behaviors. A supplier organization collects and coordinates customer information, sales information, marketing effectiveness, responsiveness to customers, and market trends. It helps in maintaining satisfactory relationships with customers and requires the commitment of both management and the entire workforce. Also referred to as *relationship marketing* or *one-to-one marketing*, CRM is a concept greatly influenced by Peppers, Rogers, and Dorf.[1] McKenna offers the following perspective:

> *Differentiation, from the customer's viewpoint, is not something that is product or service related as much as it is related to the way you do business. In the age of information, it is no longer possible to manufacture an image. The distinction between perception and reality is getting finer. Further, in a world where customers have so many choices, they can be fickle. This means modern marketing is a struggle for customer loyalty. Positioning must involve more than simple awareness of a hierarchy of brands and company names. It demands a special relationship with the customer and infrastructure of the marketplace.[2]*

1. CUSTOMER NEEDS

> Use quality function deployment (QFD) to capture the voice of the customer (VOC) and examine customer needs in relation to products and services offered. Analyze the results to prioritize future development in anticipation of changing customer needs. (Analyze)
>
> **Body of Knowledge V.B.1**

Anticipating Customer Expectations and Needs

Anticipating customer expectations can occur at two levels: from analyzing markets and observing social trends and from contacts with customers and suppliers. At the first level, it is staying current with or ahead of emerging trends. Contributors to potential future expectations are market researchers, social psychologists, and future-oriented societies dedicated to analyzing a wide range of prognostications.

At the customer contact level, there are two aspects to address: analysis of how well customers feel current products meet their expectations and what customers foresee as future wants and needs. Customer expectations may vary, depending on whether or not there are suppliers who can provide the product or service the customer requires or whether there is a probability that known suppliers can develop the product or service needed. Organizations that introduce a new product or service into the marketplace are not initially responding to a customer's expectations; they are concerned with building a demand for their offerings.

Data about customer needs can be found within and outside of the organization. Data found within the organization include:

- Customer complaints
- Past records of claim resolutions

- Warranty and guarantee usage

- Service records—product failure, product maintenance

- Customer contact personnel

- Listening post data

- Customer satisfaction surveys or other feedback

- Market research

Data obtained from outside the organization include:

- Data about competitors' customers

- Research—magazine and newspaper articles, information from trade journals

- Public information—for example, customers' and competitors' annual reports

- Advertising media—brochures, TV and radio, websites

- Industry market research

Each data source listed above could well be considered when constructing the *voice of the customer* (VOC) for any particular product or service. The VOC should not only help capture customer needs/wants (requirements) but also provide insight on how well the organization's product and services meet those needs/wants. Read the following three scenarios and, from a customer's perspective, ask what factors or features:

- May be satisfiers?

- May be dissatisfiers?

- Would meet my priorities?

- Would just meet my needs?

- Would truly excite or delight me?

In the first scenario, Alpha is a distributor of replacement parts for household appliances. Alpha's perception of customers' expectations is as follows: the part needed is in stock, the part needs to work as intended, the part needs to be the same or of higher quality as the part it replaces, there is a very short waiting time, courteous treatment is given, the supplier offers some instruction on how to install the part, and the price for the part is fair.

In the second scenario, Beta, a manufacturer of toy action figures, is launching a new action figure. Beta's customers are toy distributors who expect, for example, that Beta has made a sound judgment that the new action figure will rapidly become a high-demand item, the quality of the product will be the same or higher compared to previous products from Beta, delivery will be on time to meet the holiday market (assuming the demand will build), and Beta is prepared to manufacture and ship additional product to distributors on short notice if demand exceeds original projections.

Epsilon, a department store, buys an initial shipment of the new toy from its toy distributor. Epsilon expects that Beta will heavily promote the item, that the toy will generate interest and demand, and that Epsilon will make a profit. It also expects the distributor to be able to deliver rush orders if demand exceeds original estimates.

One of Epsilon's customers is Peggy, the mother of seven-year-old Billy. Peggy expects to find something new and different to buy for Billy that costs less than $25 and is not too heavy to carry. Peggy is shopping in the first week of December. Searching the toy department, she sees several items that may meet her needs. Several action figures look familiar, probably from last year's promotions. One item, Captain Saturn, appears to be new and is unknown to her. It is selling for $19.95 and weighs only a couple of pounds. But will Billy want that? The parking meter is about to expire, so she leaves without buying anything.

A couple of weeks pass. Billy has been avidly following the TV adventures of Captain Saturn. He has taken much notice of the advertisements for the new action figure now available. Desire builds, and Billy pesters his mother for the toy.

A week before the holiday, Peggy ventures into the horde of holiday shoppers in search of Captain Saturn. She expects to find the toy, and at the same price as before. A mob of angry shoppers surround a large sign notifying potential buyers that the captain is presently sold out. Orders are being taken on a first-come basis, at a price of $34.95, with no guarantee the item will be delivered before the holiday. Peggy quits, empty-handed.

A block away, a street vendor is offering "Captain Saturn in the original carton" for $50, cash only, no returns. Frustrated, Peggy buys one. The toy survives only two hours of Billy's vigorous play. It was a knockoff, not the authentic Beta model.

In our third scenario, Omega College, a small, privately endowed institution, offers associate's and bachelor's degrees in business. Following its strategic planning goals, Omega has decided it must offer a new degree program to address the local business need for management candidates with an emphasis on quality management. The new program will be offered on an accelerated basis, with all of the students' work done online. This is to accommodate employed people who normally could not attend either a full daytime or an evening program. Omega expects that its projected enrollment will more than support the costs of launching the new program, including hiring faculty.

Susan and the eleven other students enrolled in the first class of the new program expect to learn material that will qualify them for good-paying management positions upon graduation. They speculate that the teachers from the business world will be more interesting, realistic, and up-to-date than typical college professors. These students expect a more practical education than theoretical. The degree program will cost more than the traditional business degree program.

These scenarios emphasize the importance of identifying who the customers are and, then, what expectations need to be considered. Should Alpha be concerned if its supplier produces parts made from inferior materials? Should Beta be concerned whether the TV network has plans to renew Captain Saturn for another season? Why should the Omega College administrators be concerned about the job market for quality-educated managers three years from now?

These questions, and more, are valid considerations as an organization supplying products and services anticipates and projects future needs and priorities. Thought must be given to whether the products or services offered only marginally satisfy a customer or have the potential for generating real excitement. What are the possibilities for disappointing the customer? How will the customers' expectations, priorities, and needs fit with the supplier's priorities and needs?

Is it possible that with today's speed to market and the growing ephemeral nature of customer demand that many of these questions do not matter? Consider that cultural drivers may make these questions more useful for organizations who desire to reach their desired level of excellence.

Insofar as feasible, start with data from customers (gathered with one or more of the tools discussed later). One method for transforming these data into information is to document and assess these answers and the impact on the supplier's organization using the quality function deployment matrix.

Quality Function Deployment

Quality function deployment (QFD) is a methodology that helps translate a customer voice input on needs/wants from qualitative constructs into operational requirements. Using a tool called the house of quality, we are able to look into the relationships between customer needs and product characteristics and use these to set priorities in the way a product is designed or delivered. In this way, QFD translates the customers' voice into product and service characteristics that will result in increased levels of customer satisfaction. Viewing Figure 17.1, we see that:

- Data for section A, the customers' wants and needs, is obtained from several VOC sources—for example, customer listening systems, surveys, and customer focus groups.

- Each listed customer want is given an importance weighting in section B.

- Through research, interviews, focus groups, and so on, data are obtained in order to rate customers' perceptions, in section C, of the wants listed in section A relative to competitors' products/services (the horizontal connection between A and C).

- "How things are done"—the critical characteristics of the process that meet the customers' needs (the voice of the company)—is shown in columns in section D of the matrix.

- In the cells of the relationships section of the matrix, section E, where the rows and columns of the matrix intersect, relationship codes are inserted. Usually, these codes are classified as 9 = *strongly related*, 3 = *moderately related*, or 1 = *weakly related*.

- Section F shows totals of the vertical columns, representing the sums of the weighted totals of the relationships (where coded) between the customers' wants and the organization's voice of the company (characteristics of the process/product).

- The house of quality is completed by adding a roof, section G, which is a matrix to correlate the interrelationship between company descriptors. Code symbols depict the strength of the correlated relationships. See a completed sample QFD in Figure 17.2.

The QFD matrix may be changed and/or expanded according to the objectives of the analysis. If desired, customer requirements can be prioritized by importance,

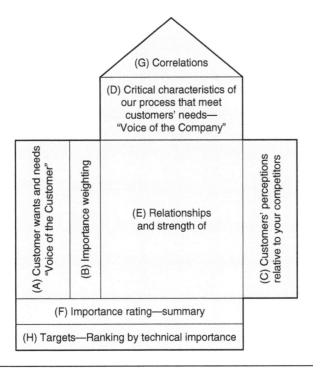

Figure 17.1 Quality function deployment matrix "house of quality."

competitive analysis, and market potential by adding an additional matrix to the right-hand side of the QFD matrix. The company descriptors can be prioritized by importance, target values, and competitive evaluation with a matrix added to the bottom of the QFD matrix. To summarize, the QFD approach and deployment steps are:

1. Plan—determine the objective(s), and determine what data are needed.

2. Collect data.

3. Analyze and understand the data using the QFD matrix to generate information.

4. Deploy the information throughout the organization (depending on the objectives).

5. Employ the information in making decisions.

6. Evaluate the value of the information generated and evaluate the process.

7. Improve the process.

The completed QFD matrix can also indicate which activities for problem-solving or continual improvement should be given the highest priority. This graphic representation helps management and personnel involved in an improvement effort understand how an improvement will affect customer satisfaction and helps prevent deviations from that objective. See Figure 17.3 for a diagram of the cascading matrices involved in the deployment of the voice of customer through design, parts planning, process planning, and production.

Figure 17.2   Sample QFD matrix for an automobile door.

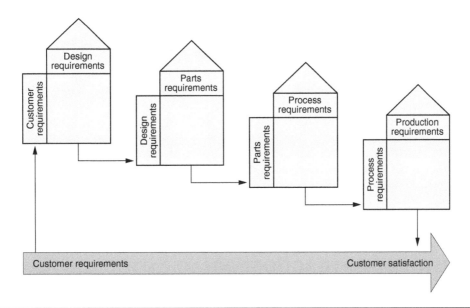

Figure 17.3   Quality function deployment using voice of customer (VOC).

QFD has been used to develop products that delight the customers by providing features that are beyond their stated requirements. In many cases, the customers did not know these options were possible, so they were not on a list of needs or priorities. By comparing a customer's requirements to product and service features, the company typically focuses on identifying and prioritizing the agreements and gaps. From this analysis, innovative new offerings are more likely to become apparent. These can provide a greater probability of moving the company into the "delighting" quality level. Findings from a competitive analysis may also identify opportunities for significant improvement.

A simpler but less comprehensive analysis may be done using a kind of priority matrix for each unique product and service offered, for each type of customer. To set up a sample priority matrix, title a spreadsheet with the name of the product or service and the type of customer. Label seven columns, reading left to right:

a. Product/service factor/feature

b. Potential to satisfy customers (brief commentary)

c. Estimated rating of customers' perception of value (scale: 0 = *none*, 1 = *low* to 5 = *high*)

d. Potential to dissatisfy customers (brief commentary)

e. Estimated rating of customers' negative perception (same scale, only with minus prefix for any 1s through 5s)

f. Estimated overall rating of impact on customers (arithmetic sum of the two ratings from *c* and *e* above)

g. Comments about increasing, sustaining, decreasing, or eliminating the factor/feature from the suppliers' perspective

List every factor/feature of the organization's products and services, including those already perceived as negative. For each line, rate the positive value perceived by the customer and the negative value perceived, with comments about each. Sum the two ratings and make comments about the impact on the organization if the feature/factor was increased, sustained, decreased, or eliminated, based on the perceptions of the customers.

A glance at the completed table provides a perception of how customers may rate present expectations, needs, and value of the organization's products or services. Creating the same type of table for a new product or service and using data from focus groups or other sources can help head off a potentially disastrous product/service launch. Likewise, using this approach with competitor data may yield valuable insights as to what the organization must do to meet or exceed the competition.

2. CUSTOMER SATISFACTION AND LOYALTY

> Develop systems to capture positive and negative customer feedback and experiences, using tools such as listening posts, focus groups, complaints and warranty data, surveys, and interviews. Use customer value analysis to calculate the financial impact of existing customers and the potential results of losing those customers. Develop corrective actions and proactive methods to improve customer satisfaction, loyalty, and retention levels. (Create)
>
> **Body of Knowledge V.B.2**

Voice of the Customer as a System

If you ask three people to describe what VOC is in their organization, how it is chartered, and how it is actually used, you will likely get three diverse approaches in the responses. Here are a few ideas to support a robust VOC system.

- Create a standing cross-functional team for VOC.

- All customer touchpoints and functions should be represented, with participation of leaders, managers, and frontline staff as appropriate.

- Charter should detail meeting frequency (weekly/monthly/quarterly).

- Primary charter of the team is to identify/monitor customer current and future needs, as well as measure customer perceptions on how well those needs are met.

- Charter should check effectiveness of actions taken as a result of improvements implemented.

- Dedicated staff need to be assigned to VOC team to organize and analyze data and translate it into useful information for VOC team and other stakeholders.

- Synergy results from bringing all "owners" of customer information sources into a centralized group, where context is shared ownership in meeting customers' needs.

- Be outcome focused. Strive to get the right information to the right people.

Figure 17.4 shows a framework for moving from data inputs to useful information outputs, especially in a setting of cross-functional collaboration as just described. Getting the right information into the hands of the right people is critical for a high-performing customer-focused organization. Some examples include:

- Frontline workers in tech support get feedback on their strengths and weaknesses from customers they served.

- Tech support manager gets feedback on performance for each employee in department and uses results to coach higher performance.

- Senior management can see when additional resources are needed to help tech support be more effective.

- Information streams are directed to foster more effective corrective action, prevention, and process improvement.

- Information streams on changing customer requirements and new market opportunities are identified to support strategic planning.

Other Models for Gathering and Deploying Voice of the Customer Information

Juran on Planning for Quality details a process for optimizing product design.[3] Juran's model uses a spreadsheet (matrix) approach, the concepts of which could be adapted to the measurement and analysis of customer satisfaction.

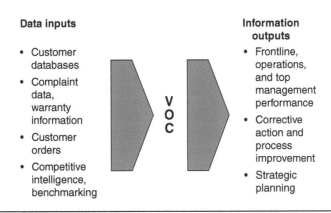

Figure 17.4 Robust VOC system.

GOAL/QPC's VOC research report describes a structured approach for gathering, analyzing, and deploying the VOC, which, if desired, can be linked with QFD.[4]

Criteria category 3.2 of the Baldrige Performance Excellence Program (BPEP) examines "How do you engage customers to serve their needs and build relationships?" Readers are encouraged to obtain a copy of the criteria and become acquainted with the report's entire contents.

Determining Customer Satisfaction Levels

Customer satisfaction levels are impossible to assess unless customers' needs, expectations, and priorities have been determined. Once customer requirements are known, we can ask customers to provide their perceptions of how well we met their needs.

Leading organizations have measured and tracked customer satisfaction levels for decades. In that time we have seen a progression of goals. At first it was measuring customer satisfaction, then measuring value received, then measuring customer loyalty, whether that meant repeat purchase intent or willingness to recommend. Increasingly, there is great interest in measuring and improving the customer experience. All of these concepts are still excellent indicators of the state of the customer/provider relationship, and each can help identify valuable insights to strengthening the customer relationship.

Regardless of the evolving objective, measurement results are used to identify problems and opportunities, measure the performance of products, employees, managers and executives; and reveal competitive strengths and weaknesses. Organizations have also integrated findings (from customer surveys and other VOC sources) into their corporate strategies, new product development, manufacturing quality, product and service delivery, and competitive positioning. Marketing decisions are made on the basis of statistical analysis that shows which factors are most important in their customers' buying decisions.

Customer satisfaction measurement is an integral part of the quality management process as companies use customer satisfaction information to drive improvement initiatives. Figure 17.5 outlines a system for utilizing customer feedback. Leading-edge customer satisfaction systems include several key elements:

- There are formal processes for collecting and analyzing customer data and for communicating results to the appropriate business functions for action. Data can be used for company or market segment analysis to develop marketing strategies or used at the account level to gain an understanding of the customer's opinion of the company.

- Feedback on how well an organization is meeting requirements is gathered by using some combination of the methods listed and described below. Most companies use several methods for collecting customer satisfaction data. By using several sources, the companies are better able to validate results and increase their credibility.

- Because each method of gathering customer feedback has its benefits, disadvantages, and specific applications, most companies choose a combination of methods to get a more complete picture. Once information has been gathered, it can be analyzed in a manner

Customer Information Feedback System

Figure 17.5 System for utilizing customer feedback.

consistent with process and project objectives. This can range from simple top-line reporting to using advanced, sophisticated techniques.

- To be useful, data and the information derived from data must be stored appropriately and made available to those who need it.

Analyzing Customer Satisfaction Data

Kano Model. One method used to analyze customer satisfaction data is the *Kano model* (Figure 17.6). The model was developed by Noriaki Kano to show the relationship between three types of product characteristics, or qualities.[5] The impetus for this two-dimensional modeling is that objective measures of quality such as *satisfaction due to fulfillment* versus *dissatisfaction due to unfulfillment* cannot explain consumer behavior. To account for both objective and subjective (or emotional) aspects of satisfaction, two axes are used: a vertical axis for the degree of emotional *satisfied feeling* and a horizontal axis for objective *state of physical fulfillment*. Aspects of the product or service are mapped into three main areas:

Attractive quality elements—Quality elements that when fulfilled provide satisfaction but when not fulfilled are acceptable. We call this *attractive quality*. These are shown in the upper two quadrants.

One-dimensional quality elements—Quality elements that result in satisfaction when fulfilled and in dissatisfaction when not fulfilled. We call this *one-dimensional quality*, the conventional way of recognizing quality.

Must-be quality elements—Quality elements that are absolutely expected (taken for granted when fulfilled) but result in dissatisfaction when not fulfilled. We call this *must-be quality*, shown in the bottom two quadrants.

Although the above quality element categories are the most common, two other categories are possible, bringing the number of areas for quality elements to five:

Indifferent quality elements—Quality elements that result in neither satisfaction nor dissatisfaction regardless of whether they are fulfilled or not. We call these *indifferent quality elements*.

Reverse quality elements—Quality elements that result in dissatisfaction when fulfilled and satisfaction when not fulfilled. We call these *reverse quality elements*. They are so named because sometimes users evaluate an element as *dissatisfying* while producers have made an effort to fulfill such an element.

The three main areas can be mapped onto the two-dimensional axes as in Figure 17.6. The presence or absence of *must-be* characteristics is shown by the curved line in the lower quadrants. When a must-be characteristic is not present or is not present in sufficient quantity, dissatisfaction exists. As the characteristic becomes more available or of a higher quality, customer satisfaction increases, but only to a neutral state, represented by the horizontal line. In other words, the factor can only satisfy, not delight, the customer.

One-dimensional factors drive satisfaction in direct relationship to their presence, and thus, they are represented by a straight line. For example, as the interest rate on a savings account rises, so does satisfaction.

The curved line in the upper left to center area represents *delighters*. If absent, these factors have no impact on satisfaction. When present, however, these features delight the customer. An example would be automobile cup holders. When

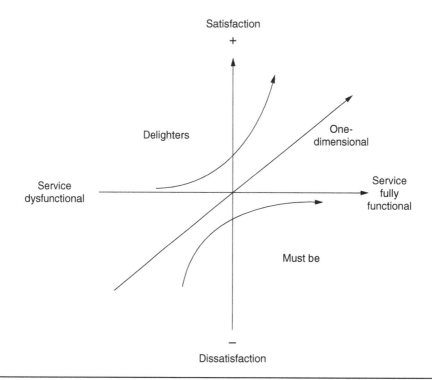

Figure 17.6 The Kano model.

first introduced, cup holders were delighters. This example also demonstrates an important point about delighters. As they become more available, they tend to move from the upper-left side of the model to the lower left. Today, an automobile without cup holders would not be well received in the market. Cup holders have become a *must-be* feature.

Listening Post Data. Most organizations have many people within who regularly or occasionally interact with customers. For example, company engineer to customer's engineer, salesperson to buyer, CEO to CEO, and delivery person to customer's receiving person. In many of these interactions, the customer's employees express opinions, suggestions, complaints, or compliments about the supplier's organization or the products/services quality, delivery, and price—even about the personal attention they receive (or do not). Excepting severe negative expressions, these comments, casually and informally made, are seldom captured. By not having a formal process for collecting and analyzing this data (for example, trending), an organization may be unable to spot the early stage of an eventual customer problem. They also miss compliments that should get back to the people responsible as positive feedback. Listen-capture-analyze-learn-improve (LCALI), a process that does just this, is discussed next.

LCALI. This is a listening post process to capture and use the casual remarks often mentioned in conversations with customers. These remarks are usually forgotten once mentioned, yet they may be the spark of new needs or wants, or hint that a problem may be brewing. Westcott says, "Most companies have no systematic way to actively listen to customers, record what they hear, analyze the data, disseminate the information internally, and act on the information."[6] Without a process like LCALI, opportunities are lost, such as:

- An idea for a new product or service

- A suggestion for improvement of an existing product or service

- Displeasure with some feature or aspect of an existing product or service

- An observation about packaging, the delivery process, or company image

- Comments about the seller's sales approach, customer service, or inquiry handling

- Minor annoyances (long wait times, inconvenient parking, business hours)

- Actions of the seller's personnel that pleased the customer

- Comments about a competitor's product or service

- Hints that the customer may soon leave

These are but a few of the possible types of comments that may casually come up during the course of communication between the seller and the buyer (between the producer's personnel and buyer's personnel or the actual consumer). The key is to:

- Train the seller organization's personnel to tune into these remarks and know what requires immediate action (requires corrective action) versus what is casual commentary.

- Have a process for recording the casual remarks, collecting them, and analyzing them (for example, trending, severity prioritizing).

- Get the information learned to the right people in the organization to take action.

When casual customer information is captured, categorized, and trended over time, patterns evolve that can materially affect your product and service design, production, delivery, and customer satisfaction. For example, a CEO of an engineering consulting firm, after an introduction to the LCALI process, admitted that had his firm used the process earlier, the firm could have saved over a million dollars. Four months prior, the firm's project manager was talking on the phone to the customer's engineer and heard the engineer was looking around for another job because he could "see the handwriting on the wall." The consulting engineer, feeling that the customer's engineer's problem was not his concern (not in his job description) did nothing with the information.

Shortly thereafter, the customer's organization was bought out by a conglomerate in another part of the country. The remnants of the business the buyer wanted from the sale were moved across the country. All projects underway were abandoned. Only three people were relocated; the rest were terminated.

The engineering consulting firm had invested (consulting time and travel expenses) over a year on a project with the customer, very heavily in the last two months. Expensive tools and equipment belonging to the firm were lost when the customer's operation closed. Costly legal actions were underway to attempt to recoup some of the engineering consulting firm's losses (over a million dollars projected).

In another situation, a pharmaceutical company's delivery driver heard from a customer's receiving clerk that the customer's warehousing supervisor was upset with the way the product came in shrink-wrapped. Slow-moving product, within unopened shrink-wrapped pallets, tended to develop condensation (sweat), causing some of the product to become unusable. The warehouse supervisor had not complained to anyone in his company because he did not want to cause a problem. Lately, however, the supervisor had been criticized about the amount of product scrapped before its normal expiration date. He had casually griped to the receiving clerk, who passed on the gripe to the delivery truck driver.

The truck driver, trained to tune into such comments, duly recorded the information he had heard and turned in the record to the official listening post person at the pharmaceutical company. The listening post person took the following actions: She officially informed the shipping department of the problem by initiating a corrective action request. She reported the comment to the organization's person in charge of analyzing such comments. He found that similar comments had been rumored previously from other customers. He initiated a preventive action request to review the packaging procedure. He informed the sales rep for the customer's account so the customer could be informed that a potential problem had been noted and action was being taken. He updated the listening post person on the actions taken. He informed the truck driver's supervisor of the actions being taken so the driver could be recognized for his contribution.

Figure 17.7 shows a sample form used in the LCALI process.

Customer Focus Teams. Customer focus teams improve the ability of an organization to execute the strategies of customer relationship management. Often, these teams provide a point of focus for customers that cuts across different functions.

Customer/Client Contact Record (CCR)   [CCR no.]

A. Identification   [Cust./client no.]

Contact   *[Person's name]*   *[Title]*
from: *[Location]*   *[Phone]*
               [Customer/client's name]   *[Fax]*
               [Address]   *[E-mail]*
               [City]   *[State/province]*   *[Country]*

Field   *[Name]*   *[Position]*
listener: *[Dept./location]*   *[Mail stop]*   *[Phone]*
               [Supervisor's name]   *[Title]*

B. Context/situation/place of contact

❏ Complaint   ❏ Compliment   ❏ General observation *[What?]*
❏ Letter: *[Date]*   ❏ Phone call: *[Date]*   ❏ Face-to-face: *[Date]*   ❏ Other: *[Date]*
[Describe context in greater detail if "other" is checked:]

C. Quote or best recollection of words from customer/client and nature of the contact

❏ Related to specific order/product: *[Order no.]*   *[Date]*   *[Product]*
❏ Related to specific representative of this organization: *[Who]*   *[Date]*
[Record words used by customer/client's contact. If a direct quote, use quotation marks.]

[Describe any details that will make the understanding of the customer/client's perspective clear to persons reading this CCR. Note if customer/client specifically requested notification of resolution or other feedback. Use back of form if needed.]

[Field listener's commentary (viewpoint, opinion, interpretation)]

D. Action activity

Triage: ❏ Action needed now   ❏ Investigate further   ❏ Watch trend
             (Corrective action)   (Preventive action)
Action assigned to: *[Name]*   *[Location]*   *[Phone]*   *[Date]*
Follow-up: *[How?]*   *[Date]*   *[Date]*   *[Date]*   *[Date]*
Status reports: *[How?]*   *[Date]*   *[Date]*   *[Date]*   *[Date]*

E. Resolution and closeout

[State how problem/question was resolved:]   *[By whom]*   *[Date]*
[Corrective action no.]   *[Preventive action no.]*   *[Returned material auth. no.]*   *[Other?]*
[Procedure/work instruction affected]   *[Date to be changed]*   *[By whom]*
[Forms/computer programs affected]   *[Date to be changed]*   *[By whom]*
[Status/feedback to be provided—how?]   *[To whom]*   *[By whom]*   *[By date]*
[Closeout code] [Closed by:—print]   *[Signature]*   *[Date]*

Figure 17.7   A customer/client contact record, a sample LCALI form.

Source: Reprinted with permission of R. T. Westcott & Associates.

Typical team composition includes an account manager, customer service representative, field engineer/tech support, and plant representatives. The purpose of the customer focus team is to provide a near-seamless interface in the customer relationship. Further, it ensures that all the key stakeholders in the supplying organization are in alignment on strategy and actions on behalf of the customer.[7]

Focus Groups. *Focus groups* are qualitative group discussions, usually with eight to ten participants generally recruited based on segmentation criteria, such as level of product use, age, income, and/or gender. A discussion guide that outlines questions is prepared in advance. The questions are asked and facilitated by a focus group moderator. Depending on the research design, between two and ten groups may be conducted with different customer segments in different geographic areas. Focus groups can identify important recurring themes with regard to product or service likes and dislikes and important service and product factors (customer requirements), as well as opportunities for product/service performance improvement.

The focus group has many of the benefits and uses of the in-person interview and the added benefit of a group's synergy at a lower cost per response. Focus groups are often used as a first step in developing surveys, especially to identify specific product and service requirements. Focus groups of internal customers can provide input to improve business, manufacturing, development, administrative, and even sales processes.

External customer focus groups are usually conducted in specialized facilities, with respondents and moderator in one room and with clients behind a one-way mirror in another. Typically, focus groups require a skilled facilitator to ensure that the sessions stay on track and are not unduly influenced by a few participants.

Complaint Handling

Empirical data from *Consumer Complaint Handling in America, an Update Study* shows the importance of effective complaint-handling systems. The data show the importance of making it easy and convenient for customers to complain when they experience problems and for complaint handling to be effective and efficient as well. For example, for a product costing over one hundred dollars, the research results show that 9.5% of noncomplainants experiencing problems would repurchase. Repurchase intent increases to 19% for those who complain yet whose issues remain unresolved and jumps way up to 54.3% when complaints are resolved satisfactorily. Additional research by the U.S. Office of Consumer Affairs/Technical Assistance Research Programs (TARP) shows the speed of complaint resolution also affects repurchase intent and is significantly higher when resolution is achieved quickly.[8]

Capturing, Differentiating, and Using Data from Customers

A study indicated a majority of surveyed firms rely on reactive feedback methods (complaint monitoring, toll-free call centers, and warranty systems) to bring the VOC into their organization. Proactive feedback methods, such as written surveys, telephoning, and visiting customers, were less common. Proactive methods (such as customer surveys) are important to provide an accurate measure of problem frequency in the population as reactive methods suffer from self-selection bias (for example, most with a problem never bother to complain).

Many organizations strive to improve performance and increase customer satisfaction because of competitive and financial performance pressures. Businesses collect customer data using many tools and from many functions in the organization. The organization's systems for gathering data, as well as for analyzing and disseminating this information, are key to an effective use of customer data (essentially VOC, though not all will call it that).

Customer data that can be useful in determining customer satisfaction may be from:

- Product warranty registrations

- Complaints, when logged and tracked

- Customer surveys

- Transaction data

- Data from established listening posts

- Lost-customer analysis

When integrated and analyzed, this information is extremely valuable to the organization. Unfortunately, individual departments may feel that they own this information and may not share it with others who could benefit. Regarded separately, the data streams might suggest one course of action but if considered collectively could suggest another course. Organizations need to integrate, process, and trend data and then disseminate the resulting information in a manner that facilitates the maximum positive impact on the organization.

Techniques and Tools Used to Collect the Data

Survey Research. Some of the most common applications of surveys include satisfaction surveys, customer satisfaction tracking, and customer attrition (lost-customer) surveys. Quantitative research provides empirical data from which statistical inferences can be drawn and extrapolated to the population at large. Typically, rating-scale questions and multiple-choice questions are thought of as quantitative. If not a census of everyone, a sample for quantitative research must be random and large enough to draw statistical inferences. Most quantitative surveys include four types of questions: outcome questions (such as overall satisfaction, net promoter score [NPS], etc.), process questions (such as satisfaction with delivery performance), open-ended questions (often used to clarify reasons for positive or negative ratings), and classification questions (such as industry segment, age, or income level).

Qualitative research is very useful in identifying key themes related to the research issues and in capturing affect (likes, dislikes, and preferences). Qualitative research, however, does not allow for statistical inferences that can be projected back to the population.

Survey Methods. There are a variety of survey methods, including:[9]

- *Written/mail surveys.* A common survey method is the written customer satisfaction or mail survey. Many companies periodically mail out companywide surveys, tabulate the results, and provide feedback to all areas of the organization. Some companies survey their customers annually; others send out questionnaires monthly to a random sample of customers.

Mail surveys take longer to implement than phone surveys and some in-person interviews but are the least obtrusive of all survey techniques because respondents can complete the survey at a time of their own choosing. Mail surveys are less expensive than personal interviews and telephone surveys.

Maximizing the response rate of a mail survey is a key concern. Prior notification, a well-written cover letter, and a follow-up survey mailing to nonrespondents in the sample are some of the most effective tactics to boost response rates. (The follow-up only works if the organization can identify who did and who did not respond.) With customer satisfaction surveys, response rates between 30% and 50% are attainable.

Mail surveys can include both quantitative and qualitative questions, but the quality of open-ended qualitative data is not as good as that of telephone and in-person surveys because there is no interviewer to probe or clarify incomplete or vague responses. Mail surveys tend to produce a low response rate, in general.

To be effective, written surveys must be relatively short. This limits the number of questions dedicated to specific areas of the business and minimizes the recipient's desire to throw away the survey. The responses to a single-mailing written survey are not random, as the least and most satisfied customers are most likely to respond. To overcome this problem, some companies may send a second survey mailing or use other methods (phone or in-person) in order to attain a higher response rate.

A variation on the use of a written survey is the captive audience survey. In this approach, an audience of customers, or potential customers, is present for another purpose—for example, a new product demonstration or training in product use. As part of the program, the audience is asked to complete a survey. A high response rate is usually achieved. The question is, how representative of the customer base is the audience that took the survey?

- *Telephone surveys.* Phone surveys can be effective for collecting information about the organization as a whole or about functional areas such as sales and services. Interviewers call customer decision-makers and influencers directly to find out how well their requirements are being met. The survey can be conducted and the findings made available more quickly than mail surveys. Phone surveys are subject to fewer nonresponse biases than mail surveys.

Because response rates are higher, sample sizes can be smaller. Interviewers know for certain who answered the survey questions. Phone survey open-ended comment data quality is good given adequate interviewer training and supervision. Care must be taken with phone surveys to ensure that each interviewer conducts surveys in a consistent manner to minimize potentially biased interviewer effects. It can be more difficult to ask respondents to evaluate complex concepts by phone than it is by mail or in person because visual props are not available.

There is a practical time limit for telephone calls; however, maximum survey length is generally longer than that for mail surveys but shorter than that for in-person interviews. Phone surveys have a higher cost per response than well-executed written surveys but are less expensive than in-person interviews. It should be noted that telephone calls are intrusive by nature, and there has been an increasing resistance to them, especially when consumers are called during their mealtime! Widespread adoption of voice mail and answering machines has necessitated increased attempts to attain reasonable survey response rates. Finally, in many consumer markets, customers have unlisted telephone numbers, cell phones, or no phone service. Even with these disadvantages, the telephone survey continues to be popular and is an excellent source of input for measuring customer perceptions of performance and satisfaction.

There are negatives to telephone surveys: With *caller identification*, the recipient can eliminate the call before any contact is made. Further, without eye contact and with less guilt, some respondents may cut the call short or just hang up when they detect a survey request. There is a growing trend for businesses to conduct automated phone surveys on an opt-in basis immediately following a call to technical support or customer service.

• *In-person interviews (one-to-one)*. The face-to-face interview is the most powerful of all survey methods. It can be used to identify qualitative issues most important to customers so these issues can then be included in preparing quantitative written or telephone surveys. The in-person interview is also an effective method for gathering quantitative information. A skilled interviewer can quickly elicit information critical to improving the sales process. The interviewer can pursue the areas of greatest importance, probe for details, and discuss new ideas and approaches. The in-person interview is an excellent tool for getting input from both external and internal customers. Open-end data quality is unsurpassed. Face-to-face interviewers have the advantage of making eye contact and using body language to encourage respondents to provide more detail in their answers.

The cost of conducting a large number of in-person interviews virtually precludes the value of this technique to gather statistically significant data. This is especially true if the company has a large population of customers or if customers are widely dispersed, as scheduling logistics and geography tend to magnify both the costs and time requirements to complete a project.

Perhaps the greatest advantage of face-to-face surveys is when they can be used with a manageable number of core customers to strengthen relationships with those customers who are most vital to the company's success. The technique also requires the use of skilled, unbiased interviewers. This often means using outside contractors or that employees selected for interviewing are properly trained to be successful. In addition, these types of surveys allow for the longest interviews with minimal respondent fatigue. Unlike with focus groups, the attitudes expressed are truly owned by the respondent and not in any way influenced by groupthink or a dominant participant.

• *E-mail and web-based surveys*. The most popular survey method today is the electronic e-mail-based survey. Usually, an e-mail is sent to the customer including a link to a web-based survey. E-mail surveys have the advantage of being the lowest cost and are the quickest to complete. No one has to print questionnaires, stuff envelopes, or manually enter data. Today's e-mail survey software supports the research design, data collection, analysis, and reporting phases of the project.

The negatives for e-mail surveys include low response rates, poor open-ended data quality, and a requirement to keep the surveys very short to prevent people from not responding. Most survey software provides the ability to send follow-up surveys to those who do not respond in a reasonable time following the initial e-mailing.

Web-based surveys may be posted on customer feedback pages of the company's website, open to anyone who happens to find the survey. While reactive, this feedback can be useful in much the same way as complaints and compliments received by phone or mail.

- *Comment cards/suggestion boxes.* Comment cards and suggestion boxes were once relied upon as a key source of customer feedback. While sometimes still used at some hotels, restaurants, or medical offices, data gathering is more sophisticated today. While comment card-type surveys are almost always very brief and easy to complete, they are generally only completed when the customer had a significant negative experience or, conversely, an extremely delighted experience. The majority of customers simply do not take the time to complete this type of survey. Comment cards in some industries have been replaced with e-mail-based surveys (sent to hotel loyalty program members or to patients after a visit to the dentist). Retail and fast-food businesses often provide customers with incentives (contests/coupons off next visit) for going online and providing feedback about their latest visit. Another replacement for comment cards are wall-mounted touch screens for passing customers to provide simple (*poor-okay-excellent*) responses.

- *Observation. Murmurs*, a technique with origins in Japan, is used to gather information on customer behavior. In the late 1980s, Honda dispatched a team of engineers to the parking lots of Disney's theme parks to discover customers' requirements for their car trunks. The engineers reportedly watched people drive into the theme parks and unload their trunks. On departure, the engineers observed how people packed and loaded their gear into the trunks. As a result, many new design ideas were integrated into Honda trunk designs to add benefits and make them easier for customers to use.

- *Mystery shoppers.* This method can be very useful in monitoring the effectiveness of policy deployment, training, and new product/program launches. Shoppers (either internal or third-party employees) pretend to be customers with specific needs, with the aim to get a firsthand view of the service process in action (not just the way it is supposed to work). Mystery shoppers can be trained to minimize personal biases and focus performance ratings on the basis of carefully defined (objective) service levels. However, high shopper scores do not imply that the organization's performance is universally aligned with customers' needs and expectations. When a mystery shopper uncovers a performance nonconformance to policies, training, and so on, or when a serious deficiency is noted, management needs to take appropriate action. Mystery shoppers are used to verify that sales personnel are properly trained and have been taught the organization's policies and procedures.

- *Internet.* Finch suggests a six-step process for gathering customer information from internet conversations. He says, "Anyone with internet access, even the novice, can locate and extract conversational information related to product quality issues."[10]

- *Social media.* Customer opinions abound on social platforms such as Twitter, Facebook, Instagram, and the like. Sometimes a customer gives rave reviews but more likely in social media would be customer rants. Certain incidents about poor customer service go viral (for example, airlines with flight delays stranding customers for up to fourteen hours; then the plane is boarded and then is delayed for mechanical or other reasons). As such, social media can magnify the impact of both negative and positive experiences. Some companies now pay celebrities to promote their products on social media. More progressive companies not only monitor customer issues shared by social media but also attempt to mitigate the impact of negative publicity.

• *Customer councils.* Sometimes also called a *customer advisory board*, many companies have established customer councils that meet periodically to discuss common issues and concerns. These councils are an excellent way to develop customer-supplier partnerships. Council meetings provide a forum for in-depth discussions of the organization's sales process and for identifying ways in which sales can add value to the products and services. Because council members usually come from the organization's largest and best customers, other forms of customer feedback would be needed to represent the attitudes of all customers.

• *Panels.* A panel is a group of customers recruited by an organization to provide ad hoc feedback on performance or product development ideas. Panel composition can vary depending on strategic intent. Panels frequently include customers who are strategic business partners, are accustomed to communicating openly, and are familiar with the sponsoring organization's business practices and technical capabilities. Like focus groups, data gathered from panels should not be extrapolated to the total population of customers.

• *Joint planning meetings.* One of the most effective ways to identify customer requirements and gather satisfaction feedback is by conducting joint planning meetings (sometimes referred to as a customer review). Although joint planning meetings are known by many names, and the process might vary slightly, common characteristics exist. Joint planning meetings begin with a meeting between representatives of a key customer and the sales and service team for that account. The meeting objective is to determine how the organization can better meet the customers' requirements and expectations. A skilled facilitator leads the participants through a planning process to create a prioritized list of improvement activities. At follow-up meetings, the customers provide feedback on how well the improvements worked, and the participants work together to identify more areas on which to focus. The organization consolidates input from all of the joint planning sessions to identify common issues that can be addressed on a companywide basis.

This method is most useful when salespeople or teams support one or a few large customers. Importantly, the objective of these planning meetings is improvement; customers must never perceive that the intent is to gain additional business. Users of the method do report, however, that it can identify additional business opportunities.

The discipline of customer relationship management forces an organization to reevaluate its methods of measuring the "customers'" satisfaction. Satisfaction surveys conducted only with purchasing customers can be too limited in these enhanced business relationships. The nature of the customer/supplier interface will be dramatically expanded from the traditional seller/purchaser relationship to include cross-functional teams from both organizations. As a result, surveys will increasingly need to examine the needs of a cross-section of stakeholders from the customer's organization. In addition, organizations will be increasingly likely to implement internal satisfaction measurement systems using in-person surveys as a vehicle to improve communications and customer satisfaction and to strengthen relationships with core customers.[11]

Customer Value Analysis. Gale and Wood describe seven tools of customer value analysis:

1. The *market-perceived quality profile* is an "indicator of how well you are performing overall for customers in your targeted market."

2. The *market-perceived price profile* is a weighted indicator of how customers perceive different competitors' performance on given price attributes.

3. The *customer-value map* is a map that reveals any significant cluster of business units receiving premium prices that are not fully supported by superior perceived quality.

4. The *won/lost* analysis is an analysis of those factors that won the sale or lost the sale.

5. The *head-to-head area chart of customer value* is a "chart of customer value displaying where you are doing well and where you do worse against a single competitor."

6. The *key events time line* is a chronological list of the events that changed the market's perception of performance on each quality attribute, both yours and your competitor's.

7. A *what/who matrix* is a method for tracking who is responsible for the actions that will make success in customer value possible.

Using these tools will "enable an organization to navigate strategically even in confusing times."[12]

Numerous factors represent value to different customers under a variety of situations. The characteristics shown in Table 17.1 illustrate different perspectives on what the customer considers important.

Unconditional Guarantees. Unlike warranties, which are conditional (time limited, conditions of use, period of use), an unconditional guarantee informs the customer that:

1. If a product fails, it will be replaced with an item of the same or equivalent value, or money will be refunded, or the item will be repaired, and/or any damage or inconvenience to the customer will be rectified or reimbursed.

2. If a service is substandard, the work performed will be redone or money will be refunded, and/or any damage or inconvenience to the customer will be rectified or reimbursed.

3. The customer will not be challenged about the claim.

4. The customer will receive a sincere apology.

5. The settlement will be quick and fair.

Unconditional guarantees provide a unique opportunity to demonstrate the application of your organization's policy, restore/enhance customer loyalty, foster

Table 17.1   Perspectives of value to customers.

Characteristics—Product (examples)	Performance Reasonable price Durability Safety	Serviceability Ease/flexibility of use Simplicity of design, aesthetics Ease of disposal
Characteristics—Service (examples)	Responsiveness Reliability Competence Access Courtesy Communication (sensitivity, genuine interest/concern)	Credibility/image Confidentiality/security Understanding the customer Accuracy/completeness Timeliness

stories of positive experiences, gather detailed customer data, and sell additional products/services. Also, the guarantee conveys the belief that your organization is sufficiently confident of your product or service quality to offer such a guarantee.

Big Data. Big data analysis can be used for insights to help make better decisions. One application of big data is comparative analysis, where we might want to compare our products, services, and brand with the competition. This could involve looking at user behavior metrics to learn how consumers are engaging in real time with businesses in your sector. Three important aspects of big data are volume, velocity, and variety. Volume has to do with the amount of data that is getting generated. Velocity is related to the speed that these data are generated. Variety refers to the different types of data getting generated.

Data Mining. Data mining is a computer search of a large customer database to seek patterns of heretofore undetected relationships and correlations among the data stored in the records. Geographical information systems as an output when combined with data mining can produce smart maps.

Other. A variety of other sources of valuable information exist about current and potential customers. Some of these are product/warranty registration cards, call center data, complaint systems, customer databases, and data generated from the sales force's customer visits.

Each of these sources has useful applications in terms of generating customer satisfaction metrics, as well as providing input for strategic planning, process improvement, and corrective action. Today's organizations increasingly have information about their customers—problems experienced, needs, and wants, as well as competitive intelligence from many sources. It is important that each data stream be considered for the value it might hold for various stakeholders throughout the organization.

Two challenges in using big data and/or data mining are:

1) Be careful that customers' preferences are not used in a manner they would not approve, such as revealing teen pregnancies prior to disclosure to their parents (a real case).[13]

2) Ensure the data are accurate, you know what you are looking for, and you have verified the big data projections with actual customers.[14]

Corrective and Preventive Action

Collecting data without doing something with them is waste. Data have to be processed in some way before they become actionable information. Each of the tools and techniques discussed involve manipulation and analysis of the data produced. Much as the data from the tracking of nonconforming product detected in manufacturing processes are captured, analyzed, and targeted for corrective and/or preventive action, customer data should be treated similarly. In the listening post approach described earlier, trended data, as appropriate, become the basis for a corrective and/or preventive action. Data gathered by the other tools also form the basis for actions to make changes and improvements.

Just as it is important to select appropriate customer data-gathering tools and techniques, it is also important to establish the processes by which the data will be recorded, monitored, collected, manipulated (sorted, collated, categorized), analyzed, correlated, measured, summarized, and reported. Many organizations have implemented customer satisfaction measurement and reporting systems. These systems alert management to critical failures in satisfying customers. They also provide information to management in deciding whether a negative trend is developing. The information can assist management in determining whether efforts should be made to ratchet up the quality of its products/services to meet customers' ever-changing requirements and perceptions of satisfaction.

Computer software providers have produced a number of products for use in collecting customer data, processing them, and reporting out either detailed customer information or a synthesis of customer information. Typically, many of these programs are focused on areas where large volumes of data are to be processed—for example, from large surveys, from product registration cards, or from a complaint desk function.

Pitfalls Encountered in Determining Customer Satisfaction

The common mistake most often made by organizations is assuming that they know how satisfied the customers are and what the customers want. This perception is usually based on the existence of a long-term relationship and/or on the absence of complaints.

Another mistake is designing surveys using questions that the organization wants the customer to answer. Better survey design suggests that the customers be asked what is most important to them. Then consider what they want in creating the survey questions. (Focus groups, discussed earlier, are often used to obtain the customer perspective.) As a quality vice president from a Baldrige Award winner once said, "We tended to include survey questions to which we already knew the answers." A similar mistake is developing the survey questions in such a way as to lead the customer to answer the way the organization wants. The design of unbiased and intelligent survey questions is paramount. Another common mistake is to survey samples of customers that are neither random nor representative. This results in responses that are not statistically valid. Surveys with low response rates always raise the question of whether the results really represent the entire population. For example, if a mail or e-mail survey nets a 30% response rate, what do the results tell you about the other 70% who did not respond? The answer, in general, is very little or nothing!

Poor question definition and invalid statistical samples can lead the organization to focus its improvement efforts in the wrong area or on areas that are not important to the customer. This wastes resources without achieving improved customer satisfaction or competitive position.

Relying too heavily on reactive data (such as complaint data) is a common mistake. The problem is that complaint data (and other reactive techniques) cannot be used to estimate the reactions of the total population. For example, complaints might help identify key problems that need to be addressed, but they fail to quantify the true frequency at which a problem occurs. Typically, twenty-five to fifty times more customers experience a problem than those who bother with, or succeed in, registering a complaint with management.[15]

A failure to use the customer's language is another deficiency: often the constructs evaluated in surveys are generated internally using company jargon. These constructs would be worded differently if they were in the customers' language. The use of jargon will likely result in the customers not understanding the organization's intent, and question validity is compromised.

Organizations often use poor research design. Sometimes survey objectives (problem statements) are not well thought out. It is very important to consider how the survey information will be used and what decisions will be made based on results. Every question to be included should meet the "need to know" rather than just "nice to know" test. Scrutinizing every question by asking, "Why are we asking this?" helps prevent asking questions of limited value.

Once they receive the research results, some companies use them ineffectively. Frequently, there is a failure to act on valid, insightful information. Sadly, it is quite common for organizations to conduct surveys but fail to act (strategic planning, process improvement, and corrective and preventive action opportunities). A failure to disseminate the right information to the right persons in the organization (including process owners) is a common reason for this type of breakdown. Other pitfalls include a failure by leadership to set expectations for action, as well as a lack of discipline in applying a rigorous plan-do-check-act (PDCA) cycle to the survey process.

Customer Retention/Loyalty

Customer-driven organizations that address the importance of the customer relationship enjoy significant competitive advantages. Several well-known companies, such as L. L. Bean and Nordstrom, are frequently cited for their outstanding customer service—and enjoy the benefits afforded by greater than usual customer loyalty.

Operating a customer-focused organization implies there is an integrated system of plans, processes, and practices designed to deliver the organization's services and products in a way that creates retained and committed customers, at a profit. Customer satisfaction is the focus of the entire organization. Can you identify the satisfaction level of your customers (individually or by segment)?

Look at Table 17.2[16] and assume that having most customers at level 4, with many at level 5, is desirable. The extent to which everyone is focused on the customers, in thought and action, is critical. For example, applying the concept of open-book management:[17]

- Do employees know the costs of delivering less than exemplary service and products?

- How many level 1s have been lost in the past year?

- How many level 2s come and go?

- How many level 3s are there in the customer base?

- What does it cost to bring in new customers to replace departed customers?

- What are restitution costs when the customer is dissatisfied?

- Does this customer ever come back?

- What is it costing the company when your competitors cut into your share of the market?

- What is lost when delivery dates are missed?

- If the company is doing well now, how much better might profits be if there were greater customer focus—more level 4s and 5s?

Increasing and growing customer retention and loyalty are key objectives for the customer-focused organization. In addition to the five-point scale demonstrated in Table 17.2 for customer satisfaction, organizations often establish metrics for "ease of doing business," repeat purchase intent, and willingness to recommend. Both of the latter are metrics for customer loyalty. One of the most popular approaches to measuring customer loyalty is using the net promoter score (NPS).

NPS is based on a direct question: "How likely are you to recommend our company's product/service to your friends and colleagues?" The scoring is based on a 0 to 10 scale, with those rating a score of 9 or 10 considered *promoters*, those rating a 7 or 8 considered *passives*, and those rating from 0 to 6 considered *detractors*. To calculate the NPS, take the total number of promoters minus the detractors, with the result divided by total number of respondents, times one hundred. If the total number of promoters exceeds the total number of detractors, a positive NPS score will result. In general, the higher the score, the better. When the NPS question is asked in a survey, it is often very helpful to ask detractors the reasons for their low ratings. This feedback can be used to identify ideas to improve future scores and the actual likelihood more customers are willing to advocate. Similarly, promoters can be asked the reasons for their ratings. Sometimes strategies can be created around the results that increase the frequency that customer delight is experienced.

Information is vital. The VOC is critical in a competitive environment. Typically, companies have no systematic way to actively listen to customers, record

Table 17.2   Levels of customer satisfaction.

Level	Is your customer	Then your customer
1	Dissatisfied	Has probably departed forever
2	Marginally satisfied	Is casual (any supplier will do)
3	Basically satisfied	Is borderline, uncommitted
4	Delighted	Is a return customer (retained)
5	A committed advocate	Is loyal, appreciates what you do, and tells others

Source: Reprinted with permission of R. T. Westcott & Associates.

what has been heard, and analyze, distribute, and act on the information. In his book *Moments of Truth*, Jan Carlzon talks about the often unrecognized myriad opportunities all employees have for gathering customer information.[18] Karl Albrecht further defines the moment of truth as "any episode in which the customer comes in contact with any aspect of the organization and gets an impression of the quality of its service. A moment of truth is typically neither positive nor negative in and of itself. It is the outcome that counts."[19] In truth, the outcome will either meet, exceed, or fail to meet the customer's expectations.

Without a system (including training employees to listen to the VOC) for collecting, analyzing, and disseminating the information and taking action, the organization is operating blindly. Without a measure, or at least a sense, of how satisfied customers are, the door is open to the competition. Investigating reasons for returned product is but a small part of the picture. A customer's offhand remark to the company's salesperson or delivery person can appear insignificant in itself. These comments, however, heard as a moment of truth, can alert the company to a potential problem before it turns into a formal complaint. A call requesting clarification from a customer's engineer to your company's engineer can indicate present or potential shortcomings in identifying customer requirements. Scattered remarks from a variety of customers' personnel to several different people in your company, while not appearing important when looked at individually, can, when collected and analyzed, form a pattern pointing to needed preventive action. Earl Naumann, in *Creating Customer Value*, says, "A firm that has no customer satisfaction program and no interest in starting one should be the delight of the firm's competitors."[20] To protect their customer base, organizations may:

- *Reward usage.* This can take the form of discount coupons, provided inside a product pack, for buying additional quantities of the same product.

- *Reward loyalty.* Airlines' frequent-flier programs are an example of this phenomenon.

- *Provide unpaid services.* Some organizations offer free lessons on how to use their products.

- *Establish personal relationships.* Publicly honoring loyal customers during company events, greeting them on their birthdays and anniversaries, and giving them preferential treatment (for example, upgrading economy class fliers to business class when space is available) are examples of ways in which organizations build personal relationships with customers.

Customer Lifetime Value

Retaining customers costs money but is still much less expensive than going after new customers. Reichheld discusses how to put a dollar value on retained customers. Factors such as acquisition cost, base profit, revenue growth, operating costs, referrals, and price premium are considerations mentioned.[21]

Customer Experience Management

The ideas and tools defining the "customer satisfaction and loyalty" landscape continue to evolve, and they are helping organizations foster stronger ties with their customers. Perhaps the most significant shift is toward customer experience management. An article from *Forbes* magazine describes the customer experience as the "cumulative impact of multiple touchpoints" over the course of a customer's interaction with an organization. Some companies are known to segment the customer experience into interactions through the web and social media, while others define human interaction such as over-the-phone customer service or face-to-face retail service as the customer experience.[22]

Customer experience takes into account the dynamic nature between what a company provides and what the customer receives. A service or product performance failure today could result in a customer defection tomorrow, plus negative word-of-mouth. On the other hand, a strong promoter might choose to invest in working through a problem with the provider. Organizations should look at things from customers' perspectives to better understand significant pain points and drivers of delight. Then they should work to cause less pain and create more customer delight.

Customer journey mapping is a tool that helps providers step into customers' shoes and see things the way a customer sees them. A customer journey map is a visual representation of the journey a customer has with your brand, products, services, and people. It helps to identify different outcomes at different touchpoints that have an impact on customer experience. Maps can be created for different types of customers (personas). Journey mapping includes key moments of the experience and positive and negative impacts, as well as resulting attitudes and emotions.

Reputational Risk

Perhaps the most important construct on the topic of customer satisfaction and loyalty is growing and maintaining the organization's reputation and customer goodwill. While reputation and customer goodwill are considered intangible assets, they are critical to the organization's health. A significant loss of goodwill can translate into huge drops in sales revenues and market share. A stellar reputation can be destroyed in moments. Reputational risk is the risk of loss resulting from damages to a firm's reputation, whether in lost revenue; increased operating, capital, or regulatory costs; or destruction of shareholder value. From a risk management mindset, goodwill must be preserved, especially when there are problems in the news headlines, and factors of reputational risk are in play. Social media and 24/7 news cycles ensure bad news about your product or service will spread quickly, and the media attention will intensify. Corporate apologies, rapid recovery and corrective action, remedies, and true humility and compassion are just some of the actions required to mitigate the reputation crisis. Some examples of damaged reputations include:

- *Boeing's 737 Max airplane crashes.* After two similar plane crashes, the FAA grounded all Boeing 737 Max aircraft in March of 2019. For some airlines, much of their fleet was grounded and flights canceled (lost airline revenue). Airlines considered canceling billions of dollars' worth of 737 Max air frame orders (lost sales for Boeing). Many air travelers are afraid and reluctant to fly on the 737 Max in the future (lost confidence). All in all, it has been a huge reputational mess for Boeing.

- *Johnson & Johnson Tylenol scare.* In 1982, an employee of Johnson & Johnson was found to have laced some of the company's Tylenol product with cyanide, causing the deaths of seven people. This resulted in widespread panic, as it was not known how extensively contaminated product was distributed. At the time Tylenol held 35% market share of the U.S. over-the-counter analgesic market. By the end of the episode, the company's market value had fallen by $1 billion.

- *JetBlue Tarmac incident.* In February 2007, a JetBlue plane sat on the tarmac for eleven hours at John F. Kennedy International Airport. Tarmac delays are problematic for the airline industry, creating hardships for passengers and bad publicity for the airlines. This high-profile incident ultimately led to new federal rules in April 2010.

- *United Airlines dragged doctor debacle.* In April 2017, United Airlines flight 3411 from Chicago to Louisville was overbooked. Apparently, the airline asked randomly selected passengers to voluntarily give up their seats to accommodate airline employees needing to get to Louisville. One passenger, a doctor, was not willing to give up his seat and was forcibly dragged off the plane. Video of this incident, recorded by other passengers, was posted to social media and went viral. The consequence was severe damage to United's reputation.

3. CUSTOMER SERVICE PRINCIPLES

> Demonstrate strategies that support customer service principles: courtesy, politeness, smiles, cheerfulness, attention to detail, active listening, empathy, rapid response, and easy access for information and service. (Apply)
>
> **Body of Knowledge V.B.3**

Creating a Customer Service–Oriented Organization

Customer service is much more than just delivering what the customer wants. Customer service, when fully embraced, involves not only delivering what was ordered but also truly caring about the customer. *Caring* is about customers' perceptions of your organization—its products and services, its people, its reputation. Caring is about the customers' well-being—health, safety, security. Caring is also understanding as much as possible about what the customer needs and wants, even in the future.

The trend continues toward ultimately serving the unique needs of each customer. The organization that is most successful in achieving that end, to the mutual advantage of both the customer and the organization, usually wins the privilege of keeping that customer.

Figure 17.8 Successful customer-centric organizations excel in six critical areas.
Source: Jeff Israel.

Customers fall into a number of different categories, yet there are no organizations without customers. And, since all organizations (for-profit and not-for-profit) have customers, a primary focus of any organization must be on providing satisfactory to excellent service to its customers. Many organizations in classifications other than service mistakenly believe and wrongly act as if their business does not involve serving customers.

In the eyes of today's customer, customer service transcends the product or service an organization provides. It is a predominant factor in the buying decision, often overriding price. It is a primary factor that distinguishes one organization from another. In many cases, superior customer service justifies an organization charging higher prices. However, even with all this at stake, most organizations conduct strategic planning without considering key elements vital to attaining customer focus through the creation and deployment of viable service strategies. A holistic systems view of the essential elements of a customer-centric organization is needed, especially for organizations that believe customer satisfaction is the basis of what sets them apart from the competition.[23] Figure 17.8 illustrates the elements of a successful customer-centric model and is described below.

Leadership: vision and support—Leadership is committed to customer service. It has a vision for service, evident in consistency and daily actions:

- The top management of the organization sets the tone and the pace. There must be visible personal involvement of the senior leaders in championing exemplary customer service. Employees, or volunteers, depending on the organization, must see their leaders supporting customer service excellence—in words, in actions, and with appropriate funding. In spite of the hundreds of articles, the extensive advertising campaigns, and other media hype, there is still more talking than walking.

- Top management's commitment is expressed in the organization's vision and/or mission statement. This statement clearly positions customers, and service to customers, as the primary reasons for being.

Equip, enable, and engage employees—The organization works to empower employees and help them succeed in serving customers. This includes equipping, enabling, and engaging them for this journey.

- The concepts and practices of superior customer service start within the organization. When internal customers receive quality service from internal providers, the beneficial results can be more easily related to external customers.

- The organization's leadership involves its members/employees in shaping external customer service excellence. Management style evolves toward empowering the people in the organization to act in providing the best service possible. Management's role is to support, conceptually turning the organization's structure upside down from its traditional pyramidal shape.

- The organization dedicates itself to training its people. Everyone is educated in the products and services provided by the organization. They not only understand what these products and services are but why and how the customer uses them. Everyone in the organization is trained in customer service practices, including interpersonal skills (basic courtesy, politeness, pleasantness, and conflict resolution), problem-solving, and customer inquiry and complaint response techniques. Every individual in the organization is made aware of his or her role in the customer service process and treated as an important owner of the process. Every individual is kept well informed as to how the organization is doing in achieving its customer service objectives. Exemplary customer service performance is recognized and rewarded, frequently.

Master service delivery processes—Mastery both from employee and customer points-of-view. Mapping service processes the way customers experience service to identify and reduce customer pain and increase delight.

- The organization adopts the goal of eliminating unwanted variation (customer pain) associated with the service delivery process and also looks for new ways to delight customers. Both practices are key to growing customer goodwill.

- The organization uses service process mapping, ideally some combination of traditional process mapping (i.e., order process, repair process, etc.); mapping moments of truth (from the customer's point of view); and identifying customer expectations for critical moments of truth or creating customer journey maps.

Performance measurement (VOC)—Understanding customer requirements and measuring how well those needs and expectations are actually met.

- The organization's system of tracking, measuring, analyzing, reporting, and reacting ensures that actions supporting the strategic plans are measured and evaluated. The means for collecting, analyzing, and disseminating the VOC is integral to the achievement of the strategic goals. Both customer service initiatives and the processes for achieving the plans are continually examined for opportunities to improve.

- The organization employs multiple means for obtaining customer feedback. It collects, correlates, analyzes, and disseminates crucial information for management's action. Complaints are actively solicited and acted on.

- The organization establishes a benchmarking process. It seeks out others who are perceived as best in class for specific processes. It charters benchmarking teams to learn about how these other organizations achieve their results and translate these findings into improvements within their own organization.

Resource and infrastructure development—Appropriate investments in information technology (IT), professional development, and facilities design/layout, providing the tools and environment for employees to succeed.

- The organization investigates the critical resources (training and infrastructure) needed by the frontline to foster success in serving the customer.

- The organization may look to integrate information management systems so customer support employees can quickly find the information they need to help the customer without tabbing through multiple systems.

- The organization commits to adequate staffing levels to handle customer inquiries and complaints.

Create and deploy service strategies—An assessment of the current state of the service culture is called for. Manage stakeholders accountable for different customer touchpoints, evaluate current capabilities, have group discussion, and conduct a strengths-weaknesses-opportunities-threats (SWOT) analysis. If consensus exists, group develops plans to close the gap between the current and desired future states:

- The organization's strategic goals and objectives reinforce the vision and mission. These plans, cascaded downward through the organization, are translated into actions to support the goals and objectives.

- Managers responsible for the customer experience in every touchpoint conduct individual and then collective assessment of the current state for key customer focus indicators. One assessment tool available to everyone is the "Are We Making Progress Tool" (NIST), which is modeled on the Malcolm Baldrige criteria.[24]

Customer Service Skills

All organizations occasionally encounter an unhappy customer. Making the effort to successfully resolve customer complaints shows the customer that you care and can be used as a continual improvement tool. Here is a five-step recovery program:

1. *Apologize.* First and foremost, say that you are sincerely sorry for the inconvenience the customer has experienced. Also, personally accept responsibility for the problem and its resolution.

2. *Restate.* Restate the problem as the customer described it to you to make certain that you understand exactly what the customer means. Then tell or show the customer that you will do everything possible to solve the problem and resolve the complaint as soon as feasibly possible.

3. *Empathize.* Make certain that you communicate clearly to your customers so that they understand that you know how they feel.

4. *Make restitution.* Not only tell your customers that you will take immediate action to resolve their complaints (for example, refunding their money), but tell and show them that you will make it up to them in some special way. For example, provide a free gift or a discount on their next purchase.

5. *Follow up.* Later, check to see whether your customers are now satisfied. This area is where most programs fail.

Training customer service representatives (CSRs) is vital to building and retaining customers. The organization's principles and policies and the CSR skills needed are exemplified in the following checklist.

Will the action I take:

- Meet the customer's need?

- Save the customer time and/or money?

- Earn my organization the customer's loyalty?

- Help obtain future business?

Do I treat customers as people? Have I:

- Looked at the situation/transaction from the customer's perspective?

- Been objective and calm?

- Listened carefully and been responsive and efficient?

- Taken the time and made the effort to get all of the information needed to serve the customer?

- Been sensitive to the customer's unspoken needs and alert to the customer's disagreement and/or disappointment?

- Confirmed that I heard and understand the message from the customer?

- Made the effort to know my organization's products, services, processes, and procedures to maximize my ability to assist the customer?

- Carefully avoided making excuses when a problem affects the customer?

- Been clear that I share the customer's need to resolve any problem, real or imagined, that concerns the customer about my organization or what it offers?

- Been helpful and informative, letting the customer know what I will do to rectify the problem?

- Asked the customer whether what I propose to do will satisfy the customer's needs and wants?

- Taken the appropriate action in a timely manner?

- Checked back with the customer to see if the action I took resolved the problem and that the customer is satisfied with the response?

- Thanked the customer for bringing the problem to my attention and allowing me to respond?

- Communicated the problem and the solution to appropriate persons in my organization to facilitate preventing a recurrence of the problem?

4. MULTIPLE AND DIVERSE CUSTOMER MANAGEMENT

Establish and monitor priorities to avoid or resolve conflicting customer requirements and demands. Develop methods and systems for managing capacity and resources to meet the needs of multiple customers. Describe the impact that diverse customer groups can have on all aspects of product and service development and delivery. (Evaluate)

Body of Knowledge V.B.4

Managing Multiple Customers

Most businesses have more than one external customer, each with his or her own needs/expectations for the product or service being purchased. To meet the needs/ expectations of its customers, an organization must first understand its own business. This begins with knowing what it takes, including costs, to produce the product or provide the service being offered. Next, the organization needs to determine the needs and expectations of specific customers or customer segments. This can be done by studying the industry—for example, by forming focus groups in which industry representatives express their needs. An organization should be aware that customers purchasing the same product might have very different needs.

As an example, the supplier of bookkeeping computer software could have customers from the medical device manufacturing industry, nonprofit foundations, and educational institutions. Each of these types of customers will obviously have different requirements, even though certain features of the software product might perform well in most industry categories. The medical device manufacturers would have special product traceability requirements to consider. The not-for-profit foundation needs complete security over sources of contributions.

Educational institutions require features to manage their costs and delayed revenue related to student loans.

In addition to different product requirements, customers might have varying delivery requirements. Some customers might need truckloads of product but are flexible with delivery lead times, whereas others might want small volumes of material delivered just in time. A supplier must weigh these types of logistical problems and consider the additional costs that could be incurred in either case. Other customers might require the same product but at different stages of completion. For example, one customer might prefer to purchase material that is less finished, lower in purity, and so on because these materials meet its needs at the best value. When selling partially finished product, suppliers might find it necessary to modify their pricing structure to prevent others from buying and finishing the product and becoming strong competitors.

Organizations need to evaluate each potential sales opportunity to make an informed decision as to whether it is worthwhile to pursue. Specifically, they should ask, "Does this potential customer fit well with our existing service processes and capabilities?" Once management has decided on which areas to focus, customers can be ranked so that research efforts can anticipate the needs of key customers. Generally, key customers are those that generate the most profits or have a high potential for generating profits and/or are high-visibility organizations. The value of a customer should be projected over the long term because business with a customer can lead to other business with that customer or to a referral of a new customer.

Resolving Conflict

Many times, potential or real conflicts arise between organizations and their customers. Having multiple customers who compete with one another can also present special challenges for a supplier. Conflicts can result when delivery schedules overlap or when material or other resources are in short supply.

Consider this example: A supplier of products to more than one automotive customer may find it has to take special precautions. For each such customer it must carefully train its people and segregate product during processing in order to maintain the level of security imposed by each competing customer.

Establishing a relationship based on trust is critical to avoiding or resolving conflict with a customer. A customer must know that confidential or proprietary information is safeguarded from competitors. A supplier should have procedures for protecting proprietary information, such as by limiting access to drawings and specifications and restricting competitors' access to a customer's product. An organization without these provisions faces legal liability from patent or copyright infringement or violations of a contract with the customer.

Beyond safeguarding proprietary or protected information, however, there is an economic aspect to managing customer conflict. If the systems and resources required to resolve conflict with a demanding customer exceed the economic benefit of meeting the customer's needs and resolving the conflict, it might appear to be more expedient to take no steps to resolve the conflict and let that customer go to a competitor. When making such a decision, the intangible impact should be considered. A supplier needs to consider how the loss of that customer will affect business. Unhappy customers talk about their experience with many more people than do satisfied ones, and this needs to be considered when dealing with customers. In some industries, ceasing to do business with a customer (sometimes referred to as "firing the customer") might not have adverse effects, but in a small retail company that is heavily dependent on word of mouth for its reputation and future business, this solution could be disastrous. Sometimes, instead of firing an unprofitable customer, the best course is to try to renegotiate terms first. Sit down with the customer; share financial data demonstrating the costs of doing business with them; and, work together to ensure the customer gets a realistic price for goods/services, and the supplier earns a fair margin on said goods/services.

When conflicts arise, high priority should be given to communicating with the customer in a calm manner, conducting root cause investigations, and implementing corrective action. Results of corrective action should be fed back to the customer, and response action should not be discontinued until both parties are satisfied that the conflict has been resolved. Customer service representatives should be trained to deal with irate customers and need to be given the information and authority to solve or resolve customer problems immediately. Passing problems along to others does not help relieve the customer's concern—the faster the problem can be dealt with, the happier (or less disturbed) the customer will be.

Resolving conflict with a customer helps establish trust and promotes a long-term relationship. This is a competitive advantage in industries in which customers are reducing supply bases to deal with fewer suppliers. A supplier should develop a relationship with its customers and clearly understand their needs. When conflicts arise, the supplier should try to understand the customer's point of view and negotiate a resolution.

The biggest mistake a supplier can make is taking the position that the customer is unreasonable and therefore failing to react to resolve the conflict or making a half-hearted attempt at conflict resolution. Many times, this lack of action is rooted in the supplier's focus on optimizing their internal processes even if these processes do not serve the customer well. Conflict resolution is seldom possible in an environment in which the supplier tells the customer, "That's the way we do it, take it or leave it." Unfortunately, this scenario is still all too common.

The most important criterion for both multiple customer management and resolving conflict is excellent interpersonal relations. That means management's commitment to training and support. For example, an organization that responds quickly, pleasantly, and professionally to a customer's complaint can often demonstrate its policy of exemplary customer service and can turn an irate customer into a good repeat customer who will bring friends along. The intangible benefits are high and must be considered in all customer relations.

Managing Capacity and Resources

Does the organization have the capacity and the resources to properly serve the existing customer base? What would be your answer if there was a rapid increase in orders due to a new fad, introduction of a new product line, acquisition of another company, a competitor's demise, and so on?

Good customer relations means not only providing a quality product or service but also being able to deliver the needed quantity when and where the customers' requirements dictate. Predicting and providing for future demand is tricky, but necessary. Factors that can contribute to building and sustaining the needed capacity are:

- Customer-focused organization culture
- Leadership commitment
- Strategic planning and deployment process
- Continual environmental scanning
- Sound financial management
- Continual risk assessment
- Effective quality system
- Understanding and improving your processes
- Trend and pattern analysis
- Knowing your process capability
- Understanding present and emerging customer needs
- Understanding and working with suppliers

For an example of the impact diverse customer groups may have on product and service development and delivery, consider the following scenario: Marketing efforts are anticipated to result in adding a new customer product line and a new customer segment. The sole manufacturing plant is working at near 100% capacity now. What to do before the expected wave of new orders for the new products arrives? Management considers:

- Adopting lean techniques and tools to reduce cycle time and free up space for the needed new equipment and personnel.

- Initiating a study, based on activity-based costing, to determine if any of the existing product lines are unprofitable and can be phased out.

- Renting a local facility and setting up a miniplant to start producing the new product line. When the new products become a stable source of income, a more permanent facility for making the new products can be found or built, perhaps closer to the customers.

- Outsourcing either the manufacture of the new products or, more likely, some of the existing functions to make room for manufacturing to expand to accommodate the new products.

- Reassessing the product lines currently offered in relation to the new product line to determine whether the business should be restructured and one or more of the existing product lines sold because of lack of fit to the strategy of the reconstituted core business.

- Hiring an organizational development consultant to diagnose the existing organizational culture and recommend effective approaches to assimilating the new product lines, new technologies involved, new procedures, and new people.

In meeting the challenges of today's marketplace, many organizations will have to develop the competence and capacity to provide for mass customization. The benefits that will accrue to the organization that does so may include:

- Competitive edge

- Greater attraction to buyers

- Increase in customers' perceived value

- Greater agility in response to changing customer perceptions and demands

- Prestigious reputation for one-to-one selling

- Increased profitability

Customers are your most valued assets; attend to their needs or nothing else matters!

REFERENCES

1. D. Peppers, M. Rogers, and D. Dorf, "Is Your Company Ready for One-to-One Marketing?," *Harvard Business Review* 77, no. 3 (January–February 1999).

2. R. McKenna, *Relationship Marketing: Successful Strategies for the Age of the Customer* (Reading, MA: Basic Books, 1991).

3. J. M. Juran, *Juran on Planning for Quality* (New York: Free Press, 1988).

4. Goal QPC, *The Six Sigma Memory Jogger II* (Salem, NH: Goal QPC, 2002 [1994]), 258–62.

5. N. Kano, N. Seraku, F. Takahashi, and S. Tshuji, "Attractive Quality and Must-Be Quality," Best on Quality, IAQ book series vol. 7 (Milwaukee: ASQC Quality Press, 1996), 165–86, in English (no longer in print, but provided via ASQ librarian on December 3, 2018).

6. R. T. Westcott, "Tapping the Many Voices of the Customer," *Informed Outlook*, June 2000, 20–23.

7. J. T. Israel, "Feedback to Improve Core Customer Relationships: A Framework to Implement Face-to-Face Surveys," *ASQ 51st Annual Quality Congress Transactions*, May 6, 1997, 420.

8. U.S. Office of Consumer Affairs/Technical Assistance Research Programs, *Consumer Complaint Handling in America: An Update Study, Part II* (Washington, DC: U.S. Office of Consumer Affairs, March 31, 1986), 42–43.

9. Much of the material under this heading has been adapted from articles by D. M. Stowell in *The Quality Management Forum*, a publication of the ASQ Quality Management Division.

10. B. J. Finch, "A New Way to Listen to the Customer," *Quality Progress* (May 1997): 73–76.

11. Israel, "Feedback," 425.

12. B. T. Gale, and R. C. Wood, *Managing Customer Value: Creating Quality and Service That Customers Can See* (New York: Free Press, 1994).

13. K. Hill, "How Target Figured Out a Teen Girl Was Pregnant before Her Father Did," *Forbes*, March 31, 2016, accessed August 11, 2019, https://www.forbes.com/sites/kash mirhill/2012/02/16/how-target-figured-out-a-teen-girl-was-pregnant-before-her-father -did/#337b70736668.

14. B. O'Neill, "Brian O'Neill," July 29, 2019, accessed August 11, 2019, https://designing foranalytics.com/resources/failure-rates-for-analytics-bi-iot-and-big-data-projects-85 -yikes/.

15. T. G. Vavra, *Improving Your Measurement of Customer Satisfaction: A Guide to Creating, Conducting, Analyzing, and Reporting Customer Satisfaction Measurement Programs* (Milwaukee: ASQ Quality Press, 1997), 16–17.

16. R. Westcott, "Safeguard Your Customer Base," *Quality Management Forum* (Summer 1998): 10–13.

17. J. Case, *Open-Book Management: The Coming Business Revolution* (New York: HarperBusiness, 1995).

18. J. Carlzon, *Moments of Truth: New Strategies for Today's Customer-Driven Economy* (New York: HarperBusiness, 1987).

19. K. Albrecht, *At America's Service: How Your Company Can Join the Customer Service Revolution* (New York: Warner Books, 1988).

20. E. Naumann, *Creating Customer Value: The Path to Sustainable Competitive Advantage* (Milwaukee: ASQC Quality Press, 1995).

21. F. F. Reichheld, *The Loyalty Effect: The Hidden Force behind Growth, Profits, and Lasting Value* (Boston: Harvard Business School Press, 1996).

22. M. Zwilling, "'Customer Experience' Is Today's Business Benchmark," *Forbes*, March 10, 2014.

23. W. Davidow and B. Uttal, *Total Customer Service: The Ultimate Weapon* (New York: Harper & Row, 1989).

24. The "Are We Making Progress" assessment tool may be found at https://www.nist.gov/baldrige/self-assessing/improvement-tools/are-we-making-progress.

See Appendix A for additional references for this chapter.

Part VI
Supply Chain Management

Chapter 18	Supply Chain Management
	Contributor: Heather McCain

World-class supply chains organize, plan, and deliver on the basis of what customers value.

—Gene Tyndall, Christopher Gopal, Wolfgang Partsch, and John Kamauff

Chapter 18
Supply Chain Management

A systems view of an organization recognizes that performance is a function of taking in inputs (marketplace and customer requirements, operating funds, raw materials and supplies, and employees) and effectively and efficiently converting them to outputs deemed of value by customers. It is, therefore, in the best interest of organizations that they select and work with suppliers in ways that will ensure high quality of those inputs to reduce the risk of unwanted waste. Strategic sourcing is a process for reducing the total cost of purchased materials, goods, and services while maintaining and/or improving levels of operating efficiency, quality, technical innovation, customer service, and safety.[1] Strategic sourcing requires the purchasing organization to work with suppliers to develop strategies that are mutually beneficial.

According to ASQ's *Quality Glossary*, a supplier is a source of materials, service, or information input provided to a process. External suppliers may be used at any stage in the design, production, and/or delivery process. *Supply chain management* (SCM) is a system in which supplier quality is managed by using a proactive and collaborative approach. This management approach begins early in the product design and supplier selection process. It continues through the entire life cycle of a product and for the duration of the relationship with that particular supplier.[2] SCM, defined as the process of effectively integrating and managing the supply chain, is a series of processes including planning, sourcing, making, delivering, and returning. This chapter focuses on the planning, sourcing, and delivering aspects of SCM.[3]

The ASQ *Quality Glossary* also defines supplier quality as the supplier's ability to deliver goods or services that will satisfy customers' needs. Supplier performance is recognized as being about more than just a low purchase price. The costs of transactions, communication, problem resolution, and of switching suppliers all have an impact on overall cost. The reliability of supplier delivery as well as their own internal operational policies, such as inventory levels, all affect overall supply chain performance. If suppliers have proven to be effective at controlling the quality of their output, the purchasing organization can reduce the amount of monitoring of the supplier.

A progressive supplier management process must be supported by top management of all companies involved, and the relationship must be based on mutual trust. More funds will typically be spent in developing the relationship in order to prevent problems later. This means that total cost of doing business has to be considered. As Deming stated in his fourteen points for management, we must "end the practice of awarding business on the basis of price tag alone."[4] Supplier life cycle management is critical for support of business needs. The life cycle includes selecting, evaluating, and developing suppliers as well as reevaluating suppliers over time to ensure business needs are met.[5]

Many of the concepts presented in this chapter are especially focused on the manufacturing industry. This industry has the special situation wherein much of what it purchases is actually incorporated into its own products, as opposed to simply being used as a component of the processes of doing business. Because there is a higher inherent risk, or potential impact, in the manufacturing customer-supplier relationship, organizations such as the Automotive Industry Action Group (AIAG) have developed detailed supplier management guidelines such as CQI-19. This supplier management process guideline defines the minimum quality-related requirements for subtier suppliers and provides explicit guidance on effective identification and control of pass-through characteristics (PTC).[6] The medical device industry has also established requirements for suppliers. For example, 21 CFR Part 820 requires medical device companies marketing products in the United States to have a quality management system. Within this regulation there is a Purchasing Controls Section 820.50, which requires manufacturers to develop and maintain procedures that ensure all purchased or otherwise received products and services adhere to a specific set of requirements.[7] Other industries have guidelines or requirements, and some nonmanufacturing organizations have also created quality requirements for items such as records, data, and software code.

A. SUPPLIER SELECTION AND APPROVAL

> Define and outline criteria for selecting, approving, and classifying suppliers, including internal rating programs and external certification standards. (Analyze)
>
> **Body of Knowledge VI.A**

Supplier Selection

The process for selecting new suppliers should be based on the type of organization, the risk associated with the product/service provided, the type of product or service being purchased, product market requirements, uniqueness of the product or service, and total cost. For example, if the item is a standard product (available off the shelf) and does not have a critical impact on the purchaser's performance, then purchase price and availability may be all that needs to be considered. Selection may be as easy as finding companies listed on the internet or an industrial directory and requesting a quote. An example of such a product might be standard office supplies; for a service organization it might be a lawn care service. There may also be inherent product market requirements that must be met by any supplier in order to be considered.

This simple view, however, does not suffice for the many purchased products and services that will have a significant performance impact. Aluminum billets for an extruder of automotive brake parts, a new university online research database, or equipment maintenance for an airline are examples in which the qualification and selection process must be carefully thought through and carried out. In some cases customers may dictate that a particular supplier be used (as is typical for steel used to make automotive components) or meet environmental or social sustainability goals, coined the Triple Bottom Line.[8] But in most cases the purchaser must define what criteria will be applied, then make a final decision to determine ways that prospective suppliers will be evaluated against the criteria. The ASQ Customer-Supplier Division suggests the following steps to select suppliers:[9]

1. Identify all possible sources
2. Evaluate reputations
3. Prepare bidders list
4. Request bids
5. Evaluate pre-award data
6. Select the supplier
7. Update the approved supplier list
8. Prepare the contracts
9. Accept the contracts

Supplier selection criteria for a product or service category should be defined by a cross-functional team. In a manufacturing company, team members would typically be from purchasing, quality, product development, engineering, production, or materials management. Team membership could consist of personnel with technical/applications knowledge of the product or service to be purchased, as well as members of the department that will use the purchased item. The principal responsibility for selecting suppliers typically falls on purchasing, with input from product development for requirements and quality for alternative suppliers.[10]

Selection criteria will typically include the following:

- Previous experience and past performance with the product/service to be purchased

- Relative level of sophistication of the quality system, including meeting regulatory requirements or customer-mandated quality system registration (for example, ISO 9001, IATF 16949)

- Capability to produce product or provide services that consistently and predictably meet requirements

- Capacity to meet current and forecasted demand and at the desired delivery frequencies[11]

- Capacity to ramp up to meeting future demand, if necessary

- Financial stability of the supplier

- Technical support available and willingness to participate as a partner in developing and optimizing design and a long-term relationship

- Total cost of dealing with the supplier (material cost, communications methods, inventory requirements, incoming verification required)

- Supplier's past track record for business performance improvement

- Supplier's code of conduct and ability to be socially, environmentally, and ethically responsible

Data and information for determining how well a potential supplier fits the selection criteria include:

- Obtaining Dun & Bradstreet or other available financial reports

- Requesting a formal quote, which includes providing the supplier with specifications and other contractual requirements (for example, testing)

- Visits to the supplier by management and/or the selection team

- Confirmation of quality system status either by on-site assessment, a written survey, or request for a certificate of quality system registration

- Discussions with other customers served by the supplier

- Review of databases or industry sources for the product line and supplier

- Evaluation of samples obtained from the supplier (for example, prototypes, lab tests, validation testing)

This information is often used to rate suppliers using defined rating scales and prescribed weights for importance. The ratings can be inserted into a prioritization matrix, and using the consensus criteria method, the suppliers who best meet the purchaser's criteria will have the highest scores.[12]

Supplier Approval

After information has been gathered, potential suppliers are ranked and a preliminary selection made. Final selection might not be completed until the suppliers have submitted formal documentation demonstrating that certain quality system and product requirements have been met. Some organizations may require suppliers to demonstrate statistical capability over a preliminary time period. Prior to final approval, some organizations may use a checklist to ensure all documentation and information from the supplier has been submitted and reviewed.[13]

For many products and services, there is often a contract signed stipulating:

- Specifications of the items to be purchased, including quality and testing requirements

- Quantity to be purchased, or purchaser's forecasted demand level

- Price and delivery requirements, which may include schedule and future due dates

- Corrective action process to be followed

- Exclusivity constraints and nondisclosure agreement

- Terms of the rating system to be used to evaluate supplier's performance
- Time period covered by contract
- Contract terms and conditions

Once suppliers are approved, they need to be acclimated to the organization. Onboarding is the process of assimilating the supplier to your business processes so they can interface with your business efficiently and effectively. The onboarding process should help the supplier understand your processes and requirements, expectations, reporting requirements, and communication practices, as well as corrective action procedures. Orienting new suppliers to your business needs helps create a better customer-supplier relationship and a win-win environment.[14]

Suppliers not selected are to be contacted in an appropriate manner. The supplier should be informed as to why their bid was not accepted. This information should include the strengths and weaknesses in the supplier's proposal as well as reasons for not accepting the proposal. Treat all suppliers with objectivity, respect, integrity, and professionalism whether you accept their bid or not. Remember, you might need that supplier in the future.

Purchasers strive to reduce the number of suppliers for a given product or service. With fewer suppliers and longer-term relationships, purchasers can invest more time and resources in working with suppliers to improve quality and reduce costs. However, for critical items, it may be wise to identify and qualify additional sources to reduce supply chain risks.

Classifying Suppliers

It is recommended that suppliers meeting the minimum requirements of an organization are considered *approved* suppliers. Preferred suppliers produce quality better than the minimum and may receive bidding preference. A supplier who has had additional review such as a self-assessment, questionnaire, audit, on-site inspection, or has obtained certificates of compliance or conformance to a quality management system may be considered a *qualified* supplier. If a supplier is important to an organization, additional reviews of that supplier over time may result in the supplier being considered as a *certified* supplier. Certified suppliers typically have quality data records establishing that it is not necessary to perform routine inspection and test on each lot or batch received. There are eight criteria for certification:[15]

- No product-related lot rejections for at least one year
- No non-product-related rejections for at least six months
- No production-related negative incidents for at least six months
- Passed a recent on-site quality system evaluation
- Has a totally agreed on specification
- Fully documented process and quality system
- Timely copies of inspection and test data
- Process stable and in control

Supplier Capabilities

External certification standards are often required for certain industries. There are international standards that suppliers may be required to acquire. The most common are the International Organization for Standardization (ISO) standards. Certification to a particular standard means that the supplier complies with that standard's requirements. It does not guarantee that the supplier produces a quality service, material, or product. It is the responsibility of the purchasing organization to evaluate what is important to its business.

Internal rating programs may be used to assess and evaluate suppliers' capabilities and performance over time. The internal rating program is used to:

- Trigger suppliers' corrective actions
- Plan actions to improve suppliers' performance
- Comply with end customers' contractual requirements, regulatory requirements, and other external standards
- Determine whether to continue or discontinue business with a supplier
- Determine whether to change the supplier's status (approved, preferred, qualified, and certified)
- Provide a basis and method for recognition of suppliers for work done well

In deciding whether a rating system is needed and, if so, designing the system, there are several considerations, such as:

- Given the nature of the items to be purchased (value, cost, availability, and criticality) and the reputation of the suppliers providing those items, ask whether a rating system is worth the time and effort to design and maintain. Further, will a score be more meaningful to the supplier than reviewing the actual quality, cost, and delivery performance metrics?
- Is quality alone the only criterion to be used as a rating parameter?
- Are charts showing lots accepted as a percentage of lots received and deliveries received on time as a percentage of deliveries scheduled adequate? These or other quality-related statistics are converted into three or four rating levels, each with ranges of acceptability. Are these ratings sufficient, considering that they tend to relate only to the top layer of costs resulting from poor quality?
- What is required by management system standards that the purchaser maintains—for example TL9000, or any customer-specific requirements?
- Are more sophisticated quality and delivery cost indices appropriate? (For example, for each supplier, the non-value-added costs due to nonconformances, and penalty dollars associated with ranges of those costs, are part of a formula used to compute a cost index for each supplier.) Again, while this added sophistication makes for fairer comparison supplier to supplier, the index still deals with only a fraction of the total cost of poor quality.

- Is a more comprehensive approach appropriate? The method would encompass all aspects of suppliers' performance, such as quality, delivery, price, service, and the effect of nonconformances on the purchaser's as well as the customer's operations. Each factor could be subdivided into contributing factors with assigned weights. This would be the fairest of the considerations but also the most expensive and cumbersome to maintain.

When using a supplier rating system, the metrics must be meaningful, fair, objective, and easy to understand, with little chance for error in the methodology used and the interpretation of the metric and the rating system. Additionally, the rating system components should be periodically reviewed for applicability of measurements, as well as to identify potential opportunities for improvement.

B. SUPPLIER RISK MANAGEMENT

> Assess and manage supplier risk and the impact it may have on various internal processes of the organization. (Evaluate)
>
> **Body of Knowledge VI.B**

Risk management is the identification, evaluation, and prioritization of risks to eliminate or mitigate their probability or severity or to leverage opportunities.[16] According to the Project Management Institute's Body of Knowledge (PMBOK), risk is an uncertain event or condition that, if it occurs, has a positive or negative effect on one or more project objectives such as scope, schedule, cost, or quality.[17] Both positive and negative risks need to be identified and managed. For organizations leveraging a supply base, this means determining what to outsource to suppliers based on an analysis of business needs as well as risk. Some known risks in the procurement process could be specialization, reliability, intellectual property, product integration, invention, architecture, confidentiality, or regional stability. These risks are not only for the organization seeking procurement but also for the organization performing the contracted work.[18] Organizations must develop a process to determine key risks to the business, evaluate options available, and review and manage risk on an ongoing basis.

Risk Assessment

Developing a list of potential supplier risks starts with an evaluation of activities and processes used in your business and evaluating what could go wrong or what could go exceptionally well. Risk can be either negative or positive. Identifying risks includes reviewing the procurement plan, interviewing subject matter experts, analyzing the assumptions and constraints, and using risk management tools to identify risks.[19] Once a list has been created, each potential risk will need to be assessed based on the business. Items used for this assessment include severity, occurrence, probability, impact, complexity, or any items that are important to the business. Tools such as failure mode and effects analysis (FMEA), fault tree analysis, and hazard analysis may be used to assess the risks.

Risk Management

Supplier risk needs to be managed throughout the life cycle of the service or product. The simpler the procurement, the less complex risk management is generally. Risks can be related to procurement itself, such as a supplier going out of business. Risk can also be associated with the contract, such as changes in payment terms.[20] Working with your suppliers to determine possible risks is important. There are tools available to help determine and prioritize risks including risk breakdown structure, fault tree analysis, preliminary hazard analysis, and FMEA. Once a list of potential risks have been identified, they can be documented in a risk register and managed over time.

In the list of known risks, there are controllable risks and uncontrollable risks. For controllable risks, prevention activities can be implemented to deal with the risk cause. For risks that are not controllable, recovery activities will need to be developed to deal with the effects of the risk. There are a number of strategies for managing risk.[21] If the risk is positive or an opportunity, the strategies include:

- Escalate
- Exploit
- Share
- Enhance
- Accept

If the risk is negative or a threat, the strategies include:

- Escalate
- Avoid
- Transfer
- Mitigate
- Accept

Outsourcing

Outsourcing is contracting out certain processes, or subprocesses, of the organization that often:

- Do not directly contribute to the organization's core business—for example, bookkeeping for a medical consortium
- Are operations or tasks in which the organization wishes not to engage—for example, laboratory testing of raw materials, breeding animals for medical research, removal of hazardous waste material from a construction site

- Are operations or tasks for which the organization neither has the expertise nor wants to develop the expertise—for example, fundraising for a not-for-profit organization, collection services for an e-commerce organization, or repossession of autos for a finance organization

Outsourcing does not mean that the organization is free from risk. It just means that some risk or opportunities have been transferred to the supplier.[22]

C. SUPPLIER COMMUNICATIONS

> Prepare and implement specific communication methods with suppliers, including regularly scheduled meetings and routine and emergency reporting procedures. Direct, communicate, and confirm explicit expectations so that the supplier is aware of critical product and delivery requirements. (Apply)
>
> **Body of Knowledge VI.C**

If suppliers are to meet requirements, they must know and understand them. Requirements may be related to product, process, quality system, purchase transaction handling, logistics, or other related business matters. Following are some examples of requirements that should be clearly spelled out in writing, as well as communicated and/or reinforced by other means:

- *Quote requirements.* Information that is to be included in the quote, and by when and to whom the quote must be submitted.

- *Product technical requirements.* Specifications for product attributes that must be met (for example, physical, chemical, visual, performance, or reliability) and which attributes are more important and why. PTCs are special characteristics that need to be identified and communicated to suppliers.

- *Process requirements.* Special requirements that must be met related to the process that will produce/deliver the product or service.

- *Product verification and traceability requirements.* Testing that the supplier is obligated to perform, information that is to be provided to the purchaser for verification (for example, statistical data, certificates of analysis), and traceability requirements for product batches that allow for recall if necessary.

- *Quality management system requirements.* Management processes that the supplier must have in place in order to help ensure quality, including any specific quality management system standards to which the supplier must be compliant and/or certified.

- *Delivery requirements.* How orders will be placed, what labeling is required, including bar code formats, how the product is to be packaged and protected during shipment, what modes of shipping are to be used, and minimum and/or maximum batch sizes.

- *Order requirements.* The quantity of a particular product that the purchaser currently wants and the date on which it is due.

- *Corrective actions required.* Process to be followed when problems occur at the purchaser's site, for which the supplier is to perform and document a formal investigation and report back to the purchaser what was found and done to resolve the situation.

- *Safety and security safeguards required.* Special requirements needed to protect persons coming in contact with a product or service.

- *Environmental requirements.* Voluntary and involuntary environmental protection parameters relating to contamination, pollution, destruction, depletion of natural resources, introduction of a harmful organism, and so on.

- *Financial requirements.* Requirements relating to the supplier's financial stability.

- *Management requirements.* Requirements relating to the supplier management's integrity and ethical behavior (for example, adhering to the purchaser's code of conduct).

These requirements may be communicated to the supplier via:

- Formal written specifications or drawings created by the purchaser (communicated either by hard copy or electronic transfer of a CAD file), the supplier, or a third-party organization (for example, the American Society for Testing and Materials [ASTM])

- Samples of finished products or components provided to the supplier

- Supplier quality assurance (SQA) requirements manual

- Visits to customer plants by technical, quality, or logistics personnel

- Written contracts spelling out the details of products, volume to be purchased within the contract period, and the purchase price

- Terms and conditions outlining the ownership of intellectual property, warranties, disclaimers, confidentiality, and other legal considerations

- Purchase orders and releases (by phone, fax, or mail) or electronic orders placed by electronic data interchange (EDI) or through other electronic communications channels

- Other written communications

- Training provided by the purchaser's organization to supplier personnel

- Purchaser-supplier information exchanges during joint design reviews

- Purchaser furnishing order demand forecasts to suppliers

- Having the supplier visit the purchasing organization on an as-needed basis or a regular basis

- Face-to-face contact by a continuous on-site representative from the purchaser (often the case with government contracts)

The supplier should be aware of not only how normal communications are to be carried out but also what is to occur in the case of a special or critical event. Appropriate contact points (individual, method of contact) should be clearly defined for each different type of situation.

The explicit expectations and consequences to the supplier for nonconformances should be clearly spelled out in advance of the organization placing an order with the supplier. Suppliers must be made aware of the criticality of quality to the purchaser.

Suppliers must keep the purchaser informed of any change in the status of the order. Process delays in the supplier's organization, late arrival of material from the supplier's supplier, delays caused by the supplier having to rework or replace damaged product, or recalls somewhere in the supply chain are all potential disasters for the purchaser and the purchaser's customer, especially if just-in-time deliveries are expected.

D. SUPPLIER PERFORMANCE

Define, assess, and monitor supplier performance in terms of quality, cost, delivery, and service levels and establish associated metrics for defect rates, product reliability, functional performance, timeliness, responsiveness, and availability of technical support. (Evaluate)

Body of Knowledge VI.D

In order for suppliers to know how they are performing, they must receive feedback from the purchaser. Since the product or service is usually delivered to a location that is remote from where it is designed and produced, this feedback is the primary mechanism that allows the supplier to maintain performance in line with their purchaser's expectations.

This means that for suppliers providing products or services critical to quality, the purchaser must have a formal process for collecting, analyzing, and reporting supplier performance. Following are some of the more common assessments of supplier performance:

- *Questionnaires/audits.* Suppliers may be requested to fill out a survey containing questions about their organization and how their quality system is designed and what plans for improvement have been developed. The purchaser may instead conduct an on-site assessment as a means of learning more about the details of the system. The purchaser may also conduct a satisfaction survey within its own organization, asking appropriate employees to rate a particular supplier based on product performance and experiences with supplier communication and problem resolution.

• *Product data.* Suppliers are often requested to provide product quality data with each delivery, which is used in place of formal verification by the purchaser. The purchaser may then analyze the data numerically or statistically, looking at overall rates of compliance to specification as well as process stability and capability. Any verification performed by the purchaser also provides data that can be used for this analysis. Internal performance of the product (for example, number of failures when the product was used by the purchaser) can also be analyzed. A *number of defects analysis* is common for many manufacturing industries. Data from analyses of field failures that indicated the supplier was at fault can also be reported.

• *Delivery performance.* Supplier performance against delivery requirements (for example, total number of days early and total days late) can be tracked based on a comparison of receiving records against order requirements.

• *Corrective actions.* When problems are reported to suppliers with a formal request for corrective action, this triggers a tracking process for ensuring that the supplier responds. These records can be analyzed to determine whether a supplier has been timely in its responses, as well as the effectiveness of the corrective actions.

• *Product price and total cost.* Companies are always trying to reduce the cost of raw materials and services, or at least minimize increases. The ability of suppliers to continually show progress in this area can partially be done through a cost-of-quality analysis, a broader financial analysis that looks at the total cost of doing business with the supplier. Supplier-provided data on continual improvement efforts are also desired.

Supplier performance is then analyzed using a standard form (manual or computerized) into which the preceding information is placed. A numeric score is applied to each category along with a total score. The score is usually compared to some minimum level required in order to remain a supplier and a category label applied based on the score (for example, *unacceptable, acceptable, superior*). The data should also be reviewed for trends that would indicate whether the supplier is improving over the long term.

Reporting of supplier performance is usually done on a regular basis (for example, quarterly) by one of the following:

• The rating information is mailed to the suppliers.

• The rating information is provided as part of a visit to the supplier facility (for example, if there is a significant problem to be addressed).

• The information is entered into an online database so that individual suppliers are able to access their own rating.

• An electronic report is sent to suppliers.

• The report is given during regularly scheduled supplier performance meetings.

522   *Part VI   Supply Chain Management*

Figure 18.1 is an example of a supplier performance report that allows a supplier to quickly see its performance over the past year, as well as compare itself to the purchaser's other suppliers.

Suppliers who receive unacceptable ratings are often given a probationary period in which to resolve their problems, and if they do not take action or are unable to improve, they will usually be replaced. For some products, however, a particular supplier may be the only option, which requires a creative approach in working with them. Suppliers who consistently perform exceptionally well may be given supplier performance awards.

Metrics in common use to measure supplier performance may include:

- Defects (parts per million [ppm] defective)

- Accuracy (order processing, billing)

- Timeliness (traditional delivery, just-in-time delivery, stock replenishment)

- Completeness (order quantity delivered, required paperwork submitted)

- Responsiveness (to inquiries, to corrective actions, complaint resolution)

- Returns for rework or repair

- Technical support made available (field adjustments, end-user training)

- Supplier's process capability (C_{pk})

- Supplier's process performance (P_{pk})

- Cost/price responsiveness

- Compliance

- Warranty performance

ABC Company
Supplier Performance Report for:

Fourth Quarter 2014

Supplier: XYZ Company, Anywhere U.S.

Category	Possible score	Actual score
Product quality	30	25
Delivery	30	30
Quality system	20	15
Corrective action	20	20
	100	**90**

Performance for past three quarters:	80, 80, 85
Average score of all suppliers:	88
Performance of best supplier:	95

Performance categories:

Preferred partner	95–100
Acceptable	80–94
Probation	<80

Figure 18.1   Supplier performance report.

Questions to ask when determining the frequency with which suppliers should be measured include:

- What is the purpose of the metric? What is needed by when? How critical is the item(s) to be purchased?

- How much time and money will this measurement require to maintain and use?

- How much of a time interval should there be between taking measurements?

- Can the measurement be used in controlling the overall process? Can an unfavorable trend be corrected, and how quickly?

- What are the risks and consequences of not using the measurement?

- Will the measurement be consistently used over time for trend analysis?

Suppliers can also be provided with benchmarking data that help them understand the levels of performance that can be achieved. Care must, of course, be taken to not violate any confidentiality issues. Letting suppliers know about the best performance being achieved by other suppliers regarding measures such as on-time delivery, ppm defect rates, and corrective action effectiveness provides the supplier with an opportunity to know how they compare.

Supplier performance metrics achieve several things. They:

- Reinforce the terms of the contract (a purchaser's order accepted by the supplier is a contract)

- Serve to link the supplier organization with the strategic objectives of the purchaser

- Aid in detecting current or emerging problems

- Help the purchaser's process owners in understanding the overall process—which factors are important

- Help in making the decisions needed from the purchaser to keep the supply chain viable

Each organization typically has its own indices used for tracking supplier performance. Following are some examples:

- *Past performance index* (PPI). This index can be based both on quality and/or delivery and/or best-value measures. It is used for individual materials and can be calculated for each supplier that provides the material. Suppliers can then be compared using the index.

- *Supplier performance index* (SPI). This index can also include both quality and/or delivery measures. It tracks all materials provided by a supplier in order to show overall performance trends.

- *Commodity performance index* (CPI). This index is often used when there is no past performance history.

- *Quality performance index* (QPI). This index can be organized by product or by supplier and takes into account things such as manufacturing floor failures, scrap, supplier corrective action, and failures at receiving inspection.

- *Delivery performance index* (DPI). This index shows delivery trends and can be organized by product or by supplier. Late, early, and on-time deliveries are considered on the basis of requested delivery dates.

A purchaser's action taken resulting from nonconformances may be one or more of the following:

- Return defectives at the supplier's expense.

- Accept nonconforming products temporarily until the product can be replaced.

- Accept nonconforming product at a discounted price.

- Accept nonconforming product that has been modified, adjusted, or repaired at the supplier's expense.

- Scrap nonconforming product received and deduct price charged from supplier's total invoice.

- Bill supplier for purchaser's internal costs related to the nonconformances.

- Scrap nonconforming product in accordance with purchaser's policy and procedures.

- Make arrangements with the supplier for the purchaser to provide technical assistance or training to improve quality.

E. SUPPLIER IMPROVEMENT

> Define and conduct supplier audits, evaluate corrective and preventive action plans, provide feedback, and monitor process improvements. (Evaluate)
>
> **Body of Knowledge VI.E**

Whether it is to help resolve problems or is simply a part of ongoing continual improvement, ensuring that supplier performance improves is required if an organization is to maintain competitiveness. Improvements may be related to products, processes, systems, value and competitive pricing, or strategies. Feedback to suppliers is an important component for their improvement, helping them to understand strengths and weaknesses from the purchaser's perspective.

When the transaction is business-to-business, evaluate the purchasing process as well as supplier performance. Look at:

- Is the purchasing process measured solely on reducing costs, the head of purchasing measured on "Don't pay too much. Don't run out. And never shut down a line"?

- Is the focus on suppliers absorbing storage costs, causing higher prices?

- Is the total cost of procurement considered (price + poor quality + poor delivery)?

- Are specifications given the suppliers correct and adequately defined?

- Are buyer-supplier relationships more adversarial than collaborative?

Supplier Audits

A focus on the supplier's quality system is one means of supplier improvement and can be done through assessment and scoring of the appropriate processes. Suppliers that are audited against a quality system standard may be asked to improve particular aspects of the system (for example, better qualification of critical processes or use of statistical process control). Some industries require that registered companies develop their suppliers based on the requirements of the industry quality management standard (for example, IATF 16949 for automotive, AS9100 for aerospace, and TL 9000 for telecommunications).

Audits that are performed against a company's standards or other criteria, such as the Baldrige criteria, typically measure strengths and weaknesses. Suppliers are given a score, and some purchasers require scores to be above a minimum in order to award business.

Assessments done of a supplier's quality system must be done by personnel who are adequately qualified in the assessment process as well as the particular standard being used for the assessment. Perhaps more importantly, they must have the ability to communicate with supplier personnel in a manner that will result in a willingness to listen to the results, rather than feeling criticized.

Supplier audits should be planned, executed, reported, and closed in order to be successful. Planning needs to be aligned with organizational needs as well as risk. Communication with the supplier is key to ensure that audits are beneficial to all. Audits can be performed in a variety of ways, including face-to-face or virtual. How audits are performed depends on the type of organization and the needs of both the supplier and the organization.[23]

Corrective and Preventive Action

A basic aspect of supplier improvement involves the purchaser communicating problems or potential problems. For example, product performance or delivery problems can be documented and communicated to the supplier through a corrective action request. These requests usually require that the supplier respond within a specific period of time, and the response is analyzed to determine whether the actions planned or taken are appropriate to the magnitude of the problem. The purchaser can then monitor future performance to ensure that the action taken by the supplier was effective. Suppliers need to take a systematic approach to manage corrective action.

Preventive actions are taken to eliminate the causes of potential noncompliances and nonconformances from occurring. The process involving the interaction between the purchaser and supplier, as well as the supplier's internal processes, are examined for potential for producing defectives. Often, with technical assistance from the purchaser, changes are made to the supplier's process to eliminate or reduce the risk of failure to meet the purchaser's requirements. Coincidental to working to improve the supplier's process, the purchaser would examine the communication content and medium used when placing an order to ensure that all requirements are clearly transmitted and acknowledged.

Corrective actions are taken to correct a problem or nonconformance that has occurred. More than a quick fix, a corrective action seeks out the root cause(s) of the problem or nonconformance, explores solutions, and selects the best solution to implement. Assuming that the selection and implementation work as planned, the same problem should not recur.

Feedback to Suppliers

As a means of maintaining a closer working relationship, some purchasers hold regular meetings with suppliers. These meetings provide the opportunity for detailed discussions to occur that are not as effectively carried out through infrequent phone calls or e-mails between the purchaser and supplier organization. Supplier scorecards, as described previously, are often discussed in these meetings. It is important to provide regular routine feedback to suppliers. Often, suppliers only hear from purchasers when there are problems.

Monitoring Process Improvements

Purchasers may be interested in monitoring a supplier's process improvements for a number of reasons, including new business, new technology, or corrective action. Process improvements may be periodically reviewed to ensure that the desired impact was achieved and that the change was standardized.

Another approach to supplier improvement is to work very closely with those suppliers from which greater benefits would be achieved. This might involve providing technical personnel to help the supplier solve product or process problems or a joint product redesign effort. For a components manufacturer, such joint efforts might include value analysis, lean production, design for manufacturability and assembly, or other improvement techniques that will help improve product and/or reduce costs for both parties. Larger companies that have their own formal educational programs for continual improvement methods often invite or require supplier personnel to attend courses.

F. SUPPLIER CERTIFICATION, PARTNERSHIPS, AND ALLIANCES

> Define, appraise, and implement supplier certification programs that include process reviews and performance evaluations. Outline strategies for developing customer-supplier partnerships and alliances. (Evaluate)
>
> **Body of Knowledge VI.F**

Supplier Certification

The objective of a supplier certification program is to allow consistent supplier performance to be reflected in operating practices for handling received material and awarding future business. Material from a certified supplier may be verified at a very low level (for example, skip-lot sampling, whereby parts will be checked from perhaps only every fifth lot). Suppliers who are certified may also receive higher priority for new business.

The certification process involves the following major steps:

- Development of the certification criteria and process (for example, selection, evaluation, rating, communication, and reaction processes)

- Identification of supplier categories for which certification would be advantageous

- Evaluation of selected suppliers against defined criteria

- Reporting of evaluation results, awarding of certification for those who qualify, and clarification of a future interrelated process (for example, supplier reporting requirements)

- Ongoing monitoring of supplier performance, with actions taken in accordance with the defined certification process, including decertification for failure to improve or other issues

Determining which suppliers for whom certification will be available requires evaluation of the potential impact on both the purchaser and supplier. Certification should be considered if it could significantly reduce costs and enhance the business relationship. Risks or other issues such as regulatory or purchaser-mandated requirements for incoming product verification may rule out the option. Another factor is whether the level of sophistication of the supplier organization and its process technology can support the performance expected from a certified supplier.

Supplier certification programs use the assessment and feedback systems mentioned earlier in this chapter; however, there is usually a tiered rating classification (for example, *qualified*, *preferred*, and *certified*). As a supplier advances from one classification level to the next, the amount of reliance on the supplier for product verification is increased. Performance at a particular level must also be maintained for some minimum amount of time before moving to the next level.

Partnerships and Alliances

By their nature, purchaser-supplier relationships are often less than win/win and are sometimes even adversarial in nature. A customer typically wants the highest quality, the shortest cycle time, and the lowest possible price and often views suppliers as interchangeable commodity providers. Conversely, suppliers are motivated to sell goods and services at a price that provides an acceptable profit but are also motivated to build customer loyalty and create a close-knit relationship to secure future business.

Supplier management has evolved to emphasize the importance of both parties working together to build strategic relationships that are known by many terms: coalition, joint venture, strategic alliance, and partnership. According to Dominick and

Lunney, a supplier alliance is a special, formalized relationship with a supplier. An alliance implies that two parties are working together for a common purpose. The notion of partnerships goes even further, implying a shared fate, mutual benefits, and equal relationship.[24] Strategic relationships involve a cooperative undertaking between companies and can involve technology, licenses, or supply/marketing agreements.

Some common situations that might lead an organization to develop a purchaser-supplier partnership include:

- The difficulty in obtaining supplies or the need to maintain stability of product or services in a tight market.

- On the basis of a review of core competencies, a purchaser might recognize that a supplier's capabilities exceed the company's own internal capabilities. In such cases, outsourcing the production of key components or services to the supplier would be in the best interest of the purchaser.

- Cost-cutting pressures resulting from substantial price competition in the market might force a purchaser to search for ways to lower costs, both internally and externally, so that profit margins can be maintained.

- Combining resources can increase capabilities, flexibility, responsiveness, and innovation so that they exceed those realized by purchasers and suppliers engaged in more traditional purchaser-supplier relationships.

Strategic relationships are a viable option when an organization desires to attain technological breakthroughs, enter new markets, and/or develop new products or services.

The importance of creating and maintaining partnering relationships with key suppliers is reflected in the following guidelines for organizations looking for ways to effectively manage partnership relations:

- What key products/services do you purchase from suppliers and/or partners?

- How do you incorporate performance requirements into supplier and/or partner process management? What key performance requirements must your suppliers and/or partners meet to fulfill your overall requirements?

- How do you ensure that your performance requirements are met? How do you provide timely and actionable feedback to suppliers and/or partners? Include the key performance measures and/or indicators and any targets you use for supplier and/or partner assessment.

- How do you minimize overall costs associated with inspections, tests, and process and/or performance audits?

- How do you provide business assistance and/or incentives to suppliers and/or partners to help them improve their overall performance and to improve their abilities to contribute to your current and longer-term performance?

- How do you improve your supplier and/or partnering processes, including your role as supportive customer/partner, to keep current with your business needs and directions? How are improvements shared throughout your organization, as appropriate?

- Do the legal ramifications of the planned partnership prevent setting up the partnering arrangement?

In a survey of its customers, a silicon wafer manufacturer asked them several questions on the nature of purchaser-supplier partnerships. The questions addressed the nature of supplier partnerships, the expected benefits from partnerships, and the characteristics exhibited by key suppliers. Following are some of the questions and findings:

Q. *What is a supplier partnership?*

A. Nearly half the customers spoke of shared risks and rewards. Two-fifths described the nature of the relationship as embodying a mutual give-and-take (analogies ranging from marriage to virtual mergers). One-third spoke of good communications that emphasize honesty and openness. One-fifth talked of the idea of extending the factory to the supplier.

Q. *What benefits do you expect (as the customer) from a supplier partnership relationship?*

A. Nearly half indicated that the expected benefits from a partnership-type relationship would be realized through higher quality (supplier and product), guaranteed supply, and/or attaining desired purchaser-supplier synergies. About one-third expected improved communications and/or improved costs or pricing to be important benefits.

Q. *What are the characteristics of your best suppliers?*

A. The leading characteristics purchasers used to describe their best suppliers included:

- Providing high product quality (52%)

- Responsive and flexible service (48%)

- Good communications (29%)

Nearly one-fifth described their best suppliers as those who "go the extra mile" or have a "can-do" attitude, honor their commitments, and/or provide problem-solving support.[25] As shown by these answers, especially important characteristics of successful partnerships and alliances include mutual benefit, trust building, open and complete communication, and interdependence of parties.

Not all purchasers or suppliers desire to quickly enter into a partnership or alliance relationship. There is a courtship period in establishing the relationship during which a determination is made as to the viability of entering into a more formal relationship. It is worthwhile to overcome the barriers that exist, as a successful partnership can not only be economically rewarding but can also endure more mistakes and produce greater rewards than if no such relationship existed.

Even when a firm could perform an activity itself, it often makes business sense to outsource work to suppliers. When it is an essential activity, a partnership or alliance is even more critical. Typical reasons for outsourcing include:[26]

- Improving the customer organization's focus by allowing it to concentrate on essential activities

- Gaining access to world-class capabilities and skills, including better management

- Focusing on other strategies or core functions

- Sharing, and thus reducing, risks

- Freeing noncapital resources or making capital funds available

- Reducing operating costs

- Securing resources not available internally

- Increasing production capacity

- Quickly gaining needed functions, services, or product

- Eliminating a function that is difficult to manage

Steps in developing a partnership or alliance relationship include:

1. Determine materials or services for which a closer relationship would be beneficial.

2. Be aware of any legal implications.

3. Identify suppliers with whom a partnership or alliance will be pursued.

4. Define expectations and potential risks for such a relationship.

5. Communicate and negotiate with suppliers.

6. Implement arrangements that are mutually agreed upon.

7. Establish ongoing monitoring and communication to maintain the relationship.

Many of the supplier management processes previously mentioned in this chapter will apply to partnership or alliance arrangements. However, some additional activities that more closely integrate the two organizations in such arrangements include:

- Joint designing, marketing, and launching of new products/services

- Sharing of long-term strategies

- Communicating demand and resource-planning information beyond a day-to-day or week-to-week horizon

- Lending employees to each other's firm for technology transfer and development opportunities

- Sharing in financial gains achieved by the venture

Partnerships and alliances require an operating philosophy that goes beyond just successfully doing business together. Following are some of the critical aspects necessary to having a successful partnership/alliance:

• *Mutual benefit.* Both parties in a strategic relationship must profit from the relationship. Unless the relationship is satisfactory and the level of product or service provided is acceptable, neither party will desire to continue a relationship. Problems should be approached collaboratively; both parties should strive to make money while reducing cycle time. The spirit of a win/win mutual benefit must be pervasive and encourage both parties to seek creative solutions.

• *Trust building.* Both parties should be in the relationship for the long haul so that the relationship is not jeopardized by momentary problems or opportunistic behavior. Suppliers and customers must feel free to exchange ideas without fearing that proprietary information will be divulged to competitors.

• *Open and complete communication.* All responsibilities and expectations of the relationship must be clearly and frequently communicated. The most indispensable element of a customer-supplier relationship is dialogue and feedback.

• *Interdependence of parties.* Effective partnerships foster mutual assistance, joint planning, and other forms of close collaboration.

G. SUPPLIER LOGISTICS AND MATERIAL ACCEPTANCE

> Describe the impact purchased products and services can have on final product assembly or total service package, including ship-to-stock and just-in-time (JIT). Describe the incoming material inspections process. (Understand)
>
> **Body of Knowledge VI.G**

Logistics

Identification, selection, monitoring, and improvement of suppliers are part of the plan-do-check-act cycle of supplier management. An additional important piece is how the interface between purchaser and supplier is planned and implemented. Materials must be available when needed, but this must be done in a manner that considers the costs of transportation, receipt, and storage. This often requires coordination of schedules across multiple organizations in the supply chain.

Push or pull systems might be used to ensure that material is available when needed. Push systems require suppliers to ship according to purchasers' demands. Forecasts and demand must be closely aligned and communicated. Pull systems require purchasers to order product from suppliers as replacements for those items that have been used. Pull systems keep purchasers' inventory lower than the push method.

A *ship-to-stock* program utilizes supplier performance and supplier certification as a means of identifying suppliers whose materials can be received directly into the organization without verification. Material is simply moved directly to storage when received. The advantages of ship-to-stock include reduced inventory levels and elimination of incoming inspection.

Just-in-time programs eliminate raw material storage altogether on some products by having the supplier ship materials in smaller quantities more frequently and directly to the point of use. In making such decisions, the shipping lot size and frequency must consider the time in transit, cost of shipment, and cost of inventory. For example, nuts and bolts can be maintained in inventory very inexpensively, and infrequent shipments with higher inventory may make more financial sense. An automotive assembly plant, however, would probably not want to maintain a large inventory of car seats covering the full range of different colors and materials. Some organizations allow suppliers to replenish small hardware stock on premises without paperwork. The supplier is paid based on the quantity of hardware used on the final products produced.

Working on a just-in-time basis requires close coordination between purchaser and supplier. When feasible, it is best to level demand rather than have large swings (for example, created by special promotions) that require the supplier to radically adjust output levels. When the type of business makes demand leveling difficult, production plans and schedules must be communicated more frequently. This often involves electronic communications between the purchaser's and supplier's advanced-planning and enterprise resource-planning systems.

A final method being used to improve and simplify the supply chain is the move toward *modular assembly*. It is the process of transferring additional business back to suppliers, who produce a complete subassembly that was previously assembled by the purchaser. The result is that the purchaser receiving the subassembly as a completed item can more effectively integrate the subassembly into the final assembly.

Material Acceptance

Once product is delivered, purchasers need to determine whether that product meets requirements. This is accomplished by source inspection, certification of suppliers, or receiving inspection. The amount or type of inspection depends on the risk the purchaser assumes. The risk depends on the type of product purchased as well as the supplier's quality system and history (see Figure 18.2 for types of risks). Purchasers need to have a good understanding of the contract, knowledge

		Actual	
		Good	Bad
	Accept	$1 - \alpha$ Producer's confidence	β Type II error Consumer's risk
Decision			
	Reject	α Type I error Producer's risk	$1 - \beta$ Consumer's confidence

Figure 18.2   Risks in sampling.

of the product, and knowledge about the supplier to determine the appropriate material acceptance system.

Product may be directly sent to stock if a supplier is certified, the product has a *certificate of certification*,[27] or if source inspection has been completed. If a supplier is certified, the assumption is that the product meets requirements and can be sent directly to stock. Product that has a certificate of certification—which is supplier-generated data or independent lab data that demonstrate that the product meets requirements—is also sent to stock after the certification data are reviewed. Product that has been *source inspected*—or inspected by the purchaser at the supplier's facility to confirm that product complies to requirements prior to shipping—can also be directly sent to stock.

Incoming, or *receiving*, inspection is used to verify product once it is received from suppliers. Receiving inspection can be a quick check of packaging or a complete dimensional, visual, chemical, and/or electrical evaluation. Inspection rates can be 100% for product with mandated requirements or a poor quality history. Inspection rates are typically much less than 100% for suppliers with a good quality history. If inspection is necessary, the most economical way to accept product is through the use of statistical sampling plans. If the product is rejected per the sampling plan, the supplier may need to provide corrective action, including reworking the product before any additional shipments will be accepted.

Management of the Supply Chain

The role of SCM is to ensure that the right product or service, in the right quantity, of the right quality, gets to the end customer at the right time. The supplier life cycle management (SLM) model focuses on an integrated approach and plans for the acquisition of suppliers as well as supplier turnover.[28] Sometimes, it may appear that achieving effective management of the supply chain would be akin to successfully herding cats. All the linked organizations are constantly changing, as is the marketplace. It may be inevitable that there will be conflicts, incompatible objectives, and breakdowns in communication.

Integrating the entire supply chain, while it is promoted to improve operating costs and increase customer satisfaction, is a daunting task requiring very careful planning and implementation, highly effective support systems in all participating organizations, extreme patience, effective collaboration, and negotiation. This is especially important when the supply chain reaches across the globe, with the added issues of culture, politics, language, education level, and so on.

Compatible information technology is desirable, as is a centralized locale for all pertinent information. Electronic communication systems are needed to complete the linkage. The ability to track and follow material and production flows from raw material extraction until it reaches the customer is becoming increasingly important.[29] Establishing strategic partners is vital to the exchange of information and resources. Additionally, partnerships allow for shared risks as well as benefits. How customer demand will be disseminated among the organizations in the chain and how the pace of production will be planned, monitored, and synchronized is critical.

Deciding early on which organization and what person is in charge of SCM is critical. Someone has to facilitate the big decisions, or the chain can collapse. Advice on virtually every topic that has been discussed in this chapter, and some that have not, is needed to effectively attain and sustain a fully functional supply chain.

REFERENCES

1. J. L. Bossert, *The Supplier Management Handbook*, 6th ed. (Milwaukee, WI: ASQ Quality Press, 2004), 22.

2. ASQ Quality Glossary, www.asq.org.

3. American Production and Inventory Control Society (APICS), *Basics of Supply Chain Management: Participant Workbook* (Chicago: APICS, 2016).

4. W. E. Deming, *Out of the Crisis* (Cambridge, MA: MIT Center for Advanced Educational Study, 1986).

5. M. A. Durivage, *The Certified Supplier Quality Professional Handbook* (Milwaukee, WI: ASQ Quality Press, 2017), 8.

6. Automotive Industry Action Group, *CQI-19 Sub-Tier Supplier Management Process Guideline*, August 2012.

7. *FDA Group's Blog*, "A Quick Guide to FDA's Expectations for Supplier Quality," December 27, 2016.

8. J. Elkington, "25 Years Ago I Coined the Phrase 'Triple Bottom Line.' Here's Why It's Time to Rethink It," *Harvard Business Review*, June 25, 2018, p. 3.

9. Durivage, *Certified Supplier Quality Professional Handbook*, 11.

10. J. A. DeFeo, *Juran's Quality Handbook*, 7th ed. (New York: McGraw-Hill, 2017), 740.

11. L. B. Coleman Sr., *Managing Organizational Risk Using the Supplier Audit Program* (Milwaukee, WI: ASQ Quality Press, 2018).

12. N. R. Tague, *The Quality Toolbox*, 2nd ed. (Milwaukee, WI: ASQ Quality Press, 2005), 408–20.

13. Durivage, *Certified Supplier Quality Professional Handbook*, 91.

14. Ibid., 210–14.

15. DeFeo, *Juran's Quality Handbook*, 754–55.

16. ASQ Quality Glossary, www.asq.org.

17. S. Kumar, "Managing a Procurement and the Associated Risks." Paper presented at PMI® Global Congress 2003, EMEA, The Hague, South Holland, The Netherlands.

18. DeFeo, *Juran's Quality Handbook*, 370–74.

19. D. L. Lindstrom, *Procurement Project Management Success: Achieving a Higher Level of Effectiveness* (Plantation, FL: J. Ross, 2014).

20. Ibid.

21. Project Management Institute, *A Guide to the Project Management Body of Knowledge (PMBOK® Guide)*, 6th ed. (Newtown Square, PA: Project Management Institute, 2017).

22. D. Brown, and S. Wilson, *The Black Book of Outsourcing: How to Manage the Changes, Challenges, and Opportunities* (Hoboken, NJ: John Wiley & Sons, 2005).

23. Coleman, *Managing Organizational Risk*.

24. J. T. Israel, "Feedback to Improve Core Customer Relationships: A Framework to Implement Face-to-Face Surveys," *ASQ 52nd Annual Quality Congress Transactions*, May 6, 1997, 423–24.

25. Ibid.

26. Project Management Institute, *Guide to the Project Management Body of Knowledge*.

27. Bossert, *Supplier Management Handbook*.

28. Durivage, *Certified Supplier Quality Professional Handbook*.

29. UNECE (United Nations Economic Commission for Europe), "Transparency in Textile Value Chains in Relation to the Environmental, Social and Human Health Impacts of Parts, Components and Production Processes," 2017, https://www.unece. org/fil eadmin/DAM/cefact/cf_forums/2017_Rome/Mini_Conf_Agendas/ResearchPaper TraceabilityforSustainableClothing.pdf.

See Appendix A for additional references for this chapter.

Part VII
Training and Development

Chapter 19	Training and Development
	Contributors: Susan Gorveatte, Grace Duffy, Denis Devos, and Joe Wojniak

An investment in knowledge always pays the best interest.

—Benjamin Franklin

Training increases skill and competence and teaches employees the "how" of a job. Education increases their insights and understanding and teaches the "why."

—Michael Hammer and James Champy

Training—constant, intensive, lavish, and universal—is another hallmark of companies that produce great customer service.

—William Davidow and Bro Uttal

Training, if done correctly and for the right reasons, is not an expense—it's an investment.

—Russ Westcott

Chapter 19
Training and Development

Distinguishing between Training and Education

The terms *education* and *training* are often used interchangeably. Education, however, is the process of acquiring knowledge and information, usually in a formal manner. Education equips learners to acquire new knowledge by teaching them how to think. Examples are the study and understanding of human behavior, team dynamics, and the principles of statistics. On the other hand, *training* is the process of acquiring proficiency in some skill or skill set. Examples are team leadership and facilitation and the application of the seven quality control tools. Figure 19.1 compares two workers with relatively equal basic skills and abilities. What differences will emerge if, over a period of time, education is provided to one and training to the other? If the education process is successful, the worker receiving education will have broadened his or her knowledge base, therefore expanding his or her thinking processes. The worker being trained will have received specific instruction in how to perform tasks for his or her job.

The outcome of education is typically measured by testing comprehension and knowledge retention. Training is usually measured by the learner's ability to demonstrate the learned skill by producing desired outputs (for example, by correctly drawing a blood sample from a patient).

An education course may not involve much training. A training program usually involves some education in the theory or principles underlying the development and need for the skill. Taking a refresher course in preparation for the Certified Manager of Quality/Organizational Excellence (CMQ/OE) examination involves learning some skills in test taking but is primarily the assimilation, or reawakening, of knowledge in a broad range of subjects, hence mostly education. Unfortunately, the two terms are frequently used interchangeably—for example, "A Sarbanes-Oxley Training Course." Understanding which parts of the course or program are education and which parts are training is important in the design, delivery, and evaluation of the offering.

Quality management is one aspect of how a business is managed. It is a horizontal, across-the-organization view, including performance measures and integration with strategic planning. Quality management can include policies, objectives, and processes using quality planning, quality assurance, quality control, and quality improvement. To be a Big Q quality manager or director suggests a need to continually reeducate oneself and to continually acquire new skills and

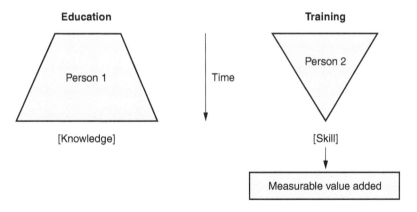

Figure 19.1   Training versus education.

sharpen proven skill sets. Also, due to the rapid increase in and importance of knowledge work, there is a need for continual education and training. Often, the competency (the sum of knowledge, experience, skills, aptitude, and attitude) of the workforce can be a factor that differentiates world-class learning organizations from their competitors.

Empowering workers to be responsible for the quality of their work has become routine in many industries. Inspection can often be eliminated when controlling the process and/or preventing defects is emphasized. This requires broader worker capabilities and effective training so that workers will know when and how to react to changing conditions.

Training and Education—Differences by Organizational Level

Often, the term *training* is not used with top management. Executive education may take the form of multiday retreats, combining learning and leisure activities, or it could consist of intensive learning events at a prestigious academic institution. For shorter-term education, executive briefings are the norm. *Forums* and *symposia* are other terms used.

Management training is the term typically used when providing education and training courses, workshops, or seminars for supervisors/managers or in preparing individuals to assume a supervisory/managerial role. Many successful companies cascade knowledge down throughout the organization by having management learn first, then having managers instruct their direct reports. It is an excellent way for management to demonstrate support, become personally involved, and better comprehend the subject matter. As the Body of Knowledge for the ASQ CMQ/OE examination suggests, managing requires an eclectic repertoire of skills (for example, technical skills for the functions managed, planning and organizing skills, staffing and people management skills, project management skills, and training, coaching, and mentoring skills). In addition, managers need to develop skills in managing conflict and negotiations, as well as build a solid understanding of variation and the use of measurements.

A. TRAINING PLANS

> Develop and implement training plans that are aligned with the organization's strategic plan and general business needs, including leadership training and alignment of personal development plans. (Create)
>
> **Body of Knowledge VII.A**

Alignment with Strategic Planning and Business Needs

For most organizations, training is a significant budget item. During downturns in business, it is often the first place where cost reduction is ordered. Therefore, it is imperative to view training as a strategic, cost-justified investment. It is the cost of not training that needs to be addressed when considering investing in training. Training is most beneficial to the organization when the training program's role in achieving the goals and objectives of the organization's strategic plan is supported by top management (for example, strategic plans include plans and budget for training).

Juran and Gryna suggest[1] consideration of the following six issues when planning for training:

1. The quality problems and challenges faced by the organization

2. The knowledge and skills needed to solve these problems and meet these challenges

3. The knowledge and skills actually possessed by the jobholders

4. The training facilities and processes already in existence

5. The prevailing climate for training in the organization, based on the record of past programs

6. What needs to be done differently to achieve the desired quality

Top management's support and personal commitment to training efforts should result in:

- The integration of training into business planning as a quality-inducing process

- Management being role models for reinforcing the daily use of quality principles throughout the organization

- Trainees grasping the connection between what they are to learn and the strategic objectives of the organization (for example, continual improvement, customer focus, product and service quality, productivity, profit, and employee training and development)

- Preparing workers to deal with changing expectations through training

- Establishing the acquiring of training skills as a requisite skill set for all management and team leaders

- Effective training design and delivery

- Consistent and frequent on-the-job recognition for work done well

- Coaching to reinforce the worker's use of posttraining skills

- Treatment of training as an investment in the future

- Application of benefits-to-cost analysis to justify training and to measure results of training; if there is no expected return on training investment (ROTI), training should not be done

- Training practitioners striving to adequately study, assess, and address the needs of the organization's mainline operations

- Measuring the training's effectiveness in terms of the improved outcomes of the organization affected by the training (for example, by collaboration/partnering between the training professionals and operations work units to achieve a mutually measurable outcome)

- Treating training as important in building and sustaining a superbly trained workforce (a significant marketing strategy that may be used to differentiate an organization from its competitors)

- Realizing the value of training and placing it high on the list of priorities for resource allocation

At the daily operating level, education might be advantageous to introduce new concepts or principles (for example, the concept of cycle time reduction and its impact on quality, or the principles of process management). Training might be warranted to build new skills, to refresh fading skills, or to qualify individuals to a prescribed standard. Such education and training at the operating level must still be traceable to the organization's strategic plans and objectives.

A proposed training and education program should be evaluated through a cost-benefit analysis. The resulting budget should be supported by top management as it identifies the trade-offs between the cost of training and the benefits that are realized by doing the training. Depending on the detail desired, the training costs can include trainee salaries, production time lost during training, facilities, training materials and equipment, and trainer or consultant costs. With a focus on the results expected from the training, benefits can include improved customer satisfaction, better product or service quality, reduced scrap, less rework, fewer returns, improved productivity, increased employee retention and improved employee morale, and a more flexible workforce.

Education and training are processes for supporting an organization's strategic objectives. Examples include building a new or updated core competency to address a threatening competitive situation, introducing a state-of-the-art technological change, or increasing customer satisfaction by reducing order response time. Organizations that use a systemic approach for translating the strategic plans and associated training objectives to the lowest levels of the organization, such as those using hoshin planning, will have the best chances for success. This process is valuable because it helps everyone in the organization better understand how training supports goals and objectives.

What Training Can and Cannot Do

An organization should be aware that training will not solve all its problems. At times, organizations attempt to use training to solve a problem when lack of skill is not the issue. Training cannot remedy a situation caused by poor performance or other root causes that are not skill related. Mager and Pipe offer a diagnostic process for analyzing and correcting performance problems.[2] Table 19.1 offers questions to help direct the actions to take.

The first consideration, before committing any resources, is to clearly differentiate whether the operating problem or situation is a performance deficiency or a knowledge/skill deficiency. It is often stated in the training field that whenever

Table 19.1 Deficiency analysis.

Question	Answer	Action
1. Why does performer fail to do job as trained?	Doesn't understand what is expected.	Ask another question.
2. Why does performer not understand what is expected?	Doesn't recall what was covered in training.	Ask another question.
3. Why doesn't performer recall content of training?	Doesn't have any notes or receive other references as to what was covered.	Ask another question.
4. Why does performer not have reference material from training?	Wasn't given any, or told where to get any.	Ask another question.
5. Were training materials given to the performer?	No. Instructor says none were available and trainees were told to "take notes."	Ask another question.
6. Why didn't performer take notes?	Performer has only sixth grade education and was not familiar with note taking.	Ask another question.
7. Why didn't instructor use handouts?	There was no formal course design and none were provided.	Ask another question.
8. Why was there no course design and no print material available for training use?	Selecting an "experienced old hand" to give the course was considered sufficient.	Ask another question.
9. In the absence of print material, why didn't performer's supervisor detect apparent reason for the performance deficiency?	The supervisor assumed the performer was ignoring or refusing to perform in accordance with the training.	Ask another question.
10. Does the performer need to be disciplined or be retrained?	Retrain, but with an improved training design, support materials, and supervisory reinforcement. Discipline is inappropriate (it was the "fault" of the system, and management's responsibility).	Redesign training. Retrain performer. Tutor supervisor on how to reinforce training.

Source: Reprinted with permission of R. T. Westcott & Associates.

a manager says that a training problem exists, much of the time the problem is found to be something in the system, not the people performing the job. Correcting deficiencies in job execution is often best achieved by changing resources, by providing more objective feedback, or by adding or removing behavioral consequences. For example, if an individual is not performing the job but could do so if his or her life depended on it, retraining is not the answer.

Planning for training should closely resemble the planning done for projects. For example:

- A need is identified

- An objective, outputs, and outcomes are stated

- Stakeholders (trainees) are identified

- Development work to be done is laid out (work breakdown structure)

- A timetable for development, delivery, and evaluation is set (Gantt chart)

- Resource requirements are specified (trainers, facilities, equipment, materials)

- Applicable metrics are established

- A budget is developed

- The plans are approved

- The training program development is monitored and measured

- Training is delivered

- Outputs are evaluated (ability to perform task)

- Outcomes are evaluated (training objective achieved)

- Lessons learned are reviewed

- Documentation of the development and delivery process, outputs, and outcomes is added to the organization's knowledge database

Training Is a Process

Whether training is conducted one-to-one, on the job, through remote electronic interface, or in a classroom, there is a process cycle, as depicted in the training system model, Figure 19.2. Steps in the process are:

1. Determine training needs:
   - Mandated or expressed need—verify and clarify
   - Needs unknown—conduct needs assessment
   - Propose training program—obtain approval and funding for design

2. Design and develop the training program:
   - Identify participants.
   - Determine objectives, content, and sequence of instruction (if to be designed internally).

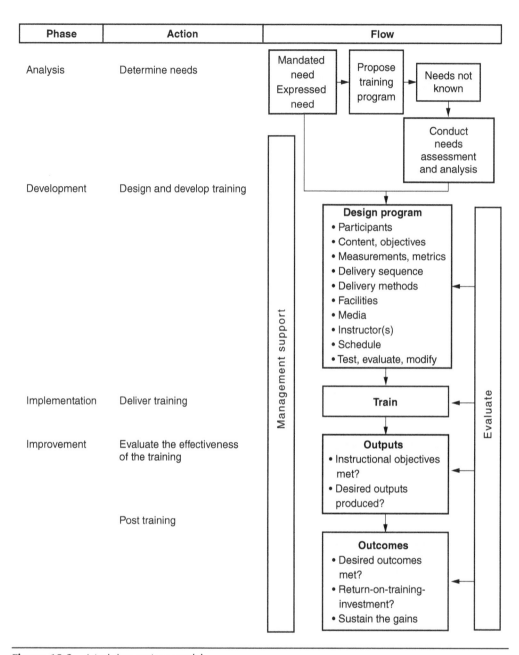

Figure 19.2 A training system model.

- Determine applicable metrics, measurement criteria, and process.
- Select/design the training delivery method(s) (if to be delivered by an internal trainer) or assess/select an appropriate external provider.
- Select/design the facilities.
- Select/design the media to be used.

- Select instructor(s)—train instructors as needed.

- Set training schedule.

- Test, evaluate, and modify the training as needed.

3. Deliver the training.

4. Evaluate the effectiveness of the training:

- Instructional objectives met? Desired outputs produced?

5. Posttraining:

- Desired outcomes met?

- Maintain the improvement—ROI?

- Sustain the gains (responsibility of the management of the work unit[s] from which trainees came).

B. TRAINING NEEDS ANALYSIS

Use various tools and techniques such as surveys, performance reviews, regulatory guidances, and gap analyses to identify and assess training needs. (Evaluate)

Body of Knowledge VII.B

When training and/or education are determined to be the best solution to the problem or situation, the next step is to determine the needs. Considerations when establishing these needs are:

- Is the need mandated by a regulatory body (for example, safety, hazardous materials, food quality, toxic material use)? Is the need clearly defined?

- Is the need mandated by management in support of a specific strategic objective (for example, customer contact skills or an International Organization of Standardization (ISO) 9001–based quality system)? Is the need clearly defined?

- If not mandated, is the need directed toward correcting a knowledge/skill deficiency? If so, who are the affected individuals? How many individuals are affected? Where are they located? What do they need to learn to do? What do they presently know about how to do what they are expected to do? What is the expected outcome of the training? Within what time frame must the individuals be trained? Need all individuals affected be trained at one time, together, or individually, or just in time?

- What delivery method is most appropriate for the needed training (instructor-led classroom training, self-directed, on-the-job training [OJT], or other)?

- What facilities, methods/programs, trainers, materials, equipment, and so on are available?

- What presently unavailable resources are needed to achieve the training or education objective?

- If primarily a training need, does a cost-benefit analysis justify the training? How will the training be funded (budget, appropriation, grant or subsidy, or other)?

- How should the training effectiveness be measured and evaluated (for example, demonstration of skills learned, on-the-job performance improvement, or ROTI)?

- What top management commitment and personal involvement are necessary to successfully execute the training and education plans?

A design can be determined once needs have been established, the number of individuals to be affected has been identified, the availability of personnel and facilities has been confirmed, and so on. The needs, timing, resources available, funding, and operating constraints will affect the method of delivery selected. Here are a few examples:

- Two newly hired workers, who need basic safety, housekeeping, and ISO 9001–quality system orientation, when reporting for work might be asked to watch three DVDs and successfully complete a quiz to demonstrate assimilation and understanding of the learning points. (Education)

- All machine operators need to learn how to use a new onboard statistical process control computer terminal to be installed at their machines. Training is needed just before the new system goes online. Appropriate just-in-time training might consist of instructor-led classroom training with each individual demonstrating the requisite skills to perform the task. (Training)

- One-to-one OJT by a skilled operator is one solution for an experienced machine operator transferred to a new work cell where unfamiliar machinery is in use. Another solution could be to send the operator to a course offered by the machinery manufacturer. (Training)

As these examples imply, the variety of designs and the media possible for training and/or education is extensive. For a large percentage of skill-related needs, the use of OJT by a skilled trainer/supervisor and the introduction of job aids (for example, checklists, work instructions, and diagrams) is often an effective solution.

Fade-out is a significant issue. It is the decline of a learned skill as time elapses between training delivery and on-the-job use of the learned skill. For this reason, it is best to schedule training just prior to participants' need for the skill, on the job. Likewise, when a skill is infrequently used, the skill fades out, and refresher training may be needed.

Purposes of a Needs Assessment and Analysis

Training may be indicated for one or more of the following reasons:

- To comply with new or changed regulatory and/or customer requirements

- To address new or changed systems, processes, procedures, methods, equipment, or tools

- To add or modify skills

- To refresh previous training to ensure maintenance of a specific skill

- To qualify and/or certify an individual to a specific workmanship standard

- To correct a skill deficiency noted in an individual's performance appraisal

In addition, there are often needs to satisfy that are not strictly training. These education needs could be to:

- Provide company orientation for new or transferred employees.

- Provide knowledge of theories and concepts pertinent to the organization's products or services and practices, such as theory pertaining to electrical currents and transmission.

- Provide knowledge of required and/or acceptable work behaviors.

- Mentor an individual in personal development planning and/or career advancement.

Assessing Training Needs

An assessment of training needs can range from a companywide periodic assessment in which the analysis provides data for an annual training plan and budget to a simple observation that a given employee does not know how to perform an assigned task. Many companies address their training needs by matching people to jobs on the basis of formal education acquired, then training them in the specific requirements of the job. For this to be successful, the needs assessment should begin with top management and the organization's strategic plan. The following issues may be appropriate to address:

- Strategic plans, goals, business objectives, and action plans

- Major changes anticipated for the short and long term

- Primary customers served

- Plans for entering a new market (requiring workforce retraining)

- Products or services produced and technologies used presently

- Organizational structure

- Decision-makers

- Impact of political realities (internal and external)

- Microcultures and policies of each business unit

- Budget approval process

- Present core competencies of employees

- Future core competencies employees will need

- History and significance of technical training in the organization

- Competitor's approach to training and education

- Industry standards and regulations affecting technical training

A proper assessment of needs helps prioritize resources to ensure that they are available to address the most critical training needs. Finally, the needs assessment process must be deployed to each business unit, which in turn cascades it downward until the training needs of individual employees are addressed.

Needs Assessment Techniques and Tools

There are many techniques and tools for determining training needs and for separating out nontraining needs. Data obtained from these needs assessment and analysis tools provide information for designing program content, a baseline for evaluating training, and aid in selecting participants, instructors, facilities, equipment, and media. The KESAA factors are *knowledge, experience, skills, aptitude, and attitude*:

- Review of existing records determines the magnitude of a training and/ or education deficiency. Types of records include performance reports, job descriptions, performance appraisals, meeting minutes, process audit reports, and training programs completed. Output is a matrix showing the records accessed, the needs uncovered, and the magnitude of the need.

- Interviews of exemplary performers may be conducted to ascertain the level of competence that is attainable by performers who exhibit the most effective KESAA factors in the work units from which participants will be selected.[3] Output is a summary of the key KESAA factors for the jobs or work units targeted. See Figure 3.2 for a KESAA requisites analysis sample.

- Focus groups may be used to collect stated needs from a cross-section of key employees, conducted with small groups of eight to ten employees, using structured discussion questions, with a facilitator. Output is a summarization of the needs surfaced and the tasks, processes, and/or work unit from where the needs emanate.

- Organizational diagnosis for an entire organization examines relationships and communication—vertically, horizontally, and diagonally. The output is a summary of findings and conclusions and recommended actions.

- Job analysis consists of breaking a job down to levels of increasing specificity. Outputs are a sequenced task listing by level and job inventories.

- Task analysis involves the specification of all overt and covert behaviors pertinent to the performance of a job. Outputs can be stimulus-response tables, flowcharts, time and motion studies, and behavior observation check sheets.

- Front-end analysis can be accomplished through many techniques—for example, a performance audit, root cause analysis, or a competency analysis. The outputs provide data in a variety of formats, usually a matrix.

- Instruments for collecting data for analysis can include tests, questionnaires, surveys, checklists, simulations, games, self-completed assessments, and recorded performance reviews.

- Techniques involving personal interaction can include observations of work being performed, individual or group interviews, brainstorming, and focus groups. Outputs would be a categorization of the needs detected, where the needs are prevalent, and the perceived magnitude of the needs.

- Qualitative data analysis techniques can be used to analyze nonquantitative data, such as data expressed in words, phrases, and paragraphs.

- Critical incident analysis is the recording and analysis of personal accounts (examples of situations) of incidents pertinent to needs for training. It is similar to collecting personal stories, but briefer.

- Surveys, questionnaires, and checklists are used to collect data about a group's interests in and desires for training. While surveys are not as effective as interviews, cost, time pressure, or access may limit data collection options. The survey needs to be designed well: aligned with business goals and oriented to find out where the underlying pain points occur. Having a method of validating survey conclusions is a good idea.

For a simple approach to determine needs at the individual level:

- Talk with the performers.

- Talk with the performers' bosses.

- Talk with subordinates, peers, and customers with whom the performers have contact.

- Observe a performer and/or give the performer a test.

- Obtain needs from performance appraisals.

When the Need Is to Improve Job Performance

When conducting a needs assessment, the problem that surfaces is frequently a performance problem. Conducting a training program is not a viable solution when job behavior (and attitude), poor supervision, or an inadequacy of job design, material, tools, or equipment is the cause of deficient performance. To determine whether the deficiency is a performance problem rather than lack of knowledge and skill, apply the test questions listed in Table 19.2.

From answers to the questions in the table:

- Select a *job* solution (J) if the problem is the way the task is organized or if the tools, and so on, are inadequate. Note: The skill might not be needed at all if the job/task can be eliminated or redesigned.

- If the performer lacks the requisite knowledge/skills, select a *training* solution (T).

- If the problem is that the performer does not know what is expected of her or him, select a solution that improves performance *feedback* (F).

- If the performer is capable of doing the work but fails to do it, take action to change the *consequences* (C) of doing the job. Note: An incentive may also be considered—for example, self-assessment of performance, empowerment, or profit sharing.

Table 19.2 Distinguishing between performance and skill/knowledge issues.

Relative to Target Population (TP)	Job Solution (J)	Training Solution (T)	Feedback (F)	Consequences (C)
Does TP have time to do job well?	X	X		
Does TP have proper facilities in which to work?	X			
Does TP have the proper tools to do the work?	X			
Does TP have proper procedure, instructions, job aids?	X			
Does TP know what they are supposed to do?		X	X	
Has TP ever done the job correctly?		X	X	
Could TP do the job properly if their lives depended on it?		X		X
If TP could do the job in an exemplary way, would they?				X
Are there more negative than positive consequences in doing the job?				X
Does TP know when they are not performing as supervisor expects?			X	
Do supervisors of TP have requisite knowledge/skills?		X	X	X

Source: Reprinted with permission of R. T. Westcott & Associates.

- Frequently, performers know how to get the job done but receive more negative than positive consequences for doing so and really do not know what is expected of them. A solution is to train supervisors in how to provide performance feedback and positive consequences for work done well (a T, F, and C for supervisors).

An effective tool for needs analysis is the individual development plan (IDP). This proactive tool anticipates the knowledge, skills, and abilities required for the future growth of the employee. Development plans can be related to the current job description (job enlargement) or be targeted toward job enhancement as the employee is groomed for career growth. The reactive analysis tool of performance counseling is more appropriate for the *consequences* identified in Table 19.2.

An IDP focuses on developing a quality talent pool by allowing each individual to create a systematic strategy to improve skills and overall performance. The IDP is a quality tool that creates direction and ongoing dialogue with future quality leaders. They help identify improvement needs and align them with internal talent needs and future opportunities in the organization. IDPs help cultivate talent and enable individuals to advance more quickly to meet the critical needs of the organization while fulfilling their personal skills development and career goals. An IDP is a tailored plan created by employees in collaboration with their immediate managers to establish clear goals, deadlines, and measurable action items. Managers undertake a quality control function during performance appraisals and ensure that employees at all levels have the *knowledge, skills, and abilities* (KSA) to perform their roles.

There are three major elements in a structured IDP:

1. Development goals

2. Time lines to accomplish each development goal

3. Activities necessary for development

Start the process by thinking about what you do well and what you should improve to enhance performance. Identify strengths, interests, and opportunities for improvement. Form a concise list of KSA improvements related primarily to your job requirements and career goals. Set goals that are specific, measurable, achievable, relevant, and timely. Commit to a few specific goals. Managers should provide clarifying feedback to ensure that your goals align with those of the organization and that nothing stands in the way of success.

As employees fulfill strategically planned tasks, challenging new assignments and education experiences, the person gains KSAs that lead to higher performance, increased career satisfaction, and rapid advancement. As managers use IDPs, the organization enhances its overall performance while forming a deeper talent pool to meet the quality leadership needs of tomorrow.[4] Of course, a situation might be detected in which both a knowledge/skill deficiency and a performance problem exist. The performance problem should be resolved first so that training efforts are not wasted.

Caveats

Ineffective or poor assessment of needs can negatively impact a training program. Following are examples of corrective actions focused on preventing these problems:

- Training plan is changed to address specific organizational goals and objectives.

- Training is necessary to address a specific process or task need.

- Identified job skills are deficient, and training is needed immediately.

- The work problem has been clearly identified, and training is the right solution, regardless of the organizational levels of those persons to be trained.

- It is planned that the right participants will be trained in the right skills, by the right trainers, for the right reasons, and at the right time.

- Any purchased or outsourced training is keyed to appropriate business needs and constraints.

- Training is effectively designed, delivered, evaluated, and reinforced to meet the organization's needs. That is, training appropriately addresses the identified gaps.

If the value to be gained by training does not exceed the cost, a less expensive training method should be used, or the training should not take place. People should not be trained until there is an immediate way for them to use the skill. Most of the skills-acquisition process should focus on learning by doing, but sequencing learning activities in the order they are performed on the job is not always best. Building from simpler to more complex subtasks may be a better way to build toward achieving mastery of complex tasks.

Circulating a list of available or potential courses for employees to indicate their preference *is not* a needs assessment. Employees often do not know what they need. This may be true if:

- Little or no effective performance feedback is provided, so the employee does not have a clear view of what is expected of her or him or of her or his performance related to that expectation.

- Employee is unaware of organizational objectives and conditions that could affect his or her job (for example, new product introduction, new process/equipment, new regulations).

- Receiving the list is perceived to mean the employee must check off something.

- The perception is that something additional will be expected if a course is attended.

- The courses listed appear to have no relation to the employee's work.

- Attending a course may be just a way of getting out of doing work.

The skill level of the intended training participants should be assessed so that training can be structured to build on present skill levels. People should not be trained in a skill they already can demonstrate. Finally, if there is a performance problem and lack of skill is not an issue, some other solution is indicated.

C. TRAINING MATERIALS, DEVELOPMENT, AND DELIVERY

Use various tools, resources, and methodologies to develop training materials and curriculum that address adult learning principles and the learning needs of an increasingly diverse workforce. Describe various methods of training delivery: classroom, workbooks, simulations, computer delivered, on the job, and self-directed. Use mentoring and coaching to support training outcomes. (Apply)

Body of Knowledge VII.C

Leadership of Quality Training in Support of Organizational Goals

In most organizations the quality manager is the in-house expert on quality issues and, as such, is expected to be involved in helping identify the quality subject training needs for other managers. The quality manager should either ensure that the quality-related technical content of a training program meets the training needs for the organization or negotiate how quality goals are to be met by other functional managers within the organization.

It is not enough simply for training to be conducted; it is extremely important that follow-up activities require the manager to use the knowledge or skill gained in the training session. If a manager is not required to employ the new skill immediately, only a small portion of the training is likely to be retained. Additionally, a manager must be given the opportunity to apply the new skill in the environment in which it is expected to be used. The training should be reinforced and evaluated periodically to ensure that the concepts are understood, and the skills are practiced.

Training for managers differs from that for other employees because managers often are not expected to do the things that are the subject of the training, but rather are expected to be able to oversee proper application of the training. A simple example involves training in statistical process control (SPC).

An operator or engineer would be expected to apply the skills learned in training to record the data and control the process. To do this, the operator and/or engineer would need to understand control chart rules and what action to take when out-of-control conditions are shown on the chart. A manager, however, needs to not only oversee the worker's proper use of SPC but interpret the data at a higher level. For example, a manager or the manager's engineer designate must determine whether the average or range chart control limits are so broad that action is required at the machine to improve capability even when the process is in control. The manager may also create communication systems so SPC charts can be properly employed within the organization. For significant changes, managers will need to understand the SPC system well enough to approve investments to drive continuous improvement and improve process capability.

The ISO 9000 series quality system standards, and other standards, have heightened awareness of the need for work competency (education, training, and experience) and qualifying personnel who conduct activities pertaining to quality, as defined in the organization's quality plan, procedures, and practices. Typical basic training topics for all employees include quality principles and practices, problem-solving methods, the basic quality tools, working as a team member, team protocols, and interpersonal skills. Training is also needed in the technical aspects of a job.

Skills required in day-to-day activities can be acquired through formal training or through *on-the-job training* (OJT). When practical, employee training may be more effective when formal training is combined with OJT. Both formal training and OJT need a defined structure, clear objectives, and a method for demonstrating competency. Regardless of the training system used, the trainer must be qualified to teach the topic/skill to be trained (including underlying concepts and the reason for training), must know how to properly use requisite tools and references (including any equipment used to deliver training), and should be aware of how to best train adults. Knowles has delineated theories of learning and teaching for adults that need to be taken into consideration for organizational training and distance learning programs.[5] Knowles' ideas are based on adults having self-direction and internal motivation. Thus, the instructor operates less as a director and more of a guide, providing direction to learners and making sure that the material links to their experiences.

Nonmanagerial employees tend to receive more specific OJT than do managers. OJT can be highly effective because the training is typically conducted in the actual work environment—on the same equipment and using the same processes used in day-to-day activities.[6] Historically, OJT normally has been conducted by a manager or other employee familiar with job requirements. Organizations are utilizing external training providers particularly for industry-specific subject matter such as standard practices, test methods, and regulations.

Training could be ineffective, abbreviated, or superficial if:

- The time that can be devoted to the training effort is limited.

- The trainer lacks the competency to conduct training in the subject matter.

- Training is not planned.

- Training is not given adequate priority in order to ensure implementation.

- The trainer lacks firsthand knowledge of all the things that must be done to do the job successfully.

There are a few precepts for performer-level training:

- Trainers need to understand that the learner is always in control of what is learned. For a training program or an OJT learning experience to be fully effective, the learners need to see clearly how what is being taught will benefit them and fulfill a felt need in them.[7] This is true of both managers and other employees, but because managers have the authority to set directions, a failure to recognize this fact can effectively nullify the training efforts.

- A training program should address benefits in terms of the trainee's needs and is also aligned with the strategic plan and general business needs of the organization. The information presented must be reinforced with hands-on application of the skills. Although hands-on activities can be simulated in a classroom setting, it is better, when feasible, to do these activities in the work environment, as described in this example.

A program for teaching internal quality auditing to employees consists of several steps. First, the program establishes the purposes and benefits of internal auditing to the participants and to the organization. Second, the program examines the elements of auditing and explains how to establish an audit schedule, prepare a checklist, conduct an opening meeting, perform the audit, hold the closing meeting, report audit results, and follow up on any problems detected. Classroom training is supplemented with exercises and role playing to demonstrate and reinforce the skills presented. The procedures the organization follows in preparing for an actual audit—for example, preparing a checklist—are to be followed. Training continues with employees demonstrating competence in all of the skills learned by performing an actual audit in a unit of the organization. The trainer(s) should supervise and coach participants throughout the entire auditing process, including the audit team's issuance of the audit report and audit follow-up activities.

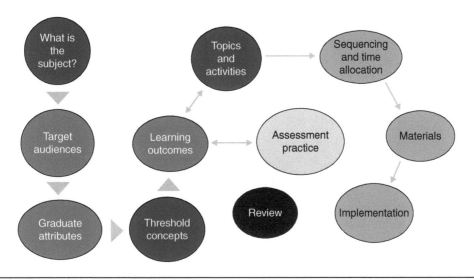

Figure 19.3 A curriculum development process.

Source: CHEPSAA (Consortium for Health Policy and Systems Analysis in Africa), "Principles and Practice of Good Curriculum Design," December 12, 2013, cited in *Power*, "Maximize the ROI of Coaching and Training."

Designing the Training Program

ASQ's self-directed learning series *CMQ/OE Program* presents in Module 7 a five-phase instructional design model called *ADDIE*, representing:

1. *A.* The *analysis* phase provides the opportunity to get the target training audience, including prospective participants and their managers, directly involved in determining what training should take place, how it should be delivered, and who should participate.

2. *D.* The *design* phase is where decisions regarding course content, delivery methods, measurement and evaluation, and implementation strategies are made.

3. *D.* In the *development* phase, training materials are created, purchased, and/or modified to meet the training need.

4. *I.* During *implementation,* the training is delivered to the target audience.

5. *E. Evaluation* consists of determining what results were achieved because of attendance and participation in the training encounter.

Following a needs assessment/analysis, the next step is to design (or purchase) a cost-effective training program. The intent of the program is to produce the desired outputs and outcomes with the least expenditure of resources.

A training program can be as simple as planning for one-to-one OJT training for an individual or as involved as training large groups of employees in a new process or the use of new equipment. Regardless, there should be a defined training plan and documented evidence that the training was successfully completed.

The major factors to consider in designing a training program are:

- Who needs the training (participants)? How many are there, and where are they located?

- Why do they need the training? What are they doing now? At what skill level are they now?

- What do they need to learn? How much of what they need is knowledge, and how much is pure skill attainment?

- What measurement(s) will best indicate that participants can do the tasks to which they are assigned (apply the skills acquired)?

- What basis will be used to evaluate the success of the training program?

- What method is best for delivering the training within the organization's resource constraints (for example, classroom, on-the-job training, outside training provider, or other method)?

- Where can the training best be delivered (which facility, what room, at or away from the workplace)?

- What media are best to use in delivering the training (for example, audio, visuals, video, print, intranet, or the internet)?

- Who should deliver the training? What trainer qualifications are needed? If there is no qualified trainer or facilitator available internally, will training of a trainer be needed? How many trainers are needed?

- When would training best be done? What is the best schedule, considering workplace demands?

- What is the projected ROTI? Is the planned training worth the investment? Do adjustments need to be made to ensure training costs do not overrun training benefits?

In today's fast-paced and ever-changing business environment, instructional designers are required to be more agile and to utilize iterative design models. A solid background in instructional design will be key for designing the learning of the future.

Adult Learning Principles. Before an organization can select the appropriate methods and tools to use in quality training, it must first understand how adults learn. In general, adults exert more control over their lives than do younger people, and this desire for control extends to the learning process as well. Knowles identifies six factors that influence adult learning:

1. Adults have a need to know why they should learn something.

2. Adults have a deep need to be self-directing.

3. Adults have a deeper, broader, greater, different quality of experience than youths.

4. Adults become ready to learn when they experience in their life situation a need to know or to be able to perform more effectively and satisfactorily.

5. Adults enter into a learning experience with a task-centered (or problem-centered or life-centered) orientation to learning.

6. Adults are motivated to learn by both extrinsic and intrinsic motivators.[8]

The andragogical model requires that learners be actively involved in the process of evaluating their learning outcomes. Knowles and Hartl propose the following six questions:

1. What procedures would I use with this particular group to encourage conditions of mutual respect, cooperation rather than competition, support rather than judgment, mutual trust, and fun while learning?

2. What procedures will I use to involve the learners continuously in planning?

3. What procedures will I use to help the participants diagnose their own learning needs?

4. What procedures can I use to help participants translate learning needs into learning objectives?

5. What procedures can I use to involve the learners with me in designing and managing a pattern of learning experiences?

6. What procedures can I use to involve the learners responsibly in evaluating the accomplishment of their learning objectives?[9]

Learning Objectives. Learning objectives are sometimes called *terminal objectives* because they address what will be learned by the end of the training module or program. These objectives contain a statement of the resulting observable actions planned, the measurable criterion for each action, and the conditions under which performance will be measured.

Bloom's Taxonomy of Educational Objectives categorizes objectives in three domains: cognitive (or mental skills), affective (growth in feelings, emotional areas), and psychomotor (manual, physical skills). The cognitive domain is subdivided into six behaviors:

- Remember (knowledge level)
- Understand (comprehension level)
- Apply (application level)
- Analyze (analysis level)
- Evaluate (evaluation level)
- Create (synthesis level)

The reader will recognize the cognitive domain behaviors from their use in categorizing the complexity level of the Body of Knowledge and test questions for the CMQ/OE exam. The affective domain is subdivided into five behaviors:

- Receiving
- Responding
- Valuing
- Organization
- Characterization

The psychomotor domain is useful for training that takes students out of their comfort areas. This domain has seven behaviors:

- Perception (or awareness)
- Set (or readiness to act)
- Guided response (early stages of complex skills)
- Mechanism (basic proficiency)
- Complex overt response (skillful motor acts for complex movement patterns)
- Adaptation (individual can modify to fit special needs)
- Origination (creative new movement patterns to fit a specific situation)

Lesson Plans. Lesson plans specify what material will be presented during a training session. R. S. Johnson lists the following guidelines for the successful development of lesson plans:

1. Lesson plans are crucial for [guiding the trainer to achieving] training success.

2. Every subject must be adequately researched.

3. Develop twice as much material as you think you will need.

4. Ensure that trainees know what's in it for them early on so they are motivated to learn.

5. Practice, practice, practice prior to presentation.

6. Use examples that pertain to the operation where possible.

7. Stimulate questions.

8. Use training aids.

9. Adapt the training to the group's level.

10. Never make excuses. For example, "I've never taught this material before."

11. Remain positive.

12. Follow your lesson plan.[10]

Johnson identifies four types of lesson plans: topical outline, manuscript, sentence, and key word.[11] The type of lesson plan developed depends on the instructor's experience and familiarity with the material, whether he or she has presented it previously, and the degree of formality desired in the presentation of the material. Note: Purchased training programs often include one or more suggested lesson plans.

Competency-based training methods may also be referred to as *individualized instruction, mastery learning,* or *programmed instruction.* There are fundamental differences between what students learn, how they learn, when they learn, and if they learn each task. Competency-based training focuses on these key features:

- *Outputs.* Learners know exactly what they will be able to do upon completion.

- *Learner centered.* Training is organized to accommodate individuals' needs—for example, speed of learning, need for feedback, and sequence of learning (simple to complex).

- *Job breakdown.* Jobs are subdivided into tasks with terminal performance objectives for each task.

- *Mastery.* One task is mastered by the learner before moving to the next (often moving from the simple to the more complex steps before rearranging the steps into the logical work sequence).

- *Performance.* Learners must meet a high job proficiency level, in a job-type environment, to obtain acknowledgment of completion.

- *Competency.* Competency is achieved when the learner has acquired the requisite knowledge, experience, and skill to perform a worthwhile job in a prescribed way.

E-learning is enabling training methods to be combined and is also introducing methodologies developed in the gaming industry. Gamification encourages learners to apply their learning by challenging them with real-life situations in a controlled environment. It is a more effective method of learning as it involves applying the content to reinforce key concepts in the learner's brain. Gamified e-learning courses typically have a storyline and feature challenges, rewards such as badges, and analytics. Figure 19.4 illustrates the different levels of gamified e-learning:[12]

Level 1 - Partial gamification: Gamification elements are used in parts of the course (e.g., for quizzes or activities within the course).

Level 2 - Game-based learning: The entire learning path is converted into a game.

Level 3 - Gamified learning path: This is similar to game-based learning; however, challenges aggregate and enable the learner to achieve higher levels of proficiency. Rewards such as points, badges, and leaderboards are used to encourage the learner to progress to higher levels.

Level 4 - Gamified portals: Many learners can interact via an internet-based portal.

E-learning continues to grow and is often preferred by adult learners due to the flexibility of this training and delivery method.[13]

Methods of Training Delivery

Traditionally, instructional modes have included live instructors, printed handouts, and media aids (for example, whiteboards, chalkboards, flip charts, and overhead projection of slides, or computerized projection). Lectures, discussions, role plays, simple paper-based games, case studies, workbooks, DVDs, CDs, self-directed learning with printed materials, and e-learning is often used. Lectures

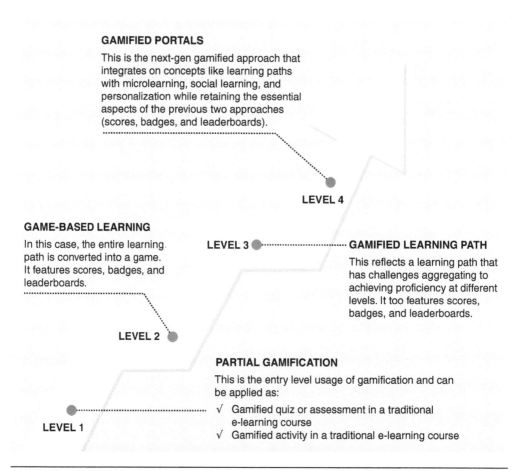

GAMIFIED PORTALS

This is the next-gen gamified approach that integrates on concepts like learning paths with microlearning, social learning, and personalization while retaining the essential aspects of the previous two approaches (scores, badges, and leaderboards).

LEVEL 4

GAME-BASED LEARNING

In this case, the entire learning path is converted into a game. It features scores, badges, and leaderboards.

LEVEL 3 .... **GAMIFIED LEARNING PATH**

This reflects a learning path that has challenges aggregating to achieving proficiency at different levels. It too features scores, badges, and leaderboards.

LEVEL 2

PARTIAL GAMIFICATION

This is the entry level usage of gamification and can be applied as:

√ Gamified quiz or assessment in a traditional e-learning course
√ Gamified activity in a traditional e-learning course

LEVEL 1

Figure 19.4   Levels of gamification.

Source: A. Pandey, "Killer Examples on How Gamification in the Workplace Is Reshaping Corporate Training," October 24, 2017, cited in Power, "Maximize the ROI of Coaching and Training."

and role playing date back to classical Greece, more than two thousand years ago. Lectures were the primary method of instruction, but creative instructors now use many other tools to enhance learning.

Learner-Controlled Instruction. Increasingly, technologies for delivering learner-controlled instruction (LCI), also called *self-directed learning* (SDL), are available. Working without an instructor and at their own pace, adult learners build toward ultimate mastery of the needed knowledge/skill. Strengths of learner-controlled instruction are due to its flexibility: when training needs to be conducted at different times, when the learners are geographically distant, when training needs to occur at multiple sites simultaneously, when consistency of skill execution is a necessity, or when refresher training is needed.

The trend toward LCI/SDL and e-learning reinforces using technology-based training, as technologies both stimulate and enable direct interaction between the individual and the material to be learned. Internet-based programs with or without learner-instructor interaction are popular for delivery of certain types of standardized training (for example, computer application and app development training). ASQ provides many media choices and topics for self-directed training.

Lectures and Presentations. A *lecture* is a one-dimensional, oral transmission of information to students by an instructor, either in person or via electronic media. They are still frequently used to convey concepts and content to students and are often used in combination with other tools. Lectures are one type of presentation, but presentations can also include other oral, visual, and multimedia formats.

Discussion Format. The discussion format allows participants freedom to present views, opinions, and ideas in an unrestrained environment. Roundtables and panel discussions are variations. These methods normally work best with a knowledgeable and experienced discussion leader. The *Socratic method* of repeated questioning is used successfully to elicit and share the accumulated knowledge and experience of course members.

Experiential Training. The focus of this form of training is on experiencing the effects typically encountered in a real-life situation. The experiential approach employs many types of structured experiences (for example, games, simulations, role plays) to facilitate learning. Typically, participants assume roles within a stated scenario designed to surface one or more learning points. They then play out the scenario to a conclusion under the eye of a skilled facilitator. A well-designed scenario will tend to produce a predictable range of responses highlighting the training content.

Coaching. Used on a one-to-one basis, or for a small group or team, and conducted at the workplace, coaching is a teaching, learning, and counseling relationship designed to develop job-related knowledge and skills and improve performance. It requires a continuous flow of instructions, comments, explanations, and suggestions from coach to trainee—with the coach demonstrating, listening, questioning, acknowledging learners' experiences, assisting, motivating, encouraging, and rewarding performance. The coaching option is used primarily to teach complex skills and operations when the number of trainees is small, and the training is needed infrequently, and as a follow-on to other forms of employee training. It has the advantage of being flexible and adaptable. Its disadvantage is that coaching may encourage older, less effective methods among younger employees.

Coaching can be applied to work groups or teams, in which it closely resembles the sports team coaching model. Finnerty outlines the following steps for effective coaching:

- Define performance goals.
- Identify the resources necessary for success.
- Observe and analyze current performance.
- Set expectations for performance improvement.
- Plan a coaching schedule.
- Meet with the individual or team to get commitment to goals, demonstrate the desired behavior, and establish boundaries.
- Give feedback on practice and performance.
- Follow up to maintain goals.[14]

Case Studies. Many kinds of learning exercises fall under the category of case studies. Such exercises illustrate the application of study content and show how different approaches can be used to solve problems. Case studies can serve to stimulate intense discussions and idea sharing.

Case studies can be developed in-house or purchased from a variety of sources. A form of mini-case study, the *critical incident*, may often be of greater value than a larger, more inclusive case study. The critical incident is usually derived from real situations within the organization for which the training is designed. A critical incident might consist of just a few sentences describing a specific type of event or condition without reference to names or locations. Critical incidents are usually inserted throughout the training to illustrate specific learning points. The advantages of critical incidents are:

- They are easier to prepare than a fully developed case study.

- Participants can usually identify with the situation (it is their organization).

- Discussion is more targeted, with less confusion generated than with the multifaceted case study.

- They take less discussion time and get to the learning points quickly.

Concerns relating to critical incidents are:

- Data used to compile critical incidents must be collected prior to course design, necessitating a plan and time to do so.

- A critical incident is a carefully crafted, succinct representation (usually written) designed to engender learning about how to respond to a specific event/situation/condition. A critical incident should not be confused with anecdotal material ("war stories") that is used extemporaneously to illustrate a point and/or to inject humor.

- Care must be taken to not target, purposely or accidentally, any person or work unit in the company. Data must appear anonymous.

Workbooks. Workbooks contain a collection of discussion topics, exercises, extra readings, and other reference material. They may be used to supplement other materials provided during classroom presentations. Workbooks can serve several purposes:

- As a learning tool actively used during the presentation to encourage note-taking (filling in the blanks); as self-tests, as a supplement to material presented in class; as a more job-specific interpretation of material presented in a generic textbook; and as a reference to be used during class testing

- To demonstrate mastery of each stage of the training: specific notes, research data, or checklists compiled by participants and signed off by the instructor

- As a guide to be used by the trained person back on the job; the guide might contain workmanship standards and other reference material

Workbooks can combine some or all of the features in the previous list. They can range from a binder for filing class handouts and making notes to a more formal reference manual.

Instructional Games, Simulations, and Role Playing. Experience has shown that adult learners prefer to practice rather than just listen to lectures and that they prefer to interact with other learners when in a group learning environment.

Instructional games are activities designed to augment other training methods in order to focus the participants' learning toward specific training results. For example, *in-box exercises* usually present each participant with a variety of papers (reports, charts, tables) that resemble what a manager might find in an in-box. The participant analyzes the documents and takes what he or she considers appropriate action for each item. Responses are either discussed in class or evaluated off-line by the instructor, with instructional notes affixed to the documents. (This method could be used to instruct future internal quality system auditors in the document analysis phase of internal auditing.)

Simulations resemble instructional games but also include correspondence between some aspect of the game and reality. *Role playing* consists of spontaneously performing in an assigned scenario.

Remote Learning. This includes educational institutions that offer low-residency or completely online learning programs. Remote learning is especially popular with nontraditional students who would not be able to attend classes in person. This type of learning requires a sustained trainee commitment and self-discipline to successfully complete.

Distance Learning. One popular form of distance learning is where students in more than one location are scheduled and linked together electronically to enable one instructor to simultaneously teach students in multiple locations. The video provides face-to-face contact between the students and the instructor. Audio interaction between student and instructor and between the students may be included.

Computer-Based Instructional Techniques. Although much training continues to be conducted using the traditional techniques of lecture, discussion, and on-the-job training, technology-based approaches are rapidly moving to the forefront. Computers, electronic communications, and the internet have created dramatic new opportunities to provide learning. New products and techniques are appearing nearly every day.

Examples of computer-related technology used include:

- Instructional modules embedded within computer software (help screens, wizards, and pop-ups)

- Learning from mistake-proofing software (spelling and grammar checkers, templates)

- Websites (offering technical knowledge, testing, articles, links to other sites)

- Internet access:

    — Online equipment use and repair instructional manuals

    — Webinars (interactive education and training modules)

    — Articles, research papers, books

    — Forums, chat rooms, and blogs

    — Massive open online course (MOOC)

- Intranets (in-house internet-like networks providing training and education)

A quality manager's activities in the area of training technology may include being familiar with the techniques available, understanding technical jargon to make wise selections, serving on multifunctional teams that develop technology-based training packages, and evaluating training programs for effectiveness.

Job Aids. Job aids are virtually any type of media that can support or substitute for formal training and/or provide reinforcement or reference after training. Often, providing a job aid can be the simplest and most cost-effective way to assist performers in doing their jobs. A few types of job aids are:

1. Procedure manual

2. Laminated checklist hung at a workstation

3. Message on a computer screen, a buzzer, or other physical/aural interruption warning of a missing step or incorrectly performed function

4. Nested (drop-down) computer help screens taking the learner to increasingly greater detail

5. Instructions printed on the back of a form giving detailed instructions for completing the form

6. Pertinent information included for each critical step described on a shop work order or traveler

7. Tool-mounting board that has a clearly marked place for each type of tool

8. Diagnostic decision tree for solving a problem

9. Audio device accessed by a learner wearing earphones that guides the learner through each task step in the sequence and at the pace expected upon achieving mastery

Rossett and Gautier-Downes cite eight situations in which job aids are appropriate:

1. The individual cannot be expected to remember how to do a task because he or she is rarely required to do it.

2. To offer support for individuals who confront lengthy, difficult, and information-intensive challenges.

3. Without the aid, the consequences of error are high.

4. Performance relies on a large body of information.

5. Performance is dependent on knowledge, procedures, or approaches that change frequently.

6. Employee turnover is high, and the task is simple.

7. Employees are expected to act in an empowered way, with emphasized or new standards in mind.

8. There is little time or few resources for training.[15]

On-the-Job Training. Much skills training occurs through OJT. The learner is usually an employee who has been newly hired, transferred, or promoted into a position and lacks the knowledge and skill to perform some specific job component(s). A more experienced employee (peer or supervisor) is usually assigned to work with the trainee. Specific tasks are demonstrated and performed in the actual work environment to help the trainee gain the knowledge or skills previously lacking.

Johnson presents six principles of OJT:

1. It is usually used for skills training.

2. It is useful for individuals or small groups.

3. Without a consistent OJT program, there is a strong possibility that people are learning incorrect techniques through trial and error or from their teammates.

4. TQM requires OJT in the workplace, whether it be on the shop floor, on a computer, or via a sales call.

5. OJT must have a plan, even though it may not be as formal as those used in the lecture method.

6. The OJT teaching process is tell them, show them, have them show you, and repeat the process until performance is satisfactory.[16]

Like all training programs, OJT programs require a needs analysis, training objectives, clear statement of responsibilities, the procedures and work instructions for the specific job/task, and the basis for measuring job/task mastery.

Inconsistencies can result in the way employees perform their duties when it is common for an employee who is familiar with the job to train another employee, without objectives or a planned system. In addition, the lack of structure can cause bad habits to be included in the training. Another problem occurs when a relatively inexperienced employee is responsible for training others. The employee might know how to do the job, but, as anyone who has done training knows, it is much more difficult to teach someone to do a job than to do it yourself.

It has been estimated that up to 75% of all training is OJT. OJT provides instant feedback on the learner's achievements, and OJT relates directly to the job/task where training is needed. The trainer should positively reinforce improvement through as many iterations as necessary for the trainee to achieve mastery.

Hands-on training can be supplemented with photos of properly completed tasks at each stage of production and/or videos of workers properly performing the tasks to enhance the learning experience. All training, even OJT, should be planned to ensure completeness, consistency, and correctness of instruction. Performance improvement is virtually assured when planned, structured OJT is combined with formal training and positive reinforcement.

Microlearning. Microlearning is effective, efficient, and gives learners an opportunity to focus on a very specific skill. While YouTube videos are not typically geared toward workplace learning, their popularity suggests that more and more, we are relying on short bits of information to help us complete our tasks. You might find a short video on YouTube that teaches you how to braid your hair. What you likely will not find is a video that includes an introduction to the history of braiding hair, why braiding hair is so important, and the five different ways you could go about it. The success and popularity of a video on braiding hair is not necessarily about the video's length but more about the fact that it places laser-like focus on a very specific task—and nothing more. This is precisely what makes effective microlearning so successful and popular.

Microlearning is not limited to video. In fact, it does not have to be multimedia at all. Even something like a poster or infographic on the wall of your breakroom is microlearning. Formats for microlearning include:

- Posters
- Infographics
- Interactive infographics
- e-learning courses
- Games
- Branching scenarios
- Videos
- Job aids
- Simulations

Microlearning is mostly careful consideration of the problem you are trying to solve—the very specific, narrowly focused problem you are trying to solve. Do not start by trying to target the format that you want. Instead, identify your learners' needs and let them drive the format of your microlearning.[17]

Other Training Delivery Techniques

Other options for providing training include:

- Using external experts to deliver a packaged program or to custom design and deliver an organization-specific program
- Training and qualifying in-house trainers to deliver an externally developed program
- Augmenting training presented by in-house trainers with known subject matter experts from outside the organization
- Utilizing webinars (training prepared for delivery via the web)
- Establishing book reading discussion groups or forums focusing on material to be learned
- Taking guided and focused tours of other organizations
- Participating in a benchmarking team, or on an internal audit team
- Inviting more experienced people from other organizations to come in and talk
- Sending individuals to a manufacturer's technical training course
- Partnering with a local college or university to bring programs to the organization

- Periodically reexamining the job(s) for ways to improve the processes and perhaps eliminate the need for training in a particular area, or simplify the training needed

- Establishing a buddy system until the trainee has mastered the job (ensure that all "buddies" are properly qualified)

- Periodically rotating jobs and cross-training workers to provide additional operation effectiveness and keep performers motivated

- Partnering with local organizations with common interests to share training costs and introduce a variety of experiences for all of the partners' employees

- Participating in e-learning is often cost effective, flexible, and scalable to small or large audiences

Keys to Making Training More Effective

Design the training with consideration for learning styles and preferences:

- *Seeing.* Participant needs to be able to see and observe or, if not, to be able to visualize what is being taught. Demonstrate, show examples, or paint a word picture to illustrate.

- *Hearing.* Participant needs to hear and understand what is being taught. Paraphrase a second time. Check with participant to determine if instruction is getting through and is understood as intended.

- *Feeling.* Participant needs to touch and feel. As appropriate, allow participant to feel surfaces and shapes. Allow for participants to feel the effect of hot/cold, wind/water, and other forces of nature. Allow for experiencing feelings: sadness, joy, anger, disappointment, enthusiasm, and other emotions.

- *Doing.* Provide hands-on opportunity for the participant to try to replicate what is instructed.

When delivering training, the trainer should remember to KISS (keep it simple, Sam or Sylvia). When participants are so enthralled with the gadgets and gizmos used in the training that they forget the training message, the trainer has gone too far. A theme-park type of production is seldom needed, practical, or economical for presenting training. Additionally, when training delivery is totally dependent on the technology, and the technology is difficult to use, it can detract from learning or disrupt the training, especially when an equipment malfunction occurs.

Training delivered by straight lecture, although a prevalent method, is often boring and fades rapidly (if it sticks at all). Trainees might understand little of the message if they are absorbed in taking notes. For this reason, the use of job aids and workbooks should be considered both to augment initial training and to provide reinforcement on the job.

Whenever possible, avoid training an individual in a skill or topic for which the learner already has competence. Doing so may mean the learner becomes disengaged or distracted from the learning process. The learner could also be disruptive when bored. If part of the training is redundant for a learner, the instructor has a few choices:

- Appoint the preinformed learner as a coinstructor for the segment where the learner could become bored. (This suggests an in-depth needs analysis, with participant interviews in which their competencies and strengths are assessed, and potential coinstructors are invited to prepare to share in the instruction of a training module.)

- Divide the participants and design the training for basic and advanced levels.

- Allow the preinformed participant to choose between remaining in the class (and participating constructively) or temporarily leaving until called back.

In skills training, the charisma of the trainer is less important than the ability of the trainer to transfer knowledge and skills to the participant. Training is not intended to be pure entertainment but does not preclude the judicious use of humor and having fun while learning.

D. TRAINING EFFECTIVENESS AND EVALUATION

> Assess training effectiveness and make improvements based on feedback from training sessions, end-of-course test results, on-the-job behavior or performance changes, and departmental or area performance improvements. (Evaluate)
>
> **Body of Knowledge VII.D**

Effectiveness of a Training Program

As indicated in the training model in Figure 19.2, all phases of the training process should be evaluated. Evaluation is essential in determining whether the training program meets the objectives of the training plan. Evaluation includes:

1. Verification of the design (for example, subject content and delivery methods)

2. Applicability of facilities, equipment and tools, and media to be used

3. Qualifications of the trainer

4. Selection of the participants

5. Measures to be used to assess training effectiveness (validation)

6. Measures to be used to assess outcomes resulting from training (verification)

Technical training effectiveness can be greatly enhanced by four key considerations:

1. Appropriate preparation of the training facilities

2. Appropriate timing of the training relative to when performance is required

No.	Level	Questions	Comments
1	Reaction	Were the participants pleased with the training?	The typical "smile" sheets collected at the end of a program, session, or module.
2	Learning	Did the participants learn what was intended for them to learn?	Were the training objectives met? Typically determined from some kind of test.
3	Behavior	Did participants change their behavior on the basis of what was taught?	Typically determined from an assessment of how learned behaviors are applied on the job.
4	Results	Was there a positive effect on the organization resulting from participants' changed behavior?	Typically measured from pretraining versus post training analysis of the organization's outcomes. Usually a "quantity" type measure (increased production, lower rejects, number of time periods without a customer complaint, and so on).
5	ROTI	Was there a measurable net dollar payback for the organization resulting from participants' application of learned behavior?	Return on training investment (ROTI) is based on the dollar value added by the investment in the training.

Figure 19.5   Levels of training evaluation.

3. Appropriate sequence of training relative to skills mastery

4. Appropriate feedback indicating performance difficulties and progress

Figure 19.5 describes five levels for evaluating training. Kirkpatrick is credited with defining the first four levels (reaction, learning, behavior, and results) for evaluating training.[18] Level 5 in Figure 19.5 is a perspective addressed by Westcott and Phillips.[19]

Level 1. The *reaction* level provides the lowest-value information and results and is frequently and easily used.

Level 2. The *learning* level is used to obtain a more in-depth assessment of whether specific training objectives were met.

Level 3. The *behavior* (job applications) level assesses whether or not the training is applied back on the job, usually after some time has passed.

Level 4. The *results* level measures the quantitative difference between the outcomes of the work units affected prior to their people receiving training (the baseline) and the outcomes sometime after the training ended. The objectives for training measured could be a decrease in scrap rate, an increase in number of savings accounts opened, increased classroom attendance, elimination of medication errors in a hospital, and so on.

Level 5. The ROTI level offers the highest-value information and results but is not used as frequently and is more difficult to assess. Level 5 is based on placing dollar values on the baseline, the results, and the improvement, then determining the value received for the dollars spent. When expressed as a ratio, a three-dollar return for every one dollar spent is a useful minimum ROTI. Quality training programs that score best at all levels are likely to be very successful.

Two formulas may be used to evaluate at level 5: the *benefits-to-cost ratio* (BCR) and the ROTI.

$$BCR = \frac{Program\ benefits}{Program\ costs}$$

$$ROTI = \frac{Net\ program\ benefits\ (total\ benefits - costs)}{Program\ costs}$$

A rule of thumb is that if ROTI is less than three dollars (or a ratio of 3:1), meaning three dollars of benefits obtained from every dollar spent, then training should not be considered (unless mandated).

Training program development costs are usually included in the first year (when training may extend over one year) unless the costs substantially exceed the first-year benefits. In this case, costs may be prorated over the period in which the training is delivered.

Unfortunately, it can be very difficult to properly assess the return on investment (ROI) for training or coaching, as the approach to training and its results can be very subjective and hard to measure. In order to be successful, it is imperative that both the trainers/coaches and trainees properly understand the big picture within the organization and how their training supports those strategies. The key to measuring ROI is to make these subjective aspects more objective. It is important to properly define the goals and objectives of the training and how they fit the strategic direction; establish a baseline against which to measure progress, along with appropriate metrics; and then create a schedule to track those metrics over time.[20]

What Causes Ineffectiveness or Failure?

The ineffectiveness or failure of a quality training program is likely to be linked to one or more of the following causes:

- Cultural resistance by line managers
- Doubt as to the usefulness of the training, which occurs when:
  - No linkage exists with the strategic plans of the organization.
  - No apparent connection is evident between the behaviors to be learned and their application on the job.
  - No projected objectives are established for posttraining improvement.
  - The question of "What's in it for me?" is inadequately addressed for participants and their supervisors.
- Lack of participation (involvement) by line managers
- Technique versus problem orientation
- Inadequacies of leaders
- Mixing of levels of participants
- Lack of application during the course

- Language too complex

- Lack of participation by the training function

- Operational and logistical deficiencies

Additional issues include:

- There is no or weak partnering among managers/supervisors, trainers, and participants mutually involved in achieving the training objectives.

- The training program is poorly planned and delivered. Problems could include:

  — Inadequate needs assessment and analysis

  — Training content (objectives, subjects, media, and demonstrations) does not match needs

  — Lack of appropriate metrics and measures for evaluation

  — Overemphasis on theory and technique versus skill application

  — Lack of practice during the course

  — Inadequacies of trainers

  — Ineffective selection of participants

- There is a lack of or inadequate reinforcement of participants' success in learning and applying learning on the job.

Rationale for Ongoing Training Evaluation

If the training is new or is a major revision to previous training, the following need to be determined:

- From the design verification phase, are there projections indicating that the training program will be worth the resources to be expended and that the outcomes will support the organization's strategic plans?

- Does it make sense to go further if the appropriate resources cannot be made available?

- Would it be more cost-effective to continue with in-house design or to consider a training provider's product?

- If going forward with the design and delivery of the program appears feasible, which of the possible alternatives available have the greatest positive impact on the organization? Which have the greatest positive impact in the short term? In the long term?

During the delivery of training, the following should be frequently evaluated:

- Is the training achieving stated objectives?

- Are the right people attending the training?

- What parts of the training are yielding the most benefit to the participants? What parts are yielding the least? Why?

- What modifications must be made in flight to correct a problem or deficiency?

- If this or similar training is to be done again, what should be done differently? Why? How?

- Are there facility problems that need to be corrected immediately?

- Is the trainer succeeding in producing trained participants? If not, why?

After the training, the following questions should be asked:

- Are the participants satisfied? If not, why?

- Are the participants' organizations satisfied? If not, why?

- Have all the training plan requirements been met?

- How can the training design and delivery be improved?

- Did the training produce the desired outcomes?

Some organizations mistakenly measure training progress by the number of training programs conducted or people that flow through a classroom rather than by how effectively the training is used to achieve the organization's strategic objectives. In other cases, organizations mistakenly measure training effectiveness by asking attendees how much they liked the course and how much they think they learned. Naturally, people will always respond that they learned the material, even when they did not. Clearly, this has nothing to do with training outcomes.[21] Just because the trainer told entertaining jokes and a fancy lunch was provided does not mean attendees will be able to apply what they have learned. True assessments of training effectiveness will prove that one has acquired a level of knowledge and knows how to apply it. Ongoing evaluation throughout a training offering can take several forms, from simply asking someone to repeat back what was heard, to using case studies and report outs to reinforce concepts, to written quizzes and tests.[22]

Training should occur just in time—that is, immediately prior to the context in which it is to be used. The longer the time that elapses between the training and the opportunity to put the knowledge/skill gained into practice, the more likely the knowledge/skill gained will fade out. In such cases, learning can be reinforced through a refresher course. A refresher course recaps previous learning in a shorter time period, at a faster pace, and in a more intense manner. Face-to-face instruction might not be required. The use of technological methods may be enough.

Most employees find value in training that helps them do a better job easier and supports their growth and development. Therefore, employees who are motivated to increase their proficiency are simultaneously working to improve their organization's competitive advantage and themselves. Note: *Never* use training as a punishment or position it so it is perceived as such.

Training and Education as Tools in the Management of Quality

An integrated training program driven by strategic organizational goals and objectives, for personnel at every organizational level, is a powerful process for continual improvement. Given the rapidity and constancy of change:

- Organizations are transitioning into learning organizations with an emphasis on acquisition of knowledge.

- Individuals are committing to lifelong learning as a personal goal.

- The viable organization's delivery of a quality service or product relies on the competence of its people. Knowledge and skills are integral to competency development and enhancement.

- The organization that has adopted a mindset that training and education of its people is an *investment*, not an *expense*, is moving toward the right goal.

Distinguishing between Training, Education, and Individual Development

Training and education have been discussed extensively in previous sections. The remaining issue is how those two topics differ from *individual development* (often called *professional development* or *career development*). First, *training* is targeted to build or enhance skills. Second, *education* is aimed at broadening one's knowledge base. *Development* infers a formal or informal program leading to or adding to an individual's repertoire of skills, knowledge, wisdom, and experience. This is accomplished through a variety of actions, often over the working lifetime of the individual. Such actions may include:

- Building experience and responsibility through a variety of occupational assignments and venues

- Gaining knowledge through formal and informal education

- Acquiring and enhancing skills

- Accumulating insights through exposure to those more expert and through networking

- Developing wisdom (this is the final stage of collecting data, synthesizing information, and building knowledge)

For the majority of people, individual development occurs though serendipity, chance encounters with growth-enhancing experiences. For a more goal-oriented individual, development occurs through following a grand plan.

Throughout much of the 1960s, 1970s, and 1980s, the development of individuals was considered to be a responsibility of employers. During those times, managers learned how to guide their employees in their career development plans. Organizations published career ladders and steps individuals should take to broaden their knowledge and skills for the employees' growth and development. This effort was not universally successful. It became apparent that the real responsibility for development rested with the individuals, not their boss. More recently, and especially with a more mobile, transient workforce, individual development is the individual's responsibility, sometimes with some support and resources from the employer.

Effectiveness of Training Delivered to Individuals

Although it is important to evaluate the effectiveness of a training program, quality practitioners are most often called upon to evaluate the effectiveness of the training itself. Whether the delivered training is in the form of classroom training or on-the-job training, it must be determined that the student has learned the material or the skill and achieved a required level of practical competence.

The delivery of training and the evaluation of its effectiveness closely follows the *plan-do-check-act* model. The first step is always to decide what knowledge or skill needs to be acquired by an individual. Most often, this applies to an individual in a new job who needs to become competent in the job as defined by the requirements of the job description. The gap between an individual's skill and the requirements of the job becomes the training *plan*. Once training is delivered (*do*), someone evaluates the degree to which the training objectives were met. Where it is determined that the individual has not achieved the level of competency expected by the training, follow-up coaching and training is performed to close that gap (*act*).

As a precondition for training to be evaluated, training outcomes must be clearly defined before the training occurs. After training is delivered, the effectiveness of that training must be evaluated for each of the expected outcomes. There are several ways to do this, but checklists can be useful. Many organizations have a training request form of some sort, where the reason for the training is defined, and the criteria for the training are listed. It is simple and effective to have the evaluation record as a part of this same form. In this way, everything is in one place, and the evaluation is less likely to be forgotten. (Lack of follow-up to evaluate training effectiveness is a very common weakness in quality management systems.) The evaluation piece can be included at the bottom of the form, or even included as a column of check boxes next to the task being trained. See the example below in Table 19.3.

In the example in Table 19.3, the training form includes the method for conducting training, along with the way to assess training effectiveness. Just as it is important to define what skills are to be trained, it can be important to define how the training is conducted and how training is evaluated. This is especially important where there can be several different individuals conducting the training and/ or evaluating the effectiveness of the training. The time elapsed between when training is conducted and when training is evaluated will depend on the nature of what is being trained. If the training involves a daily, repeatable task, the trainee

Table 19.3 Training form—example.

Required Skill	How to Teach the Skill	How to Evaluate Effectiveness	Trainer	Assessor
Recognize the machine fault, troubleshoot, and reset the machine	Teach according to machine maintenance manual #ABC and procedure #XYZ-123	Watch the employee troubleshoot at least five different fault codes	John Smith January 4, 2020	Jane Jones January 19, 2020
Complete the quarterly regulatory compliance submission #XXX for the EPA	Attend introductory training module EPA-123-456, read applicable EPA regulations and 21CFR-XXXX	Supervisor to review the first two submissions and provide feedback. Two packages are accepted by the EPA without negative comments.	Dennis Cooper January 4, 2020	Dennis Cooper August 10, 2020

will likely master the skill within a day or two and then evaluation can take place after that short time. If the training is for tasks that are less frequent, it could take months before enough of that work has been performed to properly assess training effectiveness. An example is internal quality audit training. Training effectiveness can only be evaluated by watching the trainee conduct an audit(s) and reviewing the quality of the trainee's audit reports. Because a part-time internal auditor conducts audits infrequently, it could be a year or more before the individual's competency can be fully assessed.

It is very common in manufacturing environments to create detailed work instructions and train employees against those work instructions. OJT can be conducted in many different ways, but it is always necessary to follow it up with an assessment of the competency of the trainee by the trainer watching the work being performed. Work instructions should be used as a basis for one-on-one training and not just be given to a new employee to read. Many organizations have used an approach called *training within industry* (TWI) as a vehicle for delivering simple, yet effective training. The trainer will explain the work tasks, demonstrate them, and then invite the trainee to perform the tasks. The trainer will then watch the trainee and provide coaching until he or she has fully mastered the tasks. This coaching is an iterative process and adds strength to the evaluation process. The trainee is not approved to work unaided until the trainer is fully satisfied. This shifts the onus for success from the trainee to the trainer. Under this mindset, the worker has not learned, and the instructor has not taught.[23]

Assessing and Auditing the Training System

Quality management systems generally require that training be provided for positions that could have an impact on product quality. Which positions affect quality depend upon the type of organization. For a manufacturing organization, production operators and inspectors generally are required to be trained to the work instructions and procedures that govern their work. Sometimes, specialized skills training is needed. An example of this is soldering training skills in electronics. This requires special equipment and skilled technique to ensure that product quality is not negatively affected. The training requirements need to be defined in the governing procedure and work instruction. Generally, training needs to be recorded and retained as a quality system record.

Like other aspects of the quality management system, assessing and auditing the training system starts with reviewing the organization's documented policies, procedures, and work instructions. Unless the training system itself is being audited, it is very common to audit for training while performing product or process audits. This is done by writing down the names of the personnel interviewed and then verifying their training records later in the audit. Training is often identified as a corrective action. While verifying training effectiveness is generally important, it is especially important when training has been implemented as the result of a corrective action. Training effectiveness can be assessed by incorporating short quizzes throughout the training material to assess the learner's retention of material. For skills training, the activity needs to be performed and then assessed per documented workmanship standards. Generally, training needs to be performed in a way that does not introduce defects that could be delivered to customers.

REFERENCES

1. J. M. Juran, and F. M. Gryna, eds., *Juran's Quality Control Handbook*, 4th ed. (New York: McGraw-Hill, 1988), 11.4–11.5.

2. R. F. Mager, and P. Pipe, *Analyzing Performance Problems or You Really Oughta Wanna: How to Figure Out Why People Aren't Doing What They Should Be, and What to Do about It*, 2nd ed. (Belmont, CA: David S. Lake, 1997).

3. R. T. Westcott, *Stepping Up to ISO 9004: 2000* (Chico, CA: Paton Press, 2003), 32–39.

4. S. P. Goffnett, "Steer Your Career: Employee Work Plans Feed into Organizational Success," *Quality Progress* (July 2014).

5. M. Knowles, *The Adult Learner: A Neglected Species* (Houston: Gulf, 1973; Darden, D.C., 2014); "Relevance of the Knowles Theory in Distance Education," *Creative Education* 5:809–12, http://dx.doi.org/10.4236/ce.2014.510094.

6. L. Kelly, ed., *The ASTD Technical and Skills Training Handbook* (New York: McGraw-Hill, 1995), 214.

7. R. S. Johnson, *Quality Training Practices* (Milwaukee: ASQC Quality Press, 1993), 79.

8. M. Knowles, "Adult Learning," in *The ASTD Training and Development Handbook: A Guide to Human Resources Development*, 3rd ed., ed. R. L. Craig (New York: McGraw-Hill, 1996), 171–72.

9. M. S. Knowles, and D. E. Hartl, "The Adult Learner in the Technical Environment," in Kelly, *ASTD Technical and Skills Training Handbook*, 12.

10. R. S. Johnson, *TQM: The Mechanics of Quality Processes* (Milwaukee: ASQC Quality Press, 1993), 147–48.

11. Ibid.

12. S. L. Power, "Maximize the ROI of Coaching and Training with Methodical Curriculum Design," *Quality Management Forum* 44 (February 4, 2019): 5.

13. Ibid.

14. M. F. Finnerty, "Coaching for Growth and Development," in *The ASTD Training and Development Handbook: A Guide to Human Resources Development*, ed. R. L. Craig (New York: McGraw-Hill, 1996), 423.

15. A. Rossett, and J. H. Gautier-Downes, *A Handbook of Job Aids* (San Diego: Pfeiffer, 1991).

16. R. S. Johnson, *TQM: The Mechanics of Quality Processes* (Milwaukee: ASQC Quality Press, 1993), 147–48.

17. T. Seidel, "Micro Learning Is More than a Buzzword," Association for Talent Development, TD.org, June 27, 2018.

18. D. L. Kirkpatrick, "Techniques for Evaluating Training Programs," a four-part series beginning in the November 1959 issue of the *Training Director's Journal*.

19. R. T. Westcott, "A Quality System Needs Assessment," in *In Action: Conducting Needs Assessment (17 Case Studies)*, ed. J. J. Phillips and E. F. Holton III (Alexandria, VA: American Society for Training and Development, 1995), 235; "Applied Behavior Management Training," in *In Action: Measuring Return on Investment*, vol. 1, ed. J. J. Phillips (Alexandria, VA: American Society for Training and Development, 1994), 85–104; "Behavior Management Training," in *Human Resources Management and Development Handbook*, 2nd ed. (New York: AMACOM, 1994), 897–911; and "ROQI: Overlooked Quality Tool," *Total Quality Review*, November/December, 1994, 37–44.

20. M. Weinstein, "Determining Coaching ROI," *Training Magazine*, July/August 2017, 38–41, www.TrainingMag.com.

21. J. Dew, "Learning about Learning," *Quality Progress* (July 2018): 30–35.

22. C. Hannon and S. Grossman, "Put JIB on the Job," *Quality Progress* (July 2011): 30–35.

23. Ibid.

See Appendix A for additional references for this chapter.

Chapter 20

The Certified Manager of Quality/ Organizational Excellence Body of Knowledge

Total quality management addresses the quality of management as well as the management of quality.

—V. Daniel Hunt

CERTIFIED MANAGER OF QUALITY/ORGANIZATIONAL EXCELLENCE (CMQ/OE) BODY OF KNOWLEDGE (BOK)—2019

The topics in this new BoK include descriptive details (subtext) that are used by the Exam Development Committee as guidelines for writing test questions. This subtext is also designed to help candidates prepare for the exam by identifying specific content within each topic that may be tested. The subtext is not intended to limit the subject matter or be all-inclusive of what might be covered in an exam but is intended to clarify how the topics relate to a manager's role. The descriptor in parentheses at the end of each entry refers to the maximum cognitive level at which the topic will be tested. A complete description of cognitive levels is provided at the end of this document.

I. **Leadership (28 Questions)**

A. **Organizational Structures**

Define and describe organizational designs (e.g., matrix, flat, and parallel) and the effect that a hierarchical management structure can have on an organization. (Apply)

B. **Leadership Challenges**

1. **Roles and responsibilities of leaders**

Describe typical roles, responsibilities, and competencies of people in leadership positions and how those attributes influence an organization's direction and purpose. (Analyze)

2. **Roles and responsibilities of managers**

Describe typical roles, responsibilities, and competencies of people in management positions and how those attributes contribute to an organization's success. (Analyze)

3. **Change management**

Use various change management strategies to overcome organizational roadblocks, assess impacts of global changes, achieve desired change levels, and review outcomes for effectiveness. Define and describe factors that contribute to an organization's culture. (Evaluate)

4. **Leadership techniques**

Develop and implement techniques that motivate employees and sustain their enthusiasm. Use negotiation techniques to enable parties with different or opposing outlooks to recognize common goals and work together to achieve them. Determine when and how to use influence, critical thinking skills or Socratic questioning to resolve a problem or move a project forward. (Create)

5. **Empowerment**

Apply various techniques to empower individuals and teams. Identify typical obstacles to empowerment and appropriate strategies for overcoming them. Describe and distinguish between job enrichment and job enlargement, job design and job tasks. (Analyze)

C. **Teams and Team Processes**

1. **Types of teams**

Identify and describe different types of teams and their purpose, including process improvement, self-managed, temporary or ad hoc (special project), virtual, and work groups. (Understand)

2. **Stages of team development**

Describe how the stages of team development (forming, storming, norming, performing) affect leadership style. (Apply)

3. **Team-building techniques**

Apply basic team-building steps, such as using ice-breaker activities to enhance team introductions and membership, developing a common vision and agreement on team objectives, and identifying and assigning specific roles on the team. (Apply)

4. **Team roles and responsibilities**

Define and describe typical roles related to team support and effectiveness, such as facilitator, leader, process owner, champion, project manager, and contributor. Describe member and leader responsibilities with regard to group dynamics, including keeping the team on task, recognizing hidden agendas, handling disruptive behavior, and resolving conflict. (Analyze)

5. **Team performance and evaluation**

Evaluate team performance in relation to established metrics to meet goals and objectives. Determine when and how to reward teams and celebrate their success. (Evaluate)

D. **ASQ Code of Ethics**

Identify and apply behaviors and actions that comply with this code. (Apply)

II. **Strategic Plan Development and Deployment (22 Questions)**

A. **Strategic Planning Models**

Define, describe, and use basic elements of strategic planning models, including how the guiding principles of mission, vision, and values relate to the plan. (Apply)

B. **Business Environment Analysis**

1. **Risk analysis**

Analyze an organization's strengths, weaknesses, opportunities, threats, and risks using tools such as SWOT. Identify and analyze risk factors that can influence strategic plans. (Analyze)

2. **Market forces**

Define and describe various forces that drive strategic plans, including existing competition, the entry of new competitors, rivalry among competitors, the threat of substitutes, bargaining power of buyers and suppliers, current economic conditions, global market changes, and how well the organization is positioned for growth and changing customer expectations. (Apply)

3. **Stakeholder analysis**

Identify and differentiate the perspectives, needs, and objectives of various internal and external stakeholders. Ensure that the organization's strategic objectives are aligned with those of the stakeholders. (Analyze)

4. **Technology**

Describe how changes in technology can have long-term and short-term influences on strategic planning. Identify new and upcoming technologies that may have an impact on business strategy and quality, such as automation, autonomation, Quality 4.0, cloud computing, or machine learning. (Understand)

5. **Internal capability analysis**

Identify and describe the effects that influence an organization's internal capabilities: human resources, facilities capacity, and operational capabilities. Analyze these factors in relation to strategy formation. (Analyze)

6. **Legal and regulatory factors**

Define and describe how legal and regulatory factors can influence strategic plans. (Understand)

C. **Strategic Plan Deployment**

1. **Tactical plans**

Identify basic characteristics of tactics: specific, measurable, attainable, relevant, and time specific and how these are linked to strategic objectives. Evaluate proposed plans to determine whether they meet these criteria. (Evaluate)

2. Resource allocation and deployment

Evaluate current resources to ensure they are available and deployed in support of strategic initiatives. Identify and eliminate administrative barriers to new initiatives. Ensure that all internal stakeholders understand the strategic plan and have the competencies and resources to carry out their responsibilities. (Evaluate)

3. Organizational performance measurement

Develop measurements and ensure that they are aligned with strategic goals and use the measures to evaluate the organization against the strategic plan. (Evaluate)

4. Quality in strategic deployment

Support strategic plan deployment by applying continuous improvement and other quality initiatives to drive performance outcomes throughout the organization. (Create)

III. **Management Elements and Methods (31 Questions)**

A. **Management Skills and Abilities**

1. **Principles of management**

Evaluate and use basic management principles such as planning, leading, delegating, controlling, organizing, and allocating resources. (Evaluate)

2. **Management theories and styles**

Define and describe management theories such as scientific, organizational, behavioral, learning, systems thinking, and situational complexity. Define and describe management styles such as autocratic, participative, transactional, transformational, management by fact, coaching, and contingency approach. Describe how management styles are influenced by an organization's size, industry sector, culture, and competitors. (Apply)

3. **Interdependence of functional areas**

Describe the interdependence of an organization's areas (human resources, engineering, sales, marketing, finance, research and development, purchasing, information technology, logistics, production, and service) and how those dependencies and relationships influence processes and outputs. (Understand)

4. **Human resources (HR) management**

Apply HR elements in support of ongoing professional development and role in quality system: setting goals and objectives, conducting performance evaluations, developing recognition programs, and ensuring that succession plans are in place where appropriate. (Apply)

5. Financial management

Read, interpret, and use various financial tools, including income statements, balance sheets, and product/service cost structures. Manage budgets and use the language of cost and profitability to communicate with senior management. Use potential return on investment (ROI), estimated return on assets (ROA), net present value (NPV), internal rate of return (IRR), and portfolio analysis to analyze project risk, feasibility, and priority. (Analyze)

6. Risk management

Identify the kinds of risk that can occur throughout the organization, from such diverse processes as scheduling, shipping/receiving, financials, production and operations, employee and user safety, regulatory compliance, and changes. (Apply)

7. Knowledge management (KM)

Use KM techniques in identifying core competencies that create a culture and system for collecting and sharing implicit and explicit knowledge among workers, stakeholders, competitors, and suppliers. Capture lessons learned and apply them across the organization to promote best practices. Identify typical knowledge-sharing barriers and how to overcome them. (Apply)

B. Communication Skills and Abilities

1. Communication techniques

Define and apply various modes of communication used within organizations, such as, verbal, nonverbal, written, and visual. Identify factors that can inhibit clear communication and describe ways of overcoming them. (Apply)

2. Interpersonal skills

Use skills in empathy, tact, friendliness, and objectivity. Use open-minded and nonjudgmental communication methods. Develop and use a clear writing style, active listening, and questioning and dialogue techniques that support effective communication. (Apply)

3. Communications in a global economy

Identify key challenges of communicating across different time zones, cultures, languages, terminology, and business practices and present ways of overcoming them. (Apply)

4. Communications and technology

Identify how technology affects communications, including improved information availability, its influence on interpersonal communications, and etiquette for e-communications. Deploy appropriate communication methods within virtual teams. (Apply)

C. Project Management

1. Project management basics

Use project management methodology and ensure that each project is aligned with strategic objectives. Plan the different phases of a project: initiation, planning, execution, monitoring and controlling, and closure. Ensure the project is on time and within budget. Consider alternate project management methodologies (linear, evolutionary, or iterative) as they apply to the project. (Evaluate)

2. Project planning and estimation tools

Use tools such as risk assessment matrix, benefit-cost analysis, critical path method (CPM), Gantt chart, PERT, and work breakdown structure (WBS) to plan projects and estimate related costs. (Apply)

3. Measure and monitor project activity

Use tools such as cost variance analysis, milestones, and actual versus planned budgets to monitor project activity against project plan. (Evaluate)

4. Project documentation

Use written procedures and project summaries to document projects. (Apply)

D. Quality System

1. Quality mission and policy

Develop and monitor the quality mission and policy and ensure that it is aligned with the organization's broader mission. (Create)

2. Quality planning, deployment, and documentation

Develop and deploy the quality plan and ensure that it is documented and accessible throughout the organization. (Create)

3. Quality system effectiveness

Evaluate the effectiveness of the quality system using various tools: balanced scorecard, internal audits, feedback from internal and external stakeholders (including stakeholder complaints), warranty/return data analytics, product traceability and recall reports, and management reviews. (Evaluate)

E. Quality Models and Theories

1. Quality management standards

Describe and apply the requirements and basic principles of the ISO 9000–based standards used to support quality management systems. (Apply)

2. Performance excellence models

Define and describe common elements and criteria of performance excellence models such as the European Excellence

Award (EFQM), Excellence Canada, ASQ International Team Excellence Award (ITEA), or Malcolm Baldrige National Quality Award (MBNQA). Describe how their criteria are used as management models to improve processes at an organization level. (Understand)

3. **Other quality methodologies**

Describe and differentiate methods such as total quality management (TQM), continuous improvement, and benchmarking. (Apply)

4. **Quality philosophies**

Describe and apply basic methodologies and theories proposed by quality leaders such as Shewhart, Deming, Juran, Crosby, Feigenbaum, and Ishikawa. (Apply)

IV. **Quality Management Tools (30 Questions)**

A. **Problem-Solving Tools**

1. **The seven classic quality tools**

Select, interpret, and evaluate output from these tools: Pareto charts, cause-and-effect diagrams, flowcharts, control charts, check sheets, scatter diagrams, and histograms. (Evaluate)

2. **Basic management and planning tools**

Select, interpret, and evaluate output from these tools: affinity diagrams, tree diagrams, process decision program charts (PDPCs), matrix diagrams, prioritization matrices, interrelationship digraphs, and activity network diagrams. (Evaluate)

3. **Process improvement tools**

Select, interpret, and evaluate tools such as root cause analysis, Kepner-Tregoe, PDCA, Six Sigma DMAIC (define, measure, analyze, improve, control), and failure mode and effects analysis (FMEA). (Evaluate)

4. **Innovation and creativity tools**

Use various techniques and exercises for creative decision-making and problem-solving, including brainstorming, mind mapping, lateral thinking, critical thinking, the five whys, and Design for Six Sigma (DFSS). (Apply)

5. **Cost of quality (COQ)**

Define and distinguish between prevention, appraisal, internal, and external failure cost categories and evaluate the impact that changes in one category will have on the others. (Evaluate)

B. **Process Management**

1. **Process goals**

Describe how process goals are established, monitored, and measured and evaluate their impact on product or service quality. (Evaluate)

2. Process analysis

Use various tools to analyze a process and evaluate its effectiveness on the basis of procedures, work instructions, and other documents. Evaluate the process to identify and relieve bottlenecks, increase capacity, improve throughput, reduce cycle time, and eliminate waste. (Evaluate)

3. Lean tools

Identify and use lean tools such as 5S, just-in-time (JIT), kanban, value stream mapping (VSM), quick changeover (single-minute exchange of die), poka-yoke, kaizen, standard work (training within industry), and productivity (OEE). (Apply)

4. Theory of constraints (TOC)

Define key concepts of the TOC: systems as chains, local versus system optimization, physical versus policy constraints, undesirable effects versus core problems, and solution deterioration. Classify constraints in terms of resources and expectations as defined by measures of inventory and operating expense. (Understand)

C. Measurement: Assessment and Metrics

1. Basic statistical use

Use statistical techniques to identify when, what, and how to measure projects and processes. Describe how metrics and data-gathering methods affect resources and vice versa. (Apply)

2. Sampling

Define and describe basic sampling techniques such as random and stratified. Identify when and why sampling is an appropriate technique to use. (Understand)

3. Statistical analysis

Calculate basic statistics: measures of central tendency (mean, median, mode) and measures of dispersion (range, standard deviation, and variance). Identify basic distribution types (normal, bimodal, skewed) and evaluate run charts, statistical process control (SPC) reports, and other control charts to make data-based decisions. (Evaluate)

4. Measurement systems analysis

Understand basic measurement terms such as accuracy, precision, bias, and linearity. Understand the difference between repeatability and reproducibility in gage R&R studies. (Understand)

5. Trend and pattern analysis

Interpret graphs and charts to identify cyclical, seasonal, and environmental data trends. Evaluate control chart patterns to determine shifts and other trend indicators in a process. (Evaluate)

6. Process variation

Analyze data to distinguish between common and special cause variation. (Analyze)

7. Process capability

Recognize process capability (C_p and C_{pk}) and performance indices (P_p and P_{pk}). (Understand)

8. Reliability terminology

Define and describe basic reliability measures such as infant mortality, end of life (e.g., bathtub curve), mean time between failures (MTBF), and mean time to repair (MTTR). Understand the value of estimating reliability to meet requirements or specifications. NOTE: Reliability calculations will <u>not</u> be tested. (Understand)

V. Customer-Focused Organizations (21 Questions)

A. Customer Identification and Segmentation

1. Internal customers

Define internal customers and describe the impact an organization's treatment of internal customers will have on external customers. Evaluate methods for influencing internal customers to improve products, processes, and services and evaluate the results. (Evaluate)

2. External customers

Define external customers and describe their impact on products and services. Evaluate strategies for working with them and integrating their requirements and needs to improve products, services, and processes. (Evaluate)

3. Customer segmentation

Describe and assess the process of customer segmentation and its impact on aligning service and delivery to meet customer needs. (Evaluate)

4. Qualitative assessment

Identify subjective information such as verbatim comments from customers, observation records, and focus group output. Describe how the subjective information differs from objective measures and determine when data should be captured in categories rather than numeric value. (Analyze)

B. Customer Relationship Management

1. Customer needs

Use quality function deployment (QFD) to capture the voice of the customer (VOC) and examine customer needs in relation to products and services offered. Analyze the results to prioritize future development in anticipation of changing customer needs. (Analyze)

2. Customer satisfaction and loyalty

Develop systems to capture positive and negative customer feedback and experiences, using tools such as listening posts, focus groups, complaints and warranty data, surveys, and interviews. Use customer value analysis to calculate the financial impact of existing customers and the potential results of losing those customers. Develop corrective actions and proactive methods to improve customer satisfaction, loyalty, and retention levels. (Create)

3. Customer service principles

Demonstrate strategies that support customer service principles: courtesy, politeness, smiles, cheerfulness, attention to detail, active listening, empathy, rapid response, and easy access for information and service. (Apply)

4. Multiple and diverse customer management

Establish and monitor priorities to avoid or resolve conflicting customer requirements and demands. Develop methods and systems for managing capacity and resources to meet the needs of multiple customers. Describe the impact that diverse customer groups can have on all aspects of product and service development and delivery. (Evaluate)

VI. Supply Chain Management (17 Questions)

A. Supplier Selection and Approval

Define and outline criteria for selecting, approving, and classifying suppliers, including internal rating programs and external certification standards. (Analyze)

B. Supplier Risk Management

Assess and manage supplier risk and the impact it may have on various internal processes of the organization. (Evaluate)

C. Supplier Communications

Prepare and implement specific communication methods with suppliers, including regularly scheduled meetings and routine and emergency reporting procedures. Direct, communicate, and confirm explicit expectations so that the supplier is aware of critical product and delivery requirements. (Apply)

D. Supplier Performance

Define, assess, and monitor supplier performance in terms of quality, cost, delivery, and service levels and establish associated metrics for defect rates, product reliability, functional performance, timeliness, responsiveness, and availability of technical support. (Evaluate)

E. **Supplier Improvement**

Define and conduct supplier audits, evaluate corrective and preventive action plans, provide feedback, and monitor process improvements. (Evaluate)

F. **Supplier Certification, Partnerships, and Alliances**

Define, appraise, and implement supplier certification programs that include process reviews and performance evaluations. Outline strategies for developing customer-supplier partnerships and alliances. (Evaluate)

G. **Supplier Logistics and Material Acceptance**

Describe the impact purchased products and services can have on final product assembly or total service package, including ship-to-stock and just-in-time (JIT). Describe the incoming material inspections process. (Understand)

VII. **Training and Development (16 Questions)**

A. **Training Plans**

Develop and implement training plans that are aligned with the organization's strategic plan and general business needs, including leadership training and alignment of personal development plans. (Create)

B. **Training Needs Analysis**

Use various tools and techniques such as surveys, performance reviews, regulatory guidances, and gap analyses to identify and assess training needs. (Evaluate)

C. **Training Materials, Development, and Delivery**

Use various tools, resources, and methodologies to develop training materials and curriculum that address adult learning principles and the learning needs of an increasingly diverse workforce. Describe various methods of training delivery: classroom, workbooks, simulations, computer delivered, on the job, and self-directed. Use mentoring and coaching to support training outcomes. (Apply)

D. **Training Effectiveness and Evaluation**

Assess training effectiveness and make improvements based on feedback from training sessions, end-of-course test results, on-the-job behavior or performance changes, and departmental or area performance improvements. (Evaluate)

LEVELS OF COGNITION

BASED ON BLOOM'S TAXONOMY—REVISED (2001)

In addition to **content** specifics, the subtext for each topic in this BOK also indicates the intended **complexity level** of the test questions for that topic. These levels are based on "Levels of Cognition" (from Bloom's Taxonomy—Revised, 2001) and are presented below in rank order, from least complex to most complex.

Remember: Recall or recognize terms, definitions, facts, ideas, materials, patterns, sequences, methods, principles, et cetera.

Understand: Read and understand descriptions, communications, reports, tables, diagrams, directions, regulations, et cetera.

Apply: Know when and how to use ideas, procedures, methods, formulas, principles, theories, et cetera.

Analyze: Break down information into its constituent parts and recognize their relationship to one another and how they are organized; identify sublevel factors or salient data from a complex scenario.

Evaluate: Make judgments about the value of proposed ideas, solutions, et cetera, by comparing the proposal to specific criteria or standards.

Create: Put parts or elements together in such a way as to reveal a pattern or structure not clearly there before; identify which data or information from a complex set is appropriate to examine further or from which supported conclusions can be drawn.

Appendix A
References

A list that the preparers of the CMQ/OE examination may use to create questions is available for download from http://prdweb.asq.org/certification/control/manager-of-quality/references).

QUALITY MANAGEMENT—GENERAL

(These references address multiple sections and topics from the Body of Knowledge.)

Bauer, J. E., G. L. Duffy, and R. T. Westcott, eds. *The Quality Improvement Handbook*. 2nd ed. Milwaukee: ASQ Quality Press, 2006.

Beecroft, G. D., G. L. Duffy, and J. W. Moran, eds. *The Executive Guide to Improvement and Change*. Milwaukee: ASQ Quality Press, 2003.

Cartin, T. J. *Principles and Practices of Organizational Performance Excellence*. Milwaukee: ASQ Quality Press, 1999.

Christensen, E. H., K. M. Coombes-Betz, and M. S. Stein. *The Certified Quality Process Analyst Handbook*. Milwaukee: ASQ Quality Press, 2007.

Dorf, R. C., ed. *The Technology Management Handbook*. Boca Raton, FL: CRC Press, 1999.

Duffy, G. L., ed. *The ASQ Quality Improvement Pocket Guide*. Milwaukee: ASQ Quality Press, 2013.

Evans, J. R., and W. M. Lindsay. *The Management and Control of Quality*. 6th ed. Cincinnati: South Western, 2004.

Feigenbaum, A. V. *Total Quality Control*. 3rd rev. ed. New York: McGraw-Hill, 1991.

GOAL/QPC. *The Memory Jogger II: Tools for Continuous Improvement and Effective Planning*. 2nd ed. Salem, NH: GOAL/QPC, 2010.

———. *The Process Management Memory Jogger: Building Cross-Functional Excellence*. Salem, NH: GOAL/QPC, 2008.

———. *The Six Sigma Memory Jogger II*. Salem, NH: GOAL/QPC, 2002.

———. *Value Methodology: To Reduce Cost and Improve Value through Function Analysis*. Salem, NH: GOAL/QPC, 2008.

Juran, J. M., ed. *A History of Managing for Quality: The Evolution, Trends, and Future Directions of Managing for Quality*. Milwaukee: ASQC Quality Press, 1995.

Juran, J. M., and A. B. Godfrey, eds. *Juran's Quality Handbook*. 5th ed. New York: McGraw-Hill, 1999.

Liebesman, S. *Competitive Advantage: Linked Management Systems*. Chico, CA: Paton Professional, 2011.

Pyzdek, T., and P. Keller. *The Handbook for Quality Management: A Complete Guide to Operational Excellence*. 2nd ed. New York: McGraw-Hill, 2013.

———. *The Six Sigma Handbook: A Complete Guide for Green Belts, Black Belts, and Managers at All Levels.* 3rd ed. Milwaukee: ASQ Quality Press, 2009.

ReVelle, J. B., ed. *Manufacturing Handbook of Best Practices: An Innovation, Productivity, and Quality Focus.* Boca Raton, FL: St. Lucie Press, 2002.

———. *Quality Essentials: A Reference Guide from A to Z.* Milwaukee: ASQ Quality Press, 2004.

Siebels, D. L. *The Quality Improvement Glossary.* Milwaukee: ASQ Quality Press, 2004.

Sirkin, M. *The Secret Life of Corporations: Understanding the True Nature of Business.* White Plains, NY: New Chrysalis Press, 2004.

Summers, D. C. S. *Quality.* 2nd ed. Upper Saddle River, NJ: Prentice Hall, 2000.

Tague, N. R. *The Quality Toolbox.* 2nd ed. Milwaukee: ASQ Quality Press, 2005.

Townsend, P. L., and J. E. Gebhardt. *The Executive Guide to Understanding and Implementing Employee Engagement Programs: Expand Production Capacity, Increase Revenue, and Save Jobs.* Milwaukee: ASQ Quality Press, 2007.

West, J. E., and C. A. Cianfrani. *Unlocking the Power of Your QMS: Keys to Business Process Improvement.* Milwaukee: ASQ Quality Press, 2004.

PART I   LEADERSHIP

Chapter 1   A. Organizational Structures

Ashkenas, R., D. Ulrich, T. Jich, and S. Herr. *The Boundaryless Organization: Breaking the Chains of Organizational Structure.* San Francisco: Jossey-Bass, 1995.

Harrington, H. J., and F. Voehl. *The Organizational Alignment Handbook: A Catalyst for Performance Acceleration.* Boca Raton, FL: CRC Press, 2012.

Hesselbein, F., and P. M. Cohen, eds. *Leader to Leader: Enduring Insights on Leadership from the Drucker Foundation's Award-Winning Journal.* San Francisco: Jossey-Bass, 1999.

Chapter 2   B. Leadership Challenges

Attong, M., and T. Metz. *Change or Die: The Business Process Improvement Manual.* Milwaukee: ASQ Quality Press, 2013.

Bellman, G. M. *Getting Things Done When You Are Not in Charge: How to Succeed from a Support Position.* San Francisco: Berrett-Koehler, 2001.

Benowitz, E. A. *Cliffs Quick Review Principles of Management.* Hoboken, NJ: Wiley, 2001.

Blank, W. *The 108 Skills of Natural Born Leaders.* New York: AMACOM, 2001.

Camarota, A. G. *Finding the Leader in You: A Practical Guide to Expanding Your Leadership Skills.* Milwaukee: ASQ Quality Press, 2005.

Covey, S. R. *Principle-Centered Leadership.* New York: Summit Books, 1991.

Cramer, A., and Z. Karabell. *Sustainable Excellence: The Future of Business in a Fast-Changing World.* New York: Macmillan-Rodale, 2010.

Duck, J. D. *The Change Monster: The Human Forces That Fuel or Foil Corporate Transformation and Change.* New York: Random House (Crown Business), 2001.

Ducoff, N. *No-Compromise Leadership: A Higher Standard of Leadership Thinking and Behavior.* Sanford, FL: DC Press, 2009.

Everly, G., D. Strause, and G. Everly III. *The Secrets of Resilient Leadership.* Milwaukee: ASQ Quality Press, 2009.

Gawande, A. *The Checklist Manifesto: How to Get Things Right.* New York: Metropolitan Books-Henry Holt, 2009.

Goleman, D. *Working with Emotional Intelligence.* New York: Bantam Books, 1998.

Gostick, A., and C. Elton. *The Carrot Principle: How the Best Managers Use Recognition to Engage Their People, Retain Talent, and Accelerate Performance.* New York: Free Press, 2007.

Hacker, S., and T. Roberts. *Transformational Leadership: Creating Organizations of Meaning.* Milwaukee: ASQ Quality Press, 2004.

Heath, C., and D. Heath. *Switch: How to Change Things When Change Is Hard.* New York: Crown Business, 2010.

Hersey, P. *The Situational Leader.* Escondido, CA: Center for Leadership Studies, 2004.

Hersey, P., K. Blanchard, and D. E. Johnson. *Management of Organizational Behavior: Leading Human Resources.* Upper Saddle River, NJ: Prentice Hall, 2001.

Hesselbein, F., and P. M. Cohen, eds. *Leader to Leader: Enduring Insights on Leadership from the Drucker Foundation's Award-Winning Journal.* San Francisco: Jossey-Bass, 1999.

Hirzel, R. C. "Leadership Is Personal." Paper published by the ASQ Human Development and Leadership Division. Milwaukee, 2003.

Hopen, D. "Guiding Corporate Behavior: A Leadership Obligation, Not a Choice." *Journal for Quality and Participation* 25 (Winter 2002): 15–19.

Hughes, M. *Managing and Leading Change.* New York: Routledge, 2019.

Hutton, D. *The Change Agent's Handbook.* Milwaukee: ASQ Quality Press, 1994.

Jossey-Bass. *Business Leadership: A Jossey-Bass Reader.* San Francisco: Jossey-Bass, 2003.

Kotter, J. P. *Leading Change.* Boston: Harvard Business School Press, 2012.

Kouzes, J., and B. Posner. *The Leadership Challenge.* 4th ed. San Francisco: Jossey-Bass, 2008.

Labovitz, G., and V. Rosansky. *Rapid Improvement.* Milwaukee: ASQ Quality Press, 2013.

Lee, J. *Rising Above All.* Milwaukee: ASQ Quality Press, 2013.

Miller, K. *The Change Agent's Guide to Radical Improvement.* Milwaukee: ASQ Quality Press, 2002.

Mundy, L. *A Journey to Quality Leadership.* Milwaukee: ASQ Quality Press, 2011.

Palmer, B. *Making Change Work: Practical Tools for Overcoming Human Resistance to Change.* Milwaukee: ASQ Quality Press, 2004.

Pauley, J. A., and J. Pauley. *Communication: The Key to Effective Leadership.* Milwaukee: ASQ Quality Press, 2009.

Perseus Publishing. *Best Practice: Ideas and Insights from the World's Foremost Business Thinkers.* Cambridge, MA: Perseus, 2003.

Pietenpol, D. *Leadership, Quality, and Learning.* Milwaukee: ASQ Quality Press, 2008.

Senge, P. *The Fifth Discipline.* New York: Random House, 2005.

Shearer, C. *Everyday Excellence: Creating a Better Workplace through Attitude, Action, and Appreciation.* Milwaukee: ASQ Quality Press, 2006.

Smart, B. D. *Topgrading: How Leading Companies Win by Hiring, Coaching, and Keeping the Best People.* New York: Portfolio-Penguin Group, 2005.

Weiner, E., and A. Brown. *Future Think: How to Think Clearly in a Time of Change.* Upper Saddle River, NJ: Pearson-Prentice Hall, 2006.

Weiss, A. *"Good Enough" Isn't Enough: Nine Challenges for Companies That Choose to Be Great.* New York: AMACOM, 2000.

Chapter 3   C. Teams and Team Processes

Dreo, H., P. Kunkel, and T. Mitchell. *The Virtual Teams Guidebook for Managers.* Milwaukee: ASQ Quality Press, 2003.

McDermott, L. C., N. Brawley, and W. W. Waite. *World Class Teams: Working across Borders.* New York: John Wiley & Sons, 1998.

Scholtes, P. R., B. L. Joiner, and B. J. Streibel. *The Team Handbook*. 3rd ed. Madison, WI: Joiner, 2003.

Wilson, S. "Forming Virtual Teams." *Quality Progress* (June 2003): 36–41.

Chapter 4   D. ASQ Code of Ethics

Anderson, B. *Bringing Business Ethics to Life: Achieving Corporate Social Responsibility*. Milwaukee: ASQ Quality Press, 2004.

AuBuchon, D. "Integrity in Management." *Quality Management Forum* (Fall 2004).

Geissler, P. *Managing with Conscience for Competitive Advantage*. Milwaukee: ASQ Quality Press, 2004.

Sarbanes-Oxley Act of 2002. Public Law 107-204, July 30, 2002.

Stimson, W. A. "A Deming Inspired Management Code of Ethics." *Quality Progress* (February 2005): 67–75.

PART II   STRATEGIC PLAN DEVELOPMENT AND DEPLOYMENT
Chapter 5   A. Strategic Planning Models

Cobb, C. G. *From Quality to Business Excellence: A Systems Approach to Management*. Milwaukee: ASQ Quality Press, 2003.

Colletti, J. *Hoshin Kanri Memory Jogger*. Salem, NH: GOAL/QPC, 2013.

Haines, S. G. *Strategic and Business Planning: The Systems Thinking Approach*. Amherst, MA: HRD Press, 1999.

National Institute of Standards and Technology. *Baldrige Performance Excellence Program: Criteria for Performance Excellence*. Gaithersburg, MD: NIST, 2012. (Individual copies of the criteria booklets may be obtained free of charge from: Baldrige Performance Excellence Program, NIST, Administration Building, Room A600, 100 Bureau Drive, Stop 1020, Gaithersburg, MD 20899-1020, telephone (301) 975-2036, fax (301) 948-3716, e-mail nqp@nist.gov or download from www.baldrige.nist.gov/Criteria.htm.) Note: There are separate criteria for healthcare and for education.

Chapter 6   B. Business Environment Analysis

Babcock, C. *Management Strategies for the Cloud Revolution: How Cloud Computing Is Transforming Business and Why You Can't Afford to Be Left Behind*. New York: McGraw-Hill, 2010.

Chapter 7   C. Strategic Plan Deployment

DeFeo, J. A. "Strategic Deployment." Section 13 in *Juran's Quality Handbook*. 5th ed. Edited by J. M. Juran and A. B. Godfrey. New York: McGraw-Hill, 1999.

Haines, S. G. *Strategic and Business Planning: The Systems Thinking Approach*. Amherst, MA: HRD Press, 1999.

PART III   MANAGEMENT ELEMENTS AND METHODS
Chapter 8   A. Management Skills and Abilities

Principles of Management, Management Theories, and Tools
Hersey, P., K. Blanchard, and D. E. Johnson. *Management of Organizational Behavior: Leading Human Resources*. Upper Saddle River, NJ: Prentice-Hall, 2001.

Hofstede, G., G. J. Hofstede, and M. Mikov. *Cultures and Organizations*. 4th ed. New York: McGraw-Hill, 2010.

Liker, J. *The Toyota Way: 14 Management Principles from the World's Greatest Manufacturer*. New York: McGraw-Hill, 2004.

Schein, E. H. *The Corporate Culture Survival Guide: Sense and Nonsense about Culture Change*. San Francisco: Jossey-Bass, 1999.

Schermerhorn Jr., J. R., J. G. Hunt, and R. N. Osborn. *Organizational Behavior*. 9th ed. New York: John Wiley & Sons, 2005.

Senge, P. M. *The Fifth Discipline: The Art and Practice of the Learning Organization*. New York: Doubleday, 1990.

Senge, P. M., A. Kleiner, C. Roberts, R. B. Ross, and B. J. Smith. *The Fifth Discipline Fieldbook: Strategies and Tools for Building a Learning Organization*. New York: Doubleday, 1994.

Woodson, W., P. Tillman, and B. Tillman. *Human Factors Design Handbook*. 2nd ed. New York: McGraw-Hill, 1992.

Interdependence of Functional Areas

Cobb, C. G. *From Quality to Business Excellence: A Systems Approach to Management*. Milwaukee: ASQ Quality Press, 2003.

Sirkin, M. *The Secret Life of Corporations: Understanding the True Nature of Business*. White Plains, NY: New Chrysalis Press, 2004.

Human Resources Management

Holbeche, L. *Aligning Human Resources and Business Strategy*. New York: Butterworth Heinemann, 2001.

Mathis, R. L., and J. H. Jackson. *Human Resource Management*. 11th ed. Mason, OH: Thomson South-Western, 2000.

Financial Management

Chang, R. Y., and M. W. Morgan. *Performance Scorecards: Measuring the Right Things in the Real World*. San Francisco: Jossey-Bass, 2000.

Drickhamer, D. "House of Cards." *Industry Week* (January 2005): 49–51.

Finkler, S. A. *Finance and Accounting for Nonfinancial Managers*. 3rd ed. New York: Aspen, 2003.

Garrison, R. H., and E. W. Noreen. *Managerial Accounting*. Boston: McGraw-Hill/Irwin, 2003.

George, S. "How to Speak the Language of Senior Management." *Quality Progress* (May 2003): 30–36.

Hoisington, S. H., and E. C. Menzer. "Learn to Talk Money." *Quality Progress* (May 2004): 44–49.

Kaplan, R. S., and D. P. Norton. *The Balanced Scorecard: Translating Strategy into Action*. Boston: Harvard Business School Press, 1996.

Livingston, J. L., and T. Grossman. *The Portable MBA in Finance and Accounting*. 3rd ed. New York: John Wiley & Sons, 2001.

Ryan, J. *Making the Economic Case for Quality*. ASQ White Paper. Milwaukee: ASQ, 2004.

Tracy, J. A. *Accounting for Dummies: A Reference for the Rest of Us*. 2nd ed. New York: Hungry Minds, 2001.

Risk Management

Drickhamer, D. "House of Cards." *Industry Week* (January 2005): 49–51.

Getto, G. "Risk Management Supporting Quality Management of Software Acquisition Projects." *Software Quality Professional (ASQ)* 2, no. 2 (2000): 42–53.

Goodden, R. L. *Product Liability Prevention: A Strategic Guide*. Milwaukee: ASQ Quality Press, 2000.

Hutchins, G., and D. Gould. "The Growth of Risk Management." *Quality Progress* (September 2004): 73–75.

Kolka, J. W. "ISO 9001 and 9004: A Framework for Disaster Preparedness." *Quality Progress* (February 2002): 57–62.

Snow, A. "Integrating Risk Management into the Design and Development Process." *Medical Device and Diagnostic Industry* (March 2001): 99–113.

Vinas, T., and J. Jusko. "5 Threats That Could Sink Your Company." *Industry Week* (September 2004): 53–62.

Westcott, R. T. *Stepping Up to ISO 9004:2000*. Chico, CA: Paton Press, 2005, chap. 4.

Knowledge Management

Bajaria, H. J. "Knowledge Creation and Management: Integrated Issues." *ASQ's 54th Annual Quality Conference Proceedings*. Milwaukee: ASQ, 2002.

Davenport, T. H., and L. Prusak. *Working Knowledge: How Organizations Manage What They Know*. Boston: Harvard Business School Press, 1998.

Shockley III, W. "Planning for Knowledge Management." *Quality Progress* (March 2000).

Von Krogh, G., K. Ichijo, and I. Nonaka. *Enabling Knowledge Creation: How to Unlock the Mystery of Tacit Knowledge and Release the Power of Innovation*. New York: Oxford University Press, 2000.

Wilson, L. T., and D. Asay. "Putting Quality in Knowledge Management." *Quality Progress* (January 1999): 25–31.

Product Development

Cooper, R. G. *Winning at New Products: Accelerating the Process from Idea to Launch*. 3rd ed. Cambridge, MA: Perseus, 2001.

Monczka, R. M., R. B. Handfield, T. V. Scannell, G. L. Ragatz, and D. J. Frayer. *New Product Development: Strategies for Supplier Integration*. Milwaukee: ASQ Quality Press, 2000.

Reilly, N. B. *The Team Based Product Development Guidebook*. Milwaukee: ASQ Quality Press, 1999.

Chapter 9   B. Communication Skills and Abilities

Brounstein, M. *Communicating Effectively for Dummies: A Reference for the Rest of Us*. New York: John Wiley & Sons, 2001.

Harrington, H. J., and F. Voehl. "Managing Global Quality: Directing a Worldwide Organization Demands Keen Strategy and Innovative Planning." *Quality Digest* (November 2004): 33–37.

Morrison, T., W. A. Conaway, and G. A. Borden. *Kiss, Bow, or Shake Hands: How to Do Business in Sixty Countries*. Holbrook, MA: Adams Media, 1994.

Chapter 10   C. Project Management

APLN (Agile Project Leadership Network). http://www.apln.org.

ASQ (American Society for Quality). http://www.asq.org.

Baker, S., and K. Baker. *The Complete Idiot's Guide to Project Management*. Indianapolis, IN: Alpha Books, 2000.

Barkley, B. T., and J. H. Saylor. *Customer-Driven Project Management: Building Quality into Project Processes*. 2nd ed. New York: McGraw-Hill, 2001.

Chapman, C., and S. Ward. *Project Risk Management*. New York: John Wiley & Sons, 2003.

Chatfield, C. S., and T. D. Johnson. *Microsoft Project 2000 Step by Step*. Redmond, WA: Microsoft Press, 2002.

Conklin, J. D. "Smart Project Selection." *Quality Progress* (March 2003): 81–83.

Cooper, R. G. *Winning at New Products: Accelerating the Process from Idea to Launch.* 3rd ed. Cambridge, MA: Perseus, 2001.

Dobson, M. *Project Management for the Technical Professional.* Upper Darby, PA: Project Management Institute, 2001.

Fleming, Q. W., and J. M. Koppelman. *Earned Value: Project Management.* Newtown Square, PA: Project Management Institute, 2000.

Frame, J. D. *Managing Risk in Organizations: A Guide for Managers.* New York: John Wiley & Sons, 2003.

———. *The New Project Management.* 2nd ed. San Francisco: Jossey-Bass, 2002.

Graham, R. J., and R. L. Englund. *Creating an Environment for Successful Projects.* 2nd ed. Milwaukee: ASQ Quality Press, 2003.

Kerzner, H. *Project Management: A Systems Approach to Planning, Scheduling, and Controlling.* 7th ed. New York: Van Nostrand Reinhold, 2001.

———. *Project Management: A Systems Approach to Planning, Scheduling, and Controlling.* 8th ed. New York: Van Nostrand Reinhold, 2003.

———. *Project Management: A Systems Approach to Planning, Scheduling, and Controlling.* 12th ed. New York: John Wiley & Sons, 2017.

LaBrosse, M. A. *Accelerated Project Management.* New York: HNB, 2002.

Lewis, J. P. *Project Planning, Scheduling and Control: A Hands-On Guide to Bringing Projects in on Time and on Budget.* 3rd ed. Chicago: Probus, 2001.

Lowenthal, J. N. *Six Sigma Project Management: A Pocket Guide.* Milwaukee: ASQ Quality Press, 2002.

Meredith, J. R., S. M. Shafer, and S. J. Mantel Jr. *Project Management: A Strategic Managerial Approach.* 10th ed. New York: John Wiley & Sons, 2018.

Milosevic, D. Z. *Project Management Toolbox: Tools and Techniques for the Practicing Project Manager.* New York: John Wiley & Sons, 2003.

Norman E., and S. Lawrence Pfleeger. *Software Metrics: A Rigorous and Practical Approach.* 2nd ed. London: PWS, 1997.

Phillips, J. J., T. W. Bothell, and G. L. Snead. *The Project Management Scorecard: Measuring the Success of Project Management Solutions.* New York: Butterworth Heinemann, 2002.

PMI (Project Management Institute). http://www.pmi.org.

PMI (*Project Management Magazine*). http://www.projectmanagement.com/.

PMI Standards Committee. *A Guide to the Project Management Body of Knowledge.* Upper Darby, PA: Project Management Institute, 2000.

Pyzdek, T. "Selecting Winning Projects." *Quality Digest* (August 2000): 26.

Rad, P. F., and G. Levin. *Achieving Project Management Success Using Virtual Teams.* Boca Raton, FL: J. Ross, 2003.

"Risk." *Risk Management Magazine.* http://www.rmmag.com/MGTemplate.cfm.

"Scrum." Scrum Alliance. http://www.scrumalliance.org.

Scrum Training Series. Free Online Scrum Master Training. http://www.scrumtrainingseries.com/.

Stevenson, N. *Microsoft Project for Dummies.* Foster City, CA: IDG, 2000.

Uyttewaal, E. *Dynamic Scheduling with Microsoft Project 2002.* Boca Raton, FL: J. Ross, 2003.

———. *The Portable MBA in Project Management.* New York: John Wiley & Sons, 2003.

Westcott, R. T. *Simplified Project Management for the Quality Professional.* Milwaukee: ASQ Quality Press, 2004.

Wysocki, R. K., and J. P. Lewis. *The World Class Project Manager: A Professional Development Guide.* Cambridge, MA: Perseus, 2001.

Chapter 11   D. Quality System

Arter, D. R. *Quality Audits for Improved Performance*. 3rd ed. Milwaukee: ASQ Quality Press, 2003.

Arter, D. R., C. A. Cianfrani, and J. E. West. *How to Audit the Process-Based QMS*. Milwaukee: ASQ Quality Press, 2003.

Palmes, P. C. *Continual Improvement Assessment Guide: Promoting and Sustaining Business Results*. Milwaukee: ASQ Quality Press, 2004.

———. *The Internal Auditing Pocket Guide*. Milwaukee: ASQ Quality Press, 2003.

———. *Process Driven Comprehensive Auditing*. Milwaukee: ASQ Quality Press, 2005.

West, J., and C. A. Cianfrani. *Unlocking the Power of Your QMS: Keys to Business Performance Improvement*. Milwaukee: ASQ Quality Press, 2005.

Chapter 12   E. Quality Models and Theories

Bernhart, M. S., and F. J. Maher. *ISO 26000 in Practice*. Milwaukee: ASQ Quality Press, 2011.

Blazey, M. L. *Insights to Performance Excellence 2013–2014: Understanding the Integrated Management System and the Baldrige Criteria: An Inside Look at the 2005 Baldrige Award Criteria*. Milwaukee: ASQ Quality Press, 2013.

Brown, M. G. *Baldrige Award Winning Quality: How to Interpret the Baldrige Criteria for Performance Excellence*. 14th ed. New York: Productivity Press, 2005.

Byrnes, M. A., and J. C. Baxter. *There Is Another Way! Launch a Baldrige-Based Quality Classroom*. Milwaukee: ASQ Quality Press, 2005.

Cianfrani, C. A., and J. E. West. *ISO 9001:2008 Explained Expanded: Optimizing Your QMS for Success*. Milwaukee: ASQ Quality Press, 2013.

Collins Jr., J. W., and D. S. Steiger. *The Memory Jogger 9001:2008: Implementing a Process Approach Compliant to ISO 9001:2008 Quality Management Systems*. Salem, NH: GOAL/QPC, 2011.

Crosby, P. B. *Quality Is Free*. New York: Mentor Books, 1979.

Deming, W. E. *The New Economics*. 2nd ed. Cambridge, MA: MIT Center for Advanced Educational Studies, 1994.

———. *Out of the Crisis*. Cambridge, MA: MIT Center for Advanced Engineering Study, 1986.

Imai, M. *Kaizen: The Key to Japan's Competitive Success*. New York: Random House Business Division, 1986.

Ishikawa, L. *Guide to Quality Control*. Tokyo: Asian Productivity Organization, 1982.

Leonard, D., and M. McGuire. *Executive Guide to Understanding and Implementing the Baldrige Criteria: Improve Revenue and Create Organizational Excellence*. Milwaukee: ASQ Quality Press, 2007.

Myhrberg, E. V. *A Practical Field Guide for ISO 9001:2008*. Milwaukee: ASQ Quality Press, 2009.

Russell, J. P. *Continual Improvement Assessment Guide*. Milwaukee: ASQ Quality Press, 2004.

———. *The Internal Auditing Pocket Guide*. Milwaukee: ASQ Quality Press, 2003.

West, J. E., and C. A. Cianfrani. *Unlocking the Power of Your QMS: Keys to Business Performance Improvement*. Milwaukee: ASQ Quality Press, 2005.

Westcott, R. T. *Stepping Up to ISO 9004:2000: A Practical Guide for Creating a World-Class Organization*. Chico, CA: Paton Press, 2003.

PART IV   QUALITY MANAGEMENT TOOLS
Chapter 13   A. Problem-Solving Tools

Seven Classic Quality Tools and Basic Management and Planning Tools

Andersen, B., T. Fagerhaug, B. Henriksen, and L. F. Onsøyen. *Mapping Work Processes.* Milwaukee: ASQ Quality Press, 2008.

Brassard, M., and D. Ritter. *The Memory Jogger 2.* 2nd ed. Salem, NH: GOAL/QPC, 2010.

Process Improvement Tools

ABS Consulting—L. N. Vanden Heuvel, D. K. Lorenzo, R. L. Montgomery, W. E. Hanson, and J. R. Rooney. *Root Cause Analysis Handbook.* 3rd ed. Milwaukee: ASQ Quality Press, 2008.

Andersen, B., and T. Fagerhaug. *Root Cause Analysis: Simplified Tools and Techniques.* 2nd ed. Milwaukee: ASQ Quality Press, 2006.

Barry, R., and A. C. Smith. *The Manager's Guide to Six Sigma in Healthcare: Practical Tips and Tools for Improvement.* Milwaukee: ASQ Quality Press, 2005.

Brassard, M., L. Finn, D. Ginn, and D. Ritter. *The Six Sigma Memory Jogger II: A Pocket Guide of Tools for Six Sigma Improvement Teams.* Salem, NH: GOAL/QPC, 2002.

GOAL/QPC. *The Problem Solving Memory Jogger: Seven Steps to Improved Processes.* Lawrence, MA: GOAL/QPC, 2000.

Munro, R. A. *Six Sigma for the Shop Floor.* Milwaukee: ASQ Quality Press, 2002.

Okes, D. *Root Cause Analysis: The Core of Problem Solving and Corrective Action.* 2nd ed. Milwaukee: ASQ Quality Press, 2019.

Pande, P. S., R. R. Cavanagh, and R. P. Neuman. *The Six Sigma Way: How GE, Motorola, and Other Top Companies Are Honing Their Performance.* New York: McGraw-Hill, 2000.

Pande, P. S., and L. Holpp. *What Is Six Sigma?* New York: McGraw-Hill, 2001.

Plenert, G. *Strategic Continuous Process Improvement: Which Quality Tools to Use, and When to Use Them.* New York: McGraw-Hill, 2012.

Pries, K. H. *Six Sigma for the Next Millennium.* 2nd ed. Milwaukee: ASQ Quality Press, 2009.

Six Sigma Academy. *The Black Belt Memory Jogger: A Pocket Guide for Six Sigma Success.* Salem, NH: GOAL/QPC, 2002.

Stamatis, D. H. *Failure Mode Effect Analysis: FMEA from Theory to Execution.* 2nd ed. Milwaukee: ASQ Quality Press, 2003.

Tague, N. R. *The Quality Toolbox.* 2nd ed. Milwaukee: ASQ Quality Press, 2005.

Watson, G. *Six Sigma for Business Leaders: A Guide to Implementation.* Salem, NH: GOAL/QPC, 2004.

Innovation and Creativity Tools

Cook, H. E. *Design for Six Sigma as Strategic Experimentation: Planning, Designing, and Building World-Class Products and Services.* Milwaukee: ASQ Quality Press, 2005.

GOAL/QPC. *The Design for Six Sigma Memory Jogger.* Salem, NH: GOAL/QPC, 2004.

Hidahl, J. W. "DFMA/DFSS." In *Manufacturing Handbook of Best Practices.* Edited by J. B. ReVelle. Boca Raton, FL: St. Lucie Press, 2002.

Mader, D. P. "Design for Six Sigma: You Need More than Standard Six Sigma Approaches to Optimize Your Product or Service Development." *Quality Progress* (July 2002): 82–86.

Tague, N. R. *The Quality Toolbox.* 2nd ed. Milwaukee: ASQ Quality Press, 2005.

Ungvari, S. F. "TRIZ." Chapter 19 in *Manufacturing Handbook of Best Practices: An Innovation, Productivity, and Quality Focus.* Edited by J. B. ReVelle. Boca Raton, FL: St. Lucie Press, 2002, 399–425.

Watson, G. H. *Design for Six Sigma: Innovation for Enhanced Competitiveness.* Salem, NH: GOAL/QPC, 2005.

Cost of Quality

Beecroft, G. D. "Cost of Quality and Quality Planning Affect the Bottom Line." *Quality Management Forum* (Winter 2001).

DeFeo, J. A. "The Tip of the Iceberg: When Accounting for Quality, Don't Forget the Often Hidden Costs of Poor Quality." *Quality Progress* (May 2001): 29–37.

Freiesleben, J. "Quality Problems and Their Real Costs." *Quality Progress* (December 2004): 49–55.

Gryna, F. M. "Section 8: Quality and Costs." In *Juran's Quality Handbook.* 5th ed. Edited by J. M. Juran and A. B. Godfrey. New York: McGraw-Hill, 1999.

Wood, D. C., ed. *Principles of Quality Costs: Financial Measures for Strategic Implementation of Quality Management.* 4th ed. Milwaukee: ASQ Quality Press, 2012.

Chapter 14   B. Process Management

Process Goals and Analysis

Alukal, G., and A. Manos. *Lean Kaizen: A Simplified Approach to Process Improvement.* Milwaukee: ASQ Quality Press, 2006.

Christensen, E. H., K. M. Coombes-Betz, and M. S. Stein. *The Certified Quality Process Analyst Handbook.* Milwaukee: ASQ Quality Press, 2007.

Imai, M. *Gemba Kaizen: A Commonsense Approach to a Continuous Improvement Strategy.* 2nd ed. Milwaukee: ASQ Quality Press, 2012.

Lareau, W. *Office Kaizen 2: Harnessing Leadership, Organizations, People, and Tools for Office Excellence.* Milwaukee: ASQ Quality Press, 2011.

Windsor, S. *An Introduction to Green Process Management.* Milwaukee: ASQ Quality Press, 2011.

Lean Tools

Hinckley, C. M. *Make No Mistake! An Outcome-Based Approach to Mistake-Proofing.* Portland: Productivity Press, 2001.

Lareau, W. *Office Kaizen: Transforming Office Operations into a Strategic Competitive Advantage.* Milwaukee: ASQ Quality Press, 2003.

Macinnes, R. L. *The Lean Enterprise Memory Jogger: Create Value and Eliminate Waste throughout Your Company.* Salem, NH: GOAL/QPC, 2002.

MCS Media. *The New Lean Pocket Guide XL: Tools for the Elimination of Waste!* Chelsea, MI: MCS Media, 2006.

Ohno, T. *Toyota Production System: Beyond Large-Scale Production.* Portland: Productivity Press, 1988.

ReVelle, J. B. *Manufacturing Handbook of Best Practices: An Innovation, Productivity, and Quality Focus.* Boca Raton, FL: St. Lucie Press, 2002.

Rooney, S. A., and J. K. Rooney. "Lean Glossary." *Quality Progress* (June 2005): 41–47.

Schonberger, R. J. "Make Work Cells Work for You." *Quality Progress* (April 2004): 58–63.

Tapping, D., T. Luyster, and T. Shuker. *Value Stream Management: Eight Steps to Planning, Mapping, and Sustaining Lean Improvements.* New York: Productivity Press, 2002.

Trischler, W. R. *Understanding and Applying Value-Added Assessment: Eliminating Business Process Waste.* Milwaukee: ASQC Quality Press, 1996.

Voelkel, J. G., and C. Chapman. "Value Stream Mapping." *Quality Progress* (May 2003): 65–69.

Theory of Constraints

Dettmer, W. W. *Breaking the Constraints to World-Class Performance.* Milwaukee: ASQ Quality Press, 1998.

———. *Goldratt's Theory of Constraints: A Systems Approach to Continuous Improvement*. Milwaukee: ASQ Quality Press, 1997.

Nave, D., "How to Compare Six Sigma, Lean, and the Theory of Constraints." *Quality Progress* (March 2002): 73–78.

Chapter 15   C. Measurement: Assessment and Metrics

Andersen, B. *Business Process Improvement Toolbox*. Milwaukee: ASQ Quality Press, 1999.

Anderson, M. J., and S. L. Kraber. "Eight Keys to Successful DOE." *Quality Digest* (July 1999): 39–43.

ASQ Statistics Division. *Improving Performance through Statistical Thinking*. Milwaukee: ASQ Quality Press, 2000.

Barrentine, L. B. *Concepts for R&R Studies*. 2nd ed. Milwaukee: ASQ Quality Press, 2003.

Blank, R. *Basics of Reliability*. New York: Productivity Press, 2004.

Borror, C. M., ed. *The Certified Quality Engineer Handbook*. 3rd ed. Milwaukee: ASQ Quality Press, 2009.

Brassard, M., L. Finn, D. Ginn, and D. Ritter. *Six Sigma Memory Jogger II: A Pocket Guide for Six Sigma Improvement Teams*. Salem, NH: GOAL/QPC, 2002.

Brassard, M., and D. Ritter. *The Creativity Tools Memory Jogger*. Salem, NH: GOAL/QPC, 1998.

Carey, R. G., and R. C. Lloyd. *Measuring Quality Improvement in Healthcare: A Guide to Statistical Process Control Applications*. Milwaukee: ASQ Quality Press, 2001.

Crossley, M. L. *The Desk Reference of Statistical Quality Methods*. Milwaukee: ASQ Quality Press, 2000.

Hahn, G. J., W. Q. Meeker, and N. Doganaksoy. "Speedier Reliability Analysis." *Quality Progress* (June 2003): 58–64.

Hunter, J. S. "Improving an Unstable Process." *Quality Progress* (February 2004): 68–71.

———. "Making a Decision under Uncertain Circumstances." *Quality Progress* (April 2003): 83–85.

Kimothi, S. K. *The Uncertainty of Measurements: Physical and Chemical Metrology Impact and Analysis*. Milwaukee: ASQ Quality Press, 2002.

Okes, D. *Performance Metrics: The Levers for Process Management*. Milwaukee: ASQ Quality Press, 2013.

Payne, G. C. "Calibration: What Is It?" *Quality Progress* (May 2005): 72–76.

Schilling, E. G. "Acceptance Sampling." In *Juran's Quality Handbook*. 5th ed. Edited by J. M. Juran and A. B. Godfrey. New York: McGraw-Hill, 1999, sect. 46.1–46.87.

Stephens, K. S. *The Handbook of Applied Acceptance Sampling: Plans, Procedures, and Principles*. Milwaukee: ASQ Quality Press, 2001.

West, J. E., and C. A. Cianfrani. *Unlocking the Power of Your QMS: Keys to Business Performance Improvement*. Milwaukee: ASQ Quality Press, 2005.

Wheeler, D. J. *Understanding Variation: The Key to Managing Chaos*. Knoxville: SPC Press, 1993.

Wood, D., ed. *Principles of Quality Costs: Financial Measures for Strategic Implementation of Quality Management*. 4th ed. Milwaukee: ASQ Quality Press, 2013.

PART V   CUSTOMER-FOCUSED ORGANIZATIONS

Chapter 16   A. Customer Identification and Segmentation

Westcott, R. T. "Quality-Level Agreements for Clarity of Expectations." *Informed Outlook* (December 1999): 13–15.

Chapter 17   B. Customer Relationship Management

Albrecht, K., and R. Zemke. *Service America in the New Economy.* New York: McGraw-Hill, 2002.

Allen, D. R., and T. R. Rao. *Analysis of Customer Satisfaction Data.* Milwaukee: ASQ Quality Press, 2000.

Barlow, J., and C. Møller. *A Complaint Is a Gift: Using Customer Feedback as a Strategic Tool.* San Francisco: Berrett-Koehler, 1996.

Becker, K. "Are You Hearing Voices?" *Quality Progress* (February 2005): 28–35.

Camarota, A. G. *Finding the Leader in You.* Milwaukee: ASQ Quality Press, 2004.

Cochran, C. "Leveraging Customer Complaints into Customer Loyalty." *Quality Digest* (December 2004): 26–28.

Fisher, C. M., and J. T. Schutta. *Developing New Services: Incorporating the Voice of the Customer into Strategic Service Development.* Milwaukee: ASQ Quality Press, 2003.

Fornell, C. *The Satisfied Customer: Winners and Losers in the Battle for Buyer Preference.* New York: Palgrave Macmillan, 2007.

Harris, E. K. *Customer Service: A Practical Approach.* Upper Saddle River, NJ: Prentice Hall, 2000.

Hayes, B. E. *Measuring Customer Satisfaction and Loyalty: Survey Design, Use, and Statistical Analysis Methods.* 3rd ed. Milwaukee: ASQ Quality Press, 2008.

Jeffries, R. D., and P. R. Sells. "Customer Satisfaction Measurement Instruments: In Healthcare, Does One Size Fit None?" *Quality Progress* (February 2000): 118–23.

Kessler, S. *Customer Satisfaction Toolkit for ISO 9001:2000.* Milwaukee: ASQ Quality Press, 2003.

LeBoeuf, M. *How to Win Customers and Keep Them for Life.* Rev. ed. New York: Berkeley Books, 2000.

McKenzie, R. *The Relationship-Based Enterprise: Powering Business Success through Customer Relationship Management.* New York: McGraw-Hill, 2001.

Mody, A. "New Imperative: To Keep Customers, Deliver an Exceptional Experience." *Quality Management Forum* (Fall): 5–7.

Naumann, E., and S. H. Hoisington. *Customer Centered Six Sigma: Linking Customers, Process Improvement, and Financial Results.* Milwaukee: ASQ Quality Press, 2001.

Newell, F. *Loyalty.com: Customer Relationship Management in the New Era of Internet Marketing.* New York: McGraw-Hill, 2000.

Nykamp, M. *The Customer Differential: The Complete Guide to Implementing Customer Relationship Management.* New York: AMACOM, 2001.

Plsek, P. E. "Creative Thinking for Surprising Quality: The Ability to Innovate Is a Must in Today's Competitive Marketplace." *Quality Progress* (May 2000): 67–73.

Rosenbluth, H. F., and D. M. Peters. *The Customer Comes Second: Put Your People First and Watch 'Em Kick Butt.* New York: HarperCollins, 2002.

Schultz, G. *The Customer Care and Contact Center Handbook.* Milwaukee: ASQ Quality Press, 2003.

Sewell, C., and P. B. Brown. *Customers for Life: How to Turn That One-Time Buyer into a Lifetime Customer.* New York: Doubleday, 2002.

Timm, P. R. *Seven Power Strategies for Building Customer Loyalty.* New York: AMACOM, 2001.

Ulwick, A. W. *What Customers Want: Using Outcome-Driven Innovation to Create Breakthrough Products and Services.* New York: McGraw-Hill, 2005.

Vavra, T. G. *Customer Satisfaction Measurement Simplified: A Step-by-Step Guide for ISO 9001:2000 Certification.* Milwaukee: ASQ Quality Press, 2002.

Warner, C. M. In *Real World Customer Service Strategies That Work*. Sevierville, TN: Insight, 2004.

Westcott, R. T. "Safeguard Your Customer Base." *Quality Management Forum* (Summer 1998): 10–13.

———. "Stepping Up to ISO 9004:2000: Focusing on the Customer." *Informed Outlook* (July 2001): 3–8 and (August 2001): 19–24.

———. "Tapping the Many Voices of the Customer." *Informed Outlook* (June 2000): 20–23.

———. "Unconditional Guarantee: Implications for Your Business." *Quality Management Forum* (Spring 1994): 3–6.

Wilburn, M. W. *Managing the Customer Experience: A Measurement-Based Approach*. Milwaukee: ASQ Quality Press, 2007.

Xie, M., K. C. Tan, and T. N. Goh. *Advanced QFD Applications*. Milwaukee: ASQ Quality Press, 2003.

Zeithaml, V. A., A. Parasuraman, and L. L. Berry. *Delivering Quality Service: Balancing Customer Perceptions and Expectations*. Milwaukee: ASQ Quality Press, 2002.

PART VI   SUPPLY CHAIN MANAGEMENT

Chapter 18   Supply Chain Management

Andrews, D. L. "How to Manage Cross-Cultural Change." *Chief Supply Chain Officer* (May 2005): 34–39.

Ayers, J. B. *Supply Chain Project Management: A Structured Collaborative and Measurable Approach*. 2nd ed. Boca Raton, FL: CRC Press, 2010.

Balasubramanian, R., and S. Baumgardner. "Good Supplier Management Aids New Product Launch." *Quality Progress* (June 2004): 49–57.

Barney, D. "10 Rules of Supply Chain Excellence." *Chief Supply Chain Officer* (February 2005): 22–29.

———. "Get Ripped! 20 Steps to a Lean, Mean Supply Chain Machine." *Chief Supply Chain Officer* (May 2005): 18–25.

Bolstorff, P., and R. Rosenbaum. *Supply Chain Excellence: A Handbook for Dramatic Improvement Using the SCOR Model*. 2nd ed. New York: AMACOM, 2003.

Boone, T., and R. Ganeshan. *New Directions in Supply-Chain Management: Technology, Strategy, and Implementation*. New York: AMACOM, 2002.

Bossert, J. L., ed. *The Supplier Management Handbook*. 6th ed. Milwaukee: ASQ Quality Press, 2004.

CQI-19 AIAG Sub-tier Supplier Management Process Guideline. Version I, August 2012.

Dittmann, P. J. *Supply Chain Transformation: Building and Executing an Integrated Supply Chain*. Milwaukee: ASQ Quality Press, 2013.

Dominick, C., and S. Lunney. *The Procurement Game Plan: Winning Strategies and Techniques for Supply Management Professionals*. Fort Lauderdale: J. Ross, 2012.

Fawcett, S. E., and G. M. Magnan. *Achieving World-Class Supply Chain Alignment: Benefits, Barriers, and Bridges*. Tempe, AZ: Center for Advanced Purchasing Studies, 2001. http://www.capsresearch.org.

Gilmore, D. "Integrated Supply Chains Require Effective Sales and Operations Planning." *Chief Supply Chain Officer* (May 2005): 48–47.

Gordon, S. "Seven Steps to Measure Supplier Performance." *Quality Progress* (August 2005): 20–25.

Handfield, R. B., and E. L. Nichols Jr. *Supply Chain Redesign: Transforming Supply Chains into Integrated Value Systems*. Upper Saddle River, NJ: Prentice Hall, 2002.

"How to Give a Quality Score to Your Supplier." Metric Stream. Accessed August 1, 2013. http://www.metricstream.com/insights/qualityScore.htm.

Navas, D. "The Global Supply Chain: 3PLs Lead the Way." *SCS* (May 2005): 10–17.

Norausky, P. H. *The Customer and Supplier Innovation Team Guidebook.* Milwaukee: ASQ Quality Press, 2000.

ReVelle, J. B., ed. *Manufacturing Handbook of Best Practices: An Innovation, Productivity, and Quality Focus.* Boca Raton, FL: St. Lucie Press, 2002, chaps. 16 and 17.

Stauffer, D. "Risk: The Weak Link in Your Supply Chain." *Harvard Business Review* (March 1, 2003): 3–5.

Supply Chain Metric.com. Accessed August 1, 2013. http://www.supplychainmetric.com/.

Terry, L. "Supply Chain Execution Expands Its Footprint: The Distinction between Supply Chain Planning and Supply Chain Execution Software Is Beginning to Blur, as Businesses Build Cross-Functional, Integrated Demand-Driven Networks." *SCS* (May 2005): 18–25.

Watkins, D. K. "Quality Management's Role in Global Sourcing." *Quality Progress* (April 2005): 24–31.

PART VII TRAINING AND DEVELOPMENT

Chapter 19 Training and Development

Allen, M. W. *Michael Allen's Guide to E-Learning: Building Interactive, Fun, and Effective Learning Programs for Any Company.* Hoboken, NJ: John Wiley & Sons, 2003.

Kruse, K., and J. Keil. *Technology-Based Training: The Art and Science of Design, Development, and Delivery.* San Francisco: Jossey-Bass, 2000.

Phillips, J. J. *Handbook of Training Evaluation and Measurement Methods.* 3rd ed. Woburn, MA: Butterworth-Heinemann, 1997.

———. *Return on Investment in Training and Performance Improvement Programs.* Houston: Gulf, 1997.

Rosenberg, M. J. *e-Learning: Strategies for Delivering Knowledge in the Digital Age.* New York: McGraw-Hill, 2001.

Rossett, A. *The ASTD E-Learning Handbook: Best Practices, Strategies, and Case Studies for an Emerging Field.* New York: McGraw-Hill, 2002.

———. *First Things Fast: A Handbook for Performance Analysis.* San Francisco: Pfeiffer, 1999.

———. *Training Needs Assessment.* Techniques in Training and Performance Development Series. Englewood Cliffs, NJ: Educational Technology, 1987.

Rothwell, W. J., and H. C. Kazanas. *Mastering the Instructional Design Process: A Systematic Approach.* 3rd ed. San Francisco: Pfeiffer, 2003.

Stetar, B. "Training: It's Not Always the Answer." *Quality Progress* (March 2005): 44–49.

Westcott, R. T. "Mini-Scule: If You Have No Time or Money to Provide Training, Try a Mini-Scule." *Quality Progress* (June 2005): 104.

Appendix B
Glossary and Acronyms

A

A-B-C analysis—A systematic collection and analysis of the behavior observed of an individual or a work group for the purpose of determining the cause of specific behaviors.

acceptable quality limit (AQL)—The quality level that is the worst tolerable process average when a continuing series of lots is submitted for acceptance sampling.

acceptance sampling—Inspection of a sample from a lot to decide whether to accept or not accept that lot. There are two types: attributes sampling and variables sampling. In *attributes* sampling, the presence or absence of a characteristic is noted in each of the units inspected. In *variables* sampling, the numerical magnitude of a characteristic is measured and recorded for each inspected unit; this involves reference to a continuous scale of some kind.

acceptance sampling plan—Specific plan that indicates the sampling sizes and the associated acceptance or nonacceptance criteria to be used. In attributes sampling, for example, there are single, double, multiple, sequential, chain, and skip-lot sampling plans. In variables sampling, there are single, double, and sequential sampling plans. For detailed descriptions of these plans, see ANSI/ISO/ASQ A35342.

accreditation—Certification, by a duly recognized body, of the facilities, capability, objectivity, competence, and integrity of an agency, service, or operational group or individual to provide the specific service or operation needed. For example, the Registrar Accreditation Board (United States) accredits those organizations that register companies to the ISO 9000 series standards.

accuracy—A characteristic of measurement that addresses how close an observed value is to the true value. It answers the question "Is it right?"

ACSI—The American Customer Satisfaction Index is an economic indicator, a cross-industry measure of the satisfaction of U.S. customers with the quality of the goods and services available to them—both those goods and services produced within the United States and those provided as imports from foreign firms that have substantial market shares or dollar sales.

action plan—The detailed plan to implement the actions needed to achieve strategic goals and objectives (similar to, but not as detailed as a *project plan*).

active listening—Listening closely to what others are saying (for example, rather than what you think of what they are saying or what you want to say back to them).

603

activity—A task that is performed to complete work or steps of a process.

activity attributes—A detailed set of defined characteristics that describe each project activity.

activity-based management/activity-based costing—Managing with an accounting system (activity-based costing) that allocates costs to products based on resources employed to produce the product.

activity list—A list of everything that needs to be accomplished to complete the project.

activity network diagram—See AND.

actual value—The amount of cost or effort actually expended for the project at a point in time.

ADDIE—An instructional design model (*analysis, design, development, implementation,* and *evaluation*).

ad hoc team—See *temporary team.*

adult learning principles—Key principles of how adults learn that have an impact on how education and training of adults should be designed.

Advanced Product Quality Planning (APQP)—Methodology used to guide the process of developing and launching a new product/process (automotive industry). Defines the phases: conceptualize, design, develop, validate, and launch new product and process designs.

affinity diagram—A management and planning tool used to organize ideas into natural groupings in a way that stimulates new, creative ideas. Also known as the *KJ method.*

agile—An approach or method, first implemented in software development, to focus on getting software functionality quickly to customers.

agile approach—Means to change rapidly to meet changing customer and business direction. Also see *lean approach.*

Agile Manifesto—The basic principles and beliefs of agile methods.

AIAG—Automotive Industry Action Group.

alignment—Action taken to ensure that a process or activity allows traceability from an action level upward to support the organization's strategic goals and objectives.

alliance—An alliance can be the first step toward a partnership. See *partnership/alliance.*

alpha risk—Type 1 error; rejecting a process or lot when it is acceptable. Also see *producer's risk.*

analogies—A technique used to generate new ideas by translating concepts from one application to another.

analysis of variance (ANOVA)—A basic statistical technique for analyzing experimental data. It subdivides the total variation of a data set into meaningful component parts associated with specific sources of variation in order to test a hypothesis on the parameters of the model or to estimate variance components. There are three models: fixed, random, and mixed.

analytical thinking—Breaking down a problem or situation into discrete parts to understand how each part contributes to the whole.

AND—activity network diagram. A management and planning tool used to diagram the sequential relationships of events or processes or deliverables. The critical path method (CPM) and the program evaluation review technique (PERT) are derived from the arrow diagram.

andon board—A visual device (usually lights) displaying status alerts that can easily be seen by those who should respond.

AOQ—Average outgoing quality.

AOQL—Average outgoing quality limit.

APICS—American Production and Inventory Control Society.

appraisal cost—Costs incurred to determine the degree of conformance to quality requirements.

AQL—See *acceptable quality limit.*

AS9100—An international quality management standard for the aeronautics industry embracing the ISO 9001 standard.

ASME—American Society of Mechanical Engineers.

ASQ—American Society for Quality, a society of individual and organizational members dedicated to the ongoing development, advancement, and promotion of quality concepts, principles, and technologies.

assessment—An estimate or determination of the significance, importance, or value of something.

assignable cause—See *common cause* or *special cause.*

assumptions log—A list of all of the assumptions and constraints for the project throughout its entire life cycle. These can include product, process, or project assumptions and any restrictions (constraints) on the schedule, cost, or product implementation choices.

ASTD—American Society for Training and Development.

ASTM—American Society for Testing and Materials.

attribute data—Does/does not exist data. The control charts based on attribute data include fraction defective chart, number of affected units chart, count chart, count-per-unit chart, quality score chart, and demerit chart.

audit—A planned, independent, and documented assessment to determine whether agreed-on requirements are being met. Common types of audits are of the quality management system, processes, products, and services. When an audit is to check on conformance to a standard, specifications, contract terms, or regulations, it may be called a *compliance audit.*

auditee—The individual or organization being audited.

auditor—An individual or organization carrying out an audit.

audit program—The organized structure, commitment, schedules, and documented methods used to plan and perform audits.

audit scope—The depth or extent and boundaries within which the audit will be conducted.

audit team—The group of trained individuals conducting an audit under the direction of a team leader, relevant to a particular system, product, process, service, contract, project, or standard.

audit types—*Internal* or *first party* (organization being audited by itself), *external* or *second party* (an organization conducting an audit of a supplier, customer, or other company), and *external* or *third party* (audit conducted by a registrar or another party).

autocratic management—Autocratic managers are concerned with developing an efficient workplace and often have little concern for people (theory X assumptions about people). They typically make decisions without input from subordinates. These managers rely on their positional power.

autonomation—Use of specially equipped automated machines capable of detecting a defect in a single part, stopping the process, and signaling for assistance. See *jidoka*.

availability—The ability of a process or equipment to be in a state to perform its designated function under stated conditions at a given time. Availability can be expressed by the ratio:

$$\frac{\text{Uptime}}{\text{Downtime}}$$

average—The sum of all the pertinent data divided by the number of observations collected. Also see *mean*.

average chart—A control chart in which the subgroup average, X-bar, is used to evaluate the stability of the process level.

average outgoing quality (AOQ)—The expected average quality level of outgoing product for a given value of incoming product quality.

average outgoing quality limit (AOQL)—The maximum average outgoing quality over all possible levels of incoming quality for a given acceptance sampling plan and disposal specification.

B

balanced scorecard—Translates an organization's mission and strategy into a comprehensive set of performance measures to provide a basis for strategic measurement and management, typically using four balanced views: financial, customers, internal business processes, and learning and growth.

balance sheet—A financial statement showing the assets, liabilities, and owner's equity of a business entity.

Baldrige Performance Excellence Program (BPEP)—The Baldrige National Quality Award was established by Congress in 1987 to raise awareness of quality management and to recognize U.S. companies that have implemented successful quality management systems. A *Criteria for Performance Excellence* is published each year. Three awards may be given annually in each of five categories: manufacturing businesses, service businesses, small businesses, education institutions, and healthcare organizations. The award is named after the late secretary of commerce Malcolm Baldrige, a proponent of quality management. The U.S. Commerce Department's National Institute of Standards and Technology manages the award and ASQ administers it. The major emphasis in determining success is achieving results.

basis of estimates—The definition of supporting details for any estimate, including any basic assumptions about what was and was not included in the estimate.

batch processing/batch and queue—Running large batches of a single product through the process at one time, resulting in queues awaiting next steps in the process.

BATF—Bureau of Alcohol, Tobacco, and Firearms.

bathtub curve—Also called *life-history curve* or *Weibull curve*. A graphic demonstration of the relationship of failures over the life of a product versus the probable failure rate. Includes three phases: early or infant failure (break-in), a stable rate during normal use, and wear out.

behavioral theories—Motivational theories, notably those of Abraham Maslow, Frederick Herzberg, Douglas McGregor, and others.

behavior management—The management methodology and practices adapted from B. F. Skinner's theories: a practice used in managing people.

benchmarking—An improvement process in which a company measures its performance against that of best-in-class organizations (or others that are good performers), determines how those organizations achieved their performance levels, and uses the information to improve its own performance. Areas often benchmarked include strategies, operations, processes, and procedures.

benefit-cost analysis—Collection of the dollar value of benefits derived from an initiative and the associated costs incurred, then computing the ratio of benefits to cost.

beta risk—Type 2 error; the possibility that a bad product will be accepted by a consumer. See *consumer's risk*.

bias—A characteristic of measurement that refers to a systematic difference.

Big Q, little q—A term used to contrast the difference between managing for quality in all processes and products (Big Q) and managing for quality in a limited capacity (little q).

binomial distribution—Defines the probability of successes from a given number of trials.

Black Belt—Full-time leader responsible for implementing Six Sigma process improvement projects using pertinent methodologies, such as DMAIC, DOE, and others. Usually, the Black Belt trains the Green Belts and often serves for a two-year assignment overseeing eight to ten Six Sigma projects.

blemish—An imperfection that is severe enough to be noticed but should not cause any real impairment with respect to intended normal or reasonably foreseeable use. (See also *defect*, *imperfection*, and *nonconformity*.)

block diagram—A diagram that shows the operation, interrelationships, and interdependencies of components in a system. Boxes, or blocks (hence the name), represent the components; connecting lines between the blocks represent interfaces. There are two types of block diagrams: a *functional* block diagram, which shows a system's subsystems and lower-level products, their interrelationships, and interfaces with other systems; and a *reliability* block diagram, which is similar to the functional block diagram except that it is modified to emphasize those aspects influencing reliability.

Bloom's Taxonomy (levels of cognition)—See Appendix A.

body language—The expression of thoughts and emotions through movement or positioning of the body.

bottom line—An essential point or primary consideration. The line at the bottom of a financial statement that states the net profit or loss incurred.

boundaryless organization—An organization without the internal or external boundaries limiting traditional structures. (Also known as a *network organization*, a *modular corporation*, or a *virtual corporation*.)

BPR—Business process reengineering. See *reengineering*.

brainstorming—A problem-solving tool that teams use to generate as many ideas as possible related to a particular subject. Team members begin by offering all their ideas; the ideas are not discussed or reviewed until after the brainstorming session.

breakthrough—A method of solving chronic problems that results from the effective execution of a strategy designed to reach the next level of quality. Such change often requires a paradigm shift within the organization.

brownfields—Abandoned, idle, or underused commercial or industrial facilities or sites, often where use is complicated by real or potential environmental contamination.

BSI—British Standards Institute.

budget variance—The difference between budgeted and actual expenditures at a point in time.

burndown chart—A graph that shows the work left to be completed in the project.

business partnering—The creation of cooperative business alliances between constituencies within an organization or between an organization and its customers or suppliers. Partnering occurs through a pooling of resources in a trusting atmosphere focused on continuous, mutual improvement. See also *customer-supplier partnership*.

business processes—Processes that focus on what the organization does as a business and how it goes about doing it; the functional processes (generating output within a single department) and cross-functional processes (generating output across several functions or departments).

C

calibration—The comparison of a measurement instrument or system of unverified accuracy to a measurement instrument or system of a known accuracy to detect any variation from the true value.

capability maturity model (CMM)—Description of key elements of an effective software process, covering planning practices, engineering, management of software development, and maintenance.

capability ratio (C_p)—The specification tolerance width divided by the process capability.

capital expenditure—Money for improvements that will have a useful life of more than a year.

cascading training—Training implemented in an organization from the top down, where each level acts as trainers to those below.

case study—A prepared scenario (story) that, when studied and discussed, serves to illuminate the learning points of a course of study.

cash flow statement—A financial statement showing the flow of cash in and out of an enterprise within a given time period.

catchball—A term used to describe the interactive process of reaching consensus in developing and deploying policies and plans with hoshin planning.

cause-and-effect diagram—A tool for analyzing process variables. It is also referred to as the *Ishikawa diagram* because Kaoru Ishikawa developed it and the *fishbone diagram* because the complete diagram resembles a fish skeleton. The diagram illustrates the main causes and subcauses leading to an effect (symptom). The cause-and-effect diagram is one of the seven tools of quality.

CBT—Computer-based training. Training delivered via computer software.

c-chart—Count control chart. See also *attribute data*.

CDC—Centers for Disease Control and Prevention.

cell—A layout of workstations and/or various machines for different operations (usually in a U shape) in which multitasking operators proceed with a part from machine to machine to perform a series of sequential steps to produce a whole product or major subassembly.

cellular team—The cross-trained individuals who work within a cell.

CE mark—A mark placed on a product signifying that the product complies with the essential/safety requirements of the relevant European regulations; from the French Conformité Européenne.

centralization—Relates to the locus of the decision-making authority within an organization.

central tendency—The propensity of data collected on a process to concentrate around a value situated somewhere midway between the lowest and highest values.

certification—The receipt of a document from an authorized source stating that a device, process, or operator has been certified to a known standard.

certification to a standard—A process in which an accredited, independent third-party organization conducts an on-site audit of a company's operations against the requirements of the standard to which the company wants certification. Upon successful completion of the audit, the company receives a certificate indicating that it has met the standard requirements. The third party (registrar) lists the organization receiving certification (registration). For example, an ISO 9001–based quality management system (QMS) is implemented, audited, passes, and is certified as compliant with the standard. The registrar lists the organization as having received a certificate. The organization is registered.

CFR—Code of Federal Regulations.

cGMP—current good manufacturing practices.

chain reaction—A series of interacting events described by W. Edwards Deming: improve quality > decrease costs > improve productivity > increase market share with better quality and lower price > stay in business, provide jobs, and provide more jobs.

chaku-chaku—(Japanese) Means *load-load* in a cell layout where a part is taken from one machine and loaded into the next.

champion—An individual who has accountability and responsibility for many processes or who is involved in making strategic-level decisions for the organization. The champion ensures ongoing dedication of project resources and monitors strategic alignment (also referred to as a *sponsor*).

chance cause—Same as *common cause*, a random and uncontrollable cause of variation.

change agent—The person who takes the lead in transforming an organization into a quality-focused organization by providing guidance during the planning phase, facilitating implementation, and supporting those who pioneer the changes.

change log—A log that documents all changes that occur during the project, including the approval, status, and/or disposition of each change request related to the project. This log is used to communicate change request information to the stakeholders.

change management—The strategies, processes, and practices involved in creating and managing change.

changeover—Changing a machine or process from one type of product or operation to another.

characteristic—A property that helps to identify or to differentiate between entities and that can be described or measured to determine conformance or nonconformance to requirements.

charter—A documented statement officially initiating the formation of a committee, team, project, or other effort in which a clearly stated purpose and approval is conferred.

checklist—A tool for organizing and ensuring that all important steps or actions in an operation have been taken. Checklists contain items that are important or relevant to an issue or situation. Checklists should not be confused with check sheets and data sheets.

check sheet—A simple data-recording device. The check sheet is custom designed for the particular use, allowing ease in interpreting the results. The check sheet is one of the seven tools of quality. Check sheets should not be confused with data sheets and checklists. Sometimes called a *tally sheet*.

chi-square—A measurement of how well a set of data fits a proposed distribution, such as a normal distribution.

chronic problem—A long-standing adverse situation that can be remedied by changing the status quo. For example, actions such as revising an unrealistic manufacturing process or addressing customer defections can change the status quo and remedy the situation.

clean room—Workplace or process location within which the air is filtered to a specified level and/or additional environmental controls are present to prevent failures due to contamination or to ensure the personal safety of the workers.

cloud computing—A model for enabling convenient, on-demand network access to a shared pool of configurable computing resources—for example, networks, servers, storage, applications, and services—that can be rapidly provisioned and released with minimal management effort or service provider interaction. The cloud model promotes availability and is composed of five essential characteristics, three service models, and four deployment models (National Institute of Standards and Technology, Information Technology Laboratory).

CMI—Certified mechanical inspector (ASQ).

coaching—A continual improvement technique by which people receive one-to-one learning through demonstration and practice and that is characterized by immediate feedback and correction.

code of conduct—The expected behavior that has been mutually developed and agreed on by a team and communicated to the workforce.

comment cards—Printed cards or slips of paper used to solicit and collect comments from users of a service or product.

common causes of variation—Causes that are inherent in any process all the time. A process that has only common causes of variation is said to be stable or predictable or in control. Also called *chance causes*.

companywide quality control (CWQC)—(Japanese origin). Similar to total quality management.

competence—Refers to a person's ability to learn and perform a particular activity. Competence consists of *knowledge, experience, skills, aptitude,* and *attitude* components (KESAA factors).

competency-based training—A training methodology that focuses on building mastery of a predetermined segment or module before moving on to the next.

competitive analysis—The gathering of intelligence relative to competitors in order to identify opportunities or potential threats to current and future strategy.

complaint handling—The process and practices involved in receiving and resolving complaints from customers.

complexity—In an organizational context, the number of different entities (job title, reporting levels, functional departments, and physical work locations) that compose the organization.

complexity theory—The theory concerned with the interaction among the parts of a system, as well as the interaction between the system and its environment.

compliance—An affirmative indication or judgment that the supplier of a product or service has met the requirements of the relevant specifications, contract, or regulation; also the state of meeting the requirements.

computer-based training—Any instruction delivered via a computing device.

concurrent engineering—A process in which an organization designs a product or service using input and evaluations from business units and functions early in the process, anticipating problems and balancing the needs of all parties. The emphasis is on upstream prevention versus downstream correction. Sometimes called *simultaneous engineering*.

conflict resolution—A process for resolving disagreements in a manner acceptable to all parties.

conformance—An affirmative indication or judgment that a product or service has met the requirements of a relevant specification, contract, or regulation.

consensus—Finding a proposal acceptable enough that all team members can support the decision, and no member opposes it.

constancy of purpose—Occurs when goals and objectives are properly aligned to the organizational vision and mission (first of Deming's fourteen steps).

constraint—A constraint may range from the intangible (for example, beliefs, culture) to the tangible (for example, posted rule prohibiting smoking, buildup of work in process awaiting the availability of a machine or operator).

constraint management—Identifying a constraint and working to remove or diminish the constraint while dealing with resistance to change.

construct—A formally proposed concept representing relationships between empirically verifiable events and based on observed facts.

consultative—A decision-making approach in which a person talks to others and considers their input before making a decision.

consumer's risk—For a sampling plan, refers to the probability of acceptance of a lot the quality of which has a designated numerical value representing a level that is seldom desirable. Usually, the designated value will be the lot tolerance percent defective (LTPD). Also called *beta risk* or *type 2 error*.

content analysis—A qualitative analytical technique for categorizing and analyzing the contents of documents.

continual process improvement (CPI)—The actions taken throughout an organization to increase the effectiveness and efficiency of activities and processes in order to provide added benefits to the customer and organization. It is considered a subset of total quality management and operates according to the premise that organizations can always make improvements. Continual improvement can also be equated with reducing process variation.

continuous probability distribution—A graph or formula representing the probability of a particular numeric value of continuous (variable) data, based on a particular type of process that produces the data.

continuous quality improvement (CQI)—A philosophy and actions for repeatedly improving an organization's capabilities and processes with the objective of customer satisfaction.

contract review—Systematic activities carried out by an organization before agreeing to a contract to ensure that requirements for quality are adequately defined, free from ambiguity, documented, and can be realized by the supplier.

control chart—A basic tool that consists of a chart with upper and lower control limits on which values of some statistical measure for a series of samples or subgroups are plotted. It frequently shows a central line to help detect a trend of plotted values toward either control limit. It is used to monitor and analyze variation in a process to see whether the process is in statistical control.

control limits—(1) Calculated boundaries of a process within specified confidence levels, expressed as upper control limit (UCL) and lower control limit (LCL). (2) The limits on a control chart used as criteria for signaling the need for action or for judging whether a set of data does or does not indicate a "state of statistical control."

control plan—The control plan is a document that describes the actions (measurements, inspections, quality checks, or monitoring of process parameters) required at each phase of a process to ensure the process outputs will conform to predetermined requirements.

core competency—Pertains to the unique features and characteristics of an organization's overall capability.

corporate culture—See *organization culture*.

correction—When a problem occurs (1) find out how bad it is, (2) decide what to do to keep it from having a larger impact, and (3) determine what to do with what has already been affected. Doing 1 and 2 is containment action and 3 is remedial action. This is correcting the problem but not the causes.

corrective action—Once a problem has been corrected, decide whether or not it was of enough significant importance (based on frequency, impact, risk, and so on) to warrant investigating the causes and take action to eliminate the root cause(s) and symptom(s) of an existing deviation or nonconformity to prevent recurrence.

correlation—Refers to the measure of the strength of the relationship between two sets of numbers or variables (a *scatter chart* may be used in the analysis).

correlation coefficient—Describes the magnitude and direction of the relationship between two variables.

cost-benefit analysis—Compares the potential or actual benefits with the estimated or real cost associated with a problem solution or process improvement, as a ratio or in dollars.

cost driver—A factor in the project that drives cost within the project.

cost estimate—A quantitative estimate of the cost (typically measured in monetary units) to complete an activity or a set of activities on the project's activities list.

cost forecast—The expected total cost of completing all work, expressed as the sum of the actual cost to date and the estimated cost to complete the work.

cost of poor quality—The costs associated with providing poor-quality products or services.

cost of quality (COQ)—The total costs incurred relating to the quality of a product or service. There are four categories of quality costs: *internal failure costs* (costs associated with defects found before delivery of the product or service), *external failure costs* (costs associated with defects found during or after product or service delivery), *appraisal costs* (costs incurred to determine the degree of conformance to quality requirements), and *prevention costs* (costs incurred to keep failure and appraisal costs to a minimum).

count chart—A control chart for evaluating the stability of a process in terms of the count of events of a given classification occurring in a sample.

count-per-unit chart—A control chart for evaluating the stability of a process in terms of the average count of events of a given classification per unit occurring in a sample.

C_p—A widely used process capability index. It is expressed as:

$$\frac{\text{Upper spec limit} - \text{Lower spec limit}}{6\sigma}$$

C_{pk}—A widely used process capability index. It is expressed as:

$$\frac{(\text{Ratio with smallest answer}) \text{ Upper specification limit} - X\text{-bar}}{3\sigma}$$

or

$$\frac{X\text{-bar} - \text{Lower specification limit}}{3\sigma}$$

Crawford slip method—A method of anonymously gathering and presenting data from a group.

creativity, stages of—One model gives the following stages: generate, percolate, illuminate, and verify. May also be defined as visualization, exploration, combination, and modification.

criteria—Stated objectives, guidelines, principles, procedures, and/or standards used for measuring a project, process, product, or performance.

criterion—A standard, rule, or test on which a judgment or decision can be based.

critical activity—Any activity in the project plan that must be completed by the specified date or the project will be delayed.

critical incident—An event that has greater than normal significance, often used as a learning or feedback opportunity.

critical path—Refers to the sequence of tasks that takes the longest time and determines a project's completion date.

critical path method (CPM)—An activity-oriented project management tool that uses arrow-diagramming techniques to demonstrate both the time and cost required to complete a project. It provides one time estimate—normal time—and allows for computing the critical path.

critical success factors (CSF)—Factors identified by the organization as critical to the organization's success in achieving its strategic goals and objectives.

critical thinking—The careful analysis, evaluation, reasoning (both deductive and inductive), clear thinking, and systems thinking leading to effective decisions.

critical-to-quality (CTQ)—Characteristics that, from a customer's perception of quality, are critical to the achievement of quality goals, objectives, standards, and/or specifications.

cross-functional team—A group consisting of members from more than one department, work unit, or technical discipline that is organized to accomplish a project.

CSR—Customer service representative.

culture—See *organization culture.*

culture change—Major proposed or actual change in organizational operating principles, behavior, and attitude.

cumulative sum control chart (CUSUM)—A control chart on which the plotted value is the cumulative sum of deviations of successive samples from a target value. The ordinate of each plotted point represents the algebraic sum of the previous ordinate and the most recent deviations from the target.

current reality tree—A technique used in applying Goldratt's theory of constraints to identify undesirable effects (similar to root cause analysis).

customer—Recipient of a product or service provided by a supplier. See also *external customer* and *internal customer.*

customer council—A group usually composed of representatives from an organization's largest customers who meet to discuss common issues.

customer delight—The result achieved when customer requirements are exceeded in unexpected ways the customer finds valuable.

customer loyalty/retention—The result of an organization's plans, processes, practices, and efforts designed to deliver their services or products in ways that create retained and committed customers.

customer-oriented organization—An organization whose mission, purpose, and actions are dedicated to serving and satisfying its customers.

customer relationship management (CRM)—Refers to an organization's knowledge of its customers' unique requirements and expectations and using that knowledge to develop a closer and more profitable link to business processes and strategies.

customer satisfaction—The result of delivering a product or service that meets customer requirements, needs, and expectations.

customer segmentation—Refers to the process of differentiating customers based on one or more characteristics for the purpose of developing a marketing strategy to address specific segments. The intent is to better address customers' needs and improve customer satisfaction and organizational effectiveness.

customer service—Activities dealing with customer questions; also may be the designation of the department that takes customer orders or provides postdelivery services.

customer-supplier partnership—A long-term relationship between a buyer and supplier characterized by teamwork and mutual confidence. The supplier is considered an extension of the buyer's organization. The partnership is based on several commitments. The buyer provides long-term contracts and uses fewer suppliers. The supplier implements quality assurance processes so that incoming inspection can be minimized. The supplier also helps the buyer reduce costs and improve product and process designs.

customer value—There are four factors of influence on customer value: price, product/ service quality, innovation, and organization image relative to competition. When customers are satisfied with their perception of the balance of the product/service meeting their need or want, the quality is satisfactory, and the price is right for them, customer value has been achieved.

cycle time—Refers to the elapsed time that it takes to complete a process from the start of the process to completion.

cycle time reduction—To reduce the time that it takes, from start to finish, to complete a particular process.

D

daily stand-up meeting—A short meeting where members are encouraged to stand due to the intended short nature of the meeting. The purpose is to quickly assess the status of the project. Used in the Scrum agile method, as well as other project types.

data—Quantitative or qualitative facts presented in descriptive, numeric, or graphic form. Two types of numerical data are *measured*, or *variable* data, and *counted*, or *attribute* data.

data mining—The process of searching a large computer database (for example, a customer database) for previously undetected patterns and relationships, with the intent to transform the data into information for making decisions about strategy.

decision matrix—A matrix used by teams to evaluate problems or possible solutions. For example, after a matrix is drawn to evaluate possible solutions, the team lists them in the far left vertical column. Next, the team selects criteria to rate the possible solutions, writing them across the top row. Then, each possible solution is rated on a scale of 1 to 5 for each criterion and the rating recorded in the corresponding grid. Finally, the ratings of all the criteria for each possible solution are added to determine its total score. The total score is then used to help decide which solution deserves the most attention.

defect—A product's or service's nonfulfillment of an intended requirement or reasonable expectation for use, including safety considerations. They are often classified, such as:

- Class 1, *critical*, leads directly to severe injury or catastrophic economic loss.

- Class 2, *serious*, leads directly to significant injury or significant economic loss.

- Class 3, *major*, is related to major problems with respect to intended normal or reasonably foreseeable use.

- Class 4, *minor*, is related to minor problems with respect to intended normal or reasonably foreseeable use. See also *blemish, imperfection,* and *nonconformity.*

defective—A product that contains one or more defects relative to the quality characteristics being measured.

delighter—Feature of a delivered product or service that unexpectedly pleases a customer.

demerit chart—A control chart for evaluating a process in terms of a demerit (or quality score), such as a weighted sum of counts of various classified nonconformities.

Deming cycle—See *plan-do-check-act cycle.*

Deming Prize—Award given annually to organizations that, according to the award guidelines, have successfully applied companywide quality control based on statistical quality control and will keep up with it in the future. Although the award is named in honor of W. Edwards Deming, its criteria are not specifically related to Deming's teachings. There are three separate divisions for the award: the Deming Application Prize, the Deming Prize for Individuals, and the Deming Prize for Overseas Companies. The award process is overseen by the Deming Prize Committee of the Union of Japanese Scientists and Engineers in Tokyo.

demographics—Variables among buyers in the consumer market, which include geographic location, age, sex, marital status, family size, social class, education, nationality, occupation, and income.

dependability—The degree to which a product is operable and capable of performing its required function at any randomly chosen time during its specified operating life, provided that the product is available at the start of that period. (Nonoperation-related influences are not included.) Dependability can be expressed by the ratio

$$\frac{\text{Time available}}{\text{Time available} + \text{Time required}}$$

deployment—Used in strategic planning to describe the process of cascading *goals, objectives,* and *action plans* throughout an organization.

design documentation—The documentation of the product's architecture, describing the components of the system (or product), the internal interfaces between those components, their external interfaces with components outside the system, and the allocation of requirements to those components or interfaces.

design failure mode and effects analysis (DFMEA)—See *FMEA.*

design for manufacturing (DFM)—The design of a product for ease in manufacturing. Also called *design for assembly* (DFA).

Design for Six Sigma (DFSS)—The aim is for a robust design that is consistent with applicable manufacturing processes and ensures a fully capable process that will produce quality products.

designing-in quality versus inspecting-in quality—See *prevention versus detection.*

design of experiments (DOE)—A branch of applied statistics dealing with planning, conducting, analyzing, and interpreting controlled tests to evaluate the factors that control the value of a parameter or group of parameters.

design review—Documented, comprehensive, and systematic examination of a design to evaluate its capability to fulfill the requirements for quality.

desired quality—Refers to the additional features and benefits a customer discovers when using a product or service that lead to increased customer satisfaction. If missing, a customer may become dissatisfied.

deviation—A nonconformance or departure of a characteristic from specified product, process, or system requirements.

diagnostic journey and remedial journey—A two-phase investigation used by teams to solve chronic quality problems. In the first phase, the diagnostic journey, the team moves from the symptom of a problem to its cause. In the second phase, the remedial journey, the team moves from the cause to a remedy.

dimensions of quality—Different ways in which quality may be viewed—for example, meaning of quality, characteristics of quality, or drivers of quality.

DiSC—A profiling instrument that measures characteristic ways in which a person behaves in a particular environment. Four dimensions measured are dominance, influence, steadiness, and conscientiousness.

discrete probability distribution—The measured process variable takes on a finite or limited number of values; no other possible values exist. A discrete variable could be the number of people in a room.

disposition of nonconformity—Action taken to deal with an existing nonconformity; action may include correct (repair), rework, regrade, scrap, obtain a concession, or amend a requirement.

dissatisfiers—Those features or functions that the customer or employee has come to expect, which, if they are no longer present, would result in dissatisfaction.

distance learning—Learning where student(s) and instructor(s) are not colocated; interaction through electronic means.

distribution—Describes the amount of potential variation in outputs of a process; it is usually described in terms of its shape, average, and standard deviation.

DMAIC—A methodology used in a Six Sigma initiative: *define, measure, analyze, improve, control.*

Dodge–Romig sampling plans—Plans for acceptance sampling developed by Harold F. Dodge and Harry G. Romig. Four sets of tables were published in 1940: single-sampling lot tolerance tables, double-sampling lot tolerance tables, single-sampling average outgoing quality limit tables, and double-sampling average outgoing quality limit tables.

downsizing—The planned reduction in workforce due to economics, competition, merger, sale, restructuring, or reengineering.

DPMO—Defects per million opportunities.

DPPM—Defective parts per million.

drivers of quality—Crucial factors that when controlled, the product or service will be controlled. These factors might include processes, customers, products, services, employee satisfaction, total organizational focus on providing quality products/services, and so on.

duration estimate—A quantitative estimate of the length of calendar time it will take to complete an activity, a set of activities, a phase, or a project.

E

earned value analysis (EVA)—A methodology used to measure project performance by comparing planned work with actual work accomplished to determine if performance is adhering to plan.

education—Refers to the individual learner's process to acquire new or refreshed knowledge. See also *training*.

efficiency—Ratio of output to the total input in a process, with an objective to use less resources, such as time and cost.

eighty-twenty (80-20) rule—A term referring to the Pareto principle, which suggests that most effects come from relatively few causes; that is, 80% of the effects come from 20% of the possible causes.

eliminate non-value-added steps in the process—Reduce waste and cut costs.

eliminate or reduce buffer stocks and inventories—Smooth process flow, reduce costs, improve quality, and increase customer satisfaction.

employee involvement—A practice within an organization whereby employees regularly participate in making decisions on how their work areas operate, including making suggestions for improvement, planning, objectives setting, and performance monitoring.

empowerment—A condition whereby employees are given the authority to make decisions and take action in their work areas, within stated bounds, without prior approval. For example, an operator can stop a production process upon detecting a problem, or a customer service representative can send out a replacement product if a customer calls with a problem.

end users—External customers who purchase products/services for their own use— *consumers*.

engineering change order (ECO)—An order to make a change in a process, product, or service after the initial release of the product or service design. See *concurrent engineering* for a process for reducing ECOs.

entropy—Tendency of a system or process to run down and collapse.

environmental analysis/scanning—Identifying and monitoring factors from both inside and outside the organization that may have an impact on the long-term viability of the organization.

environmental management system (EMS)—A management system for addressing the environmental policies, objectives, principles, procedures, authority, responsibility, accountability, and implementation of an organization's practices for managing its impact on the environment in which it operates.

EPA—Environmental Protection Agency.

equity theory—A theory that states that job motivation depends on how equitable the individual believes the rewards or punishment to be.

error proofing—See *poka-yoke.*

ethics—An individual or an organization's adherence to a belief or documented code of conduct that is based on moral principles and tries to balance what is fair for individuals and the organization with what is right for society.

EU—European Union.

event—The starting or ending point for a task or group of tasks. An occurrence of some attribute.

executive education—Usually refers to the education (and training) provided to top management.

exit criteria—The activities, deliverables, and elements that must be in place to move to the next phase of the project.

expectancy theory—A motivational theory inferring that what people do is based on what they expect to gain from the activity.

expected quality—Also known as *basic quality,* the minimum benefit or value a customer expects to receive from a product or service.

experimental design—A formal plan that details the specifics for conducting an experiment, such as which responses, factors, levels, blocks, treatments, and tools are to be used.

explicit knowledge—Represented by the captured and recorded tools of the day—for example, procedures, processes, standards, and other like documents. See also *tacit knowledge.*

exponential distribution—A continuous distribution where data are more likely to occur below the average than above it. Typically used to describe the break-in portion of the bathtub curve.

external audit—Audit performed by anyone or any organization outside the organization being audited. See *second-party audit* or *third-party audit.*

external customer—A person or organization who receives a product, a service, or information but is not part of the organization supplying it. See also *internal customer.*

external failure costs—Costs associated with defects found during or after delivery of the product or service.

F

facilitator—A trained individual who is responsible for creating favorable conditions that will enable a team to reach its purpose or achieve its goals by bringing together the necessary tools, information, and resources to get the job done. A facilitator addresses the processes a team uses to achieve its purpose.

factor analysis—A statistical technique that examines the relationships between a single dependent variable and multiple independent variables. For example, it is used to determine which questions on a questionnaire are related to a specific question such as "Would you buy this product again?"

failure mode analysis (FMA)—A procedure for determining which malfunction symptoms appear immediately before or after a failure of a critical parameter in a system. After all the possible causes are listed for each symptom, the product is designed to eliminate the problems.

failure mode and effects analysis (FMEA)—A procedure in which each potential failure mode of every subitem of an item is analyzed to determine its effect on other subitems and on the required function of the item. Typically, two types of FMEAs are used: DFMEA (design) and PFMEA (process).

failure mode effects and criticality analysis (FMECA)—A procedure that is performed after a failure mode and effects analysis to classify each potential failure effect according to its severity and probability of occurrence.

false customer—An individual or group within a process that performs activities that do not add value to the product or service.

fault tree analysis (FTA)—Technique for evaluating the possible causes that might lead to the failure of a product or service.

FDA—Food and Drug Administration.

feasibility study—Examination of technical and cost data to determine the economic potential and practicality of a project or application of equipment. NPV may be used in this analysis.

feedback—The interpersonal communication response to information received (written or oral); it may be based on fact or feeling and helps the party who is receiving the information judge how well he/she is being understood by the other party. More generally, feedback is information about a process or performance and is used to make decisions that are directed toward improving or adjusting the process or performance as necessary.

feedback loops—Pertains to open-loop and closed-loop feedback. Open-loop feedback focuses on how to detect or measure problems in the inputs and how to plan for contingencies. Closed-loop feedback focuses on how to measure the outputs and how to determine the control points where adjustment can be made.

filters—Relative to human-to-human communication, those perceptions (based on culture, language, demographics, experience, and so on) that affect how a message is transmitted by the sender and how a message is interpreted by the receiver.

finding—A conclusion of importance based on observation(s) and/or research, for example, an audit finding.

first-party audit—Audit of a process or product/service by auditing personnel employed by the organization in which the audit is performed. Also called *internal audit*.

fishbone diagram—See *cause-and-effect diagram*.

fitness for use—A term used to indicate that a product or service fits the customer's defined purpose for that product or service.

5S—(Japanese) Five practices for maintaining a clean and efficient workplace. Briefly the term embraces: *seiri* (sort/separate), *seiton* (arrange and identify), *seiso* (clean up), *seiketsu* (standardize), *shitsuke* (develop habit of always following first four Ss).

five whys—A repetitive questioning technique to probe deeper to surface the root cause of a problem by asking *why* five times (more or fewer, as needed).

flexibility/agility—Concept and practice of configuring facilities, equipment, people, and support services to cope with inevitable change. Enables organization to reduce costs, respond more effectively to reduce costs, respond more effectively to marketplace demands, withstand economic fluctuations, and facilitate continual improvement.

flowchart—A graphic representation of the steps in a process. Flowcharts are drawn to better understand processes. The flowchart is one of the seven basic tools of quality.

focus group—A discussion group consisting of eight to ten participants, usually invited from a segment of the customer base to discuss an existing or planned product or service, led by a facilitator working from predetermined questions (focus groups may also be used to gather information in a context other than customers). Information from a focus group is often used as a basis for forming survey questions.

force field analysis—A technique for analyzing the forces that aid or hinder an organization in reaching an objective.

formal communication—The officially sanctioned information within an organization, which includes publications, memoranda, training materials/events, public relations information, and company meetings.

fourteen (14) points—W. Edwards Deming's fourteen management practices to help organizations increase their quality and productivity. They are:

1. Create constancy of purpose for improving products and services.

2. Adopt a new philosophy.

3. Cease dependence on inspection to achieve quality.

4. End the practice of awarding business on price alone; instead, minimize total cost by working with a single supplier.

5. Improve constantly and forever every process for planning, production, and service.

6. Institute training on the job.

7. Adopt and institute leadership.

8. Drive out fear.

9. Break down barriers between staff areas.

10. Eliminate slogans, exhortations, and targets for the workforce.

11. Eliminate numerical quotas for the workforce and numerical goals for management.

12. Remove barriers that rob people of pride of workmanship and eliminate the annual rating or merit system.

13. Institute a vigorous program of education and self-improvement for everyone.

14. Put everybody in the company to work to accomplish the transformation.

fraction defective chart (*p*-chart)—An attribute control chart used to track the proportion of defective units.

frequency distribution—Set of all the various values from individual observations and the frequency of their occurrence in the sample population. Statistically, a display of a large volume of data so that the central tendency (average or mean) and distribution are clear.

functional organization—An organization organized by discrete functions—for example, marketing/sales, engineering, production, finance, and human resources.

funnel experiment—An experiment that demonstrates the effects of tampering. Marbles are dropped through a funnel in an attempt to hit a flat-surfaced target below. The experiment shows that adjusting a stable process to compensate for an undesirable result, or an extraordinarily good result, will produce output that is worse than if the process had been left alone.

future reality tree—A technique used in the application of Goldratt's theory of constraints to show what to change and how to identify any new unfavorable aspects to be addressed prior to the change.

G

gage blocks—Standards of precise dimensions, used in combination to form usable length combinations. The blocks are traceable to national standards in the country of use (NIST in the United States).

gage repeatability and reproducibility (GR&R)—The evaluation of a gaging instrument's accuracy by determining whether the measurements taken with the gage are repeatable (that is, there is close agreement among a number of consecutive measurements of the output for the same value of the input under the same operating conditions) and reproducible (that is, there is close agreement among repeated measurements of the output for the same value of input made under the same operating conditions over a period of time). *Repeatability* is the variation in results on a single gage when the same part is measured repeatedly by the same person. *Reproducibility* is the variation from person to person using the same gage. May also go by MSA or measurement systems analysis.

gainsharing—A type of program that rewards individuals financially on the basis of organizational performance.

Gantt chart—A type of bar chart used in process/project planning and control to display planned work and finished work in relation to time. Also called a *milestone chart* when interim checkpoints are added. May be used in the planning stage as well as in tracking progress.

gap analysis—A range of techniques that compares a company's existing state to its desired state (as expressed by its long-term plans) to help determine what needs to be done to remove or minimize the gap between them.

gatekeeper—The role of an individual (often a facilitator) in a group meeting in helping ensure effective interpersonal interactions (for example, someone's ideas are not ignored due to the team moving on to the next topic too quickly).

Gemba (Japanese for workplace)—Management is urged to go to gemba to get out to where the work is being done to better understand a problem and appreciate the process involved in making the product or delivering the service.

geographic information system (GIS)—A computer-based method of collecting and displaying data in relation to a specific point or location on Earth to which each datum is related—the computer program maps the data.

geographic organization—An organization structured by geography, territory, region, or the like.

geometric dimensioning and tolerancing (GDT)—A method used to minimize production costs by considering the functions or relationships of part features in order to define dimensions and tolerances.

goal—A statement of general intent, aim, or desire; it is the point toward which management directs its mission, efforts, and resources; goals are usually nonquantitative. A goal is measured by the objectives supporting the goal.

goal-question-metric (GQM)—A method used to define measurement of a project, process, or product on three levels (conceptual, operational, quantitative).

go/no-go—State of a unit or product. Two parameters are possible: *go* conforms to specifications, and *no-go* does not conform to specifications.

grade—A planned or recognized difference in requirements for quality.

grapevine—The informal communication channels over which information flows within an organization, usually without a known origin and without any confirmation of its accuracy or completeness (sometimes referred to as the *rumor mill*).

Green Belt—An individual trained on the improvement methodology of Six Sigma who will lead a process or quality improvement team.

group dynamics—The interaction (behavior) of individuals within a team.

groupthink—Most or all team members coalesce in supporting an idea or decision that has not been fully explored, or some members secretly disagree but go along with the other members in apparent support.

H

Hawthorne effect—Concept that every change in workplace environment results (initially, at least) in increased productivity. This demonstrates the importance of human factors in motivating the workforce. (Based on studies by Elton Mayo at the Hawthorne Plant of Western Electric Company in Chicago in 1924.)

heijunka—Act of leveling the variety or volume of items produced in a process over time. Used to avoid excessive batching of product types, volume fluctuations, and excess inventory.

hierarchy structure—Describes an organization that is organized around functional departments/product lines or around customers/customer segments and is characterized by top-down management (also referred to as a *bureaucratic model* or *pyramid structure*).

histogram—A graphic summary of variation in a set of data. The pictorial nature of the histogram lets people see patterns that are difficult to see in a simple table of numbers. The histogram is one of the seven tools of quality.

hold point—A point, defined in an appropriate document, beyond which an activity must not proceed without the approval of a designated organization or authority.

horizontal structure—Describes an organization that is organized along a process flow or value-added chain, eliminating hierarchy and functional boundaries (also referred to as *systems structure*).

hoshin kanri, hoshin planning—Japanese-based strategic planning/policy deployment process that involves consensus at all levels as plans are cascaded throughout the organization, resulting in improved actionable plans and continual monitoring and measurement.

house of quality—A diagram (named for its house-shaped appearance) that clarifies the relationships between customer needs and product features. It helps correlate market or customer requirements and analysis of competitive products with higher-level technical and product characteristics and makes it possible to bring several factors into a single figure. Also known as *quality function deployment* (QFD).

human relations theory—A theory focusing on the importance of human factors in motivating employees.

hygiene factors—A term used by Frederick Herzberg to label dissatisfiers. See *dissatisfiers*.

I

IEEE—Institute of Electrical and Electronics Engineers.

imagineering—Creative process used to develop, in the mind's eye, a process without waste.

imperfection—A quality characteristic's departure from its intended level or state without any association to conformance to specification requirements or to the usability of a product or service. See also *blemish*, *defect*, and *nonconformity*.

implied warranty—Implicit promise, not necessarily documented, that states that a product must reasonably operate or comply with the ordinary purposes for which it is intended or used.

in-control process—A process in which the statistical measure being evaluated is in a state of statistical control; that is, the variations among the observed sampling results can be attributed to a constant system of chance/common causes. The process may also be described as *stable*. See also *out-of-control process*.

incremental improvement—Improvements implemented on a continual basis. See *kaizen*.

indicators—Predetermined measures used to determine how well an organization is meeting its customers' needs and its operational and financial performance objectives. Such indicators can be either *leading* or *lagging* indicators. *Indicators* may also refer to devices used to measure lengths or flow.

indirect customers—Customers who do not receive process output directly but are affected if the process output is incorrect or late.

individual development—A process that may include education and training but also includes many additional interventions and experiences to enable an individual to grow and mature intellectually and emotionally, as well as professionally.

informal communication—The unofficial communication that takes place in an organization as people talk freely and easily; examples include impromptu meetings and personal conversations (verbal or e-mail).

information—Data transformed into an ordered format that makes it usable and allows one to draw conclusions.

information system—Technology-based systems used to support operations, aid day-to-day decision-making, and support strategic analysis. Other names often seen include *management information system, decision system, information technology* (IT), *data processing.*

input—Material, product, or service that is obtained from an upstream internal provider or an external supplier and is used by the receiver to produce an output.

inspection—Measuring, examining, testing, and gauging one or more characteristics of a product or service and comparing the results with specified requirements to determine whether conformity is achieved for each characteristic.

intellectual property—The concepts, ideas, thought, processes, and programs that are definable, measurable, and proprietary in nature (includes copyrights, patents, trademarks, computer software).

interactive multimedia—A term encompassing technology that allows the presentation of facts and images with physical interaction by the viewers; for example, taking a simulated certification exam on a computer or receiving training embedded in transaction processing software.

interdependence—Shared dependence between two or more items.

interfaces—Interaction between individuals, departments, work units, outside organizations, and so on that allows the meaningful exchange of information.

intermediate customers—Distributors, dealers, or brokers who make products and services available to the end user by repairing, repackaging, reselling, or creating finished goods from components or subassemblies.

internal audit—An audit conducted within an organization by members of the organization to measure its strengths or weaknesses against its own procedures and/or external standards—a first-party audit.

internal capability analysis—A detailed view of the internal workings of the organization; for example, determining how well the capabilities of the organization match to strategic needs.

internal customer—The recipient (person or department) of another person's or department's output (product, service, or information) within an organization. See also *external customer.*

internal failure costs—Costs associated with defects found before the product or service is delivered.

internal rate of return (IRR)—An organization's acceptable rate of return from investments. Also, the discount rate that causes net present value to equal zero.

International Organization for Standardization (ISO)—Based in Geneva, Switzerland, it is the worldwide controller of ISO standards.

interrelationship digraph—A management and planning tool that displays the relationship between factors in a complex situation. It identifies meaningful categories from a mass of ideas and is useful when relationships are difficult to determine. May also be called a relations diagram.

intervention—An action taken by a leader or a facilitator to support the effective functioning of a team or work group.

inventory—A term encompassing all forms of physical accumulation of materials, supplies, work in process, and finished goods held in temporary storage or warehoused. The term is also used by Goldratt to mean "all the money the system invests in things it intends to sell" (see *theory of constraints*).

Ishikawa diagram—See *cause-and-effect diagram.*

is/is not matrix—A tool that helps to differentiate what is distinctive about a problem.

ISO—A prefix for a series of standards published by the International Organization for Standardization. *Iso* also means *equal* in Greek.

ISO 14000 series—A set of standards and guidelines relevant to developing and sustaining an environmental management system.

ISO 9000 series standards—A set of individual but related international standards and guidelines on quality management and quality assurance developed to help companies effectively document the quality system elements to be implemented to maintain an efficient quality system. The standards, initially published in 1987 and revised in 1994, 2000, and 2008–2009, are not specific to any particular industry, product, or service. The standards were developed by the International Organization for Standardization, a specialized international agency for standardization composed of the national standards bodies of countries worldwide.

issue log—A log that documents all of the project's issues, including problems, gaps, inconsistencies, delays, quality concerns, and conflicts that require action. The issue log is used to record, track, and manage issues from creation, through analysis, to resolution.

iterative project management methodology—A project management methodology in which agile or iterative methods are used and where small groups of functionality are implemented quickly, and then the process iterates for the next set of a small group of functionality.

J

jidoka—Japanese method of autonomous control involving the adding of intelligent features to machines to start or stop operations as control parameters are reached and to signal operators when necessary.

job aid—Any device, document, or other media that can be provided to a worker to aid in correctly performing tasks (for example, a laminated setup instruction card hanging on a machine, photos of product at different stages of assembly, or a metric conversion table).

job description—A narrative explanation of the work, responsibilities, and basic requirements of a job.

job enlargement—Expanding the variety of tasks performed by an employee.

job enrichment—Increasing the worker's responsibilities and authority in work to be done.

job specification—A list of the important functional and quality attributes (knowledge, skills, aptitudes, and personal characteristics) needed to succeed in the job.

joint planning meeting—A meeting involving representatives of a key customer and the sales and service team for that account to determine how better to meet the customer's requirements and expectations.

Juran's trilogy—See *quality trilogy.*

JUSE—Union of Japanese Scientists and Engineers.

just-in-time (JIT) manufacturing—An optimal material requirement planning system for a manufacturing process in which there is little or no manufacturing material inventory on hand at the manufacturing site and little or no incoming inspection.

just-in-time training—Providing job training coincidental with, or immediately prior to, an employee's assignment to a new or expanded task.

K

kaikaku—A Japanese term that means a breakthrough improvement in eliminating waste.

kaizen—A Japanese term that means incremental and unending improvement by doing little things better and setting and achieving increasingly higher standards. The term was made famous by Masaaki Imai in his book *Kaizen: The Key to Japan's Competitive Success.*

kaizen blitz/event—An intense, short-time-frame (typically three to five consecutive days) team approach to employ the concepts and techniques of continual improvement (for example, to reduce cycle time or increase throughput).

kanban—A system inspired by Taiichi Ohno's (Toyota) visit to a U.S. supermarket. The system signals the need to replenish stock or materials or to produce more of an item (also called a *pull* approach).

Kano model—A representation of the three levels of customer satisfaction defined as dissatisfaction, neutrality, and delight. Named after Noriaki Kano.

kansei engineering—A Japanese term referring to the translation of consumers' psychological feelings about a product into perceptual design elements (sensory engineering, emotional usability).

KESAA factors—See *competence.*

key result area (KRA)—Critical customer requirements that are important for the organization's success. Also known as *key success factor* (KSF).

KJ method—See *affinity diagram.*

knowledge management—Involves transforming data into information and the acquisition or creation of knowledge, as well as the processes and technology employed in identifying, categorizing, storing, retrieving, disseminating, and using information and knowledge for the purposes of improving decisions and plans.

L

lateral thinking—A process that includes recognizing patterns, becoming unencumbered with old ideas, and creating new ones.

LCALI—A process for operating a listening post system for capturing and using formerly unavailable customer data. LCALI stands for *listen, capture, analyze, learn,* and *improve.*

leader—An individual recognized by others as the person to lead an effort. Normally one cannot be a leader without one or more followers. The term is often used interchangeably with *manager*. A leader may or may not hold an officially designated management-type position. See *manager*.

leadership—An essential factor in a quality improvement effort. Organization leaders must establish a vision, communicate that vision to those in the organization, and provide the tools, knowledge, and motivation necessary to accomplish the vision.

lean approach/lean thinking—A focus on reducing cycle time and waste using a number of different techniques and tools—for example, value stream mapping and identifying and eliminating monuments and non-value-added steps.

lean manufacturing—Applying the lean approach to improving manufacturing operations.

learner-controlled instruction (LCI)—When a learner works without an instructor, at an individual pace, building mastery of a task. Computer-based training is a form of LCI. Also called *self-directed learning*.

learning curve—The time it takes to achieve mastery of a task, a body of knowledge, or a skill.

learning organization—An organization that has a policy to continue to learn and improve its products, services, processes, and outcomes—"an organization that is continually expanding its capacity to create its future" (Senge).

lesson plan—A detailed plan created to guide an instructor in delivering training and/ or education.

lessons learned register—A list that documents the knowledge gained from reflecting on activities, processes, or projects after they have been implemented, through performing root cause analysis of identified issues or defects, or through other empirical analysis methods. That knowledge may then be used to prevent future problems or repeat successful actions.

life cycle—A product life cycle is the total time frame from product concept to the end of its intended use; a project life cycle is typically divided into six stages: concept, planning, design, implementation, evaluation, and closeout.

life history curve—See *bathtub curve*.

linear project management methodology—A project management approach where the entire sequence of activities and phases are performed in a linear fashion. The entire set of defined requirements are elicited, designed, developed, tested, implemented, and made operational.

linear regression—The mathematical application of the concept of a scatter diagram where the correlation is actually a cause-and-effect relationship.

linear responsibility matrix—A matrix providing a three-dimensional view of project tasks, responsible person, and level of relationship.

line balancing—A method of proportionately distributing workloads within the value stream to meet *takt* time.

listening post data—Customer data and information gathered from designated organizational listening posts.

little q, Big Q—The difference between managing for quality in a limited capacity (q) to managing for quality across all business processes and products (Q). Attributed to J. M. Juran.

long-term goals—Goals that an organization hopes to achieve in the future, usually in three to five years. They are commonly referred to as *strategic goals*.

lost customer analysis—Analysis to determine why a customer or segment of customers was lost or defected to a competitor.

lot—A defined quantity of product accumulated under conditions that are considered uniform for sampling purposes.

lot tolerance percent defective (LTPD)—See *consumer's risk*.

lower control limit (LCL)—Control limit for points below the central line in a control chart.

M

macroprocesses—Broad, far-ranging processes that often cross functional boundaries.

maintainability—The probability that a given maintenance action for an item under given usage conditions can be performed within a stated time interval when the maintenance is performed under stated conditions using stated procedures and resources. Maintainability has two categories: *serviceability*, the ease of conducting scheduled inspections and servicing, and *repairability*, the ease of restoring service after a failure.

Malcolm Baldrige National Quality Award (MBNQA)—Earned by the organization qualifying under the criteria of the Baldrige Performance Excellence Program of NIST.

management by fact—A business philosophy that decisions should be based on data.

management by policy—The organizational infrastructure that ensures that the right things are done at the right time.

management by walking around (MBWA)—A manager's planned, but usually unannounced, walk-through of the organization to gather information from employees and make observations; may be viewed in a positive light by virtue of giving employees opportunity to interact with top management; has the potential of being viewed negatively if punitive action is taken as a result of information gathered.

management levels—A typical hierarchy of management levels is top management (executive level, upper management, top team), middle management (directors, general managers, plant managers, department managers), and first-level supervision (persons directly supervising workers).

management representative—A person appointed to act on management's behalf to manage the quality/environment system. Also, this person usually handles the interface with a registration body.

management responsibility categories—Planning, organizing, staffing, directing, and controlling (POSDC).

management review—Scheduled formal review and evaluation by management of the status and adequacy of the quality/environmental management system(s) in relation to the organization's strategic objectives and policies.

management styles—The predominant personal styles used by managers; styles may be based on prevalent management theories and assumptions about people. Style categories include authoritarian, autocratic, combative, conciliatory, consensual, consultative, democratic, disruptive, ethical, facilitating, intimidating, judicial, laissez-faire, participative, promotional, secretive, shared, or shareholder management.

management training—Usually refers to training and/or education provided to any management or professional-level person from frontline supervision up to, but usually not including, executives.

manager—An individual who manages and is responsible for resources (people, facilities, equipment, material, money, time). A person officially designated with a management-type position title. A manager is granted authority from above, whereas a leader's role is derived by virtue of having followers. The terms *manager* and *leader* are often and unfortunately used interchangeably.

market-perceived quality—The customer's opinion of your products or services as compared to those of your competitors.

Master Black Belt (MBB)—Six Sigma quality expert responsible for strategic implementation within the organization. The MBB is qualified to instruct other Six Sigma Black Belts and Green Belts on the methodologies, tools, and applications in all functions and levels of the organization, and acts as a resource on process management.

material review board (MRB)—A quality control committee or team, usually employed in manufacturing or other materials-processing installations, that has the responsibility and authority to deal with items or materials that do not conform to fitness-for-use specifications. An equivalent, the *error review board*, is sometimes used in software development.

matrix chart/diagram—A management and planning tool that shows the relationships among various groups of data; it yields information about the relationships and the importance of task/method elements of the subjects. Typically, a matrix displays the relationship between two topics—with, perhaps, the impact of a third element—such as a personnel requirements matrix. There are many varieties of matrices—for example, see *quality function deployment*.

matrix structure—Describes an organization that is organized into functional and product/project departments; it brings together teams of people to work on projects and is driven by product or project scope. Basically, functional departments obtain, train, maintain, and sustain the appropriate people, who are deployed, as needed, to product/project departments or work units. A given person may be based in a functional department (say, software developers) and deployed to one or more product/project work teams (say, a new product development team and also a team working on improving the QMS).

mean—A measure of central tendency, the arithmetic average of all measurements in a data set.

means (in hoshin planning usage)—The step of identifying the ways by which multi-year objectives will be met, leading to the development of action plans.

mean time between failures (MTBF)—The average time interval between failures for repairable product for a defined unit of measure (for example, operating hours, cycles, or miles).

measurement—Refers to the reference standard or sample used for the comparison of properties.

median—The middle number or center value of a set of data when all the data are arranged in sequence.

mentor—A person who voluntarily assumes a role of trusted advisor and teacher to another person. The mentor may or may not be the mentored person's organizational superior or even in the same organization. Usually, the only reward the mentor receives is self-gratification in having helped someone else.

metric—A standard of measurement or evaluation.

metrology—Science and practice of measurements.

micromanaging—Managing every little detail (for example, executive approving requisition for paper clips).

microprocesses—Narrow processes made up of detailed steps and activities that could be accomplished by a single person.

milestone—A specific time when a critical event is to occur; a symbol placed on a milestone chart to locate the point when a critical event is to occur. (An upward-pointing triangle signifies the scheduled time of an event; a downward-pointing triangle signifies completion of an event.)

milestone chart—A Gantt chart on which event starting and ending times are indicated.

milestone list—A list of key scheduled dates for designated project events (milestones) used to determine if key progress checkpoints have been reached on schedule.

mind mapping—A technique for creating a visual representation of a multitude of issues or concerns by forming a map of the interrelated ideas.

mission statement—An explanation of the core purpose or reasons for existing as an organization; it provides the focus for the organization and defines its scope of business. The mission may define customers or markets served, distinctive competence, or technologies used.

mistake proofing—See *poka-yoke*.

mitigation—Risk response strategy that decreases risk by lowering the probability of a risk event's occurrence or reduces the effect of the event should it occur.

mode—The value that occurs most frequently in a data set.

moment of truth (MOT)—An MOT is described by Jan Carlzon, former CEO of Scandinavian Air Services in the 1980s, as "any episode where a customer comes into contact with any aspect of your company, no matter how distant, and by this contact, has an opportunity to form an opinion about your company."

monitoring—Systematic and periodic or continuous surveillance or testing of a product or process to determine the level of compliance with industry, engineering, or regulatory requirements. No action is implied.

monument—The point in a process that necessitates a product waiting in a queue before processing further; a barrier to continuous flow.

motivation—Two types of motivation are *extrinsic* and *intrinsic*. Motivating a person means providing a work environment in which the person feels motivated; that is, one person cannot directly motivate another person.

muda—(Japanese). An activity that consumes resources but creates no value; the seven categories of muda (waste) are correction, processing, inventory, waiting, overproduction, internal transport, and wasted motion.

multi-attribute evaluation—Simpler than QFD, this process rank orders and weights customer requirements relative to the competition. In addition, it estimates the cost of each requirement in order to prioritize improvement actions.

multivariate control chart—A control chart for evaluating the stability of a process in terms of the levels of two or more variables or characteristics.

multivoting—A decision-making tool that enables a group to sort through a long list of ideas to identify priorities.

murmurs—A technique to gather information on consumer behavior by watching customers use the product or service.

Myers-Briggs Type Indicator (MBTI)—A method and instrument for identifying a person's personality type based on Carl Jung's theory of personality preferences.

mystery shopper—A person who pretends to be a regular shopper in order to get an unrestrained view of how a company's service process works.

N

n—Sample size (the number of units in a sample).

NAICS—North American Industry Classification System; a system replacing the Standard Industrial Classification (SIC), used to classify organizations according to the products or services produced.

natural team—A work group having responsibility for a particular process.

n-**chart**—Number defective chart for attribute data, used where each unit is inspected from a given lot.

negotiation—A process in which individuals or groups work together to achieve common goals.

net present value (NPV)—A discounted cash flow technique for finding the present value of each future year's cash flow.

next operation as customer (NOAC)—Concept that the organization comprises service/product providers and service/product receivers, or internal customers.

NIST—National Institute of Standards and Technology (United States).

nominal group technique—A technique similar to brainstorming, used by teams to generate ideas on a particular subject. Team members are asked to silently come up with as many ideas as possible and write them down. Each member is then asked to share one idea, which is recorded. After all the ideas are recorded, they are discussed and prioritized by the group.

nonconformity—The result of nonfulfillment of a specified requirement. See also *blemish*, *defect*, and *imperfection*.

nondestructive testing (NDT) and evaluation—Testing and evaluation methods that do not damage or destroy the product being tested.

non-value-added—Tasks or activities that can be eliminated with no deterioration in product or service functionality, performance, or quality in the eyes of the customer.

norm (behavioral)—Expectation of how a person or group will behave in a given situation based on established protocols, rules of conduct, or accepted social practices.

normal distribution—A bell-shaped distribution for continuous data where most of the data are concentrated around the average, and it is equally likely that an observation will occur above or below the average.

np-**chart**—A control chart for attribute data showing the number of defective units in a subgroup. Requires a constant subgroup size.

O

objective—A quantitative statement of future expectations and an indication of when the expectations should be achieved; it supports goals, clarifying and measuring what people must accomplish.

objective evidence—Verifiable qualitative or quantitative observations, information, records, or statements of fact pertaining to the quality of an item or service or to the existence and implementation of a quality system element.

objective setting—See *S.M.A.R.T. W.A.Y.*

observation—An item or incidence of objective evidence found during an audit.

OC (operating characteristic) curve—For a sampling plan, the OC curve indicates the probability of accepting a lot based on the sample size to be taken and the fraction defective in the batch.

one-to-one marketing—The concept of knowing customers' unique requirements and expectations and marketing to these. See also *customer relationship management.*

on-the-job training (OJT)—Training conducted at the workstation, typically done one-on-one.

open book management—An approach to managing that exposes employees to the organization's financial information, provides instruction in business literacy, and enables employees to better understand their role and contribution and its impact on the organization.

operating characteristic curve—See *OC curve.*

operating expense—All the money the system spends turning inventory into throughput (Goldratt's theory of constraints).

optimization—Achieving planned process results that meet the needs of the customer and supplier alike and minimize their combined costs.

organization culture—The collective beliefs, values, attitudes, manners, customs, behaviors, and artifacts unique to an organization.

organization development (OD)—An organization-wide (usually) planned effort, managed from the top, to increase organization effectiveness and health through interventions in the organization's processes using behavioral science knowledge and methodologies.

original equipment manufacturer (OEM)—An organization that uses product components from one or more other outside organizations to build a product it sells under its own name and brand. For example, an organization that furnishes the completed seats that are installed in the automobile that is sold under the auto assembler's brand is an OEM. Sometimes the term is misused to refer to the outside organization that supplies only components.

OSHA—Occupational Safety and Health Administration (United States).

outcome—The measurable result of a project, a quality initiative, or an improvement. Usually, some time passes between the completion of the action and the realization of the outcome—for example, improved productivity, quality, customer satisfaction, profits, and so on.

out-of-control process—A process in which the statistical measure being evaluated is not in a state of statistical control (that is, the variations among the observed sampling results cannot all be attributed to a constant system of chance causes; special or assignable causes exist). See also *in-control process*.

out of spec—A term used to indicate that a unit does not meet a given specification.

output—The deliverables resulting from a process, project, quality initiative, improvement, and so on. Outputs include data, information, documents, decisions, and tangible products. Outputs are generated both from the planning and management of the activity and the delivered product, service, or program. *Output* is also the item, document, or material delivered by an internal provider (supplier) to an internal receiver (customer).

outsourcing—A strategy and an action to relieve an organization of processes and tasks in order to reduce costs, improve quality, reduce cycle time (for example, by parallel processing), reduce the need for specialized skills, and increase efficiency. Often, the primary intent is to save money through cheaper labor costs.

overall equipment effectiveness (OEE)—Method for measuring effectiveness and efficiency of processes.

P

panels—Groups of customers recruited by an organization to provide ad hoc feedback on performance or product development ideas.

paradigm—The standards, rules, attitudes, culture, and so on that influence the way an organization lives and behaves.

paradigm shift—Advent and acceptance of a totally new model that is theory or custom shattering and displaces and/or discredits older theories and models—for example, a major organizational culture change such as adopting the BPEP criteria as the new business model.

parallel structure—Describes an organizational model in which groups, such as quality circles or a quality council, exist in the organization in addition to and simultaneously with the line organization. Also referred to as *collateral structure*.

parameter design (Taguchi)—The use of design of experiments in identifying the major contributors to variation.

Pareto chart—A basic tool used to graphically rank causes from most significant (or frequent) to least significant (or frequent). It utilizes a vertical bar graph in which the bar height reflects the frequency or impact of causes.

Parkinson's law—States that work expands to fit the organization developed to perform it, and there is a tendency for each work unit within the organization to try to build up its importance by expanding the number of jobs and personnel it controls. Sometimes expressed as "work expands to fit the available time."

participative management—A style of managing whereby the manager tends to work from theory Y assumptions about people, involving the workers in decisions made. See *theory Y.*

partnership/alliance—A strategy and a formal relationship between a supplier and a customer to engender cooperation for their mutual benefit, such as reducing costs of ownership, maintenance of minimum stocks, just-in-time deliveries, joint participation in design, exchange of information on materials and technologies, new production methods, quality improvement strategies, and the exploitation of market synergy.

payback period—The number of years it will take the results of a project or capital investment to recover the investment from net cash flows.

***p*-chart**—Fraction defective chart (also called a *proportion chart* or *percent chart*).

PDSA cycle—Plan-do-study-act cycle (a variation of PDCA). See *plan-do-check-act cycle.*

performance appraisal/evaluation—A formal method of measuring employees' progress against performance standards and providing feedback to them.

performance management system—A system that supports and contributes to the creation of high-performance work and work systems by translating behavioral principles into procedures.

performance plan—A performance management tool that describes desired performance and provides a way to assess the performance objectively.

PERT (program/project evaluation and reporting technique) chart—An enhanced AND that graphically demonstrates the relationship among project elements. Unlike the critical path method (CPM), PERT uses three time estimates rather than one.

phase gate review—A periodic review of the project deliverables, typically at the end of the phase, to assess whether the project is making appropriate progress and if it should progress into the next phase.

physical resource assignments—A list of the materials, equipment, supplies, locations, and other physical resources that are planned for use during the project.

pilot test—Small-scale implementation of a process or an operation to test its capability, design, and performance to requirements.

plan-do-check-act (PDCA) cycle—A four-step process for quality improvement. In the first step (*plan*), a plan to effect improvement is developed. In the second step (*do*), the plan is carried out, preferably on a small scale. In the third step (*check*), the effects of the plan are observed. As part of the last step (*act*), the results are studied to determine what was learned and what can be predicted. The plan-do-check-act cycle is sometimes referred to as the Shewhart cycle because Walter A. Shewhart discussed the concept in his book *Statistical Method from the Viewpoint of Quality Control* and as the Deming cycle because W. Edwards Deming introduced the concept in Japan. The Japanese subsequently called it the Deming cycle. Sometimes referred to as *plan-do-study-act* (PDSA).

Poisson distribution—A distribution used for discrete data, applicable when there are many opportunities for occurrence of an event but a low probability (less than 0.10) on each trial.

poka-yoke—(Japanese). A term that means to mistake proof a process by building safeguards into the system that avoid or immediately find errors. It comes from *poka*, which means *error*, and *yokeru*, which means *to avoid*.

PONC—Price of nonconformance: the cost of not doing things right the first time.

population—A group of people, objects, observations, or measurements about which one wishes to draw conclusions.

portfolio analysis—A process of comparing the value of proposed projects or acquisitions relative to the financial impacts on current projects as well as the potential for impact on resources of the proposed projects or acquisitions.

P_{pk}—Potential process capability statistic used in the validation stage of a new product launch (uses the same formula as C_{pk}, but a higher value is expected due to the smaller time span and fewer data from the sample).

ppm—Parts per million.

precision—A characteristic of measurement that addresses the consistency or repeatability of a measurement system when the identical item is measured a number of times.

precontrol—A control process, with simple rules, based on tolerances. It is effective for any process in which a worker can measure a quality characteristic (dimension, color, strength) and can adjust the process to change that characteristic and where there is either continuous output or discrete output totaling three or more pieces.

prerequisite tree—A technique used to identify obstacles in the application of Goldratt's theory of constraints.

prevention costs—Costs incurred to keep internal and external failure costs and appraisal costs to a minimum.

prevention versus detection—A term used to contrast two types of quality activities. *Prevention* refers to those activities designed to prevent nonconformances in products and services. *Detection* refers to those activities designed to detect nonconformances already in products and services. Another phrase used to describe this distinction is *designing-in quality versus inspecting-in quality*.

preventive action—Reviewing procedures, processes, and products/services to evaluate risks and take action to eliminate the potential causes of a nonconformity, defect, or other undesirable situation in order to prevent occurrence.

primary customer—The individual or group who directly receives the output of a process.

principled negotiation—Based on a win-win orientation, it includes:

- Separate the people from the problem.
- Focus on interest, not position.
- Understand what both sides want to achieve.
- Invent options for mutual gain.
- Insist on objective criteria.

priorities matrix—A tool used to choose between several options that have many useful benefits but where not all of them are of equal value.

probability—Likelihood of occurrence.

probability distribution—A mathematical formula that relates the values of characteristics to their probability of occurrence in a population.

problem-solving—A rational process for identifying, describing, analyzing, and resolving situations in which something has gone wrong without explanation.

problem-solving model seven steps—(1) identify the problem; (2) list possible root causes; (3) search out the most likely root causes; (4) identify potential solutions; (5) select and implement a solution; (6) follow up to evaluate the effect; (7) standardize the process.

procedure—A document that answers the questions: What has to be done? Where is it to be done? When is it to be done? Who is to do it? Why do it? (contrasted with a work instruction, which answers, How is it to be done? With what materials and tools is it to be done?) In the absence of a work instruction, the instructions may be embedded in the procedure.

process—An activity or group of activities that takes an input, adds value to it, and provides an output to an internal or external customer; a planned and repetitive sequence of steps by which a defined product or service is delivered.

process analysis—Defining and quantifying the process capability from data derived from mapping and measurement of the work performed by the process.

process capability—A statistical measure of the inherent process variability for a given characteristic. See C_p, C_{pk}, and P_{pk}.

process capability index—The value of the tolerance specified for the characteristic divided by the process capability. There are several types of process capability indexes, including the widely used C_p and C_{pk}.

process control—Methodology for keeping a process within prescribed boundaries and minimizing the inherent variation in the process.

process decision program chart (PDPC)—A management and contingency planning tool that identifies all events that can go wrong and the appropriate countermeasures for these events. It graphically represents all sequences that can lead to an undesirable effect.

process improvement—The act of changing a process to reduce variability and cycle time and make the process more effective, efficient, and productive.

process improvement team (PIT)—A natural work group or cross-functional team whose responsibility is to achieve needed improvements in existing processes. The life span of the team is based on the completion of the team's purpose and specific objectives.

process management—The collection of practices used to implement and improve process effectiveness; it focuses on holding the gains achieved through process improvement and assuring process integrity.

process mapping—The flowcharting of a work process in detail, including key control measurements.

process organization—A form of departmentalization where each department specializes in one phase of the process.

process owner—The manager or leader who is responsible for ensuring that a total process is effective and efficient.

process quality audit—An analysis of elements of a process and appraisal of completeness, correctness of conditions, and probable effectiveness.

process reengineering—See *reengineering*.

process village—Refers to an area where machines are grouped by type of operation performed by the machines (contrast with a cell layout).

producer's risk—For a sampling plan, the probability of not accepting a lot, the quality of which has a designated numerical value representing a level that is generally desirable. Usually, the designated value will be the acceptable quality level. Also called *alpha risk* and *type 1 error*.

production part approval process (PPAP)—Documents used to demonstrate to the customer that the new product/process is ready for full-blown production and to obtain approval to release it for production. Started in the automotive industry and is now moving into usage in other industries.

productivity—The amount of resources used to produce a product.

product life cycle management (PLM)—Concern for a product's viability, reliability, use, and disposition from its design through manufacturing, delivery, customer use, and ultimate discard.

product organization—A departmentalization where each department focuses on a specific product type or family.

product orientation—A tendency to see customers' needs in terms of a product they want to buy, not in terms of the services, value, or benefits the product will produce.

product quality audit—A quantitative assessment of conformance to required product characteristics.

product/service liability—The obligation of a company to make restitution for loss related to personal injury, property damage, or other harm caused by its product or service.

product warranty—The organization's stated policy that it will replace, repair, or reimburse a customer for a defective product, providing the product defect occurs under certain conditions and within a stated period of time.

professional development plan—An individual development tool for an employee. Working together, the employee and management create a plan that coordinates the individual's career needs and aspirations with organizational demands.

profit and loss statement—A financial statement showing the income and expenses resulting in a profit or loss for an organization within a specified period of time.

profound knowledge, system of—As defined by W. Edwards Deming, states that learning cannot be based on experience only; it requires comparisons of results to a prediction, plan, or an expression of theory. Predicting why something happens is essential to understand results and to continually improve. The four components of the system of profound knowledge are appreciation for a system, knowledge of variation, theory of knowledge, and understanding of psychology.

program evaluation and review technique (PERT)—An event-oriented project management planning and measurement technique that utilizes an arrow diagram

(AND) to identify all major project events and demonstrates a range of times needed to complete a project. It uses three time estimates on each project activity: optimistic, most likely, and pessimistic.

project—A temporary endeavor undertaken to create a unique product, service, or result (PMI 2017).

project calendars—Calendars that identify working days and/or shifts that are available for scheduling project activities.

project charter—A formal document that describes the project goals, scope, resources, deliverables, and potential benefits used to gain approval to embark on the project.

project communications—All of the reports, minutes, metrics, and other information products used to communicate with various stakeholders during the project.

project life cycle—Six sequential phases of project management: concept, planning, design, implementation, evaluation, and closeout.

project management—The management of activities and events involved throughout a project's life cycle.

project plan—All the documents that compose the details of why the project is to be initiated, what the project is to accomplish, when and where it is to be implemented, who will have responsibility, how the implementation will be carried out, how much it will cost, what resources are required, and how the project's progress and results will be measured.

project schedule—A listing of the project's activities with each activity's planned start and end dates, duration, assigned staff, and assigned resources. The project schedule may also include milestone dates.

project schedule network diagram—A graphic representation that shows each activity's predecessor/successor relationships (dependencies), including lag times between the activities in a project schedule. (Also called an activity network diagram or AND.)

project scope statement—The description of the project's boundaries, defining what is included within the project, along with a list of the project's major deliverables, assumptions, and constraints. The project scope statement may also describe any identified project limitations, including any items discussed with stakeholders that were determined to be outside the scope of the project.

project team—A designated group of people working together to produce a planned project's outputs and ultimate outcome.

project team assignments—A list of the project team members with their assigned roles and responsibilities.

psychographic customer characteristics—Variables among buyers in the consumer market that address lifestyle issues and include consumer interests, activities, and opinions.

pull system—See *kanban*.

Q

quality—A subjective term for which each person has his or her own definition. In technical usage, quality can have two primary meanings: (1) the characteristics of a product or service that bear on its ability to satisfy stated or implied needs, and (2) a product or service free of deficiencies.

quality assessment—The process of identifying business practices, attitudes, and activities that are enhancing or inhibiting the continual achievement of quality improvement in an organization.

quality assurance/quality control (QA/QC)—Two terms that have many interpretations because of the multiple definitions for the words *assurance* and *control*. For example, *assurance* can mean the act of giving confidence, the state of being certain, or the act of making certain; *control* can mean an evaluation to indicate needed corrective responses, the act of guiding, or the state of a process in which the variability is attributable to a constant system of chance causes. One definition of *quality assurance* is all the planned and systematic activities implemented within the quality system that can be demonstrated to provide confidence that a product or service will fulfill requirements for quality. One definition for *quality control* is the operational techniques and activities used to fulfill requirements for quality. Often, however, *quality assurance* and *quality control* are used interchangeably, referring to the actions performed to ensure the quality of a product, service, or process.

quality audit/assessment—A systematic, independent examination and review to determine whether quality activities and related results comply with planned arrangements and whether these arrangements are implemented effectively and are suitable to achieve the objectives.

quality auditor—A person trained in the auditing/assessing of the appropriate application of quality principles, policies, protocols, and practices supporting the producing of high-quality products or services that meet customer needs and expectations and comply with applicable standards.

quality characteristics—The unique characteristics of products and services by which customers evaluate their perception of quality.

quality circles—Quality improvement or self-improvement study groups composed of a small number of employees—ten or fewer—and their supervisor, who meet regularly with an aim to improve a process.

quality control—See *quality assurance*.

quality control measurement—A document containing the results of quality control activities that provides information about the project's compliance with quality requirements, including regulations and standards.

quality cost reports—A system of collecting quality costs that uses a spreadsheet to list the elements of quality costs against a spread of the departments, areas, or projects in which the costs occur and summarizes the data to enable trend analysis and decision-making. The reports help organizations review prevention costs, appraisal costs, and internal and external failure costs.

quality costs—See *cost of quality*.

quality council—The group driving the quality improvement effort and usually having oversight responsibility for the implementation and maintenance of the quality management system; operates in parallel with the normal operation of the business. Sometimes called *quality steering committee*.

quality engineering—The analysis of a manufacturing system at all stages to maximize the quality of the process itself and the products it produces.

quality function—The entire spectrum of activities through which an organization achieves its quality goals and objectives, no matter where these activities are performed.

quality function deployment (QFD)—A multifaceted matrix in which customer requirements are translated into appropriate technical requirements for each stage of product development and production. The QFD process is often referred to as "listening to the voice of the customer." See also *house of quality*.

quality function mission—Derived from and an input into the organization's mission, the quality function mission statement includes a customer focus, a supplier focus, and an employee focus. The statement represents the basic direction the organization intends to follow regarding quality.

quality improvement—Actions taken in any or all parts of the organization to increase the effectiveness and efficiency of activities and processes in order to provide added benefits to both the organization and its customers.

quality inspection—A number of possible activities used with an intent to ascertain or verify compliance to stated standards, prescribed measurements, or acceptable practices.

quality level agreement (QLA)—Internal service/product providers assist their internal customers in clearly delineating the level of service/product required in quantitatively measurable terms. A QLA may contain specifications for accuracy, completeness, timeliness, usability, service availability, or responsiveness to needs. The QLA provides, in writing, what a service/product receiver expects from an upstream provider, furnishes data to measure whether the quality acceptance level has been met, and is the basis for trending progress toward improvement and ultimate recognition for quality achievement.

quality loss function—A parabolic approximation of the quality loss that occurs when a quality characteristic deviates from its target value. The quality loss function is expressed in monetary units—the cost of deviating from the target increases as a quadratic function the further the quality characteristic moves from the target. The formula used to compute the quality loss function depends on the type of quality characteristic being used. The quality loss function was first introduced in this form by Genichi Taguchi.

quality management—All activities of the overall management function that determine the quality principles, policy, mission, objectives, responsibilities, and practices that when implemented through quality planning, quality assurance, quality control, and continual quality improvement within the quality system provide quality products and services leading to customer satisfaction and organizational benefits.

quality management system (QMS)—The organizational structure, processes, procedures, and resources designed and implemented to maintain and continually improve quality management, products, and services.

quality manual—Document stating the organization's quality policy and describing the quality system of an organization.

quality metrics—Quantitative measurements that give an organization the ability to set objectives and evaluate actual performance versus plan.

quality plan—The document, or documents, stating the specific quality practices, resources, specifications, and sequence of activities relevant to a particular product, project, or contract. The types of documents differ widely depending on the industry, type and size of organization, type of product or service produced, and other factors.

quality planning—The activity of establishing quality objectives and quality requirements.

quality policy—An organization's formally stated beliefs about quality and the acceptable behavior that will lead to the expected result.

quality principles—Rules, guidelines, or concepts that an organization believes in, collectively. The principles are formulated by senior management with input from others and are communicated and understood at every level of the organization.

quality report—A report summarizing the results of one or more quality control activities. A quality report may include items such as: quality related issues; project, process, or product improvement; recommendations; corrective or preventive action recommendations.

quality score chart (Q chart)—A control chart for evaluating the stability of a process in terms of a quality score. The quality score is the weighted sum of the count of events of various classifications in which each classification is assigned a weight.

quality steering committee—See *quality council.*

quality trilogy—A three-point approach to managing for quality. The three points are *quality planning* (developing the products and processes required to meet customer needs), *quality control* (meeting product and process objectives), and *quality improvement* (achieving unprecedented levels of performance). Attributed to Joseph M. Juran.

questionnaire—See *survey.*

queue processing—Processing in batches (contrast with continuous flow processing).

queue time—Wait time of product awaiting the next step in a process.

quincunx—A teaching tool that creates frequency distributions. Beads tumble over numerous horizontal rows of pins, which force the beads to the right or left. After a random journey, the beads are dropped into vertical slots. After many beads are dropped, a frequency distribution results. In the classroom, quincunxes are often used to simulate a manufacturing process. The quincunx was invented by English scientist Francis Galton in the 1890s.

R

radar chart—A visual method to show in graphic form the size of gaps between a number of both current organization performance indicators and ideal performance indicators. The resulting chart resembles a radar screen or a spider's web.

random cause—Cause of variation due to chance and not assignable to any factor. See *common cause.*

random number generator—Used to select a stated quantity of random numbers from a table of random numbers. The resulting selection is then used to pull specific items or records corresponding to the selected numbers to comprise a random sample.

random sampling—A sampling method in which every element in the population has an equal chance of being included.

range—A measure of dispersion, the highest value minus the lowest value.

range chart (R chart)—A control chart in which the subgroup range, *R*, is used to evaluate the stability of the variability within a process.

ratio analysis—The process of relating isolated business numbers, such as sales, margins, expenses, debt, and profits, to make them meaningful.

rational subgroup—A subgroup that is expected to be as free as possible from assignable causes (usually consecutive items).

recognition and reward system—Management's recognition of work done well by individuals or groups and any monetary or nonmonetary reward that is provided to those persons recognized.

record—Document or electronic medium that furnishes objective evidence of activities performed or results achieved—for example, a filled-in form.

red bead experiment—An experiment developed by W. Edwards Deming to illustrate that it is impossible to put employees in rank order of performance for the coming year based on their performance during the past year because performance differences must be attributed to the system, not to employees. Four thousand red and white beads, 20% red, in a bin, and six people are needed for the experiment. The participants' goal is to produce white beads because the customer will not accept red beads. One person begins by stirring the beads and then, blindfolded, selects a sample of fifty beads. That person passes the bin to the next person, who repeats the process, and so on. When everyone has his or her sample, the number of red beads for each is counted. The limits of variation between employees that can be attributed to the system are calculated. Everyone will fall within the calculated limits of variation that could arise from the system. The calculations will show that there is no evidence one person will be a better performer than another in the future. The experiment shows that it would be a waste of management's time to try to find out why, say, John produced four red beads and Jane produced fifteen; instead, management should improve the system, making it possible for everyone to produce more white beads.

reengineering—Completely redesigning or restructuring a whole organization, an organizational component, or a complete process. It's a "start all over again from the beginning" approach, sometimes called a *breakthrough*. In terms of improvement approaches, reengineering is contrasted with incremental improvement (kaizen).

Registrar Accreditation Board (RAB)—An organization that evaluates the competency and reliability of registrar organizations that audit and register client organizations to an appropriate standard, such as ISO 9001 or ISO 14001.

registration—See *certification to a standard*.

regression analysis—A statistical technique for estimating the parameters of an equation relating a particular variable to one or more variables.

reinforcement of behavior—The process of providing positive consequences when an individual is applying the correct knowledge and skills to the job. It has been described as *catching people doing things right and recognizing their behavior*. Caution: Less than desirable behavior can also be reinforced unintentionally.

reliability—In measurement systems analysis, the ability of an instrument to produce the same results over repeated administration—consistency. In reliability engineering it is the probability of a product performing its intended function under stated conditions for a given period of time. See also *mean time between failures.*

reliability engineering—Science of including those factors in the basic design that will ensure the required degree of reliability, availability, and maintainability.

remedial journey—See *diagnostic journey.*

remedy—Something that eliminates or counteracts a problem cause: a solution.

repair—Action taken on a nonconforming product so that it will fulfill the intended usage requirements, although it may not conform to the originally specified requirements. See *rework.*

repeatability and reproducibility (R&R)—A measurement validation process to determine how much variation exists in the measurement system (including the variation in product, the gage used to measure, and the individuals using the gage).

reproducibility—Variation in the average of the measurements made by different appraisers using the same measuring instrument when measuring identical characteristics on the same part.

requirements documentation—Documentation of the requirements to be implemented by the project, including business-level, stakeholder-level and product-level requirements. The definition of what the product or service must do (functional requirements); what the product or service must be (quality and product attributes like reliability, security, safety, performance, usability, accuracy, accessibility, maintainability, supportability, and so on); what restrictions are there on the choices that project staff can make when implementing the product or service (design constraints).

requirements traceability matrix—The documentation of the identified relationships between each requirement's source and the resulting requirement, derived requirements, designs, code, tests, and implemented deliverables.

resistance to change—A person or group's unwillingness to change beliefs, habits, and ways of doing things.

resource breakdown structure—A hierarchical decomposition of the staffing and resources available to the team. When used for staffing, the resource breakdown structure describes the composition of the available staff, which can be used to help identify knowledge availability and identify any potential skill gaps. When used for nonhuman, physical resources, the resource breakdown structure describes the composition of identified resources by category and type.

resource calendar—A resource calendar identifies the availability of specific resources by type or specific attributes. For example, a staffing resource calendar identifies when staff members are available by excluding vacation days and days when staff members are otherwise engaged in other work.

resource requirements—A description of the staff and nonhuman physical resources needed, by types and quantities, to implement an activity, work package, set of work packages, or the entire project.

resource requirements matrix—A tool used to relate the resources required to the project tasks requiring them (used to indicate types of individuals needed, material needed, subcontractors, and so on).

response surface—A graphic representation of the relationship between important independent variables, controlled factors, and a dependent variable.

RETAD—Rapid exchange of tooling and dies; the same concept as *SMED*.

return on assets (ROA)—A measure of the return generated by the earning power of the organization's investment in assets, such as facilities, large equipment, and so on.

return on equity (ROE)—The net profit after taxes, divided by the previous year's tangible stockholders' equity, and then multiplied by one hundred to provide a percentage (also referred to as *return on net worth*).

return on investment (ROI)—An umbrella term for a variety of ratios measuring an organization's business performance and calculated by dividing some measure of return by a measure of investment and then multiplying by one hundred to provide a percentage. In its most basic form, ROI indicates what remains from all money taken in after all expenses are paid.

return on net assets (RONA)—Measure of an organization's earning power from investments in assets calculated by dividing net profit after taxes by the previous year's tangible total assets, multiplied by one hundred to provide a percentage.

return on training investment (ROTI)—A measure of the return generated by the benefits obtained by the organization's investment in training.

reverse engineering—Developing new design specifications by inspection and analysis of the process steps (from last to first) used to produce an existing product.

rework—Action taken on a nonconforming product so that it will fulfill the specified requirements (may also pertain to a service).

right the first time—The concept that it is beneficial and more cost-effective to take the necessary steps up front to ensure that a product or service meets its requirements than to provide a product or service that will need rework or fail to meet customers' needs. In other words, an organization should engage in defect prevention more than defect detection.

risk—A probable event that could have an impact on the successful completion of a project or a product.

risk assessment/management—The process of determining what present or potential risks are possible in a situation (for example, project plan) and what actions might be taken to eliminate or mitigate them.

risk priority number (RPN)—The priority of risks assessed expressed as a number.

risk probability—The likelihood that the risk will occur.

risk register—A list that describes detailed information about the threats and opportunities that may have an impact on the success of the project.

risk report—A report on the sources of overall project risks, with a summary of information about identified risks.

robustness—The condition of a product or process design that remains relatively stable with a minimum of variation even though factors that influence operations or usage, such as environment and wear, are constantly changing.

role playing—A training technique whereby selected participants, designated to assume a particular role, spontaneously interact in an assigned scenario.

root cause analysis (RCA)—A set of quality techniques that can be used to distinguish the cause of defects or problems. It is a structured approach that focuses on finding the decisive or original source of a problem or condition.

run—Consecutive points on one side of the centerline on an SPC chart.

run chart—A line graph showing data collected during a run or an uninterrupted sequence of events. A trend is indicated when the series of collected data points up or down.

S

sales leveling—A strategy of establishing a long-term relationship with customers to lead to contracts for fixed amounts and scheduled deliveries in order to smooth the flow and eliminate surges.

sample—A finite number of items of a similar type taken from a population for the purpose of examination to determine whether all members of the population would conform to quality requirements or specifications.

sample plan—Documented plan showing the scheduled number of samples to be taken from a lot for the purpose of acceptance or rejection of the lot. There are several pre-designed sampling plans available.

sample size—The number of units in a sample chosen from a population.

sampling—The process of drawing conclusions about a population based on a part of the population.

satisfier—Term used to describe the quality level received by a customer when a product or service meets requirements.

SCAMPER—A list of seven questions used by a team to stimulate creativity. *S* for Substitute, *C* for Combine, *A* for Adapt, *M* for Modify/Magnify, *P* for Put to another use, *E* for Eliminate (or Minimize), *R* for Rearrange or Reverse.

scatter diagram—A graphic technique used to analyze the relationship between two variables. Two sets of data are plotted on a graph, with the y-axis being used for the variable to be predicted and the x-axis for the variable being used to make the prediction. The graph will show possible relationships (although two variables might appear to be related, they might not be; those who know most about the variables must make that evaluation). The scatter diagram is one of the seven tools of quality.

scenario planning—A strategic planning process that generates multiple stories/scenarios about possible future conditions, allowing an organization to look at the potential impact on them and different ways they could respond.

schedule data—Measurements and information collected and used to describe and control the project's schedule.

schedule forecast—The expected total schedule for completing all work, expressed as the sum of the actual schedule to date and the estimated future schedule to complete the work.

schedule variance—A measure of the difference between the planned schedule to date and the actual work accomplished to date.

scientific management—Finding the one best way to perform a task so as to increase effectiveness, quality, productivity, and efficiency.

scope—The total number of products, services, processes, people, and operations that will be affected by an initiative, project, or other action.

scope creep—In a project, job, or other work situation, the gradual expansion of responsibilities and workload, often invisible in early stages until the additional time and cost appear as a variation from estimates.

scorecard—Any evaluation device that formally specifies criteria and a means for rating performance.

Scrum—An agile framework that focuses on achieving complex projects quickly.

Scrum development team—the team of participants that work on a project applying the Scrum approach. It is a self-organizing team.

Scrum master—The person in charge of facilitating and guiding the Scrum team to understand the use of the Scrum method.

secondary customer—Individuals or groups from outside the process boundaries who receive process output but who are not the reason for the process's existence.

second-party audit/assessment—An action carried out by a customer on its suppliers.

segmentation—See *customer segmentation*.

SEI capability maturity model—A model used to determine current process capabilities and identify critical software issues for improvement.

selective listening—One hears what one is predisposed to hear.

self-control—Three elements comprise workers' self-control: knowing what they are supposed to do, knowing what they are actually doing and how well, and being able to control the process.

self-directed learning—See *learner-controlled instruction*.

self-inspection—The process by which employees inspect their own work according to specified rules.

self-managed team—A team that requires little supervision and manages itself and the day-to-day work it does; self-directed teams are responsible for whole work processes, with each individual performing multiple tasks.

sensor—In an inspection or monitoring system, a device that detects a condition out of the normal and provides a notification signal of the changed condition.

service level agreement (SLA)—See *quality level agreement*.

setup time—The time taken to change over a process to run a different product or service.

seven basic tools of quality—Tools that help organizations understand their processes in order to improve them. The tools are the cause-and-effect diagram, check sheet, control chart, flowchart, histogram, Pareto chart, and scatter diagram. See individual entries.

seven management tools of quality—The tools used primarily for planning and managing are the activity network diagram (AND), or arrow diagram, affinity diagram (KJ method), interrelationship digraph, matrix diagram, priorities matrix, process decision program chart (PDPC), and tree diagram.

shape—(1) Pattern or outline formed by the relative position of a large number of individual values obtained from a process; (2) removal of material from an item using a shaper or shaver tool.

shared leadership—Management approach in which the manager believes that the many functions of management can be effectively spread among various teams or individuals.

Shewhart cycle—See *plan-do-check-act cycle.*

shift—Abrupt change in an important variable in a process. Examples include broken tools, dropped gages, parts slipping, oil stops flowing, missed ingredient in a mix.

ship-to-stock program—An arrangement with a qualified supplier whereby the supplier ships material directly to the buyer without the buyer's incoming inspection; often a result of evaluating and approving the supplier for certification.

SIC—Standard Industrial Classification. Replaced by *NAICS.*

sigma—Greek letter (Σ) that stands for the standard deviation of a process.

silo—(as in functional silo). An organization where cross-functional collaboration and cooperation is minimal and where the functional silos tend to work toward their own objectives, sometimes to the detriment of the organization as a whole. The allusion to *silo* is the mental picture of a vertical farm structure dedicated to serving one purpose without due regard to its relation to the farm as a whole entity.

single-minute exchange of die (SMED)—A goal to be achieved in reducing the setup time required for a changeover to a new process; the methodologies employed in devising and implementing ways to reduce setup.

single-piece flow—A method whereby the product proceeds through the process one piece at a time rather than in large batches, eliminating queues and costly waste.

SIPOC analysis—A macrolevel analysis of the suppliers, inputs, processes, outputs, and customers.

situational leadership—Leadership theory that maintains that leadership style should change based on the person and the situation involved, with the leader displaying varying degrees of directive and supportive behavior.

Six Sigma approach—A quality philosophy; a collection of techniques and tools for use in reducing variation; a program of improvement.

Six Sigma quality—Term generally used to indicate that a process is well controlled—that is, within process limits $\pm3\Sigma$ from the centerline in a control chart and requirements/tolerance limits $\pm6\Sigma$ from the centerline. The term was originated by Motorola.

skewness—Measure of a distribution's symmetry, a skewed distribution has a longer tail on the right or left side, with its hump (probability) pushed to the opposite side.

skip-level meeting—Evaluation technique that occurs when a member of senior management meets with persons two or more organizational levels below, without the intervening management present, to allow open expression about the effectiveness of the organization.

skip-lot sampling—An acceptance sampling plan in which some set number of lots in a series is accepted without inspection. When the set number of lots is received without inspection, the next lot is inspected unless problems surface that merit all lots being inspected until the problem is eliminated and confidence is restored.

slack time—The time an activity can be delayed without delaying the entire project; it is determined by calculating the difference between the latest allowable date and the earliest expected date. Also called *float*.

S.M.A.R.T. W.A.Y.—A template for setting objectives—*specific, measurable, achievable, realistic, time, worth, assign, yield*.

Society of Automotive Engineers (SAE)—International society for the exchange of ideas advancing the engineering of powered transportation systems.

spaghetti chart—A before-improvement chart of existing steps in a process, with lines showing the many back-and-forth interrelationships (the resulting chart resembles cooked spaghetti). It is used to identify the redundancies and other wasted movements of people and material.

span of control—How many subordinates a manager can effectively and efficiently manage.

special causes—Causes of variation that arise because of special circumstances. They are not an inherent part of a process. Special causes are also referred to as *assignable causes*, as contrasted with *common causes*.

special characteristics—Any characteristics that may affect safety and/or regulatory requirements, degradation, customer satisfaction, annoyance, and/or other criteria.

specification—The engineering requirement used for judging the acceptability of a particular product/service based on product characteristics such as appearance, performance, and size. In statistical analysis, specification refers to the document that prescribes the requirements to which the product or service has to conform.

sponsor—The person who supports a team's plans, activities, and outcomes—the team's "backer." The sponsor provides for resources and helps define the mission and scope to set limits. The sponsor may be the same individual as the "champion."

sprint—A short iteration, usually a month or less, to deliver some functionality.

sprint retrospective—A Scrum meeting at the end of the sprint used to identify improvements to the Scrum and sprint processes.

sprint review meeting—A Scrum meeting held to inspect the product or output of the sprint.

stable process—Process that is in control, with only common causes of variation present.

stakeholder—People, departments, and outside organizations that have an investment or interest in the success of—or may be affected by actions taken by—the organization.

stakeholder analysis—The identification of stakeholders and delineation of their needs.

stakeholder requirements matrix—A matrix for capturing and categorizing the needs of identified stakeholders.

standard—A statement, specification, or quantity of material against which measured outputs from a process may be judged as acceptable or unacceptable.

standard deviation—A calculated measure of variability that shows how much the data are spread around the mean.

standardized work—Documented and agreed-on work instructions and practices that embody the present best-known methods and work sequence to be followed by all performers of each manufacturing or assembly step in a process.

statement of work (SOW)—A description of the actual work to be accomplished. It is derived from the work breakdown structure and, when combined with the project specifications, becomes the basis for the contractual agreement on the project. See also *scope*.

statistical confidence—The level of accuracy expected of an analysis of data. Most frequently it is expressed as either a "95% level of significance" or "5% confidence level." Also called *statistical significance*.

statistical process control (SPC)—The application of statistical techniques to control a process.

statistical quality control (SQC)—The application of statistical techniques to control quality. Often, the term *statistical process control* is used interchangeably with *statistical quality control*, although statistical quality control includes acceptance sampling as well as statistical process control.

statistical thinking—A philosophy of learning and action based on fundamental principles:

* All work occurs in a system of interconnected processes.

* Variation exists in all processes.

* Understanding and reducing variation are vital to improvement.

steering committee—A special group established to guide and track initiatives or projects.

storyboarding—A technique that visually displays thoughts and ideas and groups them into sequenced categories (scenes), making all aspects of a process visible at once. Often used to communicate to others the activities performed by a team as they improve a process.

strategic fit review—A process by which senior managers assess the future of each project or initiative proposed for a particular organization in terms of its ability to advance the mission, strategies, goals, and objectives of the organization.

strategic planning—A process for identifying and setting an organization's long-range vision, mission, goals, and objectives and identifying the actions needed to ultimately achieve the goals.

stratified random sampling—A technique for segmenting (stratifying) a population prior to drawing a random sample from each strata, the purpose being to increase precision when members of different strata would, if not stratified, cause an unrealistic distortion.

structural variation—Variation caused by regular, systematic changes in output, such as seasonal patterns and unaccustomed "blips" in long-term trends.

suboptimization—The result occurring when an individual business function fails to focus on the overall organizational objectives for producing higher efficiency and effectiveness of the entire system and instead focuses on the individual function's improvement.

supplier—Source of materials, services, or information input provided to a process. Internal suppliers provide materials or services to internal customers.

supplier audits—Reviews that are planned and carried out to verify the effectiveness of a supplier's quality program, drive improvement, and increase value.

supplier certification—Process of evaluating the performance of a supplier with the intent of authorizing the supplier to self-certify shipments if such authorization is granted.

supplier performance—The monitoring and measurement of supplier conformance to standards, good manufacturing practices, industry norms, and the customer's purchase contract, often with the use of specialized performance metrics and/or supplier audits.

supplier quality assurance—Confidence that a supplier's product or service will fulfill its customers' needs. This confidence is achieved by creating a relationship between the customer and supplier that ensures that the product will be fit for use with minimal corrective action and inspection. According to J. M. Juran, there are nine primary activities needed: (1) define product and program quality requirements, (2) evaluate alternative suppliers, (3) select suppliers, (4) conduct joint quality planning, (5) cooperate with the supplier during the execution of the contract, (6) obtain proof of conformance to requirements, (7) certify qualified suppliers, (8) conduct quality improvement programs as required, and (9) create and use supplier quality ratings.

supplier selection strategy and criteria—Selection of new suppliers is based on the type and uniqueness of the product or service to be purchased and the total cost. Suppliers of commodity-type items and basic supplies may be selected from directories and catalogs. For more sophisticated products and services, stringent evaluation criteria may be established.

supply chain—The series of processes and/or organizations that are involved in producing and delivering a product to the final user.

supply chain management (SCM)—The process of effectively integrating and managing components of the supply chain.

support systems—Starting with top management commitment and visible involvement, support systems are a cascading series of interrelated practices or actions aimed at building and sustaining support for continual quality improvement.

surveillance—Continual monitoring of a process.

surveillance audit—The regular audits conducted by registrars to confirm that a company registered to the ISO 9001 standard still complies; usually conducted on a six-month or one-year cycle.

survey—Act of examining a process or of questioning a selected sample of individuals to obtain data about a process, product, or service. A survey is generally conducted on a selected sample of a population to collect information about predetermined questions. A customer satisfaction survey is one example. Surveys may be conducted orally by a survey taker, by paper and pencil, by computer online, and so on. Responses are tabulated and analyzed to surface significant areas for change.

SWOT analysis—An assessment of an organization's key *strengths, weaknesses, opportunities,* and *threats.* It considers factors such as the organization's industry, competitive position, functional areas, and management.

symptom—An indication of a problem or opportunity.

system—A network of interdependent actions, processes, or events that work together to accomplish a common mission and goal.

system of profound knowledge (SoPK)—See *profound knowledge.*

systems approach to management—A management theory that views the organization as a unified, purposeful combination of interrelated parts; managers must look at the organization as a whole and understand that activity in one part of the organization affects all parts of the organization (also known as *systems thinking*).

T

tacit knowledge—Unarticulated heuristics and assumptions used by any individual or organization. The knowledge that comes from experience over time.

tactical plans—Short-term plans, usually of one- to two-year duration, that describe actions the organization will take to meet its strategic business plan.

tactics—The techniques and processes that help an organization meet its objectives.

Taguchi loss function—Pertains to where product characteristics deviate from the target intended and losses increase according to a parabolic function. Merely attempting to produce a product within specifications does not prevent loss (loss that is inflicted on society after shipment of a product). Any points beyond the center of the process, in either direction, even though within specifications, Taguchi considers a loss.

Taguchi methods—The American Supplier Institute's trademarked term for the quality engineering methodology developed by Genichi Taguchi. In this engineering approach to quality control, Taguchi calls for off-line quality control, online quality control, and a system of experimental design to improve quality and reduce costs.

takt time—The available production time divided by the rate of customer demand. Operating to takt time sets the production pace to customer demand.

tally sheet—Another name for check sheet.

tampering—Action taken to compensate for variation within the control limits of a stable system. Tampering increases rather than decreases variation, as evidenced in the funnel experiment.

TARP—U.S. Office of Consumer Affairs/Technical Assistance Research Programs.

task—A specific, definable activity to perform an assigned function, usually within a specified time frame.

taxonomy—Classification of terms or objects.

team—A group of two or more people who are organized to work together and held accountable for the accomplishment of a task and specific performance objective.

team-based organization/structure—A function or entire entity that consists primarily of multiple teams.

team building/development—The process of transforming a group of people into a coordinated team and developing the team to achieve its purpose.

team charter—A document that established the team and defines the values, agreements, scope of work, processes, and guidelines of the team.

team dynamics—Interactions that occur among team members under different conditions.

team facilitation—Process of dealing with both the role of the facilitator on the team and the techniques and tools for facilitating the team. See *facilitator*.

team growth, stages of—Refers to the four development stages through which groups typically progress: *forming*, *storming*, *norming*, and *performing*. Knowledge of the stages helps team members accept the normal problems that occur on the path from forming a group to becoming a team. It is suggested that *adjourning* be added to the list to deal with closing down a team's work.

team leader—A person designated to be responsible for the ongoing work and success of the team and keeping the team focused on the task assigned.

team performance evaluation, recognition, and rewards—Special metrics are needed to evaluate the work of a team (to avoid focus on any individual on the team) and as a basis for the recognition and reward for team effort and achievements.

telecommuting—Working individually, or as part of a group, performing at least some work away from the organization's primary location and accomplishing tasks with the aid of electronic technologies.

temporary/ad hoc team—A team, usually small, formed to address a short-term objective or emergency situation.

test and evaluation documents—Documents that define the inputs to the quality control activities, including checklists, requirements traceability, acceptance criteria, test plans, test cases, test procedures, and so on.

theory of constraints (TOC)—Eliyahu Goldratt's theory deals with techniques and tools for identifying and eliminating the constraints (bottlenecks) in a process to achieve greater flow of money.

theory of knowledge (TOK)—A belief that management is about prediction, and people learn not only from experience but also from theory. When people study a process and develop a theory, they can compare their predictions with their observations; profound learning results.

theory X and theory Y—A theory developed by Douglas McGregor that maintains that there are two contrasting assumptions about people, each of which is based on the manager's view of human nature. Theory X managers take a negative view and assume that most employees do not like work and try to avoid it. Theory Y managers take a positive view and believe that employees want to work, will seek and accept responsibility, and can offer creative solutions to organizational problems.

third-party audit—External audits conducted by personnel who are neither employees of the organization nor a supplier but are usually employees of certification bodies or of registrars.

three-sixty-degree (360°) feedback process—A people performance evaluation method that provides feedback from the perspectives of self, peers, direct reports, superiors, customers, and suppliers.

throughput—The rate at which the entire system generates money through sales of product or service (Goldratt's theory of constraints).

throughput time—The total time required (processing + queue) from concept to launch, or from order received to delivery, or raw materials received to delivery to customer.

TickIT—A certification of quality management systems that conform to the requirements of the ISO 9001 standard, specifically pertaining to software development.

tier—Level, rank, sequence.

TJC—The Joint Commission, formerly the Joint Commission on Accreditation of Healthcare Organizations (JCAHO).

TL 9000—Quality management standard series for the telecommunications industry.

tolerance—The variability of a parameter permitted and tolerated above or below a nominal value.

tolerance design (Taguchi)—Provides a rational grade limit for components of a system; determines which parts and processes need to be modified and to what degree it is necessary to increase their control capacity; a method for rationally determining tolerances.

tolerance limit—The maximum and minimum limit values a product may have and still meet engineering or customer requirements.

tool—Any implement or technique used for making a desirable change to materials, process, product, or approach that contributes to a quality product or service. (A narrow definition—a device used by hand, or a fixture in a machine, that cuts, strikes, shapes, marks/tags, positions, polishes, or heat-treats material in a process.)

tool life—Minimum amount of useful production that can be expected from a tool.

top management commitment—Participation and visible involvement of the organization's highest-level officials in their organization's quality improvement efforts.

total productive maintenance (TPM)—Methodologies for reducing and eventually eliminating equipment failure, setup and adjustment, minor stops, reduced speed, product rework, and scrap; preventive maintenance.

total quality management (TQM)—A term initially coined by the Naval Air Systems Command (United States) to describe its management approach to quality improvement. Total quality management (TQM) has taken on many meanings. Simply put, TQM is a management approach to long-term success through customer satisfaction. TQM is based on the participation of all members of an organization in improving processes, products, services, and the culture in which they work. TQM benefits all organization members and society. Various methods for implementing TQM are found within the teachings of such quality leaders as Philip B. Crosby, W. Edwards Deming, Armand V. Feigenbaum, Kaoru Ishikawa, J. M. Juran, and others. The Baldrige Performance Excellence Program (United States) and other criteria-based programs embody the principles of TQM.

traceability—The ability to track the history, application, or location of an item or activity, and like items or activities, by means of recorded identification.

training—The skills that employees need to learn in order to perform or improve the performance of their current job or tasks and the process of providing those skills.

training evaluation—The techniques and tools used and the process of evaluating the effectiveness of training.

training needs assessment—The techniques and tools used and the process of determining an organization's training needs.

transactional leadership—A style of leading whereby the leader sees the work as being done through clear definition of tasks and responsibilities and the provision of resources as needed.

transformational leadership—A style of leading whereby the leader articulates the vision and values necessary for the organization to succeed.

transition tree—A technique used in applying Goldratt's theory of constraints.

tree diagram—A management and planning tool that shows the hierarchy of subtasks required to achieve an objective.

trend—Consecutive points plotted against a time period that show a pattern and help to identify any unexpected occurrences. Trend plotting of sequential data points shows the direction and rate of change of an organization, work unit, or process over time.

trend analysis—The charting of data over time to identify a tendency or direction.

trilogy—See *quality trilogy*.

TRIZ—(Russian). A theory of problem-solving that aids in the solution of inventive problems. A set of analytical and knowledge-based tools that are typically hidden subconsciously in the minds of creative inventors.

t-**test**—A method for testing hypotheses about the population mean; the *t*-statistic measures the deviation between the sample and population means, in terms of the number of standard errors.

type I error—An incorrect decision to reject something (such as a statistical hypothesis or a lot of products) when it is acceptable. Also known as *producer's risk* and *alpha risk*.

type II error—An incorrect decision to accept something when it is unacceptable. Also known as *consumer's risk* and *beta risk*.

U

u-**chart**—Count per unit chart. Attribute control chart used to show the average number of defects in a sample; uses variable sample size. A *c*-chart uses a fixed sample size.

unconditional guarantee—An organizational policy of providing customers unquestioned remedy for any product or service deficiency.

unity of command—The concept that a subordinate should be responsible to only one superior. Note: A matrix-type organization negates this concept.

upper control limit (UCL)—Control limit for points above the central line in a control chart.

upper specification limit (USL)—Maximum limit for dimensions as specified for a product to be acceptable.

USDA—U.S. Department of Agriculture.

V

validation—Confirmation by examination of objective evidence that specific requirements and/or a specified intended use are met.

validity—Refers to the ability of a feedback instrument, and validation action taken, to measure what it was intended to measure. Validity may be measured three ways: (1) criterion related, (2) construct related, and (3) content related.

value-added—Parts of the process that add worth from the external customers' perspective.

value chain—See *supply chain*.

values—Statements that clarify the behaviors that the organization expects in order to move toward its vision and mission. Values reflect an organization's personality and culture.

value stream—The primary actions required to bring a product from concept to placing the product in the hands of the end user.

value stream mapping—The technique for mapping the value stream, typically done for the present perception and then the future perspective.

variable control chart—Data resulting from the measurement of a parameter or a variable. Control charts based on variable data include average (X-*bar*) chart, individuals (X) chart, range (R) chart, sample standard deviation (s) chart, and CUSUM chart.

variable cost—Cost that varies with production quantity, such as material and direct labor.

variables—Quantities that are subject to change.

variable sampling plan—A plan in which a sample is taken and a measurement of a specified quality characteristic is made on each unit. The measurements are summarized into a simple statistic, and the observed value is compared with an allowable value defined in the plan.

variance—The difference between a planned amount (usually money or time) and the actual amount. In math, the measure of dispersion of observations based on the mean of the squared deviations from the arithmetic mean. The square of the standard deviation, given by formula.

variation—A change in data, a characteristic, or a function that is caused by one of four factors: *special causes, common causes, tampering,* or *structural variation.* See individual entries.

velocity—The average rate of productivity per day.

verification—The act of reviewing, inspecting, testing, checking, auditing, or otherwise establishing and documenting whether items, processes, services, or documents conform to specified requirements.

vertically integrate—To bring together more of the steps involved in producing a product in order to form a continuous chain owned by the same firm; typically involves taking on activities that were previously in the external portion of the supply chain.

virtual team—A boundaryless team functioning without a commonly shared physical structure or physical contact, using electronic technology to link the team members.

vision—A statement that explains what the company wants to become and what it hopes to achieve.

visual control—A technique of positioning all tools, parts, production activities, and performance indicators so that the status of a process can be understood at a glance by everyone; providing visual cues to aid the performer in correctly processing a step or series of steps to reduce cycle time, to cut costs, to smooth flow of work, and to improve quality.

vital few, useful many—A term used by J. M. Juran to describe his use of the Pareto principle, which he first defined in 1950. (The principle was used much earlier in economics and inventory control methodologies.) The principle suggests that most effects come from relatively few causes; that is, 80% of the effects come from 20% of the possible causes. The 20% of the possible causes are referred to as the *vital few*; the remaining causes are referred to as the *useful many*. When Juran first defined this principle, he referred to the remaining causes as the *trivial many*, but realizing that no problems are trivial in quality assurance, he changed it to *useful many*.

voice of the customer—The perceived understanding of the customers' needs and expectations (*voice*) interpreted and passed downward throughout the organization to ensure, at all levels, that the organization is responding to the customers' voice.

W

walkabout—A visual group technique used during strategic planning for resolving resource planning conflicts among organizational components.

walk the talk—Not only talking about what one believes in but also being observed acting out those beliefs. Employees' buy-in to the TQM concept is more likely when management is seen involved in the process every day.

warranty—A manufacturers' published statement that defective or deficient product or service experienced by the customer, within a prescribed time period, will be remedied by the manufacturer.

waste—Activities that consume resources but add no value; visible waste (for example, scrap, rework, downtime) and invisible waste (for example, inefficient setups, wait times of people and machines, inventory).

Weibull distribution—A distribution of continuous data that can take on many different shapes and is used to describe a variety of patterns; in relation to the bathtub curve, used to define when the "infant mortality" rate has ended and a steady state has been reached (decreasing failure rate).

WIIFM—"What's in it for me?" Ask and answer WIIFM before suggesting that a change/improvement will be acceptable to affected persons.

win-win—Outcome of a negotiation that results in both parties being better off.

wisdom—The culmination of the continuum from data to information to knowledge to wisdom.

work analysis—The analysis, classification, and study of the way work is done. Work may be categorized as value-added (necessary work), or non-value-added (rework, unnecessary work, idle). Collected data may be summarized on a Pareto chart showing how people within the studied population work. The need for and value of all work is then questioned and opportunities for improvement identified. A time use analysis may also be included in the study.

workbook—A collection of exercises, questions, or problems to be solved during training; a participant's repository for documents used in training (for example, handouts).

work breakdown structure (WBS)—A project management technique by which a project is divided into tasks, subtasks, and units of work to be performed, displayed on a chart.

work group—A team type composed of people from one functional area who work together on a daily basis and whose goal is to improve the processes of their function.

work instruction—A document that answers the question "How is the work to be done?" See *procedure*.

world-class quality—A term used to indicate a standard of excellence; the best of the best.

X

x-axis—Horizontal axis on a control chart, run chart, or other chart.

X-bar chart—Average chart.

Y

y-axis—Vertical axis on a control chart, run chart, or other chart.

yield—Ratio between salable goods produced and the quantity of raw materials and/or components input at the beginning of the process.

Z

zero defects—A performance standard popularized by Philip B. Crosby to address a dual attitude in the workplace: people are willing to accept imperfection in some areas, while in other areas they expect the number of defects to be zero. This dual attitude has developed because of the conditioning that people are human and humans make mistakes. The zero-defects methodology states, however, that if people commit themselves to watching details and avoiding errors, they can move closer to the goal of perfection.

zero investment improvement—Another name for a *kaizen blitz*.

Index

Note: Page numbers followed by *f* or *t* refer to figures or tables, respectively.

A

ABC (activity-based costing), 183, 364, 402*t*
A-B-C analysis, 145–147, 146*f*
ABM (activity-based management), 183
absolutes of quality management (Juran), 321
acceptable quality limit (AQL), 418
acceptance sampling, 417, 440, 532*f*, 533
accommodation, in conflict management, 42, 43*f*
accountability, team member, 66
accrual basis bookkeeping, 175
accuracy, of measurements, 428, 442
Accuride, 389, 391
achieved availability, 441
achievement, as motivation, 38. *See also* rewards and
    recognition
action plans. *See also* corrective and preventive
    action
    process management, 402*t*
    project management, 271*f*–272*f*, 273
    strategic planning, 90*f*, 91, 95, 121–122, 123*f*–124*f*,
      126–127
active listening, 211–212, 215–216
activity-based costing (ABC), 183, 364, 402*t*
activity-based management (ABM), 183
activity network diagrams (AND), 247*t*, 254,
    336–337, 337*f*, 402*t*
ADA (Americans with Disabilities Act), 156, 165
adaptability, of leadership, 20
ad hoc teams, 58
adjourning stage of teams, 65
administration
    administrative expenses, reporting, 177
    management role in, 22
    team, 78
adult learning principles, 556–557
Advanced Product Quality Planning (APQP), 173,
    402*t*
advertising and marketing
    communication via, 215
    data mining for, 431
    information technology informing, 221
    knowledge management for, 198
    management competence with, 24
    marketing function responsibility for, 156

    market segmentation in, 457, 463
    one-to-one marketing, 457, 469
    recruitment, 166, 167
    relationship marketing, 469
    strategic planning for, 89, 463
advisers, 17
affiliation, as motivation, 38
affinity diagrams, 332, 337, 338*f*, 402*t*, 466
agendas, team, 66, 67, 75
agile project management, 234–237. *See also* Scrum
    project management
agility, in process management, 404*t*
Aguayo, Rafael, 445
AI (artificial intelligence), 113, 221
AIAG (Automotive Industry Action Group), 511
Albrecht, Karl, 495
alignment
    mistake-proofing against misalignment, 395
    of performance measures, 130, 225
    of project management with objectives, 232, 236,
      238
alliances, supplier, 527–531
alpha risk (type 1 errors), 417–418
altruism, as motivation, 38
Altshuller, Genrich, 45–46, 359
American Productivity and Quality Center (APQC),
    300, 367
American Society for Quality (ASQ)
    ADDIE training design model, 555
    certification and professional development
      courses of, 169
    CMQ/OE Body of Knowledge (*See* Certified
      Management of Quality/Organizational
      Excellence Body of Knowledge)
    code of ethics, 83–85
    Customer-Supplier Division selection criteria,
      512
    financial management for quality assistance
      from, 174, 185
    Knowledge Center, xxi
    Professional Ethics and Qualifications
      Committee, 84
    Quality Glossary, 510
    on strategic plan deployment, 134
    website, xxi, 303

American Society for Testing and Materials (ASTM), 519
Americans with Disabilities Act (ADA), 156, 165
analogies, 354, 355*f*
analysis of variance (ANOVA), 421, 423
analytical thinking, 352
AND (activity network diagrams), 247*t*, 254, 336–337, 337*f*, 402*t*
Andon board, 402*t*
ANOVA (analysis of variance), 421, 423
ANSI/ASQ Z1.4, 417, 418
ANSI/ASQ Z1.9, 417
Ansoff, H. Igor, 88
Anthony, M., 463
AOQL (average outgoing quality limit), 417
apologies, to customers, 501
appraisals
    costs of, 361, 362–363
    leadership role of, 17
appropriation requests, 247*t*, 260
APQC (American Productivity and Quality Center), 300, 367
APQP (Advanced Product Quality Planning), 173, 402*t*
aptitude
    competency analysis of, 172
    KESAA requisites analysis for, 62, 63*f*, 548–549
    team selection based on, 62, 63*f*
AQL (acceptable quality limit), 418
"Are We Making Progress Tool," 500
artifacts, of organizational culture, 34–35, 152, 153
artificial intelligence (AI), 113, 221
AR/VR (augmented reality/virtual reality), 113
AS9100D, 299, 525
ASQ. *See* American Society for Quality
assertiveness, in conflict management, 42, 43*f*
assessment. *See* evaluation; measurement and assessment
assets
    financial reporting on, 177
    return on, 182, 244
assignable cause variation, 435
assumptions, in organizational culture, 35, 152, 153
ASTM (American Society for Testing and Materials), 519
Athos, Anthony, 21
attitude
    communication of friendly, 212
    competency analysis of, 172
    KESAA requisites analysis for, 62, 63*f*, 548–549
    qualitative assessment of, 465–466
    team selection based on, 62, 63*f*
attractive quality elements, 479
Aubrey, C. A., 50, 79–80
audits
    external, 285, 286
    financial statements for, 175
    internal or first-party, 58, 285–287, 296, 575
    postproject, 264–265
    process quality, 286

product quality, 286
quality, 285–287, 288*f*–289*f*, 296, 298, 324, 525, 575
quality auditor, 173, 285
second-party, 286
supplier, 286, 520–521, 525
teams for internal, 58
third-party, 286
training system, 575
augmented reality/virtual reality (AR/VR), 113
authenticity, in communication, 212
authority. *See also* power
    for change management, 30, 31
    empowerment for (*See* empowerment)
    line, 3
    organizational structures determining, 3, 5–6, 30
    staff, 3–4
autocratic management style, 150
automation, 113
Automotive Industry Action Group (AIAG), 511
autonomation, 113, 402*t*
autonomy, team, 59
availability, 399, 441
average, 420
average outgoing quality limit (AOQL), 417
avoidance, in conflict management, 42, 43*f*

B

B2B (business-to-business) relationships, 456
B2C (business-to-consumer) relationships, 456
Baker, Edward M., 137
balanced scorecard (BSC), 129, 184, 283–285, 284*t*, 411
balance sheets, 174–175, 176–177, 176*f*
    ratios derived from, 180
Baldrige, Malcolm, 300
Malcolm Baldrige National Quality Award
    core competencies defined for, 200
    empowerment and customer satisfaction leading to, 50
    establishment of, 300
    performance excellence criteria, 300–304, 301*f*
    profitability of winners of, 280
    quality assessment against criteria for, 285
    special project team to apply for, 61
Baldrige Performance Excellence Program (BPEP)
    customers criteria in, 302, 303, 478
    functional area interdependence in, 154
    leadership criteria in, 301–302, 303
    management by fact reflecting, 150, 409
    on management core competencies and values, 141
    measurement, analysis, and knowledge management criteria in, 302, 303, 409
    operations criteria in, 302, 303
    organizational profiles in, 301
    on performance evaluation, 129
    performance excellence criteria, 300–304, 301*f*

quality models and theories based on, 293, 300–303, 301*f*
quality not specified in, 278
results criteria in, 302, 303
strategy criteria in, 89, 129, 302, 303
total quality management foundations, 300, 305, 308
website for, 303
workforce criteria in, 302, 303
Bass, B. M., 16
batch-and-queue, 402*t*
bathtub curve, 421, 439–440, 440*f*
behavioral theories, 143
behavior management, 145–147, 146*f*
beliefs and values
    code of ethics reflecting, 83–85
    conflicts over, 42
    management's core, 141–142
    mission statements reflecting (*See* mission and value statements)
    in organizational culture, 35, 152, 153
    qualitative assessment of, 465–466
benchmarking
    benefits of, 313
    for business environment analysis, 108–110
    for change management, 35
    competitive, 310
    continuous quality improvement, 310–316, 311*t*, 312*f*, 314*f*–315*f*
    customer service performance, 500
    defined, 310
    functional, 310, 316
    generic, 310–311
    internal, 310
    management competence with, 24
    for quality assessment, 292, 310–316
    for risk assessment, 239
    sources of information, 312, 312*f*
    steps in, 311–312
    supplier performance, 523
    what it's not, 316
benefit-to-cost analysis, 240–245, 243*f*, 262, 262*f*, 541, 546, 570
Bennis, Warren, 1, 17
Berry, L. L., 115
best judgment sampling, 417
beta risk (type 2 errors), 417–418
Bhote, K. R., 449
bias, measurement, 428
big data, 113, 114, 224, 491
binomial distributions, 421, 422*f*
Blake, R. R., 148, 149*f*
Blanchard, K., 18, 147
blanket orders, 454
blockchain, 113, 114
Bloom's Taxonomy, 557, 588–589
body language, 208, 214
Body of Knowledge. *See* Certified Management of Quality/Organizational Excellence Body of Knowledge

Boeing, 496
bonding, leadership, 20
book value, 177
Boston Consulting Group, 245
boundaryless organizations, 9–10
bow tie analysis, 192–193, 193*f*–194*f*
BPEP. *See* Baldrige Performance Excellence Program
BPM (business process management), xvii–xix, xviii*f*. *See also* process management
BPMS (business process management systems), xviii, xviii*f*
BPR (business process reengineering), xvii, xviii*f*
brainstorming
    cause-and-effect diagrams with, 192
    in conflict management, 43
    imaginary, 360
    as problem-solving tools, 353
    for process management, 402*t*
    for risk assessment, 189–190, 192, 239
    in teams, 81
    for training needs analysis, 548
brainwriting, 360
breakthrough improvement, 436
Briggs, Katharine Cook, 151
BSC (balanced scorecard), 129, 184, 283–285, 284*t*, 411
buddy system, 567
budgets
    audits of adherence to, 264–265
    controlling monitoring, 141
    financial management of, 156, 183–184
    monitoring variances in, 141, 184, 262, 262*f*
    negotiation of, 41, 184
    project management, 232, 247*t*, 258–259, 259*f*, 262, 262*f*, 264–265
    strategic planning including, 91, 183
    training and development, 540, 541, 546
burndown chart, Scrum, 238
business architecture. *See also* organizational structure
    enterprise view of, xix, xx*f*
    evolution of, xviii–xix, xviii*f*
business environment analysis, 99–120
    benchmarking in, 108–110
    competitive analysis in, 107–108
    competitive intelligence gathering for, 106
    FMEA in, 103–104, 105*f*
    internal capability analysis in, 116–119, 117*f*
    of market forces, 104, 106–110
    overview of, 99, 100*f*
    of regulations, laws, and standards, 106, 119–120
    risk analysis in, 99–104, 102*f*, 105*f*
    stakeholder analysis in, 110–112, 111*f*
    strategic goals integrating, 93, 104, 112
    SWOT analyses in, 100–103, 102*f*
    of technology, 112–116
business needs, training plan alignment with, 540–541

business process management (BPM), xvii–xix, xviii*f. See also* process management
business process management systems (BPMS), xviii, xviii*f*
business process reengineering (BPR), xvii, xviii*f*
business process value stream mapping, 391
business-to-business (B2B) relationships, 456
business-to-consumer (B2C) relationships, 456

C

calibration, 428
capabilities. *See* core competencies; internal capability analysis; process capability measurements; skills and abilities; suppliers: capabilities of
capacity management, 504–506
career development, 573. *See also* training and development
Carlzon, Jan, 495
cascading, in strategic plan deployment, 127*f*
case studies, 562
cash basis bookkeeping, 175
cash flow, statements of, 174–175, 178–179
catchball, 95–96, 127, 207–208
cause-and-effect (C-E) diagrams
    critical thinking with, 45
    Ishikawa introducing, 324, 331
    as problem-solving tools, 331–332, 332*f*
    process management with, 403*t*
    risk assessment with, 191–192
cause leaders, 16
c-charts, 425
C-E diagrams. *See* cause-and-effect (C-E) diagrams
cell phones. *See* mobile technology
cells
    defined, 9
    organizational structure by, 9, 61
    work cells, 384, 385, 385*f*, 403*t*
cellular teams, 61
CE mark, 299
centralization
    of information technology, 223
    of organizational structures, 2, 5–6, 155
central tendency measures, 420
certificates of certification, 533
Certified Management of Quality/Organizational Excellence Body of Knowledge, 577–587
    on change management, 26, 578
    on code of ethics, 83, 579
    on communication, 205, 212, 217, 220, 581
    on customer identification and segmentation, 449, 454, 456, 465, 585
    on customer relationship management, 469, 476, 497, 502, 585–586
    on empowerment, 46, 578
    on financial management, 174, 581
    on human resources, 161, 580
    on internal capability analysis, 116, 579
    on interpersonal skills, 212, 581

on knowledge management, 194, 581
on leadership, 15, 36, 577–578
on management, 21, 139, 142, 154, 161, 174, 185, 194, 577, 580–581
on market forces, 104, 579
on measurement and assessment, 128, 154, 261, 409, 416, 419, 427, 429, 433, 437, 439, 584–585
on organizational structures, 2, 577
on problem-solving tools, 329, 336, 343, 360, 583
on process management, 367, 371, 383, 399, 583–584
on project management, 231, 239, 261, 265, 582
on quality, 278, 281, 283, 293, 300, 304, 580, 582–583
on regulations, laws, and standards, 119
on resource allocation, 122, 580
on risk analysis, 99, 579
on risk management, 185, 581
on stakeholder analysis, 110, 116, 579
on strategic planning, 88, 99, 104, 110, 112, 119, 121, 122, 128, 131, 579–580
on supply chain management, 511, 516, 518, 520, 524, 526, 531, 586–587
on tactical plans, 121, 579–580
on teams, 56, 64, 66, 68, 79, 578
on technology, 112, 220, 579, 581
on training and development, 540, 545, 552, 568, 587
Certified Management of Quality/Organizational Excellence examination, 538, 577
certified suppliers, 440, 514, 527, 533
chaku-chaku, 403*t*
champions
    quality, 172
    team, 70*t*
Champy, James, 537
change management
    authority for, 30, 31
    change agents for, 27, 28–29
    communication importance to, 30–31, 32, 213
    constraint management in, 32–34, 33*f*–34*f*
    cross-functional collaboration and, 29–30
    decision-making for, 31
    errors common to, 28
    geographic differences in, 35–36
    guidelines for, 27–28
    leadership of, 20, 26–36, 40
    measurement and assessment of results, 29, 35
    negotiation in, 40
    organizational culture and, 27, 28, 34–36, 154, 308
    organizational perspective of, 26–34
    organizational roadblocks to, 29–32, 32*f*
    organizational structure and, 6, 29–30
    outward vs. inward focus affecting, 30
    in project management, 236, 237
    quality management and, 295, 308
    resistance to change, causes of, 31–32

resource allocation and, 30
team implementation and, 57–58
techniques for facilitating, 26, 28–29, 31–32
changeover, 403*t*
checklists
    customer service, 501–502
    as job aids, 564
    for measurement and assessment development, 410
    for training evaluation, 574
    for training needs analysis, 548, 549
check sheets, 330, 332*f*, 403*t*, 429
chi-square test, 426
Chrysler, 196
classical organizational theory, 143
cloud computing, 113, 114, 223
cluster analysis, 462
clustered customer preferences, 461*f*, 462
clustering, 432
cluster sampling, 417
CMMI capability maturity model, 300
coaching
    coaching management style, 150
    coaching or corrective feedback, 75, 216
    by human resources, 164, 168
    by leadership, 17, 19, 78
    as management role, 23
    posttraining, 541
    project management, 237
    in teams, 77, 78
    training via, 561, 575
code of ethics, 83–85
cognitive domain, 557, 588
collaboration
    for change management, 27, 29–30
    in conflict management, 43*f*
    cross-functional, 29–30, 159
    with human resources, 164
    by leadership, 20
    in project management, 235
    in supply chain management, 533
    team, 67
comment cards, 488
commission, errors of, 396
commodity performance index (CPI), 523
common cause variation, 435
communication skills and abilities, 205–228
    barriers to communication, 207, 216–217, 218*t*–219*t*
    benefits of effective, 213
    change management requiring, 30–31, 32, 213
    communication, defined and described, 205–207
    communication path, 206*f*
    communication techniques, 205–212
    for conflict management, 44
    culture and, 205–206, 208, 209, 217, 218*t*
    direction of communication, 207–208
    distribution of information, 224–225
    for feedback, 208, 216

for financial management, 184–185
    formal vs. informal, 208–209, 235
    in global economy, 217–220, 218*t*–219*t*
    interpersonal skills and, 212–217
    of leadership, 20
    listening and, 211–212, 215–216, 217
    of management, 23
    media selection, 209–210
    methods of communication, 208–209
    nonverbal, 208, 214
    oral, 208
    overview of, 205
    for project management, 235, 236, 266
    questioning techniques, 210–212
    situational context for, 205, 210
    for strategic planning and plan deployment, 124, 207–208
    supply chain, 210, 518–520, 531, 533
    technology and, 113–114, 220–228 (*See also under* information technology)
    for total quality management, 306
    written, 208, 213–215
communities, as stakeholders, 110, 111*f*. *See also* stakeholders
competency analysis, 172
competency-based training methods, 558–559
competition
    benchmarking against (*See* benchmarking)
    business environment analysis of, 106, 107–108
    competitive analysis of, 107–108
    in conflict management, 43*f*
    customers of, identifying, 448
    internal, for resources or rewards, 30
    organizational structure influenced by, 11
    quality defined in relation to, 276
    quality driven by, 277
    strategic planning effects of, 89, 106–110
complaint handling, 484
complexity theory, 148
compromise, in conflict management, 42, 43*f*
computer-based instructional techniques, 563–564. *See also* e-learning
concurrent engineering, 159, 160*f*
conflict management
    in change management, 40
    core issues in, 44–45
    in customer relationship management, 503–504
    interest-based bargaining in, 43
    leadership for, 20, 40, 41–45
    negotiation in, 40, 43
    obstacles to, 44–45
    sources and views of conflict for, 41–42, 43*f*
    in teams, 69, 75, 76–77
    techniques for, 43–44
    third-party intervention in, 43–44
    win-win approach to, 44
conflict resolution diagrams, 402
conflicts of interest, 85
connected devices, 113, 114, 191

conscientiousness, 20, 151
consensus
  in communication, 217
  in conflict management, 43
  in strategic plan deployment, 95, 96, 125
  in team decision-making, 68, 77
constraint management, 32–34, 33f–34f. *See also*
    theory of constraints
constructive communication, 216
construct-related validity, 442
consumers, 447
consumer's risk, 417–418
content analysis, 465
content-related validity, 442–443
contingency approach management style, 150, 152
continual improvement
  continuous quality improvement model,
    309–316, 311t, 312f, 314f–315f
  internal customers assisted with, 454
  lean focus on (*See* lean)
  PDCA/PDSA cycle reflecting, 345
  regulations, laws, and standards for, 309
  supply chain, 524
  Taguchi loss function driving, 324, 324f
  total quality management focus on, 305–306
  training and development as tool for, 572–573
continuous quality improvement (CQI), 309–316
  benchmarking, 310–316, 311t, 312f, 314f–315f
  lean and *kaizen*, 309–310
  models and theories based on, 309–316
  Six Sigma, 310
control
  quality, 172–173, 278, 296, 320, 321, 323–324
  span of, 4
  statistical, 434, 438
  statistical process control, xvii, xviiif, 304, 317,
    389, 423–426, 424f, 424t, 440, 553
control charts, 333–334, 334f, 403t, 417, 423–426,
    424f, 429, 435
control limits, 426
controlling. *See also* financial management
  internal function responsible for, 156
  management role in, 24, 140, 141
control plans, 378, 379f, 403t
cooperation
  in conflict management, 42, 43f
  by leadership, 20
COQ. *See* cost of quality
core competencies. *See also* skills and abilities
  competency analysis of, 172
  defined, 200
  emotional, 19–20, 32, 39
  internal capability analysis of, 116–119, 117f
  knowledge management and, 200
  of leaders, 19–20
  of managers, 24–25, 141–142 (*See also*
    management skills and abilities)
  organizational structures focused on, 11
  team selection reflecting, 62, 63f
  technology adoption and, 115

core customers, 458
corrective and preventive action, 492, 519, 521,
    525–526, 551–552
corrective feedback, 75, 216
correlation, 335
correlation coefficients, 335
cost of quality (COQ)
  with balanced scorecard, 283
  categorizing costs, 362–364
  initiating COQ program, 363
  institutionalizing, 364
  measurements of, 363–364
  as problem-solving tool, 329, 361–364
  for process management, 403t
  quality function mission and, 280
  quality planning, control, and improvement
    using, 278
  quality system evaluation with, 283, 292
  total, 362
costs. *See also* expenses
  activity-based costing, 183, 364, 402t
  communication reducing, 213
  cost-benefit analysis, 240–245, 243f, 262, 262f,
    541, 546, 570
  cost of goods sold, 177, 181
  of customer conflicts, 503–504
  direct vs. indirect, 241
  of knowledge management, 197, 201
  of measurement, 130
  product/service cost structures, 183
  project, 240–245, 243f, 258–259, 259f, 262–263,
    262f
  of quality (*See* cost of quality)
  supplier data on, 521
  of training and development, 540, 541, 546,
    569–570
Covey, Stephen R., 14, 148–149
CPI (commodity performance index), 523
CPM (critical path method) diagrams, 247t, 254,
    255f, 336–337, 337f
CQI. *See* continuous quality improvement
Craddock, Bill, 1, 137
Crawford slip brainstorming, 353, 360
creativity
  conflict management leading to, 42
  creative thinking, 352–353
  innovation and creativity tools, 352–360
criterion-related validity, 442
critical incident analysis, 549
critical incident case studies, 562
critical path, 336–337, 384
critical path method (CPM) diagrams, 247t, 254,
    255f, 336–337, 337f
critical success factors (CSFs), 129, 129f
critical thinking, 45–46, 357
CRM. *See* customer relationship management
Crosby, Philip B., xvii, 280, 304, 321–322, 361
cross-functional collaboration, 29–30, 159
cross-functional flowcharts, 374, 376f
cross-functional teams, 73, 476–477, 512

cross-training, 567
Crystal, 237
CSFs (critical success factors), 129, 129*f*
culture
    communication affected by, 205–206, 208, 209,
        217, 218*t*
    defined, 34
    ethical issues influenced by, 83
    individualist, 54
    organizational (*See* organizational culture)
current assets, 177
current liabilities, 177
current ratio, 180
current reality trees, 401
current state value stream mapping, 392
customer advisory boards, 489
customer councils, 489
customer focus teams, 482, 484
customer identification and segmentation, 446–467
    customer segmentation, 456–464, 461*f*
        complete segmentation model, 460, 461*f*
        differentiating factors, 459–460
        historical shift to, 457
        key concepts, 460–462, 461*f*
        multiple criteria segmentation model, 460,
            461*f*
        no segmentation model, 460, 461*f*
        overview of, 457–458
        patterns of, 460–461, 461*f*
        preference segments, 461–462, 461*f*
        process of, 459–460
        strategy for, 462–464
    customer types
        importance of identifying, 448, 449*f*
        overview of, 446–447
    external customers, 447, 454–456, 464
    internal customers, 447, 449–454, 452*f*
    overview of, 446
    qualitative assessment, 465–467
customer journey mapping, 496, 499
customer panels, 489
customer relationship management (CRM),
        468–506
    capacity and resource management for,
        504–506
    conflict management in, 503–504
    customer focus, defining for, 468
    customer needs and, 469–476
        anticipating expectations and, 469–472
        quality function deployment, 472–476,
            473*f*–475*f*
    customer satisfaction and loyalty from, 469,
        472, 476–497
        complaint handling, 484
        corrective and preventive action, 492
        customer experience management, 495–496
        data capture, differentiation, and use,
            484–485
        data collection tools and techniques,
            485–491, 491*t*

    lifetime value, 495
    measurement and assessment of, 478–491,
        479*f*, 480*f*, 483*f*, 491*t*
    pitfalls in determining, 492–493
    reputational risk, 496–497
    retention and loyalty, 476, 478, 490, 493–496,
        494*t*
    voice of the customer information for,
        476–478, 477*f*
    customer segmentation and, 457
    customer service principles, 497–502, 498*f*
        service-oriented organization, 497–500, 498*f*
        skills and abilities, 500–502
    differentiation in, 469
    evolution of, xviii, xviii*f*
    management competence with, 24
    multiple and diverse customers, 502–506
    overview of, 468–469
    strategy for, 468–469
customers
    Baldrige criteria related to, 302, 303, 478
    business environment analysis of, 107, 109–110
    consumers/end users, 447
    core or key, 458
    defined, 446
    external, 447, 451, 453, 454–456, 464
    false, 447
    firing of, 504
    identification and segmentation of
        (*See* customer identification and
        segmentation)
    indirect, 446–447
    internal, 447, 449–454, 452*f*
    internal capability analysis from feedback of,
        117–118
    knowledge management of data on, 198, 202
    lifetime value of, 495
    loyalty of, 445, 453, 462, 469, 476, 478, 490,
        493–496, 494*t*
    multiple, managing, 502–503
    noncore, 458
    organizational culture focused on, 453, 468
    organizational structure by, 7, 8*f*
    past, 460
    potential, 458, 460
    primary or direct, 446, 468
    project management role of, 235, 236
    quality assessment from feedback of, 290–291,
        297, 298
    quality driven by, 277, 297
    relationship management with (*See* customer
        relationship management)
    sales function working with, 156
    satisfaction of (*See* customer satisfaction)
    secondary, 446
    as stakeholders, 110, 111*f* (*See also* stakeholders)
    strategic planning effects of, 89, 107, 109–110,
        111*f*, 117–118
    total quality management focus on, 305
    voice of (*See* voice of the customer)

customer satisfaction
  business environment analysis of, 118
  complaint handling and, 484
  corrective and preventive action for, 492
  customer experience management for, 495–496
  customer relationship management for, 469,
      472, 476–497
  customer segmentation strategy leading to,
      462
  data capture, differentiation, and use, 484–485
  data collection tools and techniques, 485–491,
      491t
  determining levels of, 478–479, 479f
  empowerment improving, 50
  internal customer treatment and, 453
  loyalty and, 445, 453, 462, 469, 476, 478, 490,
      493–496, 494t
  measurement and assessment of, 35, 290–291,
      297, 411, 413, 478–491, 479f, 480f, 483f,
      491t
  pitfalls in determining, 492–493
  project selection to achieve, 241–242
  quality defined in relation to, 276
  regulations, laws, and standards for, 299
  reputational risk and, 496–497
  retention and, 493–495, 494t
  voice of the customer information for, 476–478,
      477f
customer service
  as internal function, 156
  principles of, 497–502, 498f
  service-oriented organization, 497–500, 498f
  skills and abilities for, 500–502
customer value analysis, 490, 491t
customer-value maps, 490
CUSUM charts, 425
cycle time reduction, 384–386, 385f, 399, 403t
cyclical patterns, 430–431

D

Daniels, C., 147
data analysis. *See* measurement and assessment
databases, customer, 462, 491
data lakes, 114
data mining, 198, 199, 224, 431–432, 462, 491
Davidow, William, 537
Davis-Seaver, J., 45
deBono, E., 356
debt, long-term, 177
debt/equity ratio, 180
decentralization
  of information technology, 223
  of organizational structures, 2, 5–6
decision-making
  centralization/decentralization of, 2, 5–6, 155
  change management need for, 31
  code of ethics guiding, 83
  customer segmentation and, 460
  fact-based, in TQM, 306

information technology informing, 221–222, 222f
  negotiation for successful, 40, 41f
  in project management, 236, 241–242
  qualitative assessment for, 465
  team, 54, 59, 66, 68, 77
decision trees, 431
defect data check sheets, 330
defective parts
  lot tolerance percent defective, 418
  number of defects analysis, 521
  reducing, for cycle time reduction, 385
  as waste, 381, 399
  zero defects vs., 419
Defeo, Joseph A., 319
deferred income taxes, 177
delighters, 480–481
delivery
  supplier, 519, 521, 524
  of training and development, 545, 546, 559–568,
      571–572
delivery performance index (DPI), 524
demassification, 457
Deming, W. Edwards
  on change management, 27
  on leadership and management, 14, 18, 27, 137,
      152, 171, 307, 317–318, 510
  on measurement, 409, 435
  PDSA cycle, 319, 345
  quality theories and models, xvii, 304, 307,
      317–319, 327
  statistical process control, xvii
  system of profound knowledge, 152, 319
Deming chain reaction, 317
Deming Prize, 280, 293, 304, 305, 308
demographics, customer segmentation by,
      459–460, 461f
deployment flowcharts, 329, 331f, 374, 376f
depreciation, reserve for, 177
design
  design for manufacturing ability/and
      assembly, 357, 440
  Design for Six Sigma, 278, 358, 403t
  design of experiments, 358, 421, 423, 432
  design to unit production costs, 358
  engineering review of, 440
  FMEA of, 103, 349
  of measurements, tenets for, 415
  of organizational structure, 2–5
  quality of, 278, 321
  of training program, 543–545, 546, 555–559,
      560f, 567, 571
detection, FMEA assessing, 103
Devos, Denis, 137, 537
diagnostic journey, 321
differentiation, 469
diffused customer preferences, 461f, 462
direct customers, 446
direction
  of communication, 207–208
  management providing, 24, 140

director of quality, 172
DiSC (Dominance, Influence, Steadiness, Conscientiousness Instrument), 151
discount buyers, 455
discussion format training, 561, 566
dispersion measures, 420
dissatisfiers, 37, 143
distance learning, 563. *See also* e-learning
distributors, 454
division of labor, 4–5, 29–30
DMAIC (define, measure, analyze, improve, control) model, 345–348, 347*f*–348*f*, 403*t*–404*t*
documentation. *See also* planning; record keeping; reporting
  industry-specific, 380
  process analysis using, 377–378, 377*f*, 380, 406*t*
  project management, 265–273
  quality plan, 282–283, 406*t*
Dodge, H. F., 417
Dominance, Influence, Steadiness, Conscientiousness Instrument (DiSC), 151
Dominick, C., 527–528
Dorf, D., 469
double sampling, 418, 419*f*
downstream consequences, 362
downtime, as waste, 382, 399
DPI (delivery performance index), 524
Drucker, Peter F., 1, 25–26
Duffy, Grace, 537
dynamic systems development method (DSDM), 237

E

earned value analysis (EVA), 262–263
education
  individual development distinguished, 573
  training distinguished, 538–539, 539*f*, 573
EEOC (Equal Employment Opportunity Commission), 156
effectiveness
  performance evaluation of, 129
  of training and development, 541, 545, 546, 567–575
efficiency, performance evaluation of, 129
Einstein, Albert, 327
e-learning, 559, 560–561, 560*f*, 567. *See also* computer-based instructional techniques; webinars
e-mails
  communication via, 207, 208, 209–210, 214, 216, 226–227
  surveys via, 487–488
emojis, 214
emotional competence, 19–20, 32, 39
empathy, 20, 44, 212, 501
employee buyers, 455
employees. *See* labor; staff

empowerment
  benefits from, 50
  communication effectiveness with, 213
  for customer service, 499
  defined, 46
  job enlargement for, 46
  job enrichment for, 46
  by leadership, 46–51, 47*f*, 49*t*
  mistakes and barriers to, 49–50
  organizational culture changes with, 47, 49, 50
  organizational structure changes with, 47, 47*f*
  relationship changes with, 49, 49*t*
  total quality management based on, 305
  training and development for, 48, 539
enablers, role of, 17, 48
end users, 447
engineering
  changes in, creating waste, 383
  concurrent or simultaneous, 159, 160*f*
  design review by, 440
  human factors, 203
  as internal function, 157
  process reengineering, xvii, xviii*f*, 406*t*
  quality assurance engineer, 173
  quality control engineer, 172–173
  reliability engineer, 173
enterprise-level risks, 186*t*
enterprise resource planning (ERP), xviii, xviii*f*, 24
enterprise value stream mapping, 391
entrepreneurship, 22
environmental factors. *See also* situational context
  communication affected by, 211
  environmental scan and analysis, 93, 99–120
    (*See also* business environment analysis for details)
  management addressing, 23, 25
  for negotiations, 39
  organizational culture and, 153
  organizational structure influenced by, 12
  supplier adherence to requirements on, 519
Equal Employment Opportunity Commission (EEOC), 156
equity theory, 37
ERP (enterprise resource planning), xviii, xviii*f*, 24
ethical issues
  code of ethics on, 83–85
  in communication, 212
  management addressing, 23, 25
European Quality Award, 304, 308
EVA (earned value analysis), 262–263
evaluation. *See also* measurement and assessment
  end-of-project, 263–264
  management role in, 23
  performance (*See* performance evaluation)
  strategic planning, 89, 91, 121, 124, 128–131, 129*f*, 130*t*
  team, 59, 76, 79–81
  training and development, 541, 545, 546, 568–575, 569*f*, 574*t*
evolutionary operation (EVOP), 423

evolutionary project management, 233, 233*f*, 234
excess inventory, 381, 382
executive briefings, 539
expectancy theory, 37
expectation
    communication affected by, 206
    customer, 469–472
    quality defined in relation to, 276
expenses. *See also* costs
    financial reporting on, 177–178
    operating, 401
    quality not, 280, 292
experience
    communication affected by, 205–206, 209, 213
    competency analysis of, 172
    customer experience management, 495–496
    KESAA requisites analysis for, 62, 63*f*, 548–549
    team selection based on, 62, 63*f*
experiential learning model, 143–144, 144*f*
experiential training, 561, 567
experts, for training, 566
explicit knowledge, 195, 235
exponential distributions, 421, 422*f*
external audits, 285, 286
external business functions, 155
external customers
    defined, 447
    identification and segmentation of, 447, 454–456, 464
    internal customer treatment influencing processes for, 451, 453
    process for working with, 464
    provider relationship with, nature of, 456
    types of, 454–456
external failure costs, 362–363
external financial statements, 175
Extreme Programming (XP), 237

F

Facebook, 228, 488
face-to-face surveys, 487. *See also* interviews
face validity, 442
facilitation
    brainstorming, 189–190
    of change management, 26, 28–29, 31–32
    leadership role of, 17
    team, 56–57, 59, 69, 70*t*, 74, 76–78
    techniques for, 76–78
facilities
    engineering, 157
    internal capability analysis of, 117
    investment in, for customer service, 500
    organizational culture reflected in, 153
    organizational structure influenced by, 12
    property, plant, and equipment as, 177, 385
    for training and development, 546, 568
fact-based decision-making, 306. *See also* management by fact
factor analysis, 432, 462

fade-out of training, 546
failure costs, 361, 362–363
failure mode and effect analysis (FMEA)
    in business environment analysis, 103–104, 105*f*
    critical thinking with, 45
    defined, 103
    of design, 103, 349
    methodology of, 349
    as problem-solving tool, 343, 348–350, 351*f*
    of process, 103, 349, 351*f*, 440
    for process management, 404*t*
    quality assurance engineer applying, 173
    for risk management, 103–104, 105*f*, 188, 193, 239, 517
fairness, 84, 212
false customers, 447
Family Cleaners, 370
fault tree analysis, 517
Fayol, H., 5, 143
FDA (U.S. Food and Drug Administration), 300
feature-driven development (FDM), 237
feedback
    change management providing, 32
    coaching, constructive, or corrective, 75, 216
    communication of, 208, 216
    customer satisfaction, 478–479, 479*f*, 495
        (*See also* surveys)
    feedback loops, 128–129, 130, 130*t*, 147
        closed, 128–129, 130, 130*t*
        open, 128
    informative, 216
    internal capability analysis using, 117–118
    internal customers receiving, 454
    motivational, 75
    to new employees, 168
    on performance (*See* performance evaluation)
    in project management, 259–260
    quality assessment
        from customer feedback, 290–291, 297, 298
        from employee feedback, 291
    on strategic planning, 91, 128–129
    to suppliers, 526
    in teams, 75, 76, 79
    360°, 171, 208
    work groups monitoring, 59
Feigenbaum, Armand V., xvii, 293, 304, 322–323, 361
Felkins, P. K., 50, 79–80
financial issues
    budgets as (*See* budgets)
    communication related to, 219*t*
    costs as (*See* costs)
    customer conflicts affecting, 503–504
    empowerment effects on, 48
    exempt vs. nonexempt compensation as, 22
    human resources responsibility for, 162
    internal capability analysis of, 116, 117
    long-term investments affecting, 31
    management role overseeing, 23, 24, 25, 140, 141 (*See also* financial management)

negotiation of, 41, 184
payback period, 242, 244
pay-for-skills plans as, 80
project funding approval request, 247t, 260
strategic planning effects of, 89, 91, 116, 117, 129, 183
team rewards as, 80
financial management, 174–185. *See also* controlling
balanced scorecard for, 184
balance sheets in, 174–175, 176–177, 176f
bookkeeping methods in, 175–176
budgets in, 156, 183–184 (*See also* budgets)
communication with senior management about, 184–185
external financial statements for, 175
financial reporting in, 156, 174–179
information technology informing, 222
internal financial statements for, 175
as internal function, 156
as language of management, 174
product/service cost structures in, 183
profit and loss/income statements in, 174–175, 177–178, 178f
project management and, 240–245, 243f
for quality, 174, 184–185
ratios in, 179–183
regulations, laws, and standards for, 156, 176
statements of cash flow in, 174–175, 178–179
statements of shareholder's equity in, 175
Finnerty, M. F., 561
firing the customer, 504
first-party audits, 285–286. *See also* internal audits
fishbone diagrams. *See* cause-and-effect (C-E) diagrams
5S, 386–388, 389, 404t
five Whys, 357, 358f, 404t
flexibility
in negotiations, 40
in process management, 404t
of teams, 55
Florida Power and Light, 308
flowcharts
defined, 329
as problem-solving tools, 329, 330f–331f
for process management, 372–376, 374f–376f, 391–394, 393f, 404t, 406t
process maps as, 372–376, 374f–376f, 406t (*See also* value stream mapping)
FMEA. *See* failure mode and effect analysis
focus groups, 484, 548, 549
Follett, Mary Parker, 143
followers, role of, 17
follow-up, with customers, 501
Ford, Henry, 384, 457
Ford Production System, xvii, xviiif, 384, 388
forecasting
information technology for, 221
leadership role of, 17
long-range planning as, 89

project management, 232
supply chain, 519
trend analysis, 432
forming stage of teams, 64–65, 64f
forums, 539, 566
4S, 386
four Ms, as causes, 331
four Ps, as causes, 331
14 points for improvement (Crosby), 322
14 points for management (Deming), 317–318
Franklin, Benjamin, 537
front-end analysis, 548
F-test, 420
functional benchmarking, 310, 316
functions
benchmarking against similar, 310, 316
collaboration across, 29–30, 159
external, 155
of human resources, 161–166
integrated business processes across, 158–159, 158f, 160f
interdependence of, 154–161
internal, 155–157 (*See also specific functions*)
of management, 23–24
organizational structure by, 6–7, 7f, 154–155
project management across, 231
siloed, dysfunction with, 154
systems thinking across, 155, 159–161
teams across, 73, 476–477, 512
Furterer, Sandra L., 1, 137, 327
future reality trees, 401
future state value stream mapping, 392

G

GAAP (generally accepted accounting principles), 175
gage repeatability and reproduction (gage R&R), 427–428
Gale, B. T., 490
Galvin, Bob, 16, 150
gamification of training, 559, 560f
Gantt, Henry, 143
Gantt charts
as problem-solving tools, 337
for project planning, 247t, 252, 253f, 254
of strategic planning goals, objectives, and means, 95, 95f
gap analysis, 127, 464
Gardner, Howard, 144
Gautier-Downes, J. H., 564
Gemba Academy, 389
"Gemba" walks, 289, 404t. *See also* management by walking around
General Electric, 345
generally accepted accounting principles (GAAP), 175
generations in workforce, 117, 117f
generic benchmarking, 310–311
genetic algorithms, 432

geography
    change management variance by, 35–36
    communication across, 209, 218*t*–219*t*
    customer segmentation by, 459
    geographic information systems (GIS), 432, 462, 491
    internal capability analysis based on, 116
    organizational structure by, 7–8, 8*f*
George, Steven, 87
Gilbreth, Frank and Lillian, 143
GIS (geographic information systems), 432, 462, 491
global workplace
    communication skills and abilities in, 217–220, 218*t*–219*t*
    supply chain management in, 533
glossary and acronyms, 603–658
GMP (good manufacturing practices), 300
goal-question-metric (GQM), 410–411
goals and objectives
    budgets tied to, 184
    communication of, 207–208, 213
    conflict management on, 41, 44–45
    customer service-focused, 500
    human resources coordination of, 164
    leadership type reflecting, 16
    learning or terminal objectives, 557–558
    management role in, 12, 22–23, 140
    means matrix for, 94–95, 94*f*–95*f*
    motivation toward, 38
    negotiation on, 38–39, 40
    organizational culture reflecting, 35
    organizational structure to meet, 6
    policies for implementing (*See* policies)
    process, 367, 369–371, 369*f*, 405*t*
    project management alignment with, 232, 236, 238
    quality, 133–134, 280, 281, 295
    S.M.A.R.T.W.A.Y. to set, 68, 93, 94*t*, 405*t*
    strategic planning setting, 93, 94*t*, 104, 112, 207–208
    teams setting and working toward, 54, 56, 58, 64*f*, 65, 66, 68, 73, 75
    of training, 574, 574*t*
    training and development to achieve, 168, 553–554, 572
Goldratt, Eliyahu, 400–402
Goleman, Daniel, 19–20
good manufacturing practices (GMP), 300
goodwill, 177, 496
Gopal, Christopher, 509
Gorveatte, Susan, 537
GQM (goal-question-metric), 410–411
gross profit, 180
group interviews, 167, 465
groupthink, 81
growth strategies, change management with, 35
Gryna, F. M., 446, 540
guarantees, unconditional, 490–491
Gulledge, K. A., 149

H

HAACP (hazard analysis and critical points), 190
Hamel, Gary, 87
Hammer, Michael, 537
Harari, Owen, 445
Harrington, H. J., 446
Hartl, D. E., 557
Hawthorne effect, 143, 304
Hayakawa, S. I., 206
hazard analysis, 517
hazard analysis and critical points (HAACP), 190
head-to-head area charts of customer value, 490
Hersey, P., 18, 147
Herzberg, Frederick, 37, 143
HFE (human factors engineering), 203
hierarchical interviews, 167
hierarchy
    of knowledge management, 194–195, 195*f*
    of needs, 36–37, 37*f*, 143
high-performance work teams, 57–58
histograms, 334, 335*f*, 404*t*, 420, 429
homogeneous customer preferences, 461, 461*f*
Honda, 137, 200, 488
honesty, 84
Honey, P., 144
horizontal alignment, of performance measures, 225
horizontal organizational structures, 4–5, 6
hoshin planning
    communication in, 207–208
    for strategic planning, 91–96, 92*f*, 94*f*–95*f*, 94*t*, 125, 127, 131, 207–208
Hotelling's *t*-squared statistic, 432
house of quality, 472, 473*f*
HRA (human reliability assessment), 192
human factors engineering (HFE), 203
human relations theory, 143
human reliability assessment (HRA), 192
human resources, 161–174
    assimilation of new employee by, 168
    collaboration with other areas, 164
    competency analysis by, 172
    functions of, 161–166
    information technology informing, 222
    as internal function, 156
    job descriptions/positions by, 164–165, 172–174
    management of, 161–174, 170*f*, 188–189
    onboarding/orientation by, 168
    performance evaluation responsibility of, 162, 169, 171
    personnel selection and hiring by, 165–168, 188–189
    in quality function, 169, 171, 172–174
    risk management for, 188–189
    succession planning by, 164, 166
    training and development responsibilities of, 162, 164, 168–169, 170*f*
Hunt, V. Daniel, 577
hygiene factors, 37
hypergeometric distributions, 421, 422*f*

I

IATF 16949-2016. *See also* ISO/TS 16949
  performance evaluation criteria, 129
  quality management system requirements, 299, 525
  stakeholders in, 111
  supply chain standards, 525
icebreakers, team, 68
IDPs (individual development plans), 550–551
imaginary brainstorming, 360
Imai, Masaaki, 405t
in-box exercises, 563
income statements, 174–175, 177–178, 178f
  ratios derived from, 180
income taxes, 177
incoming inspections, 533
incremental project management, 233, 233f, 234
independent process variables, 411, 412f
indifferent quality elements, 480
indirect customers, 446–447
individual development, 169, 573
individual development plans (IDPs), 550–551
individualized instruction, 558
industrial engineering, 157
industry
  customer segmentation by, 459
  training within, 575
Industry 4.0, 113
industry-specific documentation, 380
inefficiency, as waste, 382
information errors, 395
information technology (IT)
  business environment analysis of, 113–114
  communication via, 206, 207, 208, 209–210, 213–214, 216–217, 219t, 220–228
  customer databases, 462, 491
  distribution of information via, 224–225
  as internal function, 156
  investments in, for customer service, 500
  for knowledge management, 197–198, 201
  management competence with, 24
  multifunction devices in, 227–228
  obsolescence of, 226–228
  organizational performance management informed by, 225–226
  project management documentation using, 266–267
  quality evolution and, xvii, xviiif, xviiI
  risk assessment for, 228
  in supply chain management, 533
  technology in, 223–224
  uses of, 220–222, 222f
  virtual teams using, 61–62
informative communication, 216
infrastructure development, 500
inherent availability, 441
innovation
  innovation and creativity tools, 352–360
  of leadership, 20

of management, 22
of teams, 55, 69
inspections, quality, 173, 298, 397, 417, 532–533
Instagram, 228, 488
Institute of Management Accountants Certified in Strategy and Competitive Analysis certification, 134
instructional games, 563
intangible assets, 177
integration
  of business processes, 158–159, 158f, 160f, 225
  management role in, 23
  of performance measures, 225
  of quality and organizational objectives, 279, 281
  of supply chain, 533
  in systems thinking, 147–148, 155, 159–161
  total quality management focus on, 305
integrity, 84
interdependence
  of functional areas, 154–161
  in supplier partnerships, 531
interest-based bargaining, 43
interested parties, 88, 110–112. *See also* stakeholders
interest income, 178
intermediaries, 447
internal audits, 58, 285–287, 296, 575
internal benchmarking, 310
internal business functions, 155–157. *See also specific functions*
internal capability analysis
  in business environment analysis, 116–119, 117f
  technology adoption and, 115–116
internal customers
  defined, 447
  external customer processes influenced by, 451, 453
  identification and segmentation of, 447, 449–454, 452f
  methods to energize, 453–454
  quality-level agreements, 451, 452f
  tenets for working with, 451
internal failure costs, 362–363
internal financial statements, 175
internal rate of return (IRR), 243–244
International Automotive Task Force standards. *See* IATF 16949-2016
International Organization for Standardization, 515. *See also ISO entries*
International Risk Management Institute, 227
internet
  communication via, 226 (*See also* social media)
  computer-based instructional techniques, 563
  customer data from, 488
interpersonal intelligence, 144
interpersonal skills and abilities, 212–217
interrelationship diagraphs
  constraints identified in, 32–33, 33f
  as problem-solving tools, 337–338, 339f
  for process management, 404t

interviews
  customer satisfaction, 487
  group, 167, 465
  hierarchical, 167
  human resources, 164, 166–167
  one-to-one, 167, 465, 487
  panel, 167
  peer, 167
  questions in, 167, 210–211
  for team evaluation, 79
  for training needs analysis, 548
intrapersonal intelligence, 144
inventive problem-solving, theory of, 45–46
inventory
  cycle time reduction and, 385
  defined, 401
  excess, as waste, 381, 382
  financial reporting on, 177, 181
  inventory management function, 157
  just-in-time, xvii, xviii*f*, 388–389, 404*t*, 532
  pull vs. push system for, 388, 390, 531
  supplier logistics and, 531–532
  turnover of, 181, 401
invisible waste, 382–383
IRR (internal rate of return), 243–244
Ishikawa, Kaoru, 304, 323–324, 331
Ishikawa diagrams. *See* cause-and-effect diagrams
is-is not questions, 360
ISO 9000
  functional area interdependence in, 154
  management by fact reflecting, 150
  quality management principles in, 133, 293–298
  quality models and theories based on, 293–298
  risk defined in, 187
  total quality management standards, 304
  training and development to meet, 553
ISO 9001
  ad hoc audit teams for compliance with, 58
  continual quality improvement requirements, 309
  management core competencies and values
      in, 141
  organizational structure requirements in, 11
  problem-solving tools for requirements of, 329
  quality assessments in, 285, 289–290, 296–297
  quality management system in, 277, 294–298
  risk management standards, 188, 189, 192, 193
  stakeholders in, 110, 111
ISO 9004, 294, 298
ISO 10001, 299
ISO 10002, 299
ISO 10003, 299
ISO 10012, 298
ISO 13485, 299
ISO 14001, 298
ISO 19011, 296, 298
ISO 22000, 298
ISO 26000, 85, 299
ISO 31000, 187–188, 299
ISO 31010, 189–193, 193*f*–194*f*
ISO 45001, 299

ISO 50001, 299
ISO/IEC 27001, 299
ISO/TS 9002, 294
ISO/TS 16949, 380. *See also* IATF 16949-2016
Israel, Jeff, 445
IT. *See* information technology
iterative project management, 233, 233*f*, 234–238

J

Japan
  continuous quality improvement in, 309–310
  Deming Prize in, 280, 293, 304, 305, 308
  poka-yoke in, 192, 395–398, 406*t*
  Shingo Prize for Excellence in Manufacturing
      in, 304
  statistical process control in, xvii
  total quality management in, 304, 308
  Toyota Production System in, xvii, xviii*f*, 113,
      384, 388
JC (Joint Commission), 299
JetBlue, 497
jidoka, 113
JIT (just-in-time), xvii, xviii*f*, 388–389, 404*t*, 532
job aids, 564, 567
job analysis, 548
job descriptions/positions, 164–165, 172–174
job enlargement, 46
job enrichment, 46
job performance, training to improve, 549–551,
      550*t*
Johnson, G., 35
Johnson, R. S., 558, 565
Johnson & Johnson, 497
Joint Commission (JC), 299
joint planning meetings, 489–490
journey mapping, customer, 496, 499
Jung, Carl, 151
Juran, Joseph M.
  on empowerment, 46
  on leadership and management, 153
  on measurement, 420, 421, 436
  Pareto principle, 333
  quality theories and models, xvii, 153, 304, 316,
      319–321, 361, 436, 477
  on strategic planning, 97, 540
  on training and development, 540
Juran trilogy, 319–320
just-in-time (JIT), xvii, xviii*f*, 388–389, 404*t*, 532

K

kaizen event/*kaizen* blitz, 57, 309–310, 391, 398, 405*t*
Kamauff, John, 509
kanban method, 388–390, 405*t*
Kano, Noriaki, 479
Kano model, 479–481, 480*f*
Kaplan, R. S., 283
Kepner, Charles, 344
Kepner-Tregoe, 344–345

KESAA requisites analysis, 62, 63*f*, 548–549
key customers, 458
key events time line, 490
kinesthetic intelligence, 144
King, Tim, 137
Kirkpatrick, D. L., 569
knowledge
    body of (*See* Certified Management of Quality/
        Organizational Excellence Body of
        Knowledge)
    communication affected by, 213
    competency analysis of, 172
    defined and described, 194–196
    explicit, 195, 235
    KESAA requisites analysis for, 62, 63*f*, 548–549
    knowledge mapping, 360
    management of (*See* knowledge management)
    system of profound, 152, 319
    tacit, 195, 235
    team selection based on, 62, 63*f*
    training and development of, 547 (*See also*
        training and development)
    wisdom and, 194–195, 195*f*, 196
knowledge management, 194–203
    applications of, 198–199
    Baldrige criteria for, 302
    barriers to, overcoming, 201–202
    Books of Knowledge for, 196
    capturing, sharing, and accessing information
        in, 196–197
    core competencies and, 200
    hierarchy of, 194–195, 195*f*
    initiating, 197–199
    knowledge, defined and described, 194–196
    learning organization and, 199–200
    management competence with, 24, 194–203
    measurement and assessment of, 197, 200
    processes in, 197–199, 201–202
    product development and, 202–203
    in project management, 235, 237
    technology for, 197–198, 202
    wisdom and, 194–195, 195*f*, 196
Knowles, M., 553, 556–557
Kolb, David, 143–144, 144*f*
Kotler, Philip, 457
Kouzes, J. M., 17

L

labor. *See also* staff
    division of, 4–5, 29–30
    regulations, laws, and standards for, 22, 156,
        164
    unions (*See* unions, labor)
lagging indicators, 430
language. *See also* communication skills and
        abilities
    customer segmentation by, 460
    on customer surveys, 493
    linguistic intelligence, 144

Lao-tzu, 50
Lappi, T., 236
lateral thinking, 355–356
laws. *See* regulations, laws, and standards
LCALI (listen-capture-analyze-learn-improve)
        process, 481–482, 483*f*
leadership
    Baldrige criteria for, 301–302, 303
    cause, 16
    challenges of, 14–51
    change management by, 20, 26–36, 40
    code of ethics for, 83–85
    conflict management by, 20, 40, 41–45
    core competencies of, 19–20
    critical thinking by, 45–46
    customer service commitment by, 498–499
    defined, 17
    empowerment by, 46–50, 47*f*, 49*t*
    internal capability analysis of, 117
    leader, defined, 14
    management differentiated from, 14, 17, 22, 138
        (*See also* management)
    motivation by, 20, 36–38
    negotiation by, 38–41, 41*f*, 43
    operational, 15
    organization, 15–16
    organizational structures and, 2–13
    principle-centered, 149
    problem-solving tools involving, 347, 350
    project management, 237, 238
    qualities of effective, 15, 17, 19–20
    quality management, 294–295, 303, 307
    of quality training, 553–554
    quotations on, 1
    roles and responsibilities, 15–20
    situational context for, 18–19, 147
    Socratic method by, 45
    strategic, 2, 15
    strategic planning driven by, 91, 124
    of supply chain management, 533
    in teams (*See* teams)
    techniques for, 36–46
    transactional, 16, 150
    transformational, 16, 150
leading indicators, 430
lean, 383–399
    as acronym, 383
    agile project management in, 237
    continuous quality improvement in, 309–310
    critical thinking in, 45
    cycle time reduction in, 384–386, 385*f*, 399, 403*t*
    evolution of, xvii–xviii, xviii*f*
    5S in, 386–388, 389, 404*t*
    just-in-time in, xvii, xviii*f*, 388–389, 404*t*
    kaizen event/*kaizen* blitz in, 398, 405*t*
    kanban method in, 388–390, 405*t*
    organizational culture and, 384
    overall equipment effectiveness in, 398–399,
        405*t*
    pitfalls to avoid in, 399

poka-yoke or mistake proofing in, 192, 395–398, 406*t*

process management tools, 383–399, 403*t*–407*t*

single-minute exchange of die, 388, 389, 394–395, 407*t*

technology in, 113

terminology, 383

value stream mapping in, 45, 391–394, 393*f*, 407*t*

visual management in, 387–388, 389, 407*t* (*See also kanban* method)

Lean-Six Sigma, xviii, xviii*f*

learner-controlled instruction, 560–561

learning objectives, 557–558

learning organizations, 199–200

learning styles questionnaires, 144

learning theories, 143–145, 144*f*

lectures, training, 561, 567

lesson plans, for training, 558

liabilities, 177. *See also* debt; expenses

life cycle, project, 231–232

life cycle management, supplier, 511, 533

life cycle methodologies, project management, 232–238

life history curve, 439–440, 440*f*. *See also* bathtub curve

Lincoln Electric, 309

linearity, of measurements, 428

linear project management, 232–234, 233*f*

linear regression, 423, 432

linear responsibility matrix (LRM), 247*t*, 256, 258

line authority, 3

line balancing, 405*t*

linguistic intelligence, 144

LinkedIn, 228

listen-capture-analyze-learn-improve (LCALI) process, 481–482, 483*f*

listening, 211–212, 215–216, 217

listening post data, 481–482, 483*f*

Little John/Little's law, 389

L. L. Bean, 493

Locke, E. A., 150

logical/mathematical intelligence, 144

logistics, supplier, 531–532

logistics function, 156–157

Lombardi, Vince, 93

long-range planning, 89

long-term debt, 177

long-term trend analysis, 430, 433

lot tolerance percent defective (LTPD), 418

LRM (linear responsibility matrix), 247*t*, 256, 258

Lunney, S., 528

M

machine learning, 113

Mader, D. P., 358

Mahapatra, R., 234

mail surveys, 486

maintainability, 441

management. *See also specific types of management (i.e., process management)*

core competencies and values of, 24–25, 141–142

customer service commitment by, 498–499

functions of, 23–24

hierarchy of and organizational structure, 12–13

internal capability analysis of, 117

leadership differentiated from, 14, 17, 22, 138 (*See also* leadership)

line or first-level supervision, 12, 13, 139

manager, defined, 14

middle, defined, 12, 13, 139

principles of, 139–142

problem-solving tools for, 336–342

quality assessment tools, 289–290, 296–298

regulations, laws, and standards for, 22, 25

resource stewardship of, 21, 140

roles and responsibilities of, 12–13, 21–26, 132, 138–141, 540–541

skills and abilities of (*See* management skills and abilities)

steering committees, 73

strategic plan deployment by, 124

supplier requirements for, 519

tampering by, 437

tasks of, 25–26

theories and styles of, 142–154

titles of, 21–22

top, senior, or executive, defined, 12, 138–139

training and development for, 539, 553

training and development role of, 23, 540–541

management by fact, 128, 150, 409

management by walking around (MBWA), 150. *See also* management "Gemba" walks

management "Gemba" walks, 289, 404*t*. *See also* management by walking around

management processes, wasteful, 383

management reviews, 289–290, 296–297

management skills and abilities, 138–203

for controlling, 24, 140, 141

core values and competencies, 24–25, 141–142

for directing, 24, 140

in financial management, 174–185, 176*f*, 178*f*

in functional area interdependence, 154–161

in human resources, 161–174, 170*f*, 188–189

in knowledge management, 194–203, 195*f*

in management theories and styles, 142–154, 219*t*

for organizing, 22, 23, 139, 140

overview of, 138–139

for planning, 23, 139, 140

principles of management and, 139–142

in risk management, 185–194, 186*t*, 193*f*–194*f*

roles and responsibilities requiring, 23–25, 138–141

for staffing, 23–24, 140

training and development of, 539, 553

management theories and styles, 142–154
  A-B-C analysis, 145–147, 146*f*
  autocratic, 150
  behavioral theories, 143
  behavior management, 145–147, 146*f*
  classical organizational theory, 143
  coaching, 150
  communication incompatibility with, 219*t*
  complexity theory, 148
  contingency approach, 150, 152
  human relations theory, 143
  interaction of, 149–151
  learning theories, 143–145, 144*f*
  management by fact, 150
  managerial grid, 148, 149*f*
  organizational culture reflecting, 152–154
  overview of, 142–149
  participative, 150
  scientific management, 142–143
  Seven Habits, 148–149
  situational leadership/management, 147
  systems thinking, 147–148
  tools for assessing, 151–152
  transactional, 150
  transformational, 150
managerial grid, 148, 149*f*
Mangalaraj, G., 234
Marhevko, Jd, 87, 137, 327
market forces
  benchmarking against, 108–110
  business environment analysis of, 104, 106–110
  competition as (*See* competition)
  competitive analysis of, 107–108
marketing. *See* advertising and marketing
market-perceived price profile, 490
market-perceived quality profile, 490
market research, 448
market segmentation, 457, 459, 462, 463.
        See also customer identification and
        segmentation
Marston, William, 151
mash-ups, 113
Maslow, Abraham, 36, 143
Maslow's hierarchy of needs, 36–37, 37*f*, 143
mass customization, 457, 506
master service delivery processes, 499
mastery learning, 558
material acceptance, 532–533, 532*f*
material flow value stream mapping, 391, 392
material requirements planning (MRP), xviii,
        xviii*f*, 388
material resource planning (MRP II), xviii, xviii*f*
materials management function, 156–157
matrix diagrams. *See also specific types of matrices*
  as problem-solving tools, 338–339, 340*f*
  as process management tools, 405*t*
  quality function deployment, 472–476,
    474*f*–475*f*
matrix organizational structures, 6, 9, 10*f*
Matsushita Electric, 309

MBTI (Myers-Briggs Type Indicator), 62, 151–152
MBWA (management by walking around), 150.
        See also management "Gemba" walks
McCain, Heather, 509
McClelland, D., 38
McCloskey, Robert, 215
McGregor, Douglas, 143
McKenna, R., 469
means matrix, 94–95, 94*f*–95*f*, 126
mean time between failures (MTBF), 440
mean time between maintenance actions
    (MTBMA), 441
mean time to failure (MTTF), 440
mean time to repair (MTR), 441
measles charts, 330
measurement and assessment, 409–443. *See also*
    evaluation
  alignment of, 130, 225
  audits (*See* audits)
  balanced scorecard, 129, 184, 283–285, 284*t*, 411
  Baldrige criteria for, 302, 303, 409
  benchmarking, 24, 35, 108–110, 239, 292,
    310–316, 500, 523
  bias in, 428
  budget variance, 262
  calibration for, 428
  of change, 29, 35
  checklist for developing, 410
  cost-benefit analysis, 240–245, 243*f*
  cost of quality, 363–364 (*See also* cost of quality)
  critical success factors for, 129, 129*f*
  of customer satisfaction, 35, 290–291, 297, 411,
    413, 478–491, 479*f*, 480*f*, 483*f*, 491*t*
  of customer service, 499–500
  earned value analysis, 262–263
  effects of, on performers, 413–415
  employee feedback, 291
  establishing, steps to, 412
  feedback loops for, 128–129, 130, 130*t*, 147
  financial, 179–184
  frequency of, 130
  gage repeatability and reproduction for,
    427–428
  goal-question-metric for, 410–411
  of independent process variables, 411, 412*f*
  information technology informing, 225–226
  of knowledge management, 197, 200
  management "Gemba" walks for, 289
  management reviews for, 289–290, 296–297
  management role in, 23, 24, 140, 141
  of management style, 151–152
  measure systems analysis, 427–428
  organizational alignment with, 130
  overview of, 409
  of postproject outcome, 265
  of process capability, 437–439
  of processes, 24, 108–110, 410–412
  of process management maturity, 367, 368*f*
  of process objectives, 370–371
  of process variation, 433–437

in project management, 247*t*, 259–260, 261–265, 412–413
qualitative, 409, 465–467, 485–486, 549
of quality, 281, 283–292, 296–298, 310–316, 409–443, 532–533
quantitative, 409, 465–466, 485–486
regulations, laws, and standards for, 298, 417, 418, 428
of reliability, 439–443, 440*f*, 443*f*
of resource usage, 263
rewards and recognition tied to, 79–80, 414
risk assessment, 189–193, 193*f*–194*f*, 239–240, 240*f*, 263, 516–517
sampling for, 416–419, 420, 427, 440, 532*f*, 533
self-assessments, 19, 285, 548
skip-level meetings, 290
statistics for, 409–415, 419–427, 440 (*See also* statistics)
in strategic planning, 89, 91, 121, 124, 128–131, 129*f*, 130*t*
survey data, 463, 465, 466–467, 484–488, 492–493, 520–521, 548, 549
team evaluation, 79–80
tenets for design of, 415
timeliness, 261–262
of training and development needs, 543, 545–552, 550*t*
of training and development outcomes, 541, 545, 546, 568–575, 569*f*, 574*t*
trend and pattern analysis, 429–433
by work groups, 59
media, selection of, 209–210
median, 420
meetings
joint planning, 489–490
skip-level, 290
team, 67–68
as waste, 383
mentorship, 23
Merrill, P., 45
metaphors, for organization culture, 153
microlearning, 565–566
mind mapping, 353–354, 354*f*, 405*t*
Mintzberg, Henry, 88
misalignment, 395
mission and value statements
for change management, 35–36
communication of, 207
customer service-focused, 499
examples of, 93
leadership defining, 2
management responsibility for, 12, 140
organizational culture reflected in, 153
project, 246*t*
quality-focused, 278–280, 297
strategic planning of, 91–93, 92*f*, 118
team commitment to, 55, 57, 66, 73
vision statement vs., 93
mistake-proofing, 192, 395–398, 406*t*

mobile technology
business environment analysis of, 113
communication via, 213, 217, 220–221, 226, 227–228
mode, 420
modeling, in change management, 32
modular assembly, 532
modular corporation, 9–10
monitoring
appraisal costs and, 362
of budgets, 141, 184, 262, 262*f*
of customer satisfaction data, 492
information technology for, 221
of process objectives, 370–371
in project management, 236, 259–260, 261–265
of strategic plan deployment, 131
of supplier process improvements, 526
monument, 405*t*
morphological box, 360
Morrison, T., 208
motion waste, 381, 382
motivation
dissatisfiers or hygiene factors for, 37, 143
empowerment and, 48
extrinsic, 36, 38
intrinsic, 36, 38
by leadership, 20, 36–38
by management, 23, 142–149
motivational feedback, 75
qualitative assessment of, 465–466
satisfiers for, 37, 143
six Rs for, 81
team, 81
theories of, 36–38
Motorola, 16, 150, 345
Mouton, J. S., 148, 149*f*
MRP (material requirements planning), xviii, xviii*f*, 388
MRP II (material resource planning), xviii, xviii*f*
MTBF (mean time between failures), 440
MTBMA (mean time between maintenance actions), 441
MTR (mean time to repair), 441
MTTF (mean time to failure), 440
muda, 380, 405*t*. *See also* waste
multiple regression, 423
multiple sampling, 419
multivoting, 43, 355, 356*f*
Mumford, A., 144
murmurs, 488
musical intelligence, 144
must-be quality elements, 479–481
Myers, Isabel, 151
Myers-Briggs Type Indicator (MBTI), 62, 151–152
mystery shoppers, 488

N

Nanus, Burt, 1
National Cash Register, 309

National Committee for Quality Assurance (NCQA), 299
National Institute of Standards and Technology (NIST), 428
Naumann, Earl, 495
nearest neighbor, 432
needs
    customer, 469–476
    hierarchy of, 36–37, 37*f*, 143
    techniques and tools to assess, 548–549
    for training, 543, 545–552, 550*t*
negotiation
    common uses of, 41
    in conflict management, 40, 43
    financial, 41, 184
    by leadership, 38–41, 41*f*, 43
    principled, 43
    in supply chain management, 41, 533
    in teams, 69
    techniques for, 39–40
    timing of, 39
    win-win orientation in, 39
Nerur, S., 234
net income per share, 178
net present value (NPV), 242–243, 244
net promoter score (NPS), 494
net sales, 177
network diagramming, 254, 256. *See also* activity network diagrams
network organization, 9–10
net worth, 177
neural networks, 431
NGT (nominal group technique), 355, 356*f*
NIST (National Institute of Standards and Technology), 428
noise, 216–217
nominal group technique (NGT), 355, 356*f*
noncore customers, 458
non-value-added waste, eliminating, 383–384. *See also* lean
nonverbal communication, 208, 214
Nordstrom, 493
normal distributions, 421, 422*f*, 426
norming stage of teams, 64*f*, 65
norms
    organizational (*See* organizational culture)
    team, 65, 66–67
Norton, D., 283
np-charts, 425
NPS (net promoter score), 494
NPV (net present value), 242–243, 244
number of defects analysis, 521

O

objectives. *See* goals and objectives
observation
    of customer satisfaction, 488
    for qualitative assessment, 465
    for training needs analysis, 548, 549

occasion for purchase, customer segmentation by, 460
occurrence, FMEA assessing, 103
OC (operating characteristics) curve, 418, 418*f*
OE (operating expenses), 401
OEE (overall equipment effectiveness), 398–399, 405*t*
Ohmae, Kenichi, 137
Ohno, Taiichi, 386, 388, 390
OJT (on-the-job-training), 553–554, 565, 575
Okes, D., 148
omission, errors of, 396
one-dimensional quality elements, 479–480
one-to-one interviews, 167, 465, 487
one-to-one marketing, 457, 469. *See also* customer relationship management
on-the-job-training (OJT), 553–554, 565, 575
open-mindedness, in communication, 212
operating characteristics (OC) curve, 418, 418*f*
operating expenses (OE), 401
operational availability, 441
operational excellence, 383. *See also* lean
operational leadership, 15
operational plans
    management role in, 140
    project management, 271*f*–272*f*, 273
    strategic planning, 90*f*, 91, 95, 121–122, 123*f*–124*f*, 126–127
operational quality management, 320
operations
    Baldrige criteria related to, 302, 303
    information technology for, 221, 222*f*
    internal capability analysis of, 117
    as internal function, 157
    operational process risks, 186*t*, 188–189
    quality management standards for, 296
    strategic planning for, 89
opportunities, SWOT analysis of, 101, 102*f*
order requirements, supplier, 519
organizational culture
    change management and, 27, 28, 34–36, 154, 308
    communication affected by, 209
    country culture affecting, 36
    customer-focused, 453, 468
    defined, 34
    empowerment changing, 47, 49, 50
    factors contributing to, 34–36
    internal capability analysis of, 118
    internal customer/staff treatment in, 453
    knowledge management supported by, 199, 202
    leadership shaping, 15
    lean and, 384
    management theories and styles reflected in, 152–154
    manifestations of, 152–153
    measurement and assessment and, 414
    organizational structure and, 13, 35, 153
    quality-based, 153, 305, 308

strategic planning effects of, 89, 115, 118, 125
teams changing, 58
technology adoption and, 115
organizational diagnosis, 548
organizational excellence, 383. *See also* lean
organizational profiles, 301
organizational structure, 2–13
  boundaryless, 9–10
  by cell, 9, 61
  centralization/decentralization of, 2, 5–6, 155
  classical organizational theory on, 143
  combinations of, 12
  communication affected by, 207–208, 213, 219*t*
  competition influencing, 11
  complexity of, 2
  core competencies as focus of, 11
  by customer, 7, 8*f*
  customer segmentation by, 459
  design of, 2–5
  division of labor in, 4–5, 29–30
  empowerment changing, 47, 47*f*
  environmental factors influencing, 12
  facilities influencing, 12
  formalization of, 2
  by function, 6–7, 7*f*, 154–155
  by geography, 7–8, 8*f*
  horizontal, 4–5, 6
  internal capability analysis of, 117
  knowledge management affected by, 201
  management hierarchy and, 12–13
  management role in developing, 140
  matrix, 6, 9, 10*f*
  organizational culture and, 13, 35, 153
  parallel or collateral, 6, 61
  by process, 8, 8*f*
  by product, 7, 7*f*
  for project management, 232, 235
  purpose of, 3
  regulations, laws, and standards shaping, 11
  size influencing, 10–11
  span of control in, 4
  strategy influencing, 10
  by team, 9, 59, 60*f*, 61
  technology influencing, 11
  types of, 6–12
  unions influencing, 11
  unity of command in, 3
  vertical, 3–4, 6
  workforce issues influencing, 12
organizational variation, 436–437
organization buyers, 456
organization size, customer segmentation by, 459
organization type, customer segmentation by, 459
organizers, management role as, 22, 23, 139, 140
out-of-spec materials, 382
outsourcing
  change management with, 35
  defined, 517
  reasons for, 529–530
  supplier risk management and, 517–518

overall equipment effectiveness (OEE), 398–399, 405*t*
overprocessing waste, 381, 382
overproduction waste, 380

P

panel discussions, 561
panel interviews, 167
panels, customer, 489
parallel thinking as, 356
Pareto analysis, 385
Pareto charts, 33*f*, 333, 405*t*, 429
Pareto principle, 321, 333
participative management style, 150
partnerships, supplier, 527–531, 533
Partsch, Wolfgang, 509
Pascale, Richard, 21
past customers, 460
past performance index (PPI), 523
patents, technology, 115
pattern analysis, 430–433
payback period, 242, 244
PCF (Process Classification Framework), 367
p-charts, 426
PDCA/PDSA. *See* plan-do-check-act (PDCA)/
    plan-do-study-act (PDSA)
PDPC (process decision program charts), 340, 342,
    342*f*, 406*t*
PEEP (place for everything and everything in its
    place), 386
peer interviews, 167
Peppers, D., 469
performance evaluation. *See also* measurement and
    assessment
  alignment of, 130, 225
  balanced scorecard for, 129
  communication in, 208, 210, 216
  critical success factors for, 129, 129*f*
  customer service, 499–500
  empowerment changing, 48
  feedback loops for, 128–129, 130, 130*t*
  human resources responsibility for, 162, 169, 171
  information technology informing, 225–226
  internal customers receiving, 454
  organizational alignment with, 130
  in overall equipment effectiveness, 399
  quality objectives discussed in, 134
  strategic planning, 89, 91, 121, 124, 128–131,
    129*f*, 130*t*
  supplier, 520–524
  team, 59, 76, 79–81
  360° feedback in, 171, 208
  training needs identified in, 549
performance excellence models, 300–304, 301*f*.
    See also Baldrige Performance Excellence
    Program; lean
performance management, 24
performing stage of teams, 64*f*, 65
PERT (program/project evaluation and review
    technique), 247*t*, 254, 256, 336

Phillips, J. J., 569
physical constraints, 402
picture association, 360
PIMS (Profit Impact of Market Strategy), 280
Pinterest, 228
plagiarism, 85
plan-do-check-act (PDCA)/plan-do-study-act
    (PDSA)
    for customer satisfaction surveys, 493
    Deming's adaptation of, 319, 345
    as problem-solving tools, 345, 356f
    for process management, 406t
    for quality audits, 287
    for quality management standards, 294, 296
    for risk management, 189
    Shewhart development of, 317, 345
    for strategic planning models, 91
    for supply chain management, 531
    for training and development evaluation, 574
    trend analysis and, 433
planning
    enterprise resource, xviii, xviiif, 24
    joint planning meetings, 489–490
    long-range, 89
    management skills and abilities for, 23, 139, 140
    material requirements, xviii, xviiif, 388
    material resource, xviii, xviiif
    problem-solving tools for, 336–342
    project management, 232, 239–261, 246t–247t, 262
    project planning and estimation tools, 239–261
    quality, 88, 89, 131–135, 278, 280, 281–283,
        295–296, 303, 305, 319, 477
    scenario, 89, 96, 191
    sprint, 238
    strategic (*See* strategic planning)
    succession, 164, 166
    training and development, 540–541, 543,
        550–551
PMI (Project Management Institute), 232, 234, 516
point of use (POU), 388
Poisson distributions, 421, 422f
poka-yoke, 192, 395–398, 406t
policies
    changes to, 29, 32
    code of ethics on following, 84
    communication of, 207, 208
    conflict due to, 42
    constraints from, 402
    defined, 132
    human resources responsibility for, 156, 164
    information technology, 226, 227
    knowledge management, 196, 199
    management responsibility for, 12, 132, 140
    organizational culture reflected in, 152, 153
    project management, 232
    quality, 131–133, 278, 280–281, 297
    trend analysis, 430
Porter, 107
portfolio analysis, 244–245
positive reinforcement, 145, 216, 454

Posner, B. Z., 17
potential customers, 458, 460
potential process capability, 438
POU (point of use), 388
power
    authority and, 3
    empowerment shifting (*See* empowerment)
    knowledge management perceived as, 196,
        201, 202
    as motivation, 38
    organizational culture and, 35
PPAP (production part approval process), 406t
PPI (past performance index), 523
Prahalad, C. K., 87
precision, of measurements, 428, 441
precontrol charts, 426–427
predictive project management, 232–234, 233f
preferred suppliers, 514
preliminary hazard analysis, 517
prerequisite trees, 401
presentations, training, 561
prevention costs, 361, 362–363
prices
    market-perceived price profile, 490
    supplier data on, 521
primary customers, 446, 468
principal component analysis, 432
principle-centered leadership, 149
priorities matrix
    as problem-solving tool, 339–340, 341f
    for process management, 406t
    for quality function deployment, 475–476
prioritization matrix, 245, 513
probability distributions, 420–421, 422f, 426
problem-solving
    for customer service, 501
    reasons for failures of, 328–329
    restating problem in, 501
    systematic approach to, 328
    team, 55, 75
    theory of inventive, 45–46
    tools for, 328–364
problem-solving model, 406t
problem-solving tools, 328–364
    activity network diagrams as, 336–337, 337f
    affinity diagrams as, 332, 337, 338f
    analogies as, 354, 355f
    basic management and planning tools, 336–342
    brainstorming as, 353
    cause-and-effect diagrams as, 331–332, 332f
    check sheets as, 330, 332f
    control charts as, 333–334, 334f
    costs of quality as, 329, 360–364
    creative vs analytical thinking as, 352–353
    critical thinking as, 357
    design for manufacturing ability/and assembly
        as, 357–358
    Design for Six Sigma as, 358
    failure mode and effect analysis as, 343, 348–350,
        351f

five Whys as, 357, 358*f*
flowcharts as, 329, 330*f*–331*f*
histograms as, 334, 335*f*
innovation and creativity tools, 352–360
interrelationship diagraphs as, 337–338, 339*f*
Kepner-Tregoe as, 344–345
lateral and parallel thinking as, 355–356
matrix diagrams as, 338–339, 340*f*
mind mapping as, 353–354, 354*f*
multivoting as, 355, 356*f*
nominal group technique as, 355, 356*f*
overview of, 328–329
Pareto charts as, 33*f*, 333
PDCA/PDSA cycle, 345, 356*f*
priorities matrix as, 339–340, 341*f*
process decision program charts as, 340, 342, 342*f*
process improvement model as, 350, 352
process improvement tools, 328, 343–352
root cause analysis as, 343–344, 349
SCAMPER as, 360
scatter diagrams as, 334–336, 335*f*
seven classic quality tools, 329–336
Six Sigma and DMAIC model as, 345–348, 347*f*–348*f*
storyboard technique as, 360
tree diagrams as, 342, 342*f*
TRIZ methodology as, 359, 359*t*
procedures, for process analysis, 377–378, 377*f*, 406*t*
process analysis, 371–383
control plans for, 378, 379*f*, 403*t*
flowcharting/process mapping for, 372–376, 374*f*–376*f*, 406*t*
industry-specific documentation for, 380
procedures and work instructions for, 377–378, 377*f*, 406*t*
reasons for, 371–372
waste elimination for, 380–383, 405*t*
process capability measurements, 437–439
Process Classification Framework (PCF), 367
process decision program charts (PDPC), 340, 342, 342*f*, 406*t*
process(es)
analysis of, 371–383, 403*t*, 405*t*–406*t*
benchmarking, 24, 108–110
capability of, 437–439
defined, 366
engineering of, 157 (*See also* process reengineering)
external customer management, 464
FMEA of, 103, 349, 351*f*, 440
goals and objectives of, 367, 369–371, 369*f*, 405*t*
improvement of (*See* process improvement)
integrated business, 158–159, 158*f*, 160*f*, 225
knowledge management, 197–199, 201–202
management competence auditing, 24
management of (*See* process management)
mapping of (*See* process mapping)
master service delivery, 499
measurement and assessment of, 24, 108–110, 410–412

organizational structure by, 8, 8*f*
problem-solving tools to improve, 328, 343–352
Process Classification Framework, 367
process quality audits, 286
statistical process control, xvii, xviii*f*, 304, 317, 389, 423–426, 424*f*, 424*t*, 440, 553
supplier requirements, 518
system distinction from, 366–367
team, 66–68, 74–75
total quality management centered on, 305
training and development as, 543–545, 544*f*
variation in, 433–437
work in process, 382, 385, 389
process excellence, 383. *See also* lean
process improvement
investments, 362
model, 350, 352
monitoring supplier, 526
problem-solving tools, 328, 343–352
teams, 56–57, 73–74
process management, 366–407
defined, 367
lean tools for, 383–399, 403*t*–407*t*
overview of, 366–367
process, defined, 366
process analysis for, 371–383, 403*t*, 405*t*–406*t*
Process Classification Framework for, 367
process goals and objectives in, 367, 369–371, 369*f*, 405*t*
process management maturity assessment, 367, 368*f*
for quality planning, control, and improvement, 278, 406*t*
SIPOC linkages for, 366, 367*f*, 407*t*
system distinction for, 366–367
techniques, methodologies, and tools for, summary of, 402*t*–407*t*
theory of constraints for, 399–402, 407*t*
process mapping, 372–376, 374*f*–376*f*, 406*t*. *See also* value stream mapping
process partners, 447
process reengineering, xvii, xviii*f*, 406*t*
process variation measurements, 433–437
process village, 406*t*
producer's risk, 417–418
product
backlog and sprints, 238
cost structures, 183
development of, 156, 202–203, 222
engineering of, 157
organizational structure by, 7, 7*f*
product-driven quality, 277
product quality audits, 286
product/service risks, 186*t*
quality characteristics of, 276
reliability of, 439–440
rework of, 382
supplier quality data on, 521
supplier verification and traceability of, 518

technical requirements for, 518
terminology of, xxi
product development
information technology informing, 222
as internal function, 156
knowledge management and, 202–203
production control function, 157
production part approval process (PPAP), 406*t*
productivity
human relations theory on, 143
management task of, 25
production control function handling, 157
quality evolution and, xvii–xviii, xviii*f*
scientific management approach to, 142–143
Scrum burndown chart measuring, 238
teams improving, 55, 57
theory of constraints calculation of, 401
product reliability, 439–440
product rework, 382
professional development, 169, 573. *See also*
training and development
profitability, customer segmentation by, 459
profit and loss statements, 174–175, 177–178, 178*f*
ratios derived from, 180
Profit Impact of Market Strategy (PIMS), 280
programmed instruction, 558
program/project evaluation and review technique
(PERT), 247*t*, 254, 256, 336
project budgets, 232, 247*t*, 258–259, 259*f*, 262, 262*f*,
264–265
project charter, 232, 246*t*, 267–269, 268*f*
project concept/scope statement, 246*t*, 248, 268
project deliverables, 246*t*, 248, 250*f*, 264, 412–413
project documentation, 265–273
project funding approval request, 247*t*, 260
project management, 229–273
action plans, 271*f*–272*f*, 273
agile, 234–237
basics of, 231–239
close-out actions, 264–265
cross-functional, 231
defined, 229
documentation, 265–273
end-of-project evaluation, 263–264
evolutionary or incremental, 233, 233*f*, 234
initiation of, 229–230, 232
iterative, 233, 233*f*, 234–238
life cycle methodologies, 232–238
of long-term projects, 230–231
management competence with, 24
measuring and monitoring in, 236, 247*t*,
259–260, 261–265, 412–413
negotiation in, 40
overview of, 229–231
planning the project in, 232, 239–261, 246*t*–247*t*,
262
postproject audits, 264–265
postproject outcome assessment, 265
project, defined, 232
project charter, 232, 246*t*, 267–269, 268*f*

project life cycle in, 231–232
project planning and estimation tools, 239–261
reasons for initiating, 229–230
Scrum, 237–239
of short-term projects, 230
teams, 238–239, 246*t*, 248, 269, 270, 273
waterfall, linear, or predictive, 232–234, 233*f*
Project Management Institute (PMI), 232, 234, 516
Project Management Organization, 232
project measurements, 247*t*, 259–260
project plan approval, 247*t*, 260–261
project planning and estimation tools
cost-benefit analysis, 240–245, 243*f*, 262
planning methodologies, 245–261, 246*t*–247*t*
portfolio analysis, 244–245
prioritization matrix, 245
project ranking and prioritization, 242–244
project selection decision analysis, 241–242
return on assets, 244
risk assessment, 239–240, 240*f*
strategic fit analysis, 245
project reports, 247*t*, 259–260, 264
property, plant, and equipment, 177, 385
proprietary information
code of ethics on, 85
customer conflict management and, 503
information technology and security of, 223
patents on, 115
psychographics, customer segmentation by, 460
psychomotor domain, 558
pull systems, 388, 390, 531
purchase type, customer segmentation by, 459
purchase volume, customer segmentation by, 459
purchasing function, 156–157
purpose hierarchy, 360
push systems, 531

Q

QFD (quality function deployment), 134, 282,
472–476, 473*f*–475*f*
QIPs (quality improvement projects), 436. *See also*
continual improvement
QLAs (quality-level agreements), 451, 452*f*
QPI (quality performance index), 523–524
qualified suppliers, 514
qualitative data/assessment, 409, 465–467,
485–486, 549
quality
acceptable quality limit, 418
attractive, 479
audits, 285–287, 288*f*–289*f*, 296, 298, 324, 525,
575
characteristics of, 276–277
costs of, 278, 280, 283, 292, 329, 360–364, 403*t*
of design vs. of conformance, 278, 321
drivers of, 277
economic case for, 174, 185, 280
evolution of, xvii–xix, xviii*f*
financial management for, 174, 184–185

future of, xix–xx
indifferent, 480
internal function handling, 157
as investment not expense, 280, 292
job descriptions on, 165
management competence auditing, 24
management of (*See* quality management)
market-perceived quality profile, 490
material acceptance and, 532–533, 532*f*
meanings of, 275–276
measurement and assessment of, 281, 283–292,
　　296–298, 310–316, 409–443, 532–533
mission statements on, 278–280, 297
must-be, 479–481
objectives for, 133–134, 280, 281, 295
one-dimensional, 479–480
organizational culture of, 153, 305, 308
overall equipment effectiveness accounting
　　for, 399
planning, control, and improvement of, 278,
　　281–283, 295–297, 319–324, 477
　　(*See also* continual improvement; quality
　　improvement projects)
policies on, 131–133, 278, 280–281, 297
problem-solving tools for, 329–336
product, 276, 277, 286, 521
regulations, laws, and standards for, 133, 277,
　　282, 285, 293–300, 309, 525
reverse, 480
strategic planning addressing, 88, 89, 131–135,
　　278, 280, 281–283, 303, 305
supplier, 510 (*See also* supply chain
　　management)
teams improving, 55
training and development in, 169, 173–174, 323,
　　538–539, 553–554, 572–573, 575
Quality 4.0 technology, 113–114
quality analyst, 173
quality assurance engineer, 173
quality auditor, 173, 285
quality audits, 285–287, 288*f*–289*f*, 296, 298, 324,
　　525, 575
quality circles, 324
quality control engineer, 172–173
quality coordinator, 173
quality function deployment (QFD), 134, 282,
　　472–476, 473*f*–475*f*
quality improvement projects (QIPs), 436. *See also*
　　continual improvement
quality inspector, 173
quality-level agreements (QLAs), 451, 452*f*
quality management
　　absolutes of, 321
　　benefits of implementing, 298
　　change management and, 295, 308
　　human resources in, 169, 171, 172–174
　　information technology informing, 222
　　job descriptions/positions in, 172–174
　　leadership for, 294–295, 303, 307
　　operational, 320

principles of, defining, 133
　　quality models and theories for, 293–324
　　quality system for, 275–292, 293, 406*t*
　　regulations, laws, and standards for, 133, 277,
　　　293–300, 309
　　risk-based thinking in, 183, 189
　　situational context for, 294
　　strategic, 320
　　supplier requirements for, 518
　　support systems for, 295–296
　　tools for (*See* quality management tools)
　　total (*See* total quality management)
　　training and development in, 169, 173–174,
　　　538–539, 572–573, 575
quality management tools
　　measurement and assessment, 409–443
　　problem-solving tools, 328–364
　　process management, 366–407
　　quotations on, 327
quality manager, 172
quality models and theories, 293–324
　　continuous quality improvement, 309–316,
　　　311*t*, 312*f*, 314*f*–315*f*
　　Crosby's, 321–322 (*See also* Crosby, Philip B.)
　　Deming's, 317–319 (*See also* Deming,
　　　W. Edwards)
　　Feigenbaum's, 322–323 (*See also* Feigenbaum,
　　　Armand V.)
　　Ishikawa's, 323–324 (*See also* Ishikawa, Kaoru)
　　Juran's, 319–321 (*See also* Juran, Joseph M.)
　　overview of, 293
　　performance excellence models, 300–304, 301*f*
　　quality philosophies underlying, 317–324
　　regulations, laws, and standards for, 293–300
　　Shewhart's, 317 (*See also* Shewhart, Walter A.)
　　Taguchi's, 324
　　total quality management, 304–309
quality performance index (QPI), 523–524
quality specialist, 173
quality supervisor, 173
quality system, 275–292
　　characteristics of quality, 276–277
　　defined, 293
　　drivers of quality, 277
　　little q and Big Q, 278, 321
　　meanings of quality, 275–276
　　measurement of effectiveness, 281, 283–292
　　mission and policy in, 278–281
　　overview of, 275
　　quality of design vs. of conformance, 278
　　quality planning, deployment, and
　　　documentation, 278, 281–283, 406*t*
　　quality system audits, 286–287
　　strategic planning for, 278, 280, 281–283
quality technician, 173
quality trainer, 173
quantitative data, 409, 465–466, 485–486
questionnaires. *See also* surveys
　　learning styles, 144
　　supplier, 520–521

for team evaluation, 79
for training needs analysis, 548, 549
questions
    active listening using, 211–212, 215
    close-ended, 211
    communication skills for asking, 210–212
    five Whys, 357, 358*f*, 404*t*
    goal-question-metric, 410–411
    interview, 167, 210–211
    is-is not, 360
    open-ended, 210–211
    SCAMPER, 360
    Socratic method, 45, 561
    survey, 485, 492–493 (*See also* surveys)
    "what-if," 190–191
    who, what, when, where, why, and how, 360
queue times, as waste, 382
quick assets, 177
quote requirements, supplier, 518

R

R&D. *See* research and development
random sampling, 416
range, 420
rapid application development (RAD), 237
rapid exchange of tooling and dies (RETAD), 394.
            See also single-minute exchange of die
rational subgrouping, 417
ratios, financial, 179–183
R charts, 425, 426
Reagan, Ronald, 300
receiving inspections, 533
record keeping
    bookkeeping methods, 175–176
    of customer satisfaction data, 492
    financial, 175–176
    human resources responsibility for, 163
    team, 78
    training needs analysis review of, 548
regression analysis, 421, 423, 432
regulations, laws, and standards
    business environment analysis of, 106, 119–120
    communication on, 210, 215
    financial management compliance with, 156,
        176
    human resources compliance with, 156, 164
    IATF (*See* IATF 16949-2016)
    for industry-specific documentation, 380
    ISO, 515 (*See also* ISO *entries*)
    knowledge management of, 198
    labor, 22, 156, 164
    management competence with, 25
    for measurement and assessment, 298, 417,
        418, 428
    organizational structures based on, 11
    for project management, 232, 245
    quality, 133, 277, 282, 285, 293–300, 309, 525
    risk management, 187–188, 189, 192, 193, 299
    sampling, 417, 418

strategic planning effects of, 89, 106, 110, 111,
        114, 119–120
    supply chain management, 511, 515
    technology, 114
    training and development to meet, 545, 546,
        553
Reichheld, F. F., 495
reinforcement
    of organizational culture, 153
    positive, 145, 216, 454
    reinforcement theory, 38
    team motivation with, 81
rejected parts, as waste, 381, 399
relationship diagrams, 337. *See also*
            interrelationship diagraphs
relationship marketing, 469. *See also* customer
            relationship management
reliability
    of measurements/data, 428, 441, 442*f*, 443
    measurements of, 439–443, 440*f*, 443*f*
reliability engineer, 173
remedial journey, 321
remote learning, 563. *See also* e-learning
reporting. *See also* documentation
    audit, 287
    as communication, 208, 224
    on customer satisfaction data, 492
    financial, 156, 174–179
    on process objectives, 370–371
    project management, 247*t*, 259–260, 264
    on strategic plan deployment, 131
    on supplier performance, 521–522, 522*f*
    waste in, 383
reputational risk, 496–497
research and development (R&D)
    customer segmentation, 462
    as internal function, 157
    knowledge management of, 198, 200
    market, 448
    survey research, 485
reserve for depreciation, 177
resources
    allocation of
        in change management, 30
        cost-benefit analysis for, 240–245, 243*f*
        in customer relationship management,
            504–506
        in project management, 239, 240–245
        in quality plans, 281
        in strategic plan deployment, 122, 124–127
    budgets of (*See* budgets)
    conflicts over, 42
    customer service-focused, 500
    enterprise resource planning, xviii, xviii*f*, 24
    internal capability analysis of, 117
    internal competition for, 30
    management stewardship of, 21, 140
    material resource planning, xviii, xviii*f*
    means matrix on, 94–95, 94*f*–95*f*, 126
    measuring usage of, 263

project management, 239, 240–245, 247*t*, 256, 257*f*, 263
  quality management, 281, 296–297
  resource requirements matrix, 247*t*, 256, 257*f*
  strategic planning effects of, 89, 94–95, 122, 124–127
  team motivation with, 81
  for training and development, 546
respect, 84
response surface methodology, 421, 423
responsibility
  code of ethics on, 84
  of human resources, 161–166
  of internal business functions, 155–157
  leadership roles and, 15–20
  linear responsibility matrix, 247*t*, 256, 258
  management roles and, 12–13, 21–26, 132, 138–141, 540–541
  social, of organizations, 25, 85, 112, 299
  team motivation with, 81
  team roles and, 67, 68–78, 70*t*–72*t*
restitution, to customers, 501
RETAD (rapid exchange of tooling and dies), 394. *See also* single-minute exchange of die
retail buyers, 455
retail chain buyers, 454
return on assets (ROA), 182, 244
return on investment (ROI), 174, 182, 243–244, 401
return on quality investment (ROQI), 292
return on training investment (ROTI), 541, 546, 556, 569–570, 569*f*
reverse quality elements, 480
rewards and recognition
  change management providing, 32
  for communication skills and abilities, 213
  customer, 495
  for customer service, 499
  empowerment leading to, 48, 49, 50
  equity theory on, 37
  expectancy theory on, 37
  human resources role in, 164, 168
  internal capability analysis of, 116
  internal competition for, 30
  for internal customers, 453
  for knowledge management, 202
  management theories and styles on, 143
  measurement and assessment tied to, 79–80, 414
  organizational culture influencing, 152
  for project management, 236
  for quality, 293, 300–304, 305, 308 (*See also* Malcolm Baldrige National Quality Award; Deming Prize)
  strategic planning supported by, 97
  team, 54, 59, 79–80
risk breakdown structure, 517
risk management, 185–194
  defined, 516
  FMEA for, 103–104, 105*f*, 188, 193, 239, 517
  for information technology, 228

outsourcing and, 517–518
  project management and, 239–240, 240*f*, 263
  regulations, laws, and standards for, 187–188, 189, 192, 193, 299
  reputational risk, 496–497
  risk, defined, 187
  risk analysis in, 99–104, 102*f*, 105*f*
  risk assessment for, 189–193, 193*f*–194*f*, 239–240, 240*f*, 263, 516–517
  risk-based thinking and, 188–189, 194
  risk identification in, 188–189, 517
  risk priority number in, 104
  of sampling risks, 417–419, 418*f*–419*f*, 532*f*
  situational context for, 187–188, 189
  supplier, 516–518
  team, 59
  types of risk, 186–187, 186*t*
rituals and routines
  of communication, 209
  of organizational culture, 35
ROA (return on assets), 182, 244
Rogers, M., 469
ROI (return on investment), 174, 182, 243–244, 401
role playing, 563
Romig, H. G., 417
root cause analysis, 45, 343–344, 349, 401, 406*t*
ROQI (return on quality investment), 292
Rosenbluth, Hal, 453
Rossett, A., 564
Rother, M., 392
ROTI (return on training investment), 541, 546, 556, 569–570, 569*f*
round-robin brainstorming, 353
roundtables, 561
Rs for motivation, six, 81
rule induction, 432
run charts, 333, 429, 429*f*

S

safety and security safeguards, supplier, 519
sales
  financial reporting on, 177, 181
  information technology informing, 221, 224
  as internal function, 156
  knowledge management for, 199
  leveling of, 407*t*
sampling, 416–419, 440
  acceptance, 417, 440, 532*f*, 533
  frequency of, 427
  methods of, 416–417
  reasons for not, 416
  risks in, 417–419, 418*f*–419*f*, 532*f*
  sample size for, 416–417, 420
Sarbanes-Oxley Act (2002, SOX), 176
satisfiers, 37, 143
SBPA (strategic business process architecture), xix, xx*f*
SCAMPER, 360
scatter diagrams, 334–336, 335*f*, 407*t*

scenario analysis/planning, 89, 96, 191
s charts, 425
Schein, E. H., 18, 34
Scholtes, Peter, 74
Schweiger, D. M., 150
scientific management, 142–143, 304
SCM. *See* supply chain management
scrap, 382. *See also* waste
scribes, team, 67, 69, 72*t*
Scrum project management, 237–239
secondary customers, 446
second-party audits, 286
Securities and Exchange Commission (SEC), 156, 175
selection errors, 396
self-assessment
    of leadership, 19
    of quality, 285
    of training needs, 548
self-awareness, of leadership, 19
self-confidence, of leadership, 19
self-control
    of leadership, 19
    of quality, 320
self-directed learning, 560–561
self-directed teams, 57–58
self-managed teams, 57–58, 305
self-regulation, of leadership, 19–20
Senge, Peter, 28, 54, 147–148, 199, 327, 433
sensitivity, in communication, 212
Serrano, Eileen, 327
service buyers, 456
service-level agreements (SLAs), 451, 452*f*
service process mapping, 499
service providers, 447, 455
service receivers, 447
services
    cost of quality for, 362–363
    cost structures, 183
    product/service risks, 186*t*
    quality characteristics of, 276–277
    service-driven quality, 277
    strategic planning for, 89
    technology to improve, 115
    terminology including, xxi
service users, 456
seven deadly diseases (Deming), 318
Seven Habits, 148–149
shareholders
    financial reporting to, 156, 175
    management competence with, 25
    shareholder's equity, 175, 177
    as stakeholders, 110, 111*f* (*See also* stakeholders)
Shewhart, Walter A., xvii, 304, 317, 345, 434–435
shifts, in patterns, 431
Shingo, Shigeo, 388, 395
Shingo Prize for Excellence in Manufacturing, 304
ship-to-stock programs, 531–532
Shook, J., 392
short-term trend analysis, 430, 433

sigma, 346
simulations, 563
simultaneous engineering, 159, 160*f*
single-minute exchange of die (SMED), 388, 389, 394–395, 407*t*
single-piece flow, 407*t*
single sampling, 418
SIPOC (supplier-input-process-output-customer) linkages, 366, 367*f*, 407*t*
situational context. *See also* environmental factors
    for communication, 205, 210
    for conflict management, 43
    for leadership, 18–19, 147
    for quality management, 294
    for risk management, 187–188, 189
    for strategic planning, 88
situational leadership/management, 147
six Rs for motivation, 81
Six Sigma
    continuous quality improvement in, 310
    critical thinking in, 45
    critical-to-quality process outputs in, 411, 412*f*
    defined, 345
    Design for Six Sigma, 278, 358, 403*t*
    DMAIC model, 345–348, 347*f*–348*f*, 403*t*–404*t*
    evolution and evolving principles of, xvii–xix, xviii*f*, 347–348
    leadership implementing, 16, 150, 347
    for process management, 403*t*–404*t*, 407*t*
six thinking hats, 356
skills and abilities. *See also* core competencies
    communication (*See* communication skills and abilities)
    competency analysis of, 172
    customer service, 500–502
    internal capability analysis of, 116
    interpersonal, 212–217
    KESAA requisites analysis for, 62, 63*f*, 548–549
    management (*See* management skills and abilities)
    pay-for-skills plans, 80
    project management building, 237
    social, 20, 25
    strategic planning effects of, 89, 115, 116, 124
    team selection based on, 62, 63*f*
    teams enhancing, 55
    technology adoption and, 115
    training and development to build (*See* training and development)
Skinner, B. F., 38, 145
skip-level meetings, 290
SLAs (service-level agreements), 451, 452*f*
SLM (supplier life cycle management), 511, 533
small business units, 384
Smarsh, 227
smart devices, 113, 114, 191. *See also* mobile technology
S.M.A.R.T.W.A.Y., 68, 93, 94*t*, 405*t*
SMED (single-minute exchange of die), 388, 389, 394–395, 407*t*

Smith, Fred, 87
Snapchat, 228
social media
    business environment analysis of, 113, 114
    communication via, 228
    customer data from, 488–489
social responsibilities, 25, 85, 112, 299
social skills, 20, 25
Socrates, 206
Socratic method, 45, 561
source inspections, 533
span of control, 4
SPC (statistical process control), xvii, xviii*f*, 304,
        317, 389, 423–426, 424*f*, 424*t*, 440, 553
special cause variation, 435
special project teams, 61
speed loss, 399
SPI (supplier performance index), 523
sponsors, team, 70*t*, 77
spread measures, 420
sprint planning, 238
staff
    assimilation of new, 168
    authority among, 3–4
    Baldrige criteria related to, 302, 303
    change affecting (*See* change management)
    division of labor among, 4–5, 29–30
    as employee buyers, 455
    empowerment of (*See* empowerment)
    exempt vs. nonexempt, 22
    generations in, 117, 117*f*
    human reliability assessment of, 192
    human resources for, 156, 161–174, 188–189, 222
    internal capability analysis of, 116–118, 117*f*
    internal change agents from, 27
    as internal customers, 447, 449–454, 452*f*
    job descriptions/positions for, 164–165,
        172–174
    labor laws for, 22, 156, 164
    labor unions of (*See* unions, labor)
    leadership of (*See* leadership)
    management role with, 23–24, 25, 140 (*See also*
        management)
    measurement and assessment effects on,
        413–415
    onboarding/orientation of, 168
    organizational culture and treatment of, 453
    quality assessment from feedback of, 291
    quality driven by, 277
    quality management function, 320
    recruitment of, 166, 167
    satisfaction of, 277, 453
    selection and hiring of, 165–168, 188–189
    as stakeholders, 110, 111*f* (*See also*
        stakeholders)
    strategic planning effects of, 89, 110, 111*f*,
        116–118
    teams of (*See* teams)
    total quality management involvement of,
        305

    training and development of (*See* training and
        development)
    workforce issues of
        business environment analysis of, 117
        organizational structure influenced by, 12
stakeholders. *See also specific stakeholders*
    interested parties as, 88, 110–112
    project planning for requirements of, 246*t*, 248,
        249*f*
    stakeholder analysis of, 110–112, 111*f*, 248, 249*f*,
        269–270, 270*f*, 273
    total quality management integrating, 305
standard deviation, 346, 420
standardization, 384, 386–387
standards. *See* regulations, laws, and standards
statements of cash flow, 174–175, 178–179
statements of shareholder's equity, 175
statistical control, 434, 438
statistical process control (SPC), xvii, xviii*f*, 304,
        317, 389, 423–426, 424*f*, 424*t*, 440, 553
statistics
    advanced, 421, 423
    analysis of, 419–427
    basic or simple, 409–415, 420–421
    defined, 409
    descriptive, 420
    precontrol charts, 426–427
    probability distributions, 420–421, 422*f*, 426
    process measurement, 410–412
    sampling, 420, 427, 440, 533
    statistical control, 434, 438
    statistical process control, xvii, xviii*f*, 304, 317,
        389, 423–426, 424*f*, 424*t*, 440, 553
steering committees, 73
Steiner, G. A., 97
stockholders. *See* shareholders
storming stage of teams, 64*f*, 65
storyboard technique, 360
storytelling and myths, 35, 200, 238
strategic analysis, 221, 222*f*
strategic business process architecture (SBPA), xix,
        xx*f*
strategic fit analysis, 245
strategic leadership, 2, 15
strategic plan deployment, 121–135
    cascading concept for, 127*f*
    consensus in, 95, 96, 125
    hoshin planning including, 95, 125, 127, 131
    leadership and management role in, 124,
        158
    means matrix review in, 126
    measurement and assessment of results, 121,
        124, 128–131, 129*f*, 130*t*
    monitoring of, 131
    operational/action plans for, 90*f*, 91, 95,
        121–122, 123*f*–124*f*, 126–127
    organizational culture supporting, 125
    overview of, 121
    quality in, 131–135, 282–283
    reporting on, 131

resource allocation and deployment for, 122, 124–127

tactical plans for, 90–91, 90*f*, 121–122, 123*f*–124*f*

strategic planning

Baldrige criteria for, 89, 129, 302, 303

barriers to successful, 97–98

business environment analysis for, 93, 99–120

for change management, 35

concepts of, 89–90

customer segmentation plan, 463

customer service-focused, 498, 500

defined, 88–89

deployment of, 90–91, 95–96, 121–135, 158, 282–283

information technology integrated with, 223

long-range planning vs., 89

management role in, 22, 23, 24, 158

measurement and assessment of, 89, 91, 121, 124, 128–131, 129*f*, 130*t*

models for, 88–98

organizational structures and, 10

quality included in, 88, 89, 131–135, 278, 280, 281–283, 303, 305

quotations on, 87

total quality management requirements for, 305

training and development alignment with, 540–541

strategic planning models, 88–98

barriers to successful, 97–98

deployment of, 90–91, 90*f*, 95–96, 126

feedback in, 91

goals and objectives established in, 93, 94*t*, 207–208

hoshin planning, 91–96, 92*f*, 94*f*–95*f*, 94*t*, 125, 127, 131, 207–208

leadership of, 91

means matrix in, 94–95, 94*f*–95*f*, 126

measurement and assessment of, 89, 91

mission and vision statements in, 91–93, 92*f*

operational/action plans in, 90*f*, 91, 95

overview of, 88–89

scenario analyses/planning, 89, 96

span of time in, 89, 90, 95

strategic planning, defined, 88–89

strategic planning concepts for, 89–90

strategy, defined, 88

tactical plans in, 90–91, 90*f*

traditional, 90–91, 90*f*, 127

transition to next year's planning, 95

strategic quality management, 320

strategic sourcing, 510

stratified sampling, 416

strengths-weaknesses-opportunities-threats (SWOT) analyses, 89, 100–103, 102*f*, 463, 500

structural variation, 435–436

structured "what-if" technique (SWIFT), 190–191

subject matter experts, for training, 566

succession planning, 164, 166

suggestion boxes, 488

Sullivan, Louis, 56

supplier life cycle management (SLM), 511, 533

supplier performance index (SPI), 523

suppliers

approval of, 513–514

audits of, 286, 520–521, 525

capabilities of, 515–516

certification of, 440, 514, 527, 533

classification of, 514, 527

communication by/with, 210, 518–520, 531, 533

defined, 510

feedback to, 526

improvement of, 524–526

internal capability analysis of, 117

logistics of, 531–532

material acceptance from, 532–533, 532*f*

out-of-spec material from, 382

partnerships and alliances with, 527–531, 533

performance evaluation of, 520–524

preferred, 514

qualified, 514

risk management, 516–518

selection of, 511–513

as stakeholders, 110, 111*f* (*See also* stakeholders)

supplier-input-process-output-customer (SIPOC) linkages, 366, 367*f*, 407*t*

supply chain management (SCM), 509–535

audits in, 286, 520–521, 525

certification of suppliers in, 440, 514, 527, 533

code of ethics in, 83, 85

communication in, 210, 518–520, 531, 533

corrective and preventive action in, 519, 521, 525–526

defined, 510

improvement efforts in, 524–526

inventory management function in, 157

life cycle management, 511, 533

logistics in, 531–532

management competence with, 25

material acceptance in, 532–533, 532*f*

materials management function in, 156–157

negotiation in, 41, 533

nonconforming product handling in, 524

outsourcing in, 35, 517–518, 529–530

overview of, 510–511, 533

partnerships and alliances in, 527–531, 533

performance evaluation in, 520–524

purchasing function in, 156–157

quotations on, 509

regulations, laws, and standards for, 511, 515

risk management, 516–518

strategic sourcing, 510

supplier selection and approval, 511–516

approval process, 513–514

capabilities rating, 515–516

classification of suppliers, 514

selection process and criteria, 511–513

systems thinking in, 161, 510

support, quality, 295–296

support systems technology, 114

surveys. *See also* questionnaires
    analysis and use of, 466–467
    comment card/suggestion box, 488
    customer and market, 463, 465, 466–467,
        484–488, 492–493
    e-mail and web-based, 487–488
    face-to-face, 487 (*See also* interviews)
    methods of, 485–488
    mystery shopper, 488
    qualitative, 465, 485–486
    quantitative, 465, 485–486
    supplier, 520–521
    survey research, 485
    telephone, 486–487
    for training needs analysis, 548, 549
    written/mail, 486
SWIFT (structured "what-if" technique), 190–191
swim lane charts, 329, 331*f*, 374, 376*f*
SWOT (strengths-weaknesses-opportunities-threats)
        analyses, 89, 100–103, 102*f*, 463, 500
symbols
    of organizational culture, 35
    for process capability measurements, 439
    for process mapping, 373, 374*f*
    for value stream mapping, 392
symposia, 539
system
    customer information feedback, 479*f*, 495
    defined, 366
    process distinction from, 366–367
    pull vs. push, 388, 390, 531
    quality, 275–292, 293, 406*t*
    training system model, 544*f*, 575
    voice of the customer as, 476–477, 477*f*
systematic sampling, 417
system of profound knowledge, 152, 319
systems thinking
    functional area interdependence in, 155,
        159–161
    in learning organizations, 200
    as management theory, 147–148
    in supply chain management, 161, 510
    in theory of constraints, 400–402
    in total quality management, 305

T

tabular data, 431
tacit knowledge, 195, 235
tactfulness, in communication, 212
tactical plans, 90–91, 90*f*, 121–122, 123*f*–124*f*
Taguchi, Genichi, 324
Taguchi loss function, 324, 324*f*
Tague, Nancy, 360
Taiwo, J., 45
takt time, 389, 391, 407*t*
tally sheets, 330, 332*f*
tampering, 437
TARP (U.S. Office of Consumer Affairs/Technical
        Assistance Research Programs), 484

task analysis, 548
Taylor, Frederick, 142–143
teams, 54–81
    agendas for, 66, 67, 75
    attendance at meetings of, 67
    barriers to successful, 55
    benefits of, 54–55
    cellular, 61
    champions of, 70*t*
    charter for, 73, 476
    configurations of, 56–62
    conflict management in, 69, 75, 76–77
    cross-functional, 73, 476–477, 512
    customer focus, 482, 484
    decision-making in, 54, 59, 66, 68, 77
    defined, 54
    dynamics in, 66, 78
    facilitators in, 56–57, 59, 69, 70*t*, 74, 76–78
    feedback in, 75, 76, 79
    first meeting of, guidelines for, 67–68
    goals and objectives, setting and working
        toward, 54, 56, 58, 64*f*, 65, 66, 68, 73, 75
    groupthink in, 81
    leadership of, 20, 56–57, 59, 61, 62, 69, 71*t*, 74,
        78, 81
    maintenance processes of, 66
    norms of, 65, 66–67
    organizational structure by, 9, 59, 60*f*, 61
    organizational support for, 78*f*
    overview of, 54–55
    participation in, 67, 74–75, 76
    performance evaluation of/by, 59, 76, 79–81
    process improvement, 56–57, 73–74
    process problems in, dealing with, 66–67,
        74–76
    project management, 238–239, 246*t*, 248, 269,
        270, 273
    reluctance to join, 63–64
    rewards and recognition for, 54, 59, 79–80
    roles and responsibilities in, 67, 68–78, 70*t*–72*t*
    scribes for, 67, 69, 72*t*
    selection of, 62–64, 74, 248
    self-managed, 57–58, 305
    six Rs for motivating, 81
    special project, 61
    sponsors of, 70*t*, 77
    stages of development, 64–65, 64*f*
    steering committees, 73
    structure of, 73–74
    supplier-selection, 512
    task processes of, 66
    team-building techniques, 66–68, 152
    team members, generally, 72*f*, 74, 78*f*
    temporary or ad hoc, 58
    timekeepers for, 67, 69, 71*t*
    timeliness in, 67
    training of, 57–58, 59, 73
    virtual, 61–62
    voice-of-the-customer, 476–477
    work groups, 58–61, 60*f*

technology
  adoption of new, 114–116
  artificial intelligence, 113, 221
  automation, 113
  autonomation, 113, 402*t*
  business environment analysis of, 112–116
  communications and, 113–114, 220–228 (*See also* information technology)
  computer-based instructional techniques, 563–564 (*See also* e-learning)
  data mining, 431–432 (*See also* big data; data mining)
  internal capability to implement, 115–116
  for knowledge management, 197–198, 202
  machine learning, 113
  mobile (*See* mobile technology)
  organizational structure influenced by, 11
  patents on, 115
  project management approach to, 235
  Quality 4.0, 113–114
  strategic planning effects of, 89, 112–116
  support systems, 114
telephone surveys, 486–487
temporary teams, 58
terminal objectives, 557–558
terminology, xxi, 97, 383. *See also* glossary and acronyms
theory of constraints (TOC), 399–402, 407*t*
Theory X, 143
Theory Y, 143
third-party audits, 286
threats, SWOT analysis of, 101, 102*f*
360° feedback, 171, 208
throughput, 389, 401, 407*t*
TickIT, 300
TILMAG (Transformation of Ideal Solution Elements with a Common Association Matrix), 360
time
  cycle time reduction, 384–386, 385*f*, 399, 403*t*
  downtime, as waste, 382, 399
  key events time line, 490
  long- vs. short-term trend analysis over, 430, 433
  managing within dimension of, 26
  mean time between failures, 440
  mean time between maintenance actions, 441
  mean time to failure, 440
  mean time to repair, 441
  meetings as waste of, 383
  payback period, 242, 244
  project management schedule, 232, 238, 247*t*, 252–256, 253*f*, 255*f*, 261–262
  queue times, as waste, 382
  strategic planning span of, 89, 90, 95
  takt, 389, 391, 407*t*
  time-dependent task diagrams, 247*t*, 254–256, 255*f*
  timekeeper in teams, 67, 69, 71*t*
  timeliness of communication, 213

timeliness of project, monitoring, 261–262
timing of negotiations, 39
timing of training, 568, 572
waiting waste of, 380, 382
TL 9000 R5.5, 299, 525
TOC (theory of constraints), 399–402, 407*t*
Toffler, Alvin, 457
Toffler, Heidi, 457
Toshiba, 309
total cost of quality, 362
total productive maintenance (TPM), 389, 407*t*
total quality control, 323–324
total quality management (TQM), 304–309
  award criteria approach to, 308
  Baldrige Award based on, 300, 305, 308
  barriers to implementation, 308–309
  benefits of, 306
  change management and, 36
  critical systems thinking in, 45
  element approach to, 307
  evolution of, xvii, xviii*f*
  guru approach to, 307
  implementation of, 306–309
  Japanese total quality approach to, 308
  Juran defining, 321
  management skills and abilities changed with, 138
  models and theories based on, 304–309
  organization model approach to, 307–308
  primary elements of, 305–306
tours, training, 566
Toyota, 309, 386, 390
Toyota Production System (TPS), xvii, xviii*f*, 113, 384, 388
TPM (total productive maintenance), 389, 407*t*
TQM. *See* total quality management
training and development, 537–576
  adult learning principles and, 556–557
  benefits and limitations of, 542–543, 542*t*
  business needs aligned with, 540–541
  causes of ineffectiveness or failure of, 570–571
  communication, 208, 210, 213, 218*t*
  competency-based methods of, 558–559
  corrective actions for successful, 551–552
  in cost of quality, 364
  costs and funding of, 540, 541, 546, 569–570
  curriculum development for, 555*f*
  customer service-focused, 499, 500, 501
  defined, 538
  delivery of, 545, 546, 559–568, 571–572
  design of program, 543–545, 546, 555–559, 560*f*, 567, 571
  development, terminology, 169, 573
  education distinguished, 538–539, 539*f*, 573
  effectiveness of, 541, 545, 546, 567–575
  e-learning, 559, 560–561, 560*f*, 567
    (*See also* computer-based instructional techniques; webinars)
  empowerment requiring, 48, 539
  evaluation of, 541, 545, 546, 568–575, 569*f*, 574*t*

facilitation, 77
fade-out of, 546
gamification of, 559, 560*f*
goals and objectives of, 574, 574*t*
human resources responsibility for, 162, 164,
    168–169, 170*f*
individual development distinguished, 169, 573
individual development plans for, 550–551
of individuals, evaluating, 573–575
investments in, for customer service, 500
for job performance improvement, 549–551, 550*t*
keys to improving effectiveness of, 567–568
learning objectives and, 557–558
learning theories on, 143–145, 144*f*
lesson plans for, 558
management role in, 23, 540–541
in measurement and assessment, 415
mutual investment in, 169, 170*f*
needs analysis, 543, 545–552, 550*t*
on-the-job-training, 553–554, 565, 575
organizational culture shared in, 153
planning for, 540–541, 543, 550–551
posttraining situation, 541, 545, 553, 572
as process, 543–545, 544*f*
quality-related, 169, 173–174, 323, 538–539,
    553–554, 572–573, 575
quotations on, 537
reasons for, 546–547
redundant, 567–568
return on investment in, 541, 546, 556, 569–570,
    569*f*
strategic planning alignment with, 540–541
supplier, 519, 526
team, 57–58, 59, 73
training within industry (TWI), 575
transactional leadership, 16, 150
transactional value stream mapping, 391
transformational leadership, 16, 150
Transformation of Ideal Solution Elements with a
    Common Association Matrix (TILMAG),
    360
transition trees, 402
transportation waste, 380–381, 382
tree diagrams
    constraints identified in, 33–34, 34*f*
    as problem-solving tools, 342, 342*f*
    for process management, 407*t*
    of strategic planning goals, objectives, and
        means, 95, 95*f*
Tregoe, B. B., 88, 344
trend analysis, 429–433
Triple Bottom Line, 512
TRIZ methodology, 45–46, 359, 359*t*, 407*t*
trustworthiness
    in communication, 212, 213, 217
    for conflict management, 503
    of leadership, 20
    in supplier partnerships, 531
t-test, 420
Tuckman, B. W., 64, 65

TWI (training within industry), 575
Twitter, 228, 488
Tyndall, Gene, 509
type 1 errors, 417–418
type 2 errors, 417–418

U

u-charts, 425
uncertainty risk, 187
unconditional guarantees, 490–491
undesirable effects (UDEs), 400
unions, labor
    human resources coordination with, 156, 163
    negotiation with, 38–39, 41
    organizational culture influenced by, 153
    organizational structure influenced by, 11
    steering committee representation of, 73
United Airlines, 497
unity of command, 3
universal sequence, 321
user stories, 238
U.S. Food and Drug Administration (FDA), 300
U-shaped work cells, 385, 385*f*, 403*t*
U.S. Naval Air Systems Command, 304
U.S. Office of Consumer Affairs/Technical
        Assistance Research Programs (TARP),
        484
Uttal, Bro, 537

V

validity, of measurements, 428, 442–443, 442*f*
value creation
    knowledge management and, 197
    management role in, 22
    team, 54
values. *See* beliefs and values
value stream mapping (VSM), 45, 391–394, 393*f*,
    407*t*
value streams
    management competence with, 24
    mapping of, 45, 391–394, 393*f*, 407*t*
variance, 420. *See also* analysis of variance
vertical alignment, of performance measures, 225
vertical organizational structures, 3–4, 6
vice president of quality, 172
virtual corporation, 9–10
virtual teams, 61–62
visible waste, 382
vision statements. *See also* mission and value
        statements
    for change management, 35–36
    communication of, 207
    customer service-focused, 499
    examples of, 92
    leadership defining, 2
    management responsibility for, 12, 140
    mission statements vs., 93
    organizational culture reflected in, 153

quality-focused, 297
strategic planning of, 91–93, 92f, 118
team commitment to, 57
visual management, 387–388, 389, 407t. *See also kanban* method
visual/spatial intelligence, 144
voice of the customer (VOC)
customer service performance measurement, 499–500
data sources for, 469–470
knowledge management integrating, 202
quality function deployment translating, 134, 472–476, 473f–475f
quality planning and, 477
as system, 476–477, 477f
volume buyers, 454–455
Vroom, Victor, 37
V-shaped work cells, 385
VSM (value stream mapping), 45, 391–394, 393f, 407t

W

waiting waste, 380, 382
Walton, Sam, 445
waste
costs of, 362
defined, 380
eliminating, 380–383, 405t
engineering changes creating, 383
excess inventory as, 381, 382
invisible, 382–383
management processes creating, 383
meetings as, 383
motion, 381, 382
non-value-added, 383–384
overprocessing, 381, 382
overproduction, 380
rejected or defective parts as, 381, 399
reporting-related, 383
transportation, 380–381, 382
visible, 382
waiting, 380, 382
waterfall project management, 232–234, 233f
Watson, Thomas, Jr., 87
WBS (work breakdown structure), 246t, 248, 250, 251f–252f

web-based surveys, 487–488
Weber, Max, 143
webinars, 566. *See also* e-learning
Weibull curve, 439. *See also* bathtub curve
Weibull distributions, 421, 422f
Welch, Jack, 345
Westcott, R. T., 481, 537, 569
what/who matrix, 490
who, what, when, where, why, and how questions, 360
wholesale buyers, 454
why-why diagrams, 45
WIP (work in process), 382, 385, 389
Wojniak, Joe, 537
won/lost analysis, 490
Wood, Douglas C., 327
Wood, R. C., 490
workbooks, training, 562, 567
work breakdown structure (WBS), 246t, 248, 250, 251f–252f
work cells, 384, 385, 385f, 403t
workforce. *See* staff
work groups, 58–61, 60f
working capital, 177, 181
work in process (WIP), 382, 385, 389
work instructions, 377–378, 377f, 406t, 430. *See also* policies
work orders, 282
written surveys, 486

X

x-bar charts, 425, 426
XP (Extreme Programming), 237

Y

YouTube, 228, 565

Z

zero acceptance number plans, 419
zero defects, 419
zero investment improvement (ZII), 398. *See also kaizen* event/*kaizen* blitz
Zimmerman, J. W., 88

About the Editors

Sandra L. Furterer is an Associate Professor and Department Chair at the University of Dayton in the Department of Engineering Management, Systems, and Technology. Dr. Furterer has over 25 years of experience in business process and quality improvements in multiple service industries, including healthcare, retail, consulting, information systems, and financial services. She previously was a VP of Process Improvement for two financial services firms in Columbus, Ohio. She also was the Enterprise Performance Excellence leader that deployed Lean Six Sigma in a hospital system in south Florida. She holds a PhD in Industrial Engineering from the University of Central Florida, an MBA from Xavier University, and bachelor's and master's degrees in Industrial and Systems Engineering from Ohio State. She is an ASQ Certified Manager of Quality/Organizational Excellence, an ASQ Certified Six Sigma Black Belt, an ASQ Certified Quality Engineer, an ASQ fellow, and a certified Six Sigma Master Black Belt. Dr. Furterer is an author or coauthor of several textbooks and journal articles. She has refereed conference papers and proceedings publications on systems engineering, Lean Six Sigma, process improvement, operational excellence, and engineering education. Her research interests include Lean Six Sigma, quality management, and systems engineering applied to service industries.

Douglas C. Wood is President of DC Wood Consulting, LLC, and an instructor for ASQ. He has over 35 years of experience in process engineering and quality systems planning and design in food and printing industries. His experience covers project justification, information systems design, equipment capacity, supply chain measurement and management, new product quality planning, teaching university at a master of engineering level, Lean and Six Sigma teaching and applications, and cost of quality design and operation. He holds a master of science degree in Industrial Management from the University of Central Missouri and a bachelor of science degree in Industrial Engineering from Western Michigan University. He is an ASQ Certified Manager of Quality/Organizational Excellence, an ASQ Certified Six Sigma Black Belt, an ASQ Certified Quality Engineer, and an ASQ Certified Quality Auditor. He has authored or edited books and papers on numerous quality subjects. His interests include virtual instruction, meeting facilitation, research in Cost of Quality, and psychological aspects of organizational culture development.